APPLICATIONS OF FINITE GROUPS

APPLICATIONS OF FINITE GROUPS

J. S. Lomont
Institute of Mathematical Sciences
New York University

1959

Academic Press
New York · London

First Printing, 1959
Second Printing, 1961

ACADEMIC PRESS INC.
111 FIFTH AVENUE
NEW YORK 3, N.Y.

United Kingdom Edition
Published by
ACADEMIC PRESS INC. (London) LTD.
17 OLD QUEEN STREET, LONDON SW 1

LIBRARY OF CONGRESS CATALOG CARD NUMBER:
58-12792

PRINTED IN THE UNITED STATES OF AMERICA

PREFACE

Group theory is primarily a formal mathematical tool for treating symmetry systematically. Consequently group theory is of use to physicists in treating systems of two types: (1) those which possess symmetry but are too complex to be treated in detail by analysis, and (2) those whose properties (e.g. interactions) are not known in detail. It is also useful in formulating theories for which symmetry requirements are specified a priori.

The objectives of this book are: (1) to provide a mathematical background (primarily representation theory) in finite groups which is adequate both for reading this book and for reading the physics literature, and (2) to provide a variety of instructive and interesting examples of applications of finite groups to problems of physics. It is assumed that the reader has been exposed to matrix theory and general group theory. Also a knowledge of quantum mechanics is presupposed. The definitions and theorems (except for the definition of a group) are for finite groups unless otherwise stated.

A chapter on space groups has been included because space groups can also be treated (with a few lapses of rigor) by the methods of finite groups. Also, because finite and continuous groups are rather inextricably mixed in some applications it has been necessary to include brief discussions of some continuous groups. In these discussions, however, the topological aspects of continuous groups were assiduously avoided. The handbook style appendix on Lorentz groups was included as a convenience for research workers.

Chapters 7 and 8 can be read without first reading chapters 5 and 6.

The author would like to express his gratitude to Professor W. Magnus for his untiring encouragement and for many clarifying discussions, to Professor G. W. Mackey for a lucid clarification of the theory of little groups, and to Professor E. P. Wigner for numerous useful discussions. Also, the author would like to thank Dr. J. E. Maxfield for proving several theorems on matrices, Dr. G. J. Lasher for a careful and critical proofreading of the book, Dr. J. Brooks for conscientiously reading the first few chapters, and Dr. G. S. Colladay for several useful discussions and calculations.

J. S. LOMONT

New York
February, 1959

Preface to Second Printing

Several errors in the first printing have been corrected, and the table on pages 34–35 has been expanded.

J. S. LOMONT

New York
July, 1961

CONTENTS

LIST OF SYMBOLS

*	complex conjugate
t	transpose
†	adjoint or hermitian conjugate or $*t$
$\in$	an element is contained in, e.g., $p \in S$—p is contained in the set S
$\subset$	a subset is properly contained in, e.g., $S_1 \subset S_2$—the set S_1 is properly contained in the set S_2
$\cap$	set-theoretic intersection, e.g., $S_1 \cap S_2$—the set common to the two sets S_1 and S_2
S	summation or integration
$\rightarrow$	is mapped onto
$\leftrightarrow$	corresponds to, e.g., $A \leftrightarrow D$—A corresponds to D in a one-to-one mapping
$\cdot\equiv\cdot$	is equivalent to
$\{\ \}$	set of all elements
$\otimes$	Kronecker product
$\oplus$	direct sum

Chapter I

MATRICES

The reason for starting a book on group theory with a chapter on matrices is that matrices are basic to the theory of group representations, and group representations are in turn basic to most applications of groups. Hence, we shall in this review emphasize those aspects of matrix theory which are relevant to representation theory. The principal relevant concepts are: trace, equivalence, and reducibility; therefore there will be several theorems which develop these concepts. Also, we shall be primarily interested in square, column, and row matrices whose elements (or entries) are complex numbers, hence most of our discussions will concern only such matrices. Although it will be assumed that the reader has been exposed to matrix theory, it will nonetheless be necessary to state explicitly quite a few elementary definitions in order to remove any possible ambiguities regarding elementary terminology.

Definition. (a) The *dimension* (or degree) of a square matrix D or of a column matrix v is the number of rows of the matrix and will be written dim (D) or dim (v), respectively.

(b) The dimension of a row matrix is the number of columns.

Note: We shall consider only finite-dimensional matrices here.

The d-dimensional unit (or identity) and zero square matrices will be denoted, respectively, by I_d and O_d (the subscripts will be omitted where no confusion is likely). The zero n-dimensional row and column matrices will be designated in the same way (since no confusion should result).

Definition. The *adjoint* (or hermitian conjugate) $D^\dagger$ of a matrix is the transpose of the complex conjugate:

$$D^\dagger = D^{*t},$$

where * and t signify complex conjugation and transposition, respectively, and complex conjugation of a matrix means complex conjugation of each element.

If by the commutator of two square matrices D_1 and D_2 of the same dimension we understand

$$[D_1, D_2] \equiv D_1 D_2 - D_2 D_1,$$

then we have the following definition.

Definition. A *normal* matrix is a square matrix such that its commutator with its adjoint is zero, i.e.,

$$[D, D^\dagger] = 0.$$

On the other hand, if $DD^\dagger + D^\dagger D = 0$, then $D = 0$. Some important special types of normal matrices are:

(1) unitary matrices $D^\dagger D = I$
(2) hermitian matrices $D^\dagger = D$
(3) orthogonal matrices $D^t D = I$ $D^* = D$ (We consider only real orthogonal matrices, which are therefore also real unitary matrices.)
(4) rotation matrices (These are orthogonal matrices which have positive determinants.)
(5) symmetric matrices $D^t = D$ $D^* = D$ (Again we consider only real ones.)
(6a) permutation matrices (A permutation matrix is a square matrix whose elements are all either one or zero and which has exactly one nonzero entry in each row and exactly one in each column.)

Example.

$$D = \begin{pmatrix} 0 & 1 & 0 \\ 0 & 0 & 1 \\ 1 & 0 & 0 \end{pmatrix}.$$

(6b) pseudopermutation matrices (Let us understand by this term any matrix obtained from any permutation matrix by replacing some of the ones by minus ones.)
(7) diagonal matrices (All off-diagonal elements are zero.)
(8) scalar matrices $D = \chi I$, where χ is any complex number.

Some other special types of matrices which will be of interest are

(1) unimodular (or special) matrices: $\det(D) = 1$
(2) integral matrices (Every element is an integer.)
(3) idempotent matrices $D^2 = D$
(4) nilpotent matrices $D^N = 0$, for some positive integer N
(5) monomial matrices (These are square matrices having only one nonzero entry in each row and only one in each column.)
(6) real matrices $D^* = D$
(7) skew symmetric matrices $D^t = -D$

We can now proceed to the meat of matrix theory. Subsequently, the entry in the ith row and jth column of a matrix D will be denoted by D_{ij}.

Definition. The *trace* (or spur) of a square d-dimensional matrix D (abbreviated $\operatorname{tr}(D)$) is the sum of the diagonal elements of D.

$$\operatorname{tr}(D) \equiv \sum_{i=1}^{d} D_{ii}.$$

Note. If D_1 and D_2 are square matrices of the same dimension, then

$$\operatorname{tr}(D_1 D_2) = \operatorname{tr}(D_2 D_1)$$

Note. If D is a unitary matrix of dimension d, $\operatorname{tr}(D) = \pm d$, then $D = \pm I$ (according to the sign of the trace).

Definition. Let D be a d-dimensional square matrix.

(a) The *characteristic polynomial* of D is $\det(D - \lambda I)$ (which is a dth degree polynomial in λ with leading coefficient $(-1)^d$).

(b) The *characteristic equation* of D is $|D - \lambda I| = 0$.

(c) The *eigenvalues* of D are the d roots $\lambda_1,\ldots,\lambda_d$ of the characteristic equation of D.

It can easily be shown that the eigenvalues of hermitian matrices are real and that the eigenvalues of unitary matrices have modulus one.

Theorem. If D is a d-dimensional square matrix with eigenvalues $\lambda_1,\ldots,\lambda_d$, then

$$\operatorname{tr}(D) = \sum_{i=1}^{d} \lambda_i.$$

Definition. The *degeneracy* of an eigenvalue of a square matrix D is the number of times it occurs as a root of the characteristic equation of D.

Definition. A *positive definite* square matrix is a hermitian matrix whose eigenvalues are all positive.

Theorem.
$$\det(D) = \prod_{i=1}^{d} \lambda_i.$$

Note. (1) A skew symmetric matrix of odd dimension has determinant zero.

(2) The dimension of a skew symmetric unitary matrix cannot be odd.

Corollary. A square matrix is nonsingular (or regular) if and only if it has no eigenvalues equal to zero.

Also, it may be recalled that if all the elements of a matrix are positive, then the matrix has one nondegenerate positive eigenvalue whose magnitude is larger than that of any other eigenvalue.

Definition. Two square matrices D_1 and D_2 such that

$$D_2 = S^{-1} D_1 S,$$

where S is a nonsingular square matrix, are said to be *equivalent* (or similar) (we shall write $D_2 \cdot\!\equiv\!\cdot D_1$).

Note that this implies that D_1 and D_2 must have the same dimension and that $D_1 \cdot\!\equiv\!\cdot D_2$. It may be recalled that an equivalence transformation can be geometrically interpreted as a change of axes (alias transformation) or as a point transformation (alibi transformation). Also, if two equivalent matrices D_1 and D_2 are given, then the problem of finding the general form of the transformation matrix S connecting them is quite laborious. We shall return to this problem later.

Theorem. $D_2 \cdot\equiv\cdot D_1$ implies

(1) $\operatorname{tr}(D_2) = \operatorname{tr}(D_1)$

(2) $\det(D_2) = \det(D_1)$

(3) D_2 and D_1 have the same characteristic polynomial

(4) D_2 and D_1 have the same eigenvalues.

Every square matrix D is equivalent to a simple "almost"-diagonal matrix Λ which depends on D and which is known as the Jordan canonical form of D. However, we shall not discuss this further here.

Definition. A *diagonalizable* matrix is a square matrix which is equivalent to a diagonal matrix.

No simple criterion for diagonalizability seems to be known, but a few useful relevant results are known.

Theorem. The diagonal elements of a diagonal matrix equivalent to D are the eigenvalues of D.

Theorem. A square matrix is diagonalizable if its eigenvalues are non-degenerate.

We shall say that a diagonalizable matrix D is diagonalizable by a unitary matrix if there exists a unitary matrix U such that $U^{-1}DU$ is a diagonal matrix.

Theorem. (1) A square matrix D is diagonalizable by a unitary matrix if and only if D is a normal matrix.

(2) A real square matrix D is diagonalizeable by an orthogonal matrix if and only if D is a symmetric matric.

Hence, the various special types of normal matrices listed earlier are all diagonalizable. In fact, practically all matrices which will be of interest to us will be diagonalizable. We shall now state several well-known equivalence theorems for diagonalizable matrices.

Theorem. Two diagonalizable matrices D_1 and D_2 are equivalent if and only if

$$\begin{aligned} &(1)\quad \dim(D_1) = \dim(D_2) && (= d) \\ &(2)\quad \operatorname{tr}(D_1{}^i) = \operatorname{tr}(D_2{}^i) && i = 1,\ldots,d. \end{aligned}$$

Theorem. Each of the following is a necessary and sufficient condition for a diagonalizable matrix D to be equivalent to a real matrix.

(1) The complex eigenvalues of D occur in conjugate pairs.

(2) The traces of the first d powers of D are real [where $d = \dim(D)$].

Theorem. A matrix D is equivalent to a real matrix if and only if $D \cdot\equiv\cdot D^*$.

Theorem. A matrix is equivalent only to real matrices if and only if it is a real scalar matrix.

Theorem. A diagonalizable matrix D is equivalent to an integral matrix if and only if (1) the traces of the first d powers of D are integers [$d = \dim(D)$]; (2) the eigenvalues of D are algebraic integers.

By an integer is meant a real whole number, and by an algebraic integer is meant a root of an equation of the form

$$X^N + a_{N-1}X^{N-1} + a_{N-2}X^{N-2} + \dots + a_0 = 0,$$

in which all of the a's are integers. We shall see later that crystallographic groups can be considered to have elements which are integral matrices.

Theorem. If two real matrices are equivalent, then they are equivalent with respect to a real transformation.

That is, if $D_2 = S^{-1}D_1S$, where D_1 and D_2 are real, then there exists a real matrix T such that $D_2 = T^{-1}D_1T$. In fact, if we split S into real and imaginary parts, $S = P + iQ$, and let λ be any real number such that $|P + \lambda Q| \neq 0$, then we can put $T = P + \lambda Q$.

Definition. A *projection* matrix is an idempotent matrix.

We now move on to some more difficult concepts which involve sets of matrices. Although the theorems will be stated for finite sets they hold also for infinite sets.

Definition. Let $D_1, D_2, \dots, D_N$; $D_1', D_2', \dots, D_N'$ be two sets (not necessarily finite) of square matrices. These two *sets* will be said to be *equivalent* if there exists a square matrix S such that

$$D_i' = S^{-1} D_i S \qquad i = 1, \dots, N$$

for some ordering of the second set.

Example.

$$\Gamma_1: \begin{pmatrix}1&0\\0&1\end{pmatrix}\begin{pmatrix}-1&0\\0&-1\end{pmatrix}\begin{pmatrix}-i&0\\0&i\end{pmatrix}\begin{pmatrix}i&0\\0&-i\end{pmatrix}\begin{pmatrix}0&1\\-1&0\end{pmatrix}\begin{pmatrix}0&-1\\1&0\end{pmatrix}\begin{pmatrix}0&-i\\-i&0\end{pmatrix}\begin{pmatrix}0&i\\i&0\end{pmatrix}$$

$$\Gamma_2: \begin{pmatrix}1&0\\0&1\end{pmatrix}\begin{pmatrix}-1&0\\0&-1\end{pmatrix}\begin{pmatrix}5i&8i\\-3i&-5i\end{pmatrix}\begin{pmatrix}-5i&-8i\\3i&5i\end{pmatrix}\begin{pmatrix}-7&-10\\5&7\end{pmatrix}\begin{pmatrix}7&10\\-5&-7\end{pmatrix}$$
$$\begin{pmatrix}5i&6i\\-4i&-5i\end{pmatrix}\begin{pmatrix}-5i&-6i\\4i&5i\end{pmatrix}$$

where $\Gamma_2 \cdot\!\equiv\!\cdot\, \Gamma_1$ and $S = \begin{pmatrix}1&2\\3&4\end{pmatrix}$ $\qquad S^{-1} = -\frac{1}{2}\begin{pmatrix}4&-2\\-3&1\end{pmatrix}$.

It follows that all of the matrices D_i, D_i', and S must have the same dimension. Also, it is possible to have

$$D_i' \cdot\!\equiv\!\cdot\, D_i \qquad i = 1, \dots, N$$

without having the sets equivalent.

Theorem. If two sets of real matrices are equivalent, then they are equivalent with respect to a real transformation.

This result will be essential to our group theoretic derivation of crystallographic point groups.

Theorem. If two sets of unitary (orthogonal) matrices are equivalent, then they are equivalent with respect to a unitary (orthogonal) transformation.

Theorem. If a set of unitary matrices is equivalent to a set of real matrices, then it is equivalent to a set of orthogonal matrices.

Definition. A set of matrices will be said to be diagonalizable if the set is equivalent to a set of diagonalizable matrices.

Note that a set of diagonalizable matrices need not be a diagonalizable set of matrices. In fact, there is a very simple result for normal matrices.

Theorem. A set of normal matrices of the same dimension is diagonalizable if, and only if, the commutator of every pair of matrices of the set is zero.

Such a set of matrices is called a commuting set, and one sees immediately that every set of diagonal matrices is a commuting set.

Definition. (a) A set of d-dimensional diagonal matrices $\Lambda_1, \ldots, \Lambda_N$ is *complete* if no two sets S_j and S_k of the d sets of eigenvalues $S_i = (\Lambda_{1,ii}; \Lambda_{2,ii}; \ldots; \Lambda_{N,ii})$ are equal term by term. (A single matrix with no degenerate eigenvalues is thus a complete set.)

Example.

$$\begin{pmatrix} 1 & 0 & 0 & 0 \\ 0 & 1 & 0 & 0 \\ 0 & 0 & 2 & 0 \\ 0 & 0 & 0 & 2 \end{pmatrix} \quad \begin{pmatrix} 1 & 0 & 0 & 0 \\ 0 & 2 & 0 & 0 \\ 0 & 0 & 2 & 0 \\ 0 & 0 & 0 & 1 \end{pmatrix} \quad \begin{pmatrix} 2 & 0 & 0 & 0 \\ 0 & 1 & 0 & 0 \\ 0 & 0 & 1 & 0 \\ 0 & 0 & 0 & 2 \end{pmatrix}$$

is a complete set because

$$S_1 = (1,1,2), \quad S_2 = (1,2,1), \quad S_3 = (2,2,1), \quad S_4 = (2,1,2),$$

and no two of these sets are equal term by term.

(b) A *complete commuting set* of normal matrices is a set of normal matrices which is equivalent to a complete set of diagonal matrices.

This concept is important in labelling states in the Dirac formulation of quantum mechanics.

We proceed now to the concept of reducibility and represent subarrays of a matrix by matrices. Thus we shall consider matrices whose elements are also matrices.

Definition. A *reduced* matrix is a matrix of the form

$$\begin{pmatrix} D(11) & 0 \\ D(21) & D(22) \end{pmatrix} \quad \text{or} \quad \begin{pmatrix} D(11) & D(12) \\ 0 & D(22) \end{pmatrix},$$

where $D(ij)$ is a matrix, $D(ii)$ is square, and the off-diagonal zero matrix has at least one row.

Example.

$$\begin{pmatrix} 1 & 2 & 0 \\ 3 & 4 & 0 \\ 6 & 7 & 5 \end{pmatrix} \quad \text{and} \quad \begin{pmatrix} 1 & 2 & 6 \\ 3 & 4 & 7 \\ 0 & 0 & 5 \end{pmatrix}$$

are reduced matrices.

In fact, since the Jordan canonical form of a matrix is reduced, it follows that every matrix is equivalent to a reduced matrix, or is reducible (if $d \neq 1$).

Definition. A *set* of matrices $D_1,\ldots,D_N$ (of the same dimension) is *reduced* if every matrix of the set has the reduced form

$$D_i = \begin{pmatrix} D_i(11) & 0 \\ D_i(21) & D_i(22) \end{pmatrix},$$

where $\dim D_i(11) = \dim D_j(11)$, $i,j = 1,\ldots,N$, and the zero matrices have at least one row (or, the zero matrix may be in the lower left corner of all D's instead of the upper right).

Reducibility is thus a weak substitute for diagonalizability.

Example.

$$\begin{pmatrix} 1 & 2 & 0 \\ 3 & 4 & 0 \\ 6 & 7 & 5 \end{pmatrix} \quad \begin{pmatrix} 4 & 3 & 0 \\ 1 & 2 & 0 \\ 6 & 5 & 7 \end{pmatrix}$$

is a reduced set.

We finally arrive at the concept of reducibility of a set.

Definition. A *set* of matrices is *reducible* if it is equivalent to a reduced set of matrices.

Reducibility is thus a sort of weakened diagonalizability, because every diagonalizable matrix is reducible although the converse is not true. Also, we have seen that every matrix is reducible. However, not every set of matrices is reducible. For example, the set

$$\begin{pmatrix} 1 & 0 \\ 0 & 1 \end{pmatrix}, \begin{pmatrix} -1 & 0 \\ 0 & -1 \end{pmatrix}, \begin{pmatrix} -i & 0 \\ 0 & i \end{pmatrix}, \begin{pmatrix} i & 0 \\ 0 & -i \end{pmatrix}, \begin{pmatrix} 0 & 1 \\ -1 & 0 \end{pmatrix}, \begin{pmatrix} 0 & -1 \\ 1 & 0 \end{pmatrix}, \begin{pmatrix} 0 & -i \\ -i & 0 \end{pmatrix}, \begin{pmatrix} 0 & i \\ i & 0 \end{pmatrix}$$

is not reducible. Also, any set of 1-dimensional matrices is not reducible.

Definition. A set of square matrices of the same dimension is *irreducible* if it is not reducible.

We come now to a result which is the key to the proofs of many results of representation theory, and which is known as Schur's lemma.

Lemma (Schur). Let $D_1',\ldots, D_N'$ be an irreducible set of d'-dimensional matrices; and $D_1'',\ldots, D_N''$ an irreducible set of d''-dimensional matrices. Then, if there exists a matrix S such that $D_i'S = SD_i''$ for some ordering of the second set, then it follows that either

(1) S is a zero matrix, or (2) S is a square nonsingular matrix (so $d' = d''$).

Outline of Proof. Let the d'' columns of S be denoted by $\boldsymbol{\sigma}_1, \boldsymbol{\sigma}_2, \ldots, \boldsymbol{\sigma}_{d''}$. Then by the rules of matrix multiplication we find that for a typical matrix D' and a typical matrix D''

$$D'S = (D\boldsymbol{\sigma}'_1, D\boldsymbol{\sigma}'_2, \ldots, D\boldsymbol{\sigma}'_{d''})$$

$$SD'' = \left(\sum_{k=1}^{d''} D''_{k1}\boldsymbol{\sigma}_k, \sum_{k=1}^{d''} D''_{k2}\boldsymbol{\sigma}_k, \ldots, \sum_{k=1}^{d''} D''_{kd''}\boldsymbol{\sigma}_k\right).$$

Hence

$$D'\boldsymbol{\sigma}_j = \sum_{k=1}^{d''} D''_{kj}\boldsymbol{\sigma}_k$$

and we see that the d'' $\boldsymbol{\sigma}$-vectors span a space which is invariant under the irreducible set of d'-dimensional matrices $\{D'\}$. Consequently, the $\boldsymbol{\sigma}$-vectors are the null vector or they span a d'-dimensional vector space. In the first case $S = 0$, and in the second case $d'' \geqslant d'$ and $S \neq 0$.

Let us consider the second case further. From the fact that the sets $D_1', \ldots, D_N'$ and $D_1'', \ldots, D_N''$ are irreducible it easily follows that the sets $D_1^\dagger, \ldots, D_N^\dagger$ and $D_1''^\dagger, \ldots, D_N''^\dagger$ are irreducible. Also, from the equations $D_i'S = SD_i''$ it follows directly that $D_i''^\dagger S^\dagger = S^\dagger D_i'^\dagger$. Applying the procedure of the preceding paragraph to these equations we find that $d' \geqslant d''$. Hence, $d' = d''$, and S is square. Also, since the d' columns of S span a d'-dimensional vector space, it follows that S is nonsingular.

Corollary. A matrix D which commutes with an irreducible set of matrices $D_1, \ldots, D_N$ (i.e., $[D, D_i] = 0$, $i = 1, \ldots, N$) must be a scalar matrix.

Corollary. If S_1 and S_2 are two matrices such that $D_i'S_j = S_jD_i''$ and the two sets $\{D_i'\}$ and $\{D_i''\}$ are irreducible, then $S_2 = \lambda S_1$ where λ is a number.

Theorem. Let $D_1, \ldots, D_N$ be an irreducible set of d-dimensional matrices. Then every d-dimensional matrix can be expressed as a polynomial in the matrices $D_1, \ldots, D_N$.

We shall say that a set of square matrices is equivalent to its complex conjugate if the two sets are not only equivalent in the usual sense but are also equivalent in the same order; i.e., if there exists a matrix S such that $D_i^* = S^{-1}D_iS$.

Theorem. Let $\{D_1, \ldots, D_N\}$ be an irreducible set of square unitary matrices of the same dimension which is equivalent to its complex conjugate set (with the same order). Let U be any unitary matrix such that $D_i^* = U^{-1}D_iU$ for all D_i. Then, (1) if $\{D_i\}$ is equivalent to a real set of matrices, $U^t = U$, (2) otherwise, $U^t = -U$.

We come now to the concepts of direct sum and complete reducibility.

Definition. (a) Let D, D', D'' be three square matrices. Then D is the *direct sum* of D' and D'' if

$$D = \begin{pmatrix} D' & 0 \\ 0 & D'' \end{pmatrix}$$

or

$$D = \begin{pmatrix} D'' & 0 \\ 0 & D' \end{pmatrix}$$

This is written $D = D' \oplus D''$.

(b) Let $\Gamma = \{D_1,...,D_N\}$, $\Gamma' = \{D_1',...,D'_N\}$, $\Gamma'' = \{D_1'',...,D''_N\}$ be three sets of matrices. Then Γ is the direct sum of Γ' and Γ'' (written $\Gamma = \Gamma' \oplus \Gamma''$) if

$$D_i = \begin{pmatrix} D_i' & 0 \\ 0 & D_i'' \end{pmatrix}$$

or if

$$D_i = \begin{pmatrix} D_i'' & 0 \\ 0 & D_i' \end{pmatrix}.$$

Example.

$$\Gamma = \left\{\begin{pmatrix} 1 & 0 \\ 0 & 1 \end{pmatrix}, \begin{pmatrix} -1 & 0 \\ 0 & 1 \end{pmatrix}\right\}, \Gamma' = \left\{1, -1\right\}, \Gamma'' = \left\{1,1\right\}.$$

Definition. A set of matrices is *completely reducible* if it is equivalent to the direct sum of two other sets of matrices (written $\Gamma \cdot\!\equiv\!\cdot \Gamma' \oplus \Gamma''$).

If a set is itself the direct sum of two sets, then it is completely reducible (as is Γ of the preceding example).

Note. If Γ is completely reducible it is reducible.

This statement is true because complete reducibility simply means that there is a zero matrix in both the upper right and lower left corners of the completely reduced matrix; whereas reducibility requires only one such zero matrix. The converse of this theorem is not true.

Theorem. $\Gamma \cdot\!\equiv\!\cdot \Gamma' \oplus \Gamma''$ implies $\dim(D_i) = \dim(D_i') + \dim(D_i'')$
$\operatorname{tr}(D_i) = \operatorname{tr}(D_i') + \operatorname{tr}(D_i'')$

Note. If the only matrices which commute with a set of square matrices of the same dimension are scalar matrices, then the set of matrices is not completely reducible.

One of our preceding theorems can now be generalized slightly.

Theorem. Let $\{D_1,..., D_N\}$ be a set of square unitary matrices of the same dimension which is equivalent to its complex conjugate set (in the same order), but not to a set of real matrices. Also let the set be completely reduced into irreducible unitary components, and let U be any unitary matrix such that $D_i^* = U^{-1}D_iU$. Then $U^t = -U$.

One can form not only direct sums of matrices but also direct products.

Definition. The Kronecker product (or direct product) of two square matrices D' and D'' is the matrix D whose element in the ijth row and klth column is given by

$$D_{ij,kl} = D'_{ik} D''_{jl}$$

(written $D = D' \otimes D''$). (The actual ordering of rows in D is not important for our work and consequently will not be specified.)

Theorem. (1) $\dim (D' \otimes D'') = \dim (D') \times \dim (D'')$

(2) $\mathrm{tr} (D' \otimes D'') = \mathrm{tr} (D') \times \mathrm{tr} (D'')$

(3) the eigenvalues of $D' \otimes D''$ are the products $\lambda_i' \lambda_j''$ where λ_i' and λ_j'' are eigenvalues of D' and D''.

Theorem. If $\dim D_1' = \dim D_2'$
$\dim D_1'' = \dim D_2''$,

then

$$(D_1' \otimes D_1'') (D_2' \otimes D_2'') = (D_1'D_2') \otimes (D_1''D_2'').$$

Theorem. For every D', D'' there exists a $d'd''$-dimensional permutation matrix P such that $D' \otimes D'' = P^{-1} (D'' \otimes D')P$.

Definition. If $\Gamma' = \{D_1', \ldots, D'_{N'}\}$ is a set of d'-dimensional matrices and $\Gamma'' = \{D_1'', \ldots, D''_{N''}\}$ is a set of d''-dimensional matrices, then

(a) $\Gamma' \otimes \Gamma'' = \{D_1' \otimes D_1'', \ldots, D'_{N'} \otimes D''_{N''}\}$ if $N' = N''$

(b) $\Gamma' \times \Gamma''$ = the set of all $N'N''$ matrices $D_i' \otimes D_j''$

$$i = 1, \ldots, N' \qquad j = 1, \ldots, N''$$

are called the *inner* and *outer* Kronecker products of the two sets.

If D is a square, d-dimensional matrix, then let us call the set of all d-dimensional column matrices the *carrier space* of D. This is obviously a d-dimensional vector space. Furthermore, if V is a vector of the carrier space of D, one can define its transformed vector V' by

$$v' = Dv$$

or

$$v_i' = D_{ij} v_j$$

(using the summation convention for repeated indices). Then, a kth rank tensor $F_{i_1, \ldots, i_k}$ which transforms under D will be transformed as a product of vectors,

$$F'_{i_1 \ldots i_k} = D_{i_1 j_1} D_{i_2 j_2} \ldots D_{i_k j_k} F_{j_1 \ldots j_k}.$$

That is, a kth rank tensor is transformed by the kth Kronecker power of D (call it D_k), or, the tensor F is a vector in the carrier space of D_k.

If one considers the transformation properties of the independent components of symmetric and antisymmetric kth rank tensors,* then one obtains the *symmetrized* and *antisymmetrized* kth powers of D. Call them $D_{(k)}$ and $D_{[k]}$, respectively. These matrices are also called induced and compound matrices, respectively.

Example. Let

$$D = \begin{pmatrix} D_{11} & D_{12} \\ D_{21} & D_{22} \end{pmatrix}.$$

Then a symmetric second rank tensor $F_{ij} = F_{ji}$ has at most three independent components F_{11}, F_{12}, and F_{22} which transform as follows:

$$\begin{aligned} F'_{11} &= D_{11}^2 F_{11} + D_{11} D_{12} F_{12} + D_{12} D_{11} F_{21} + D_{12}^2 F_{22} \\ &= D_{11}^2 F_{11} + 2D_{11} D_{12} F_{12} + D_{12}^2 F_{22} \\ F'_{12} &= D_{11} D_{21} F_{11} + D_{11} D_{22} F_{12} + D_{12} D_{21} F_{21} + D_{12} D_{22} F_{22} \\ &= D_{11} D_{21} F_{11} + (D_{11} D_{22} + D_{12} D_{21}) F_{12} + D_{12} D_{22} F_{22} \\ F'_{22} &= D_{21}^2 F_{11} + D_{21} D_{22} F_{12} + D_{22} D_{21} F_{21} + D_{22}^2 F_{22} \\ &= D_{21}^2 F_{11} + 2D_{21} D_{22} F_{12} + D_{22}^2 F_{22}. \end{aligned}$$

Hence, the square matrix which transforms these three independent components of F can be read off from the above equations,

$$D_{(2)} = \begin{pmatrix} D_{11}^2 & 2D_{11} D_{12} & D_{12}^2 \\ D_{11} D_{21} & D_{11} D_{22} + D_{12} D_{21} & D_{12} D_{22} \\ D_{21}^2 & 2D_{21} D_{22} & D_{22}^2 \end{pmatrix}.$$

Similarly, an antisymmetric second rank tensor has at most one nonzero independent component F_{12} (since $F_{jj} = -F_{jj}$ implies $F = 0$). It transforms as follows:

$$F'_{12} = D_{11} D_{22} F_{12} + D_{12} D_{21} F_{21} = (D_{11} D_{22} - D_{12} D_{21}) F_{12}.$$

Hence,

$$D_{[2]} = D_{11} D_{22} - D_{12} D_{21} = \det(D).$$

The dimensions of $D_{(2)}$ and $D_{[2]}$ are thus the numbers of independent components of a symmetric F_{ij} and of an antisymmetric F_{ij}, respectively. We also see that $\dim(D_{(2)}) + \dim(D_{[2]}) = \dim(D_2)$. However, it is not in general true that $\dim(D_{(k)}) + \dim(D_{[k]}) = \dim(D_k)$.

Theorem. (1) $\dim(D_{(k)}) = \binom{d+k-1}{k} = \dfrac{(d+k-1)!}{k!(d-1)!}$

* A tensor is symmetric if no interchange of the indices of any component changes the value of the component. A tensor is antisymmetric if interchange of a pair of indices of any component changes the sign of the component.

$$(2)\ \operatorname{tr}(D_{(k)}) = \frac{1}{k!}\begin{vmatrix} T_1 & -1 & 0 & 0 & 0 & \dots & 0 \\ T_2 & T_1 & -2 & 0 & 0 & \dots & 0 \\ T_3 & T_2 & T_1 & -3 & 0 & \dots & 0 \\ \cdot \\ \cdot \\ \cdot \\ T_k & T_{k-1} & \cdot & \cdot & \cdot & \dots & T_1 \end{vmatrix}$$

where $T_j = \operatorname{tr}(D^j)$.

(3) $(D_1 D_2)_{(k)} = D_{1(k)} D_{2(k)}$

(4) $\dim(D_{[k]}) = \binom{d}{k} = \dfrac{d!}{k!(d-k)!}$ if $k \leqslant d$

$$(5)\ \operatorname{tr}(D_{[k]}) = \frac{1}{k!}\begin{vmatrix} T_1 & 1 & 0 & 0 & 0 & \dots & 0 \\ T_2 & T_1 & 2 & 0 & 0 & \dots & 0 \\ T_3 & T_2 & T_1 & 3 & 0 & \dots & 0 \\ \cdot \\ \cdot \\ \cdot \\ T_k & T_{k-1} & \cdot & \cdot & \cdot & \dots & T_1 \end{vmatrix}$$

(6) $(D_1 D_2)_{[k]} = D_{1[k]} D_{2[k]}$

(7) $D_2 \cdot\!\equiv\!\cdot D_{(2)} + D_{[2]}$.

This (7) is true because any second rank tensor F_{ij} can be expressed as the sum of a symmetric tensor and an antisymmetric tensor. This is done as follows:

$$F_{ij} = \frac{F_{ij} + F_{ji}}{2} + \frac{F_{ij} - F_{ji}}{2}.$$

This simple trick does not work for higher rank tensors, but a natural generalization can be developed (see Chapter VII, Section 3).

In the same way as one forms inner Kronecker powers of a set Γ of square matrices, one can also form inner symmetrized powers $\Gamma_{(k)}$ and inner antisymmetrized powers $\Gamma_{[k]}$ of Γ.

We can also relate the antisymmetrized powers of D to the characteristic polynomial of D.

Theorem. The coefficient of λ^j in the characteristic polynomial $|D - \lambda I|$ of D is $(-1)^j \operatorname{tr}(D_{[d-j]})$.

Thus one sees that the coefficients of the characteristic polynomial of D can be expressed in terms of traces of powers of D. Hence, a knowledge of the traces of the first d powers of D enable one to determine the eigenvalues of D.

We might at this point make a remark connecting reducibility and complete reducibility with carrier spaces. If a set Γ of d-dimensional matrices is reducible, then it leaves a subspace of the carrier space of Γ invariant, i.e., no matrix of Γ transforms any vector of this subspace out of the subspace. If the reduced form of Γ is

$$\begin{pmatrix} D_i(11) & 0 \\ D_i(12) & D_i(22) \end{pmatrix},$$

then the subspace invariant under the reduced form is the set of all column matrices

$$\begin{pmatrix} 0 \\ 0 \\ \cdot \\ \cdot \\ \cdot \\ 0 \\ v_{d_1+1} \\ v_{d_1+2} \\ \cdot \\ \cdot \\ \cdot \\ v_d \end{pmatrix},$$

where $d_1 = \dim(D(11))$ and the nonzero components are arbitrary. If the set Γ is completely reducible, it leaves the above subspace invariant, and also the complementary subspace. The carrier space is then the direct sum of two invariant subspaces.

Another concept which is useful in connection with representation theory is the concept of imprimitivity.

Definition. A set $\Gamma = \{D_1, \ldots, D_N\}$ of square matrices of the same dimension is *imprimitive* if the carrier space V of Γ can be expressed as a direct sum of subspaces V_i in such a way that the effect of any matrix of Γ on any subspace V_i is to carry V_i into another one of the subspaces of the decomposition V_j, i.e.,

$$D_k V_i = V_j.$$

Example. The irreducible set of eight 2-dimensional matrices given earlier simply permutes the subspaces $V_1 = \left\{\begin{pmatrix} x \\ 0 \end{pmatrix}\right\}$, $V_2 = \left\{\begin{pmatrix} 0 \\ y \end{pmatrix}\right\}$ among themselves, and is therefore an imprimitive set of matrices.

Definition. If a set of matrices Γ is imprimitive, then the subspaces which are permuted by Γ are called a *system of imprimitivity*.

We see then that a completely reducible set is imprimitive, but the converse is not true.

While the effect of the matrices of a matrix set Γ on its carrier space is being considered, the fundamental region of Γ (if there is one) should be defined.

Definition. A *fundamental region* of a set Γ of square matrices of dimension d is a connected region V_F of the real part of its carrier space V such that

(a) V_F is d-dimensional

(b) every point of V can be obtained from a point of V_F by transforming with an element of Γ, and no point of V can be so obtained in more than one way.

Example. The set $\Gamma = \left\{\begin{pmatrix}1 & 0\\ 0 & -1\end{pmatrix}, \begin{pmatrix}1 & 0\\ 0 & -1\end{pmatrix}\right\}$ consisting of two matrices has the fundamental region $V_F = \left\{\begin{pmatrix}x\\ y\end{pmatrix}\right\} \quad \begin{matrix}-\infty \leqslant x \leqslant +\infty\\ y \geqslant 0\end{matrix}$ which is the upper half-plane of the real 2-dimensional carrier space.

Two miscellaneous aspects of matrix theory should be noted here.

Note. If D' and D'' are rectangular matrices with the same numbers of rows and columns, and if S and T are square matrices such that $D'' = SD'T$, then one can put the elements of D' and D'' in column matrices δ' and δ'' in such an order that $\delta'' = (S \otimes T^t)\,\delta$.

Definition. An *invariant vector* v of a set of square matrices $\Gamma = \{D_1, \ldots, D_N\}$ of the same dimension is a column matrix such that

$$D_i v = v \qquad (i = 1, \ldots, N)$$

(i.e., v is an eigenvector of each D in Γ) belonging to eigenenvalue 1.

Finally, let us write down two explicit forms of 3-dimensional rotation matrices. The first form will use the direction cosines l, m, n of the rotation axis plus the angle of rotation θ as parameters, and the second will use the Euler angles α, β, γ as parameters.

The first form is:

$$R(l,m,n,\theta) =$$

$$\begin{pmatrix} [1-(n^2+m^2)(1-\cos\theta)] & [-n\sin\theta+ml(1-\cos\theta)] & [m\sin\theta+nl(1-\cos\theta)]\\ [n\sin\theta+ml(1-\cos\theta)] & [1-(n^2+l^2)(1-\cos\theta)] & [-l\sin\theta+mn(1-\cos\theta)]\\ [-m\sin\theta+nl(1-\cos\theta)] & [l\sin\theta+mn(1-\cos\theta)] & [1-(m^2+l^2)(1-\cos\theta)] \end{pmatrix},$$

where $l^2 + m^2 + n^2 = 1$.

Theorem. $\operatorname{tr}(R(l,m,n,\theta)) = 1 + 2\cos\theta$
eigenvalues of $R(l,m,n,\theta) = 1,\ e^{\pm i\theta}$.

The second form is:

$$R(\alpha,\beta,\gamma) = \begin{pmatrix} [\cos\alpha\cos\beta\cos\gamma - \sin\alpha\sin\gamma] & [\cos\alpha\cos\beta\sin\gamma + \sin\alpha\cos\gamma] & [-\cos\alpha\sin\beta] \\ [-\sin\alpha\cos\beta\cos\gamma - \cos\alpha\sin\gamma] & [-\sin\alpha\cos\beta\sin\gamma + \cos\alpha\cos\gamma] & [\sin\alpha\sin\beta] \\ [\sin\beta\cos\gamma] & [\sin\beta\sin\gamma] & [\cos\beta] \end{pmatrix},$$

where $0 \leqslant \alpha < 2\pi$, $0 \leqslant \beta < \pi$, $0 \leqslant \gamma < 2\pi$.*

It is also true that any 3-dimensional rotation R can be written as the product of three rotations, one about each coordinate axis, i.e., $R = R_x R_y R_z$.

If, by an *improper* rotation matrix we mean an orthogonal matrix which is not a rotation matrix, then we can state the following result:

Note. Every improper 3-dimensional rotation matrix S can be written in the form $S = JR$, where R is a proper rotation matrix, and $J = -I$ is the inversion matrix.

If by a *reflection* matrix we understand an orthogonal matrix which has one eigenvalue equal to -1, and two eigenvalues equal to $+1$, then we can state the following theorem on 3-dimensional orthogonal matrices:

Theorem. Every rotation matrix can be written as a product of two reflections, and every improper rotation matrix can be written as a product of either one or three reflections.

Let us conclude this chapter with the following miscellaneous but useful (in connection with kinetic and potential energies) theorem on the simultaneous transformation of two matrices.

Theorem. If D_1 and D_2 are two real symmetric matrices, and if D_1 is positive definite, then there exists a real nonsingular matrix S such that $S^t D_1 S = I$ and $S^t D_2 S = \Lambda$, where Λ is a diagonal matrix whose eigenvalues are the roots of the equation

$$\det(D_2 - \lambda D_1) = 0.$$

---

* For a detailed discussion of Euler angles see: Wigner, E. P., The Application of Group Theory to the Special Functions of Mathematical Physics (Notes) (1955), p. 81.

BIBLIOGRAPHY

Aitken, A. C. (1951). "Determinants and Matrices." Interscience, New York.

Bôcher, M. (1907). "Introduction to Higher Algebra." Macmillan, New York.

Cooke, R. G. (1950). "Infinite Matrices and Sequence Spaces." Macmillan, London.

Cramer, H. (1946). "Mathematical Methods of Statistics." Princeton Univ. Press, Princeton, New Jersey.

Ferrar, W. L. (1951). "Finite Matrices." Clarendon Press, Oxford.

Gantmaher, F. R. (1953). "The Theory of Matrices." Gosudarstv. Izdat. Tehn.-Teor. Lit., Moscow.

Halmos, P. (1948). "Finite Dimensional Vector Spaces." Princeton Univ. Press, Princeton, New Jersey.

Hamburger, H. L., and Grimshaw, M. E. (1951). "Linear Transformations in n-Dimensional Vector Space." Cambridge Univ. Press, London and New York.

Higman, B. (1955). "Applied Group Theoretic and Matrix Methods." Clarendon Press, Oxford.

Hull, R. (1948). Elements of Matrices (Notes). Purdue Univ., West Lafayette, Indiana.

MacDuffee, C. C. (1933). "The Theory of Matrices." J. Springer, Berlin.

MacDuffee, C. C. (1943). "Vectors and Matrices." The Mathematical Assoc. of Am., Ithaca, New York.

Muir, T. (1890-1923). "The Theory of Determinants." Macmillan, New York.

Muir, T., and Metzler, W. H. (1933). "The Theory of Determinants." Longmans, Green, New York.

Narayan, S. (1953). "A Text Book of Matrices." S. Chand, Delhi, India.

Perlis, S. (1952). "Theory of Matrices." Addison-Wesley Press, Cambridge, Massachusetts.

Pupke, H. (1953). "Introduction to Matrix Calculus and its Physical Applications." Deutscher Verlag der Wissenschaften, Berlin.

Schmeidler, W. (1949). "Lectures on Determinants and Matrices." Akadamie-Verlag G.m.b.H., Berlin.

Schwerdtfeger, H. (1950). "Introduction to Linear Algebra and the Theory of Matrices." P. Noordhoff, Groningen.

Turnbull, H. W. (1945). "The Theory of Determinants, Matrices, and Invariants." Blackie and Son, London and Glasgow.

Turnbull, H. W., and Aitken, A. C. (1932). "An Introduction to the Theory of Canonical Matrices." Blackie and Son, London and Glasgow.

Wade, T. L. (1951). "The Algebra of Vectors and Matrices." Addison-Wesley Press, Cambridge.

Wedderburn, J. H. M. (1934). "Lectures on Matrices." Am. Mathematical Soc., New York.

Wintner, A. (1929). "Spectral Theory of Infinite Matrices." S. Hirzel, Leipzig.

Zurmuhl, R. (1950). "Matrices." Springer-Verlag, Berlin.

Chapter II

GROUPS

1. Abstract Properties

In this chapter we shall review some properties of "abstract" finite groups which are relevant to representation theory (where by "abstract" groups is meant groups whose elements are represented by symbols whose only duty is to satisfy a group multiplication table). However, the study of the representation properties of abstract groups will not be taken up until the next chapter. At the end of this chapter some applications of finite groups to problems of physics will be given.

The most important concepts (other than that of a group) which will be developed in this chapter are the concepts of homomorphism, normal subgroups, quotient group, class, class multiplication coefficient, and function on a group. For the sake of completeness, let us start off with a definition of a group.

Definition. A *group* is a set of distinct elements together with a binary multiplication law* such that

(1) multiplication is defined for every ordered pair of elements in the group
(2) multiplication is closed (i.e., the product of two elements in the group is always in the group)
(3) multiplication is single-valued
(4) multiplication is associative
(5) there exists an identity element in the group (i.e., an element I such that $IA = AI = A$ for all elements A in the group)
(6) every element has an inverse relative to the identity of (5) (i.e., if A is an element of the group, then there exists an element B such that $BA = AB = I$)
(7) equality of group elements is an equivalence relation (i.e., equality is reflexive, symmetric, transitive, and defined for all pairs of elements in the group in the sense that any two are definitely either equal or not equal).

---

* Let S be any set, and let P be the set of all ordered pairs of elements of S. Then any function F defined for all elements of P will be called a binary multiplication law for S. The values of F may or may not lie in S. Instead of writing $F(A,B)$ we shall just write AB.

We know that there can be only one identity in a group, and that there can be only one inverse for each element.

From the above definition we see that a group can be completely defined by specifying the product of every ordered pair of elements. This can be done by writing down a multiplication table for the elements.

Example.

	I	A_1	A_2	A_3	A_4	A_5	A_6	A_7
I	I	A_1	A_2	A_3	A_4	A_5	A_6	A_7
A_1	A_1	I	A_3	A_2	A_5	A_4	A_7	A_6
A_2	A_2	A_3	A_1	I	A_6	A_7	A_5	A_4
A_3	A_3	A_2	I	A_1	A_7	A_6	A_4	A_5
A_4	A_4	A_3	A_7	A_6	A_1	I	A_2	A_3
A_5	A_5	A_3	A_6	A_7	I	A_1	A_3	A_2
A_6	A_6	A_3	A_4	A_5	A_3	A_2	A_1	I
A_7	A_7	A_3	A_5	A_4	A_2	A_3	I	A_1

This is the multiplication table for a group consisting of eight elements (which are represented by the symbols $I, A_1, \ldots, A_7$). (The group is said to be of *order* eight). The entry in the ith row and jth column is the product $A_i A_j$. It should also be recalled that a group element must appear exactly once in each row and in each column of the group multiplication table. The above specified group is called the quaternion group Q and is of interest to physicists because of its connection with Hamilton's quaternions. This group will be used frequently in the following to provide examples.

The multiplication table of a group is simply a convenient way of writing down a series of equations of the form

$$A_i A_j = A_k.$$

However, it is frequently possible to define a group by using a smaller number of equations than is contained in the multiplication table. For example, the following relations hold for the elements of the quaternion group:

$$A_3^4 = I \qquad A_3^2 = A_5^2 \qquad A_3^{-1} A_5 A_3 = A_5^{-1}.$$

If one takes these equations as basic instead of the multiplication table, and if one defines the group to be the set of elements consisting of all distinct products of I, A_3, and A_5, then one finds that these elements again satisfy the multiplication table of the quaternion group.

In general a set of equations implying the group multiplication table as above is called a set of *defining relations* for the group. The A's appearing in the defining relations are called the associated *generators* of the group. Obviously, the group multiplication table itself is a set of defining relations whose associated generators are all elements of the group. We also saw that the quaternion group could be generated by the elements A_3 and A_5.

The *rank* of a group is the minimum number of generators required, and a *basis* of a group is such a minimum set of generators. The quaternion group, for example, has rank two.*

If the elements of two groups can be so arranged that they satisfy the same multiplication table, then they are essentially the same group and are said to be *isomorphic* to each other. There is then a one-one correspondence between the elements of two isomorphic groups, and this correspondence is called the *isomorphism*.

Example.

	1	−1	i	$-i$	j	$-j$	k	$-k$
1	1	−1	i	$-i$	j	$-j$	k	$-k$
−1	−1	1	$-i$	i	$-j$	j	$-k$	k
i	i	$-i$	−1	1	k	$-k$	$-j$	j
$-i$	$-i$	i	1	−1	$-k$	k	j	$-j$
j	j	$-j$	$-k$	k	−1	1	i	$-i$
$-j$	$-j$	j	k	$-k$	1	−1	$-i$	i
k	k	$-k$	j	$-j$	$-i$	i	−1	1
$-k$	$-k$	k	$-j$	j	i	$-i$	1	−1

This is isomorphic to the quaternion group via the correspondence

$$\begin{aligned} 1 &\leftrightarrow I \\ -1 &\leftrightarrow A_1 \\ i &\leftrightarrow A_2 \\ -i &\leftrightarrow A_3 \\ j &\leftrightarrow A_4 \\ -j &\leftrightarrow A_5 \\ k &\leftrightarrow A_6 \\ -k &\leftrightarrow A_7. \end{aligned}$$

(The elements i, j, and k are generalizations of the imaginary number $\sqrt{-1}$ and are called the quaternion units. A quaternion is a linear combination of quaternion units).

A group is always isomorphic to itself (one possible isomorphism being the trivial association of each element with itself). However, there are frequently nontrivial isomorphisms of a group with itself. Consequently, an isomorphism of a group with itself is given the special name *automorphism*, and the set of

* For further details on generators, see W. Magnus, "Combinatorial Group Theory," in preparation.

all automorphisms of a group is itself a group if multiplication of automorphisms is taken to be successive application of the automorphisms.

We come now to the key concept of homomorphism which is a generalization of the concept of isomorphism.

Definition. Let

$$G_1 = \{I, A_1, \ldots, A_{g_1}\}$$

$$G_2 = \{I, B_1, \ldots, B_{g_1}\}$$

be two groups. Then G_1 is *homomorphic* to G_2 if there exists a many-to-one (possibly 1-1) correspondence of G_1 onto G_2 which preserves multiplication (i.e., if $A_i \to B_i$ then $A_i A_j \to B_i B_j$).

Example. Consider the group (called D_2) of order four with the following multiplication table.

	I	B_1	B_2	B_3
I	I	B_1	B_2	B_3
B_1	B_1	I	B_3	B_2
B_2	B_2	B_3	I	B_1
B_3	B_3	B_2	B_1	I

Then Q is homomorphic to D_2 via the correspondence

$$I, A_1 \to I$$
$$A_2, A_3 \to B_1$$
$$A_4, A_5 \to B_2$$
$$A_6, A_7 \to B_3.$$

We note that homomorphism is a directed relation (larger group homomorphic to smaller) and is therefore not an equivalence relation. The smaller group is called the *homomorph* of the larger.

Definition. The *kernel* of a homomorphism is the set of elements of the larger group which is mapped onto (corresponds to) the identity element of the homomorph.

Example. In the above homomorphism of Q to D_2 the kernel consisted of the two elements I and A_1 of Q.

A homomorphism of a group onto one of its subgroups is also given a special name, *endomorphism*.

If by a *subgroup* of a group G we understand a subset of G which also is a group when used in conjunction with the multiplication law of G, then we recall that the order of a subgroup is always a divisor (with integral quotient) of the order of the whole group, and we can consider the next key concept, normal subgroup.

Definition. A *normal* (or invariant, or self-conjugate) *subgroup* H of a group G is a subgroup such that for any element A in G and any element B in H, $A^{-1}BA = B'$, where B' is also in H.

Example. $H = \{I, A_1\}$ is a normal subgroup of Q of *index* 4 (index = order of $G \div$ order of H).

We recall also that every subgroup of index 2 is a normal subgroup.

If A_1 and A_2 are elements of a group G, then by the *conjugate* of A_2 with respect to A_1 is meant the element $A_1^{-1}A_2A_1$; so a subgroup H of G is normal if and only if the conjugate of every element of H with respect to every element of G is in H. We can symbolize this neatly by saying that H is normal in G, if and only if, $A^{-1}HA = H$ for all A in G.

If G is any group, and A is any element in G, then $A^{-1}GA = G$, but it is easily seen that the correspondence $A_i \to A^{-1}A_iA$ (A fixed) is an automorphism of G. Such an automorphism, which is produced by conjugation, is called an *inner automorphism* (all others being called *outer*). We can then say that a subgroup H of a group G is normal, if, and only if, H is invariant under all inner automorphisms.

If G is any group, $H = \{B_1 \ldots B_h\}$ is any subgroup of G, and A is any element of G, then the set of elements $AH = \{AB_1, \ldots, AB_h\}$ is called a *left coset* of H. We recall that two left cosets of H are either identical or disjoint, and that the order of a left coset of H is a divisor of the order of G. We can then characterize a normal subgroup H of G as a subgroup such that every left coset AH is also a right coset HA'. In fact, H is normal, if and only if, $AH = HA$.

Furthermore, with the help of cosets we can introduce the next key concept, quotient group. First though, let us define the product and the proper product of two subsets of a group G.

Definition. (a) If $S_1 = \{B_i\}$ and $S_2 = \{C_j\}$ are two subsets of a group G, then the *product* of S_1 and S_2 is the set of all products B_iC_j.

(b) The *proper* product of S_1 and S_2 is the set of all distinct products B_iC_j.

The proper product is then always a subset of the product.

Theorem. If G is any group and H any normal subgroup of G, then, with the proper product as the law of multiplication, the distinct cosets of H form a group.

Example. Let $G = Q$, $H = \{I, A_1\}$. The distinct cosets of H are $S_1 = A_2H = \{A_2, A_3\}$, $S_2 = A_4H = \{A_4 A_5\}$, $S_3 = A_6H = \{A_6 A_7\}$, and H itself. One easily sees, for example, that $S_1S_2 = S_3$. In fact the group of cosets of H is isomorphic to D_2.

Definition. The group of distinct cosets of a normal subgroup H of a group G is called the *quotient* (*or factor*) *group* of G with respect to H, and is symbolized by G/H.

It should be observed that the order of G/H is g/h ($h =$ order of H), and that the order of a quotient group is therefore a divisor of the order of the original group.

We can now state an important theorem connecting homomorphisms, normal subgroups, and quotient groups (for which we recall that the kernel of a homomorphism must be a normal subgroup).

Theorem. Every homomorph G' of a group G is isomorphic to the quotient group G/K, where K is the kernel of the homomorphism $G \to G'$, and conversely, every quotient group G/K is a homomorph with kernel K.

The last example of a quotient group provides an example, because we had previously shown that Q was homomorphic to D_2. Since in this case H is a cyclic group of order two, we can write $Q/C_2 = D_2$.

Let us now introduce the key concept of class and tie it up with the preceding key concepts.

Definition. A class of a group is a maximal set of mutually conjugate elements.

That is, if $C = \{B_i\}$ is a class of G, then G contains no element which is conjugate to one of the elements B_i of C but is not in C; also, every two elements of C must be conjugate to each other with respect to some element of G.

Example. Q has the classes

$$C_1 = I, \quad C_2 = A_1, \quad C_3 = \{A_2, A_3\},$$
$$C_4 = \{A_4, A_5\}, \quad C_5 = \{A_6, A_7\}.$$

Again we recall that two classes are either identical or disjoint, that the order of a class is a divisor of the order of the group, and that every element of the group is in some class.

Note. The ith class of a group will subsequently be denoted by C_i, and its order by r_i. Also, the total number of classes of a group will be denoted by r.

Furthermore, every element of C_i has the same order (the *order* of an element A being the smallest positive integer α such that $A^\alpha = I$), and this order is a divisor of g/r_i ($g =$ order of the group). Also, a curious property of groups of odd order is that $(g - r)$ must be divisible by 16, as a result of which a group of odd order must have an odd number of classes. We should also recall that every class of an *Abelian* (or commutative) group has order one.

In connection with orders of elements, it should be mentioned that two groups which have the same number of elements of each order are said to be *conformal* to each other. If, then, two groups are isomorphic, they are certainly conformal, so that if they are not conformal they are not isomorphic.

Hence, in testing for nonisomorphism it is frequently sufficient to test for nonconformality.

Theorem. Let G be a group, H a subgroup of G, C a class of G, and M the subset $C \cap H$ of H. Then M is composed of whole classes of H.

We can now connect classes with normal subgroups and homomorphisms.

Theorem. A subgroup is normal if, and only if, it is composed of whole classes (i.e., a class either lies entirely within a normal subgroup or entirely without).

Example The normal subgroup $H = \{I, A_1\}$ of Q is composed of the classes C_1 and C_2 of Q.

Theorem. (1) In any homomorphism, the image of a class is entirely contained in a class of the homomorph.

(2) The order of a class of $G/H = \frac{1}{h} \sum r_i$, where the sum is extended over all classes of G which are mapped on the given class of the homomorph.

(3) If G/H is abelian, then each coset of H is composed of whole classes of G.

(4) If S_1 and S_2 are cosets of a normal subgroup H, and if S_2 contains an element conjugate to an element of S_1, then S_1 and S_2 are in the same class of G/H.

(5) If H and K are normal subgroups of G such that $G \supset H \supset K$, then
(a) H/K is isomorphic to a subgroup of G/K.
(b) G/K is homomorphic to G/H.

Let us now return to classes and sharpen one previous statement about the order of a class. Let us understand a *self-conjugate* element to be an element which is invariant under all inner automorphisms, and the *center* of a group to be the set of all self-conjugate elements (which must be a normal subgroup).

Theorem. The order of every class of a group is a divisor of the index of the center of the group.

Example. The center of Q is $\{I, A_1\}$ which has index 4, while the orders of the classes of Q are $r_1 = r_2 = 1$, $r_3 = r_4 = r_5 = 2$.

The next key concept is the concept of class multiplication.

Theorem. Every product $C_i C_j$ of two classes of a group G can be decomposed into a (set-theoretic) sum of classes; i.e.,

$$C_i C_j = \sum_{k=1}^{r} h_{ij,k} C_k,$$

where the coefficients $h_{ij,k}$ are called the *class multiplication coefficients.*

This result means that although an element of the class C_k may occur several times in the product $C_i C_j$, every element of C_k must occur in $C_i C_j$ the same number of times. Further, since an element of C_k can only occur an integral number of times in C_iC_j, it follows that the coefficients $h_{ij,k}$ must be nonnegative integers. Also, it can easily be seen that class multiplication is commutative.

Example. For Q we have

$$\begin{aligned} C_1C_i &= C_i \qquad (i = 1,\ldots,5)\\ C_2^2 &= C_1\\ C_2C_i &= C_i \qquad (i = 3,4,5)\\ C_3^2 &= 2C_1 + 2C_2\\ C_3C_4 &= 2C_5\\ C_3C_5 &= 2C_4\\ C_4^2 &= 2C_1 + 2C_2\\ C_4C_5 &= 2C_3\\ C_5^2 &= 2C_1 + 2C_2. \end{aligned}$$

From this class multiplication table we can easily read off any desired coefficient $h_{ij,k}$. For example, $h_{34,5} = 2$; whereas $h_{34,i} = 0$, for $i \neq 5$.

There are several general relations which the class multiplication coefficients of any group must satisfy, and they are listed below.

Theorem. (1) $h_{ij,k} = h_{ji,k}$

(2) $\sum_{k=1}^{r} h_{ij,k}h_{kl,m} = \sum_{k=1}^{r} h_{jl,k}h_{ik,m}$

(3) $r_ir_j = \sum_{k=1}^{r} h_{ij,k}r_k$

(4) $r_ih_{kj',i} = r_kh_{ij,k}$

(5) $h_{ij,k} = h_{i'j'k'}$

(6) $r_kh_{ij,k} = r_ih_{jk',i'}$

(7) $r_kh_{ij,k} = r_jh_{ik',j'}$

(8) $h_{ij,1} = r_i\delta_{i',j}$

where the primes denote inverse classes (i.e., $C_{i'}$, is the class which contains the inverses of the elements of the class C_i).

We can now state another connection between classes and normal subgroups.

Theorem. A set of classes $\{C_i\}$ is a normal subgroup if and only if the product of any pair of classes in the set can be expressed as an integral linear (set-theoretic) combination of classes of the set.

Thus we see that the classes C_1, C_2, and C_3 of Q form a normal subgroup of Q.

Let us define an *ambivalent* class to be a class which is its own inverse, and let r_a be the number of ambivalent classes in a group G. Thus, for Q, the classes are all ambivalent, so $r_a = 5$. For groups of odd order, however, $r_a = 1$, the only ambivalent class being the identity.

Let us further define $\zeta(A)$ to be the number of group elements whose squares are equal to the group element A; in short, $\zeta(A)$ is the number of square roots of A. For Q we have $\zeta(I) = 2$, $\zeta(A_1) = 6$, and $\zeta(A_i) = 0$ for $i = 2,\ldots,7$.

Theorem.
$$\frac{1}{g} \sum_{A \epsilon G} \zeta^2(A) = r_a.$$

For Q this says $\frac{1}{8}(2^2 + 6^2) = 5$. Another easily derived relation is:
$$\sum_{A \epsilon G} \zeta^3(A) = \sum_{A \epsilon G} \zeta^2(A^2).$$

Let us denote by $\xi(A)$ the number of group elements which commute with A, and by $r(A)$ the order of the class containing A.

Then $r(A)\,\xi(A) = g$. Thus, for Q, $\xi(I) = \xi(A_1) = 8$ and $\xi(A_i) = 4$, $i = 2,\ldots,7$.

Theorem. Every class of a group is ambivalent (i.e., $r_a = r$) if and only if
$$\sum_{A \epsilon G} \zeta^2(A) = \sum_{A \epsilon G} \xi(A).$$

For Q (whose classes are all ambivalent) this says $(2^2 + 6^2) = (2 \times 8 + 6 \times 4)$.

In general, an inequality relates $\zeta(A)$ and $\xi(A)$.

Theorem.
$$\sum_{A \epsilon G} \zeta^3(A) \leqslant \sum_{A \epsilon G} \xi^2(A).$$

For Q this becomes $(2^3 + 6^3) \leqslant (2 \times 8^2 + 6 \times 4^2)$, which is in fact an equality.

Definition. A *simply reducible* group is a group such that
$$\sum_{A \epsilon G} \zeta^3(A) = \sum_{A \epsilon G} \xi^2(A).$$

Thus, Q is a simply reducible group; and in fact, many groups of mathematical physics are simply reducible. A somewhat more interesting characterization of simply reducible groups can be given in terms of representation theory.

Theorem. Every class of a simply reducible group is ambivalent.

The only simply reducible group of odd order is therefore the trivial group of order one.

Theorem. Every homomorph of a simply reducible group is simply reducible.

There remain several miscellaneous topics for discussion, one remaining key concept, and some applications.

Let us call a subgroup H of a group G *proper* if H is neither G itself nor the identity. Also, let us call a normal subgroup *maximal* if it is proper but is not a proper subgroup of any other proper normal subgroup, and *minimal* if it is proper but contains no other proper normal subgroup. For example, Q has four proper subgroups all of which are normal (and cyclic). However, only the three normal subgroups of order four are maximal.

Theorem. Every finite group G of order greater than 1 possesses a finite series of subgroups $G, H_1, \ldots, H_s, I$, such that

$$G \supset H_1 \supset H_2 \supset \ldots \supset H_s \supset I,$$

and H_{i+1} is a maximal normal subgroup of H_i. Such a series is called a *composition series* of G, the quotient groups $G/H_1, H_1/H_2, \ldots, H_{s-1}/H_s, H_s$ are called *composition quotient groups*, the order of the composition quotient groups h_i/h_{i+1} are called the *composition indices*, and the integer $(s+1)$ is called the *length* of the composition series.

Example. Q has the composition series Q, H_1, H_2, I where $H_1 = \{I, A_1 A_2, A_3\}$ and $H_2 = \{I, A_1\}$. The composition quotient groups are

$$\frac{Q}{H_1} = C_2 \quad \frac{H_1}{H_2} = C_2 \quad H_2 = C_2,$$

where C_2 denotes the cyclic group of order two, and the equality sign in the last three equations means isomorphic. The composition indices are $2, 2, 2$ and the length is 3.

The composition series of a group is unique in a rather abstract sense according to the Jordan-Hölder theorem.

Theorem. The composition quotient groups belonging to two composition series of a group are, apart from their sequence, isomorphic in pairs.

That is, if $G \supset H_1 \supset \ldots \supset H_s \supset I$ is one composition series, and $G \supset K_1 \supset \ldots \supset K_t \supset I$ is another, then $t = s$, and corresponding to any composition quotient group K_j/K_{j+1} there is a composition quotient group H_i/H_{i+1} such that

$$\frac{K_j}{K_{j+1}} = \frac{H_i}{H_{i+1}}.$$

Definition. A *solvable* (or integrable) group is a group whose composition indices are all prime numbers (a prime number being a positive integer which is divisible only by itself and one).

Thus Q is a solvable group, and so in fact are all 3-dimensional crystallographic groups. Since the only groups of prime order are cyclic groups, we see that the composition quotient groups of a solvable group must be cyclic.

Note. (1) Every group of order < 60 is solvable.

(2) Every abelian group is solvable.

(3) If G contains a solvable normal subgroup H such that G/H is also solvable, then G is solvable.

(4) If G is a homomorph of a solvable group, it is solvable.

(5) Every subgroup of a solvable group is solvable.

Solvable groups can also be characterized in what appears to be a less restrictive manner.

Definition. A *normal series* of a group G is a series of subgroups $G, H_1, \ldots, H_s, I$ such that H_{i+1} is a proper normal subgroup of H_i.

Thus, a composition series is a normal series.

Theorem. A group is solvable if and only if it possesses a normal series whose quotient groups H_i/H_{i+1} are abelian.

This characterization is used as a definition of solvability for infinite groups.

We come now to the study of a subgroup which will be of considerable use in representation theory. By a *commutator* (in a group) is meant a group element which can be expressed as a product of group elements in the form $A^{-1}B^{-1}AB$. The commutator which was used for matrices is not used here because groups have no operation of addition. However, what we were usually interested in was whether or not the commutator of two matrices was zero. But, if D_1 and D_2 are nonsingular, then $[D_1, D_2] = 0$ if and only if $D_1 D_2 D_1^{-1} D_2^{-1} = I$. We see in particular that I is always a commutator, that if A is a commutator so is A^{-1}, and that if one element of a class is a commutator, so is every element. (Call such a class a *commutator class*.)

Theorem. A class C_i consists of commutators if and only if there exists a class C_j such that $h_{ji,j} \neq 0$.

Definition. The *commutator subgroup* (or derived group) H_c of a group is the minimal subgroup which contains all commutators of the group.

The commutator subgroup of Q is the second order subgroup $\{I, A_1\}$ in which every element is a commutator.

Theorem. H_c is normal, its quotient group is abelian, and it is contained in every normal subgroup whose quotient group is abelian.

From this theorem comes an important representation-theoretic property of H_c. We can now connect H_c with the classes of G.

Note. H_c consists of the commutator classes together with the set of all those classes which occur in the decomposition of products of commutator classes.

Note. $r_i \leqslant h_c$ (all i), $r \geqslant g/h_c$, which is true for Q because $h_c = 2$, $r_1 = r_2 = 1$, $r_3 = r_4 = r_5 = 2$, $r = 5$, and $g/h_c = 4$.

We can now give a somewhat more straightforward characterization of solvable groups. Let us call a group (of order > 1) *perfect* if it is identical with its commutator subgroup. Every perfect group is then insolvable. In general, however, we have the following result.

Theorem. The series of commutator subgroups $G, H_1, H_2, \ldots$ (H_{i+1} being the commutator subgroup of H_i) either terminates with the identity or with a perfect group. In the first case G is solvable and in the second case G is insolvable.

Thus, for Q the series is: Q; $\{I, A_1\}$; I. One can thus test the solvability of a group by constructing the series of commutator subgroups, which is quite straightforward, if laborious.

Let us now turn our attention to direct products of groups.

Definition. The *direct product* $G_1 \times G_2$ of two groups $G_1 = \{A_1, \ldots, A_{g_1}\}$, $G_2 = \{B_1, \ldots, B_{g_2}\}$ is the set of all ordered pairs (A_i, B_j) with multiplication of pairs defined by $(A_i, B_j)\ (A_k, B_l) \equiv (A_i A_j, B_k B_l)$, and is a group.

Example. $C_2 \times C_2 = D_2$ (where C_2 is the cyclic group of order two and D_2 was defined earlier).

Let us list here some simple properties of direct products.

Theorem. (1) Order $(G_1 \times G_2) = g_1 g_2$.
(2) $G_1 \times G_2$ is isomorphic to $G_2 \times G_1$.
(3) Both G_1 and G_2 are normal subgroups of $G_1 \times G_2$.
(4) The direct product of two abelian groups is abelian.
(5) The direct product of two solvable groups is solvable.
(6) The number of classes of $G_1 \times G_2$ is $r_1 r_2$.
(7) If C_1 and C_2 are classes of G_1 and G_2, respectively, then the set of elements $C_1 \times C_2$ is a class of $G_1 \times G_2$, and every class of $G_1 \times G_2$ is of this type.
(8) If H_1 and H_2 are normal subgroups of G_1 and G_2, respectively, then $H_1 \times H_2$ is a normal subgroup of $G_1 \times G_2$, and $(G_1 \times G_2)/(H_1 \times H_2)$ is isomorphic to $(G_1/H_1) \times (G_2/H_2)$.
(9) If H is a normal subgroup of G, then $G = H \times (G/H)$ if and only if G contains a subgroup K such that K is isomorphic to G/H, $H \cap K = I$, and every element of H commutes with every element of K.
(10) $(A, B)^{-1} = (A^{-1}, B^{-1})$.

Let us call a group *decomposable* if it is isomorphic to the direct product of two groups of order greater than one, and *indecomposable* otherwise. Then D_2 is decomposable and C_4 indecomposable. Then every perfect group has a unique decomposition into indecomposable factors. Also, the fundamental theorem of abelian groups is a decomposition theorem.

Theorem. Every abelian group is the direct product of cyclic groups whose orders are powers of primes (e.g., $D_2 = C_2 \times C_2$).

Returning for the moment to normal subgroups, let us call a group *simple* if it contains no proper normal subgroups, and *semisimple* if it contains no proper, normal, solvable subgroups. The lowest order of a simple group is 60. This group is the icosahedral group, which is also the lowest-order insolvable group. A conjectured property of odd-order groups is that no groups of composite (nonprime) odd order are simple.

A useful concept which should be mentioned here is that of covering group.

Definition. Let G be any group and G' any other group which contains a subgroup H' in its center such that $G'/H' = G$. Then G' is called a *covering group* of G extended by the abelian group H'.

Example. $G = D_2 \quad G' = Q \quad H' = C_2$

The center of the quaternion group is the group C_2 of order two, and the quotient group Q/C_2 is the previous mentioned group D_2 of order four.

Let us now introduce a useful generalization of the idea of a coset. By a *double coset* of G is meant any set of elements $G_1 A G_2$, where G_1 and G_2 are subgroups of G, and A is any element of G. Then, as for ordinary cosets, two double cosets $G_1 A G_2$ and $G_1 B G_2$ formed from the same pair of subgroups are either identical or disjoint. Again, G can be expressed as a (set-theoretic) sum of double cosets $G = \sum_1 G_1 A_i G_2$ where the number of cosets required in the expansion is $gg_{12}/g_1 g_2$, and $g_{12} =$ order $(G_1 \cap G_2)$. Finally, the number of distinct elements in the double coset $G_1 A G_2$ is $g_1 g_2/g_{12}$, which is independent of A.

In connection with automorphisms, let us call a group *complete* if it has no outer automorphisms and its center is the identity.

One important topic to be covered before the last key concept is the semidirect product. The semidirect product is not defined for an arbitrary pair of groups G_1 and G_2, for G_2 must be a group of automorphisms of G_1.

Definition. Let $G = \{A\}$ be any group
$\bar{\mathscr{A}}$ be the group of all automorphisms of G
$\mathscr{A} = \{\alpha\}$ be any subgroup of $\bar{\mathscr{A}}$
$\alpha(A)$ be the image of A under the automorphism α.

Then the *semidirect product*, $G \boxed{S} \mathscr{A}$, of G and $\mathscr{A}$ is the group of all ordered pairs (A, α) with multiplication defined by

$$(A, \alpha)\ (B, \beta) = (A\alpha(B), \alpha\beta).$$

Corollary. The order of $G \boxed{S} \mathscr{A}$ is the product of the orders of G and $\mathscr{A}$.

Example. Instead of using Q for an example, let us use D_2, because it leads to groups of lower order. In an automorphism the identity must always be mapped on the identity. Remarkably, in the case of D_2, every one-to-one correspondence of elements of D_2 satisfying this restriction is an automorphism of D_2. Thus the automorphism group of D_2 is of order 6, and is in fact the group D_3 with the following multiplication table (in which only the subscripts of α's are indicated).

D_3

I	1	2	3	4	5
1	5	3	4	2	I
2	4	I	5	1	3
3	2	1	I	5	4
4	3	5	1	I	2
5	I	4	2	3	1

Clearly, the elements I, α_1, and α_5 form a cyclic subgroup of order 3, C_3. This subgroup of the automorphism group of D_2 is the following set of automorphisms.

I	α_1	α_5
$I \to I$	$I \to I$	$I \to I$
$A_1 \to A_1$	$A_1 \to A_2$	$A_1 \to A_3$
$A_2 \to A_2$	$A_2 \to A_3$	$A_2 \to A_1$
$A_3 \to A_3$	$A_3 \to A_1$	$A_3 \to A_2$

Let us choose this subgroup of the automorphism group to be $\mathscr{A}$, and compute $D \boxed{S}\, \mathscr{A}$. The semidirect product is then a group of order 12 whose elements are the ordered pairs (A_i, α_j). As an example of the multiplication of these elements we have

$$(A_2, \alpha_1)(A_3, \alpha_5) = (A_2\alpha_1(A_3), \alpha_1\alpha_5) = (A_2A_1, \alpha_1\alpha_5) = (A_3, I),$$

whereas

$$(A_3, \alpha_5)(A_2, \alpha_1) = (A_2, I).$$

Hence, $D_2 \boxed{S}\, C_3$ is not abelian, even though D_2 and C_3 are. Further calculation shows that $D_2 \boxed{S}\, C_3 = T$, where T is the tetrahedral group, which has the following multiplication table, generators, and defining relations.

I	1	2	3	4	5	6	7	8	9	10	11
1	I	3	2	5	4	7	6	9	8	11	10
2	4	6	8	9	7	I	10	11	1	5	3
3	5	7	9	8	6	1	11	10	I	4	2
4	2	8	6	7	9	10	I	1	11	3	5
5	3	9	7	6	8	11	1	I	10	2	4
6	9	I	11	1	10	2	5	3	4	7	8
7	8	1	10	I	11	3	4	2	5	6	9
8	7	10	1	11	I	4	3	5	2	9	6
9	6	11	I	10	1	5	2	4	3	8	7
10	11	4	5	2	3	8	9	6	7	I	1
11	10	5	4	3	2	9	8	7	6	1	I

T

$$B_1^2 = B^3{}_2 = I \qquad (B_2B_1)^2 = B_1B_2^2$$

It might also be noted that although D_2 has 4 classes and C_3 has 3, T has only 4.

Some useful results on semidirect products are the following:

Theorem. (1) $(A, \alpha)^{-1} = (\alpha^{-1}(A^{-1}), \alpha^{-1})$.

(2) $G = H \boxed{S} \mathscr{A} = \{(A, \alpha)\}$

$H = \{(A, I)\} \qquad \mathscr{A} = \{(I, \alpha)\}$

imply that

$G = H\mathscr{A} \qquad H \cap \mathscr{A} = (I, I)$.

(3) $G = H \boxed{S} \mathscr{A}$ implies H is a normal subgroup of G.

(4) $G = H \boxed{S} \mathscr{A}$ implies $G/H = \mathscr{A}$.

(5) $G = H \boxed{S} \mathscr{A}$, H and $\mathscr{A}$ solvable implies G solvable.

The semidirect product $G \boxed{S} \bar{\mathscr{A}}$ of a group G with its total automorphism group $\bar{\mathscr{A}}$ is called the *holomorph* of G.

Let us now take up the last key concept.

Definition. A *function on a group* is a correspondence (possibly many-to-one) which associates a number with each element of the group.

Example. The following equations (correspondence) define a function on Q.

$$\begin{aligned} f(I) &= 2{\cdot}3 & f(A_4) &= \frac{41}{17} - \frac{59}{31}i \\ f(A_1) &= 39{\cdot}7 & f(A_5) &= e^{i\pi^2} \\ f(A_2) &= -7/3 & f(A_6) &= 10^{73} \\ f(A_3) &= 5i & f(A_7) &= 0. \end{aligned}$$

It will be noted that if $f(A)$ is any function on the group G, and if B is any element of G, then $\sum_{A \in G} f(A) = \sum_{A \in G} f(BA) = \sum_{A \in G} f(AB)$.

Of particular interest are the so-called class functions.

Definition. A *class function* is a function on a group which has the same value for all elements of a class.

Example.

$$\begin{aligned} f(I) &= 1 - 2i & f(A_4) &= 0 \\ f(A_1) &= \cot 79 & f(A_5) &= 0 \\ f(A_2) &= e^{-2.9i} & f(A_6) &= 11! \\ f(A_3) &= e^{-2.9i} & f(A_7) &= 11! \end{aligned}$$

is a class function on Q.

The value of a class function f on the class C_i is frequently denoted by f_i.

Let us now clean up some details relating to particular groups before turning to applications. We shall subsequently be particularly interested in the groups C_n (cyclic group of order n), D_n (dihedral group of order $2n$), T (tetrahedral group), and O (octahedral group) because every crystallographic point group is either one of these groups or a direct product of two of them.

The cyclic group C_n requires only one generator A, and one defining relation, $A^n = I$. Since C_n is abelian it has n classes, and the commutator subgroup is the identity. The dihedral group D_n can be generated by two generators A_1 and A_2, and three defining relations

$$A_1^2 = I \qquad A_2^n = I \qquad A_2 A_1 A_2 = A_1.$$

The number of classes of D_n is given by

$$\begin{aligned} r &= \tfrac{1}{2}(n+1) && n \text{ odd} \\ &= \tfrac{1}{2}n + 3 && n \text{ even.} \end{aligned}$$

Also, the order of the commutator subgroup is given by

$$\begin{aligned} h_c &= n && n \text{ odd} \\ &= \tfrac{1}{2}\, n && n \text{ even.} \end{aligned}$$

The properties of the tetrahedral group T have already been discussed, except for the order of the commutator subgroup, which is four.

The octahedral group O is a nonabelian group of order 24 which has two generators A_1 and A_2 and the defining relations

$$A_1^4 = A_2^3 = I \qquad A_1 A_2^2 A_1 = A_2 \qquad A_1 A_2 A_1 = A_2 A_1^2 A_2.$$

The octahedral group O has 5 classes and a commutator subgroup of order 12, which is in fact the tetrahedral group. The multiplication table of O is shown on the following page.

Another group of interest is the icosahedral group $\mathscr{I}$, which is a molecular point group. It is the simple insolvable group of order 60, and has five classes. Also, $\mathscr{I}$ is a perfect group. Its generators and defining relations are

$$\begin{aligned} A_1^3 = A_2^2 = A_3^2 &= I \\ (A_1 A_2)^3 = (A_2 A_3)^3 &= I \\ (A_1 A_3)^2 &= I. \end{aligned}$$

The groups C_2, D_n, and O are simply reducible, whereas C_n $(n \neq 2)$, T, and $\mathscr{I}$ are not.

It is easily seen that the set of all 3-dimensional rotation matrices is a group (infinite) if the group operation is taken to be matrix multiplication. This group is called the 3-dimensional rotation group R_3, and has as non-isomorphic finite subgroups just the groups discussed above: C_n, D_n, T, O, and $\mathscr{I}$.

The 3-dimensional orthogonal matrices form the 3-dimensional orthogonal group O_3 which has three types of finite subgroups:

(1) C_n, D_n, T, O, $\mathscr{I}$

(2) $C_n \times C_2$, $D_n \times C_2$, $T \times C_2$, $O \times C_2$, $\mathscr{I} \times C_2$

(3) subgroups H' formed from subgroups of type one by choosing any subgroup K of index 2 of a subgroup H of type one, and forming the set of elements

THE OCTAHEDRAL GROUP MULTIPLICATION TABLE

O

I	1	2	3	4	5	6	7	8	9	10	11	12	13	14	15	16	17	18	19	20	21	22	23
1	6	3	4	5	2	7	*I*	9	10	11	8	13	14	15	12	17	18	19	16	21	22	23	20
2	8	12	16	9	1	20	13	5	19	21	6	*I*	23	17	3	15	22	10	4	11	18	14	7
3	9	13	17	10	6	21	14	2	16	22	7	1	20	18	4	12	23	11	5	8	19	15	*I*
4	10	14	18	11	7	22	15	3	17	23	*I*	6	21	19	5	13	20	8	2	9	16	12	1
5	11	15	19	8	*I*	23	12	4	18	20	1	7	22	16	2	14	21	9	3	10	17	13	6
6	7	4	5	2	3	*I*	1	10	11	8	9	14	15	12	13	18	19	16	17	22	23	20	21
7	*I*	5	2	3	4	1	6	11	8	9	10	15	12	13	14	19	16	17	18	23	20	21	22
8	20	16	9	1	12	13	2	19	21	6	5	23	17	3	*I*	22	10	4	15	18	14	7	11
9	21	17	10	6	13	14	3	16	22	7	2	20	18	4	1	23	11	5	12	19	15	*I*	8
10	22	18	11	7	14	15	4	17	23	*I*	3	21	19	5	6	20	8	2	13	16	12	1	9
11	23	19	8	*I*	15	12	5	18	20	1	4	22	16	2	7	21	9	3	14	17	13	6	10
12	5	*I*	15	19	8	11	23	1	4	18	20	2	7	22	16	3	14	21	9	6	10	17	13
13	2	1	12	16	9	8	20	6	5	19	21	3	*I*	23	17	4	15	22	10	7	11	18	14
14	3	6	13	17	10	9	21	7	2	16	22	4	1	20	18	5	12	23	11	*I*	8	19	15
15	4	7	14	18	11	10	22	*I*	3	17	23	5	6	21	19	2	13	20	8	1	9	16	12
16	19	23	22	21	20	18	17	12	15	14	13	8	11	10	9	*I*	7	6	1	5	4	3	2
17	16	20	23	22	21	19	18	13	12	15	14	9	8	11	10	1	*I*	7	6	2	5	4	3
18	17	21	20	23	22	16	19	14	13	12	15	10	9	8	11	6	1	*I*	7	3	2	5	4
19	18	22	21	20	23	17	16	15	14	13	12	11	10	9	8	7	6	1	*I*	4	3	2	5
20	13	9	1	12	16	2	8	21	6	5	19	17	3	*I*	23	10	4	15	22	14	7	11	18
21	14	10	6	13	17	3	9	22	7	2	16	18	4	1	20	11	5	12	23	15	*I*	8	19
22	15	11	7	14	18	4	10	23	*I*	3	17	19	5	6	21	8	2	13	20	12	1	9	16
23	12	8	*I*	15	19	5	11	20	1	4	18	16	2	7	22	9	3	14	21	13	6	10	17

$$H' = K + J(H - K),$$

where $H - K$ is the set of elements contained in H but not in K, J is the inversion matrix, and $K + J(H - K)$ is the set-theoretic sum of the two sets of elements.

One final point to be determined is the determination of the number $N(g)$ of nonisomorphic groups of any given order g. The number $N(g)$ must be finite because there is only a finite number of ways of filling out a multiplication table with g group elements. The number $N(g)$ could in principle be determined by simply testing every possible $g \times g$ table to see if it actually represents a group. This process is, however, quite impractical for groups of reasonably high order ($g > 10$), and much more sophisticated techniques must be used. We present here only the results of these investigations.*

Number of Groups as a Function of Order

g = order of group
$N(g)$ = number of nonisomorphic groups of order g
$N_a(g)$ = number of nonisomorphic abelian groups of order g

g	$N(g)$	$N_a(g)$	g	$N(g)$	$N_a(g)$	g	$N(g)$	$N_a(g)$	g	$N(g)$	$N_a(g)$
1	1	1	19	1	1	37	1	1	55	2	1
2	1	1	20	5	2	38	2	1	56	13	3
3	1	1	21	2	1	39	2	1	57	2	1
4	2	2	22	2	1	40	14	3	58	2	1
5	1	1	23	1	1	41	1	1	59	1	1
6	2	1	24	15	3	42	6	1	60	13	2
7	1	1	25	2	2	43	1	1	61	1	1
8	5	3	26	2	1	44	4	2	62	2	2
9	2	2	27	5	3	45	2	2	63	4	2
10	2	1	28	4	2	46	2	1	64	294	11
11	1	1	29	1	1	47	1	1	65	1	1
12	5	2	30	4	1	48	52	5	66	4	1
13	1	1	31	1	1	49	2	2	67	1	1
14	2	1	32	51	7	50	5	2	68	5	2
15	1	1	33	1	1	51	1	1	69	1	1
16	14	5	34	2	1	52	5	2	70	4	1
17	1	1	35	1	1	53	1	1	71	1	1
18	5	2	36	14	4	54	15	3	72	50	6

* See Miller, G. A., *Am. J. Math.* **52**, 617 (1930); Senior, J. K., and Lunn, A. C., *Am. J. Math.* **56**, 328 (1934); and Lunn, A. C., and Senior, J. K., *Am. J. Math.* **57**, 254 (1935).

g	$N(g)$	$N_a(g)$	g	$N(g)$	$N_a(g)$	g	$N(g)$	$N_a(g)$	g	$N(g)$	$N_a(g)$
73	1	1	110	6	1	147	6	2	184	12	3
74	2	1	111	2	1	148	5	2	185	1	1
75	3	2	112	43	5	149	1	1	186	6	1
76	4	2	113	1	1	150	13	2	187	1	1
77	1	1	114	6	1	151	1	1	188	4	2
78	6	1	115	1	1	152	12	3	189	13	3
79	1	1	116	5	2	153	2	2	190	4	1
80	52	5	117	4	2	154	4	1	191	1	1
81	15	5	118	2	1	155	2	1	192	?	11
82	2	1	119	1	1	156	18	2	193	1	1
83	1	1	120	47	3	157	1	1	194	2	1
84	15	2	121	2	2	158	2	1	195	2	1
85	1	1	122	2	1	159	1	1	196	17	4
86	2	1	123	1	1	160	238	7	197	1	1
87	1	1	124	4	2	161	1	1	198	10	2
88	12	3	125	5	3	162	55	5	199	1	1
89	1	1	126	16	2	163	1	1	200	52	6
90	10	2	127	1	1	164	5	2	201	2	1
91	1	1	128	?	15	165	2	1	202	2	1
92	4	2	129	2	1	166	2	1	203	2	1
93	2	1	130	4	1	167	1	1	204	12	2
94	2	1	131	1	1	168	57	3	205	2	1
95	1	1	132	10	2	169	2	2	206	2	1
96	230	7	133	1	1	170	4	1	207	2	2
97	1	1	134	2	1	171	5	2	208	51	5
98	5	2	135	5	3	172	4	2	209	1	1
99	2	2	136	15	3	173	1	1	210	12	1
100	16	4	137	1	1	174	4	1	211	1	1
101	1	1	138	4	1	175	2	2	212	5	2
102	4	1	139	1	1	176	42	5	213	1	1
103	1	1	140	11	2	177	1	1	214	2	1
104	14	3	141	1	1	178	2	1	215	1	1
105	2	1	142	2	1	179	1	1	216		9
106	2	1	143	1	1	180	37	4	217	1	1
107	1	1	144	197	10	181	1	1	218	2	1
108	45	6	145	1	1	182	4	1	219	2	1
109	1	1	146	2	1	183	2	1	220		2

A number of the entries in this table were computed by Dr. G. Bachman

2. Applications

Of the three applications given in this chapter, the first will be completely treated, whereas the completion of the last two must be postponed until the tools of representation theory are available.

A. Thermodynamics

Let us use the eight symbols U, H, F, G, S, T, P, and V for the thermodynamic quantities, internal energy, enthalpy, Helmholtz free energy, Gibbs free energy, entropy, temperature, pressure, and volume. For the sake of definiteness, let us consider all these quantities to be functions (unspecified) of P and V (so that they can in turn be considered functions of any other two quantities). These quantities are then related by the following equations:*

$$H = U + PV \tag{2:1a}$$
$$F = U - TS \tag{2:1b}$$
$$G = U + PV - TS \tag{2:1c}$$
$$dU = Tds - PdV \tag{2:2a}$$
$$dH = Tds + VdP \tag{2:2b}$$
$$dF = -SdT - PdV \tag{2:2c}$$
$$dG = -SdT + VdP. \tag{2:2d}$$

It should be observed first that four of these equations are differential relations while three are not; second, that the last three equations are consequences of the first four; and finally, that U, H, F, and G always occur linearly, while S, T, P, and V always occur bilinearly.

What we would like to do (24, 75, 104, 149) is to find a linear transformation of the eight thermodynamic variables such that the equations into which (2:1) and (2:2) transform are equivalent to (2:1) and (2:2) (equivalent meaning here that either set of equations implies the other). The importance of such transformations is that they can be applied to any equation derived from (2:1) and (2:2) to yield other equations which must also be derivable from (2:1) and (2:2). This use of the transformation eliminates the necessity of deriving all equations directly from (2:1) and (2:2) by providing a simple scheme for generating new equations from already known ones.

To be more precise, let us define seven expressions in terms of the eight thermodynamic variables as follows:

$$Q_1 = H - U - PV$$
$$Q_2 = F - U + TS$$
$$Q_3 = G - U - PV + TS$$
$$Q_4 = dU - TdS + PdV$$
$$Q_5 = dH - TdS - VdP$$
$$Q_6 = dF + SdT + PdV$$
$$Q_7 = dG + SdT - VdP.$$

* See Epstein, P. S., "A Textbook of Thermodynamics." Wiley. New York, 1937.

Let us also define the transformed Q's by the equation

$$Q'(U,H,\ldots) = Q(DU,DH,\ldots),$$

where Q' is the transformed expression, D is the linear transformation, DU means $(D_{11}U + D_{12}H + D_{13}F + D_{14}G + D_{15}S + D_{16}T + D_{17}P + D_{18}V)$, and DH, etc., are similar expressions. For example, if

$$D = \begin{pmatrix} 0 & 0 & 0 & 1 & 0 & 0 & 0 & 0 \\ 0 & 0 & 1 & 0 & 0 & 0 & 0 & 0 \\ 0 & 1 & 0 & 0 & 0 & 0 & 0 & 0 \\ 1 & 0 & 0 & 0 & 0 & 0 & 0 & 0 \\ 0 & 0 & 0 & 0 & 0 & 1 & 0 & 0 \\ 0 & 0 & 0 & 0 & -1 & 0 & 0 & 0 \\ 0 & 0 & 0 & 0 & 0 & 0 & 0 & 1 \\ 0 & 0 & 0 & 0 & 0 & 0 & -1 & 0 \end{pmatrix},$$

which is a pseudopermutation matrix, then

$$Q_1' = F - G + PV.$$

What we should like, then, is to find a set of linear transformations $\{D\}$ of the eight thermodynamic variables which also transforms the Q's linearly. That is, we want $Q_i' = \sum_{j=1}^{7} d_{ij}Q_j$, where the d's are numbers. For example, using the above D,

$$Q_1' = F - G + PV = Q_2 - Q_3.$$

We require further that the transformed set of equations $Q_i' = 0$ be equivalent to the original set. If the Q's are transformed linearly, this is just equivalent to requiring the matrix $||d_{ij}||$ to be nonsingular. We see further that if d_1 and d_2 are two such transformations of the Q's, then the product $d_1 d_2$ must also be; and that if d is such a transformation, d^{-1} must also be. Hence, the set of linear transformations of the Q's can be made large enough to form a group. We might therefore hope to find a set of D's which is also a group.

Therefore, let us look for a group of 8-dimensional matrices which transforms the eight thermodynamic variables in such a way that the linearly transformed equations for them are equivalent to the original equations. The D given above is one such matrix.

In order to avoid getting bilinear terms in U, H, F, and G in the transformed equations, let us avoid matrices which make S', T', P', or V' functions of U, H, F, or G. This means that every D must have a 4×4 zero matrix in the lower left corner, so the group is reduced. Similarly, to avoid linear terms in S, T, P, and V, let us make the upper right corner of each D a 4×4 zero matrix. We then require the group of D's to be completely reduced, and to leave invariant the (U, H, F, G) — subspace and the (S, T, P, V) — subspace. We can then consider the transformations of U, H, F, and G and of S, T, P, and V separately.

Let us for simplicity now restrict our attention to D's which are pseudopermutation matrices, and consider to begin with the transformation of U, H, F, and G. By some detailed considerations (viz., by simply trying out pseudopermutation matrices) it can be shown that the matrices transforming U, H, F, and G must be either permutation matrices or negatives of permutation matrices. A change of sign of all variables contributes nothing new, so let us restrict our attention to transformations of U, H, F, and G which are pure permutations. From (2:1) the relation

$$U - H - F + G = 0 \qquad (2{:}3)$$

easily follows. We can now simply pick out those permutations of U, H, F, and G which leave this equation invariant (although the linear form $U - H - F + G$ may have its sign changed). One such permutation is

$$U \to G \qquad H \to F \qquad F \to H \qquad G \to U$$

which is the transformation given by the 4×4 upper left corner of the D given previously. Straightforward enumeration of all such permutations shows that there are eight, and that they form the group D_4 under multiplication. These 4×4 matrices will appear in the upper left corner of the D's.

As yet we have not shown these eight permutation transformations of U, H, F, and G are all permissible. All we have shown is that they leave the equation $U - H - F + G = 0$ invariant. The behavior of the entire set of equations (2:1) and (2:2) depends on how S, T, P, and V transform.

Some more detailed investigation shows that all eight of the transformations of U, H, F, and G can be used, and that corresponding to each such transformation of U, H, F, and G there are four transformations of S, T, P, and V. Hence, the group of pseudopermutation D's is of order 32 (with 14 classes).

Generators of the group are the seven 8-dimensional pseudopermutation matrices:

$$D_1 = D \text{ given above}$$

$$D_2 = \begin{pmatrix} \cdot & \cdot & \cdot & 1 & \cdot & \cdot & \cdot & \cdot \\ \cdot & 1 & \cdot & \cdot & \cdot & \cdot & \cdot & \cdot \\ \cdot & \cdot & 1 & \cdot & \cdot & \cdot & \cdot & \cdot \\ 1 & \cdot & \cdot & \cdot & \cdot & \cdot & \cdot & \cdot \\ \cdot & \cdot & \cdot & \cdot & \cdot & \cdot & 1 & \cdot \\ \cdot & \cdot & \cdot & \cdot & \cdot & \cdot & \cdot & 1 \\ \cdot & \cdot & \cdot & \cdot & 1 & \cdot & \cdot & \cdot \\ \cdot & \cdot & \cdot & \cdot & \cdot & 1 & \cdot & \cdot \end{pmatrix} \quad D_3 = \begin{pmatrix} 1 & \cdot & \cdot & \cdot & \cdot & \cdot & \cdot & \cdot \\ \cdot & \cdot & 1 & \cdot & \cdot & \cdot & \cdot & \cdot \\ \cdot & 1 & \cdot & \cdot & \cdot & \cdot & \cdot & \cdot \\ \cdot & \cdot & \cdot & 1 & \cdot & \cdot & \cdot & \cdot \\ \cdot & \cdot & \cdot & \cdot & \cdot & \cdot & \cdot & 1 \\ \cdot & \cdot & \cdot & \cdot & \cdot & \cdot & -1 & \cdot \\ \cdot & \cdot & \cdot & \cdot & \cdot & 1 & \cdot & \cdot \\ \cdot & \cdot & \cdot & \cdot & -1 & \cdot & \cdot & \cdot \end{pmatrix}$$

$$D_4 = \begin{pmatrix} \cdot & 1 & \cdot & \cdot & \cdot & \cdot & \cdot & \cdot \\ 1 & \cdot & \cdot & \cdot & \cdot & \cdot & \cdot & \cdot \\ \cdot & \cdot & \cdot & 1 & \cdot & \cdot & \cdot & \cdot \\ \cdot & \cdot & 1 & \cdot & \cdot & \cdot & \cdot & \cdot \\ \cdot & \cdot & \cdot & \cdot & 1 & \cdot & \cdot & \cdot \\ \cdot & \cdot & \cdot & \cdot & \cdot & 1 & \cdot & \cdot \\ \cdot & \cdot & \cdot & \cdot & \cdot & \cdot & \cdot & 1 \\ \cdot & \cdot & \cdot & \cdot & \cdot & \cdot & -1 & \cdot \end{pmatrix} D_5 = \begin{pmatrix} \cdot & \cdot & 1 & \cdot & \cdot & \cdot & \cdot & \cdot \\ \cdot & \cdot & \cdot & 1 & \cdot & \cdot & \cdot & \cdot \\ 1 & \cdot & \cdot & \cdot & \cdot & \cdot & \cdot & \cdot \\ \cdot & 1 & \cdot & \cdot & \cdot & \cdot & \cdot & \cdot \\ \cdot & \cdot & \cdot & \cdot & \cdot & 1 & \cdot & \cdot \\ \cdot & \cdot & \cdot & \cdot & -1 & \cdot & \cdot & \cdot \\ \cdot & \cdot & \cdot & \cdot & \cdot & \cdot & 1 & \cdot \\ \cdot & \cdot & \cdot & \cdot & \cdot & \cdot & \cdot & 1 \end{pmatrix}$$

$$D_6 = \begin{pmatrix} \cdot & 1 & \cdot & \cdot & \cdot & \cdot & \cdot & \cdot \\ \cdot & \cdot & \cdot & 1 & \cdot & \cdot & \cdot & \cdot \\ 1 & \cdot & \cdot & \cdot & \cdot & \cdot & \cdot & \cdot \\ \cdot & \cdot & 1 & \cdot & \cdot & \cdot & \cdot & \cdot \\ \cdot & \cdot & \cdot & \cdot & \cdot & \cdot & 1 & \cdot \\ \cdot & \cdot & \cdot & \cdot & \cdot & \cdot & \cdot & 1 \\ \cdot & \cdot & \cdot & \cdot & \cdot & 1 & \cdot & \cdot \\ \cdot & \cdot & \cdot & \cdot & -1 & \cdot & \cdot & \cdot \end{pmatrix} D_7 = \begin{pmatrix} \cdot & \cdot & 1 & \cdot & \cdot & \cdot & \cdot & \cdot \\ 1 & \cdot & \cdot & \cdot & \cdot & \cdot & \cdot & \cdot \\ \cdot & \cdot & \cdot & 1 & \cdot & \cdot & \cdot & \cdot \\ \cdot & 1 & \cdot & \cdot & \cdot & \cdot & \cdot & \cdot \\ \cdot & \cdot & \cdot & \cdot & \cdot & \cdot & \cdot & 1 \\ \cdot & \cdot & \cdot & \cdot & \cdot & \cdot & -1 & \cdot \\ \cdot & \cdot & \cdot & \cdot & 1 & \cdot & \cdot & \cdot \\ \cdot & \cdot & \cdot & \cdot & \cdot & 1 & \cdot & \cdot \end{pmatrix}.$$

These transformations can also be written in tabular form

U'	H'	F'	G'	S'	T'	P'	V'
G	F	H	U	T	$-S$	V	$-P$
G	H	F	U	P	V	S	T
U	F	H	G	V	$-P$	T	$-S$
H	U	G	F	S	T	V	$-P$
F	G	U	H	T	$-S$	P	V
H	G	U	F	P	V	T	$-S$
F	U	G	H	V	$-P$	S	T

Actually, the other transformations are not needed, because they simply introduce sign changes of (S, T) or of (P, V) which is of no help since the signs drop out in the equations.

As an example of the application of these transformations let us derive an equation from (2:1) and (2:2) and then transform it to obtain new equations.

From (2:2a) one obtains by dividing by dV

$$\left(\frac{\partial U}{\partial V}\right)_T = T\left(\frac{\partial S}{\partial V}\right)_T - P \tag{2:4a}$$

or

$$\frac{P}{T} + \frac{1}{T}\left(\frac{\partial U}{\partial V}\right)_T = \left(\frac{\partial S}{\partial V}\right)_T. \tag{2:4b}$$

Now considering F as a function of T and V we have from (2:2c)

$$\frac{\partial F}{\partial T} = -S \qquad \frac{\partial F}{\partial V} = -P. \tag{2:4c}$$

But

$$\frac{\partial^2 F}{\partial V \partial T} = \frac{\partial^2 F}{\partial T \partial V} \tag{2:4d}$$

so

$$\left(\frac{\partial S}{\partial V}\right)_T = \left(\frac{\partial P}{\partial T}\right)_V. \tag{2:4e}$$

Substituting (2:4e) in (2:4b), we get

$$\frac{P}{T} + \frac{1}{T}\left(\frac{\partial U}{\partial V}\right)_T = \left(\frac{\partial P}{\partial T}\right)_V. \tag{2:4}$$

Replacing P by $D_i P$, etc., in (2:4) we get from this equation the following seven equations.

$$\frac{V}{S} - \frac{1}{S}\left(\frac{\partial G}{\partial P}\right)_S = \left(\frac{\partial V}{\partial S}\right)_P$$

$$\frac{S}{V} + \frac{1}{V}\left(\frac{\partial G}{\partial T}\right)_V = \left(\frac{\partial S}{\partial V}\right)_T$$

$$\frac{T}{P} - \frac{1}{P}\left(\frac{\partial U}{\partial S}\right)_P = \left(\frac{\partial T}{\partial P}\right)_S$$

$$\frac{V}{T} - \frac{1}{T}\left(\frac{\partial H}{\partial P}\right)_T = \left(\frac{\partial V}{\partial T}\right)_P$$

$$\frac{P}{S} + \frac{1}{S}\left(\frac{\partial F}{\partial V}\right)_S = \left(\frac{\partial P}{\partial S}\right)_V$$

$$\frac{T}{V} - \frac{1}{V}\left(\frac{\partial H}{\partial S}\right)_V = \left(\frac{\partial T}{\partial V}\right)_S$$

$$\frac{S}{P} + \frac{1}{P}\left(\frac{\partial F}{\partial T}\right)_P = \left(\frac{\partial S}{\partial P}\right)_T.$$

B. The Dirac Equation

Let us consider the motion of a point particle of rest mass m_o according to the laws of classical special relativity theory. Let the particle have the spatial coordinate vector $\mathbf{x}\ (t)$ at time t, the velocity vector $\mathbf{v} = d\mathbf{x}/dt$, and the momentum vector $\mathbf{p} = m_0 \mathbf{v}/\sqrt{1 - v^2/c^2}$. The energy (or Hamiltonian) H of the particle, if it is not acted on by any external forces, is then given by $H = c\sqrt{\mathbf{p}^2 + m_0{}^2c^2}$.

It would be convenient to be able to express $H^2/c^2 = p^2 + m_0{}^2c^2$ as a perfect square so that H could be written without the square root. Let us see if H^2 can be expressed as the square of a linear form; i.e., let us try putting

$$p^2 + m_0^2c^2 = (\alpha_1 p_x + \alpha_2 p_y + \alpha_3 p_z + m_0 c\beta)^2, \tag{2:5a}$$

where α_1, α_2, α_3, and β are coefficients. Squaring the right side we get

$$p^2 + m_0^2c^2 = \alpha_1^2 p_x^2 + \alpha_2^2 p_y^2 + \alpha_3^2 p_z^2 + m_0^2 c^2\beta^2 \tag{2:5b}$$

$$+ (\alpha_1\alpha_2 + \alpha_2\alpha_1)p_x p_y + (\alpha_1\alpha_3 + \alpha_3\alpha_1)p_x p_z + (\alpha_2\alpha_3 + \alpha_3\alpha_2)p_y p_z$$

$$+ m_0 c(\alpha_1\beta + \beta\alpha_1)p_x + m_0 c(\alpha_2\beta + \beta\alpha_2)p_y + m_0 c(\alpha_3\beta + \beta\alpha_3)p_z,$$

where we have assumed that the α's (and β) commute with the p's, but not necessarily with each other. Clearly, our scheme will work if the α's and β satisfy the following equations:

$$\alpha_i^2 = 1 \qquad \beta^2 = 1 \tag{2:6a}$$

$$\alpha_i\alpha_j + \alpha_j\alpha_i = 0 \qquad (i \neq j) \tag{2:6b}$$

$$\alpha_i\beta + \beta\alpha_i = 0. \tag{2:6c}$$

If the α's and β were to be ordinary numbers, then from (2:6a) we see that each coefficient would have to be ± 1. But then the α's would commute and (2:6b) would become $\alpha_i\alpha_j = 0$, which would imply that either α_i or α_j would be zero, contrary to (2:6a). Hence, the α's and β's can not be ordinary numbers. Let us consider them as operators, without specifying what they operate on.

For convenience, let us introduce the operators

$$\gamma_1 = -i\beta\alpha_1 \quad \gamma_2 = -i\beta\alpha_2 \quad \gamma_3 = -i\beta\alpha_3 \quad \gamma_4 = \beta. \tag{2:7}$$

These operators then satisfy the simple relation

$$[\gamma_\mu, \gamma_\nu]_+ = 2\delta_{\mu\nu}, \tag{2:8}$$

where

$$[D_1, D_2]_+ \equiv D_1 D_2 + D_2 D_1 \tag{2:8a}$$

is called the anticommutator of two operators, and μ and ν are indices which run from 1 to 4. Every operator γ_μ is thus of order two, and anticommutes with every other γ.

Let us now consider the set of elements

$$\pm\gamma_1^{j_1}\gamma_2^{j_2}\gamma_3^{j_3}\gamma_4^{j_4}, \tag{2:9}$$

where each $j = 1$ or 2. There are then 32 such (distinct) elements, and they form a group (the Dirac group) under operator multiplication. For example,

$$(\gamma_4\gamma_2)(\gamma_3\gamma_1) = -\gamma_1\gamma_2\gamma_3\gamma_4.$$

This group is of order 32. Furthermore, if A and B are any two elements of the group, $A^{-1}BA = \pm A^{-1}AB = \pm B$ since the γ's all anticommute, and ± 1 commute. Obviously 1 and -1 each forms a class of order one. We will now see that all other classes are of order two and consist of $\pm A$. If A consists of a product of an odd number of distinct γ's then there exists some γ_j which is not contained in A, and $\gamma_j^{-1} A \gamma_j = -A$. If A is a product of an even number of distinct γ's, and if γ_j is the γ occurring on the left of the product, then $\gamma_j^{-1} A \gamma_j = -A$. Thus $\pm A$ always occur in the same class (unless $A = \pm 1$). Consequently $r_i = 2$, except for $r_1 = r_2 = 1$). Hence, $r_1 = r_2 = 1$, $r_3 = \ldots = r_{17} = 2, r = 17$. Similarly, since the γ's anticommute and ± 1 commute, one sees that the only commutators of the group are ± 1, so $h_c = 2$. The problem of finding explicit forms for the γ's will be deferred until Chapter IV, Section 1, when the tools of representation theory can be used.

In terms of the γ's the energy becomes

$$H = c\gamma_4 (i\boldsymbol{\gamma}\cdot\mathbf{p} + m_0 c). \tag{2:10}$$

If we let ψ be a function of x, y, z, and t such that the γ's (or α's) can operate on it, then the equation

$$H\psi = i\hbar \frac{\partial \psi}{\partial t}, \tag{2:11}$$

in which $\mathbf{p}$ is replaced in H by $-i\hbar\,\nabla$, is called the Dirac equation. Actually, a little more is required of the γ's for this to be the Dirac equation, but these additional restrictions will be discussed later. As is well known, the Dirac equation (2:11) is the special relativistic wave equation describing the motion of a free electron, and ψ is the electronic wave function.

C. Fermion Annihilation and Creation Operators

In quantum field theory (i.e., second quantization, or the theory of elementary particles) one frequently encounters a set of operators $a_1, \ldots, a_m$; $b_1, \ldots, b_m$, such that

$$[a_i, a_j]_+ = 0 \tag{2:12a}$$

$$[b_i, b_j]_+ = 0 \tag{2:12b}$$

$$[a_i, b_j]_+ = \delta_{ij}. \tag{2:12c}$$

The a's are called annihilation operators and the b's creation operators (although the names could be interchanged since the theory is symmetric between them so far). These operators occur in fermion fields but not in boson fields, hence the appendage, fermion.

If we form the operators

$$q_j = a_j + b_j \qquad (j = 1, \ldots, m) \tag{2:13a}$$

$$p_j = -i(a_j - b_j) \qquad (j = 1, \ldots, m), \tag{2:13b}$$

then we see that these operators satisfy the anticommutation relations

$$[q_i, q_j]_+ = [p_i, p_j]_+ = 2\delta_{ij} \tag{2:14a}$$

$$[q_i, p_j]_+ = 0. \tag{2:14b}$$

Let us represent the q's and p's collectively by $\gamma_1, \ldots, \gamma_n$, where $n = 2m$. We then have the anticommutation relations

$$[\gamma_\mu, \gamma_\nu]_+ = 2\delta_{\mu\nu} \quad (\mu, \nu = 1, \ldots, n). \tag{2:15}$$

Hence, we see that the operators

$$\pm \gamma_1^{j_1} \gamma_2^{j_2} \ldots \gamma_n^{j_n} \quad (j_k = 1, \text{ or } 2)$$

form a group $G(n)$ of order $g(n) = 2^{n+1}$. The special case $n = 4$ is the Dirac group.

Proceeding as with the Dirac group we see that $G(n)$ has $2^n + 1$ classes, and that every class except the two classes ± 1 has order two. Also, $H_c = \pm 1$ so $h_c = 2$.

Another property of the group which we shall require later is the number of square roots of 1, i.e., $\zeta(1)$. If we let J be the number of j's in $\pm \gamma_1^{j_1} \gamma_2^{j_2} \ldots \gamma_n^{j}$ which are equal to one, then we can easily deduce from the anticommutation relations (2:15) that

$$(\pm \gamma_1^{j_1} \gamma_2^{j_2} \ldots \gamma_n^{j_n})^2 = (-1)^{\frac{1}{2}J(J-1)}. \tag{2:16}$$

Furthermore, $(-1)^{\frac{1}{2}J(J-1)}$ will be positive if and only if J has one of the two forms $J = 4k$ or $J = 4k + 1$. But, the number of group elements with $J = 4k$ is just twice (because of the $\pm$ sign) the number of different ways of assigning $4k$ values of 1 among the n exponents j. Hence, the number of group elements with $J = 4k$ is $2\binom{n}{4k}$, and the number with $J = 4k + 1$ is $2\binom{n}{4k+1}$. Thus for $\zeta(1)$ we obtain

$$\zeta(1) = 2 \sum_{k=0}^{[\frac{1}{4}n]} \binom{n}{4k} + 2 \sum_{k=0}^{[\frac{1}{4}(n-1)]} \binom{n}{4k+1}, \tag{2:17}$$

where $[x]$ is the largest integer less than or equal to x. By application of some standard binomial coefficient-type tricks these sums can be evaluated, and we get finally

$$\zeta(1) = 2^n + i^{\frac{1}{2}n(\frac{1}{2}n-1)}\, 2^{\frac{1}{2}n}. \tag{2:18}$$

It should be noted that the factor $i^{\frac{1}{2}n(\frac{1}{2}n-1)}$ is always ± 1, because (since n is even) $\frac{1}{2}n$ and $\frac{1}{2}n - 1$ are two consecutive integers, one of which must therefore be even. Hence, $\frac{1}{2}n(\frac{1}{2}n - 1)$ must be even, and $i^{\frac{1}{2}n(\frac{1}{2}n-1)} = \pm 1$.

Let us for a moment consider proper normal subgroups of $G(n)$. Let H be a proper normal subgroup, and let γ be an element of H. Then, since H is composed of classes, and $\pm\gamma$ form a class, it follows that H contains $-\gamma$.

But either $\gamma^2 = -1$ or $(-\gamma)(\gamma) = -1$. Hence, -1 is also in H. Thus H_c is contained in every proper normal subgroup of $G(n)$. On the other hand, H_c contains no proper normal subgroups of $G(n)$, or, H_c is a minimal normal subgroup of $G(n)$. Since every other proper normal subgroup of $G(n)$ contains H_c, it follows that H_c is the only minimal normal subgroup of $G(n)$.

Again, we shall defer until Chapter IV the determination of an explicit form of the γ's.

BIBLIOGRAPHY

Alexandroff, P. S. (1954). "Introduction to Group Theory." Deutscher Verlag der Wissenschaften, Berlin.

Burnside, W. (1911). "Theory of Groups of Finite Order." Cambridge Univ. Press, London and New York.

Carmichael, R. D. (1937). "Introduction to the Theory of Groups of Finite Order." Ginn, New York.

Cayley, A. (1897). "Collected Papers." Cambridge Univ. Press, London and New York.

Hilton, H. (1908). "Introduction to the Theory of Groups of Finite Order." Clarendon Press, Oxford.

Kurosh, A. G. (1944). "Group Theory," (Eng. transl., 1955). Chelsea, New York.

Ledermann, W. (1949). "Introduction to the Theory of Finite Groups." Interscience, New York.

Magnus, W. (1939). "General Group Theory." B. G. Teubner, Leipzig.

Magnus, W. "Combinatorial Group Theory." In preparation.

Mathewson, L. C. (1930). "Elementary Theory of Finite Groups." Houghton Mifflin, Boston.

McIntosh, H. V. (1955). Seminar in Group Theory (Notes). Aberdeen Proving Ground, Aberdeen, Maryland.

Miller, G. A. (1934-1955). "Collected Works." Univ. of Illinois, Urbana, Illinois.

Miller, G. A., Blichfeldt, H. F., and Dickson, L. E. (1916). "Theory and Application of Finite Groups." John Wiley & Sons, New York.

Schmidt, O. J. (1933). "Abstract Theory of Groups" (in Russian). Kiev.

Specht, W. (1956). "Group Theory." J. Springer, Berlin.

Speiser, A. (1956). "Theory of Groups of Finite Order," 4th ed. Birkhauser, Basel.

Zassenhaus, H. (1937). "The Theory of Groups." B. G. Teubner, Berlin.

Chapter III

REPRESENTATIONS

The theory of group representations provides a powerful synthesis of the work of the preceding two chapters on matrices and groups. Furthermore, most applications of group theory to physical problems are, more particularly, applications of representation theory. One reason is that representation theory reduces the abstract properties of groups to numbers, with which a physicist feels more at home. Hence, representation theory is, for a physicist, the most important aspect of group theory. This theory was developed at the turn of the century almost single-handedly by the German mathematician F. G. Frobenius. The concept of representation rests on the two concepts, matrix group and homomorphism. Since homomorphisms have already been discussed in some detail, let us now discuss finite matrix groups.

1. Matrix Groups

Definition. A *matrix group* is a group in which the elements are square matrices (of the same dimension), the multiplication law is matrix multiplication, and the group inverse of an element is the matrix inverse.

Example. The set of eight matrices

$$I = \begin{pmatrix} 1 & 0 \\ 0 & 1 \end{pmatrix} \quad D_1 = \begin{pmatrix} -1 & 0 \\ 0 & -1 \end{pmatrix} \quad D_2 = \begin{pmatrix} -i & 0 \\ 0 & i \end{pmatrix} \quad D_3 = \begin{pmatrix} i & 0 \\ 0 & -i \end{pmatrix}$$

$$D_4 = \begin{pmatrix} 0 & 1 \\ -1 & 0 \end{pmatrix} \quad D_5 = \begin{pmatrix} 0 & -1 \\ 1 & 0 \end{pmatrix} \quad D_6 = \begin{pmatrix} 0 & -i \\ -i & 0 \end{pmatrix} \quad D_7 = \begin{pmatrix} 0 & i \\ i & 0 \end{pmatrix}$$

used in previous examples is a matrix group. Thus, $D_2 D_5 = D_7$; and, in fact, this group has the same multiplication table as the quaternion group Q (and is therefore isomorphic to Q).

Since the inverse of an element is the matrix inverse, and since the inverse of a group element must exist, it follows that only nonsingular matrices can be elements of matrix groups, and that the group identity is the identity matrix. Furthermore, all nonsingular matrices of dimension d form an infinite matrix group, which is called the general linear group of dimension d over the complex field, and is designated by $GL(d,C)$. Every d-dimensional matrix group is thus a subgroup of $GL(d,C)$.

Let us discuss some elementary properties of matrix groups before going on to representations.

If Γ is any matrix group, then we can construct a matrix group, the *complex conjugate* Γ^*, by replacing each matrix by its complex conjugate. Further, we obtain the *transpose* Γ^t by replacing each D by $(D^t)^{-1}$, and the *adjoint* $\Gamma^\dagger$ by replacing each D by $(D^\dagger)^{-1}$.

Theorem. Every 1-dimensional matrix group is cyclic, and the elements are all rational roots of unity.

Since the elements of a 1-dimensional matrix group are essentially numbers, and since numbers commute, it follows that such a group must be abelian. Furthermore, since some integral power of any group element must be the identity, it follows that every element must be a rational root of one. To prove that the group must be cyclic requires a little more analysis.

Theorem. The determinant of any element of a matrix group must be a rational root of unity.

Since some integral power δ of any element D must be I, it follows that $[\det(D)]^\delta = 1$ and the above result follows. This theorem is just a generalization of the last part of the preceding theorem.

Let us now consider isomorphism and equivalence of matrix groups. First of all, two matrix groups can be isomorphic without having the same dimension. For example, $\Gamma_1 = \{1, -1\}$ and $\Gamma_2 = \left\{\begin{pmatrix} 1 & 0 \\ 0 & 1 \end{pmatrix}, \begin{pmatrix} -1 & 0 \\ 0 & -1 \end{pmatrix}\right\}$ are isomorphic. Hence, two matrix groups can be isomorphic without being equivalent. They can even be isomorphic and of the same dimension without being equivalent. For example, the two groups

$$C_2 = \left\{\begin{pmatrix} 1 & 0 & 0 \\ 0 & 1 & 0 \\ 0 & 0 & 1 \end{pmatrix}, \begin{pmatrix} -1 & 0 & 0 \\ 0 & -1 & 0 \\ 0 & 0 & 1 \end{pmatrix}\right\} \qquad S = \left\{\begin{pmatrix} 1 & 0 & 0 \\ 0 & 1 & 0 \\ 0 & 0 & 1 \end{pmatrix}, \begin{pmatrix} 1 & 0 & 0 \\ 0 & 1 & 0 \\ 0 & 0 & -1 \end{pmatrix}\right\}$$

are isomorphic and of dimension 3, but are not equivalent (as can be seen from the fact that the two nonidentity matrices do not have the same trace). Further, the number of isomorphic, nonequivalent matrix groups of a given dimension is finite. On the other hand, equivalence implies isomorphism.

By a *unitary matrix group* let us understand a matrix group consisting entirely of unitary matrices. Then the following fundamental Schur-Auerbach theorem states:

Theorem. Every matrix group is equivalent to a unitary matrix group.

We shall prove this by actually constructing a transformation matrix S.

Outline of Proof. Let $\Gamma = \{D_1, \ldots, D_\gamma\}$ be the group, and define a matrix D by the equation

$$D = \sum_{i=1}^{\gamma} D_i D_i^\dagger.$$

Then, since each D_i is nonsingular, it follows that each term $D_i D_i^\dagger$ of the sum is positive definite. Hence, D itself is positive definite. Let Λ be a diagonal matrix equivalent to D, let $\Lambda^{1/2}$ be the positive definite (and hence nonsingular) matrix obtained from Λ by replacing each element of Λ by its nonnegative square root, let U be a unitary matrix such that $\Lambda = UDU^{-1}$, and let $S = \Lambda^{-1/2}U$. Then SD_iS^{-1} is unitary; i.e., S is a matrix which will transform the original matrix group into unitary form. To see that SD_iS^{-1} is unitary, let us show that $(SD_iS^{-1})(SD_iS^{-1})^\dagger = I$. In order to do this, let us put $D_i' = UD_iU^{-1}$ so that $\Lambda = \sum_{j=1}^{\gamma} D_j'D_j'^\dagger$. Then

$$\begin{aligned}(SD_iS^{-1})(SD_iS^{-1})^\dagger &= (\Lambda^{-1/2}D_i'\Lambda^{1/2})(\Lambda^{1/2}D_i'^\dagger\Lambda^{-1/2}) \\ &= \Lambda^{-1/2}D_i'\left(\sum_{j=1}^{\gamma} D_j'D_j'^\dagger\right)D_i'^\dagger\Lambda^{-1/2} \\ &= \Lambda^{-1/2}\left[\sum_{j=1}^{\gamma}(D_i'D_j')(D_i'D_j')^\dagger\right]\Lambda^{-1/2} \\ &= \Lambda^{-1/2}\left(\sum_{k=1}^{\gamma} D_k'D_k'^\dagger\right)\Lambda^{-1/2} \\ &= \Lambda^{-1/2}\Lambda\Lambda^{-1/2} = I.\end{aligned}$$

Since every unitary matrix is diagonalizable, it follows that every matrix of every (finite) matrix group is diagonalizable.

It also follows that every eigenvalue of every matrix of every matrix group is a rational root of unity.

Let us now give a criterion for the equivalence of any two matrix groups. In order to do this we will need the matrix group function called the character.

Definition. The *character* of a matrix group $\Gamma = \{D_1, \ldots, D_\gamma\}$ is a function on the group which is defined by the equation

$$\chi(D_i) \equiv \operatorname{tr}(D_i).$$

Example. For the matrix quaternion group we have:

$$\chi(I) = 2 \qquad \chi(D_1) = -2$$

$\chi(D_i) = 0$ for all other D's in the group.

We can now state the following easily proved properties of the character:

Theorem. (1) $\chi(I) = d$

(2) $|\chi(D_i)| \leqslant d$

(3) $|\chi(D_i)| = d$ implies $D_i = e^{i\theta}I$

(4) $\chi(D_i^{-1}) = \chi^*(D_i)$

(5) χ is a class function

(6) $\chi(D_i)$ is an algebraic integer (for all D_i).

We can now state our equivalence criterion.

Theorem. Two matrix groups are equivalent if and only if (1) they are isomorphic; (2) they have the same character.

The second statement means that elements which correspond under the isomorphism of part (1) must have the same trace. If there is more than one isomorphism between the groups, then any one may be used to determine an equivalence.

Example. The two matrix groups

$$\left\{\begin{pmatrix}1 & 0 & 0\\ 0 & 1 & 0\\ 0 & 0 & 1\end{pmatrix}, \begin{pmatrix}-1 & 0 & 0\\ 0 & -1 & 0\\ 0 & 0 & 1\end{pmatrix}\right\}$$

and

$$\left\{\begin{pmatrix}1 & 0 & 0\\ 0 & 1 & 0\\ 0 & 0 & 1\end{pmatrix}, \begin{pmatrix}1 & 0 & 0\\ 0 & -1 & 0\\ 0 & 0 & -1\end{pmatrix}\right\}$$

are equivalent, whereas C_2 and S are inequivalent as already seen.

We see thus that specification of the multiplication table and of the character of a matrix group actually specifies the matrix group (up to an equivalence transformation).

Let us proceed now to reducibility theorems, the first one being due to Maschke.

Theorem. If a matrix group is reducible then it is completely reducible (i.e., if the matrix group is equivalent to a matrix group in which every matrix has the reduced form $\begin{pmatrix}D_i^{(1)} & X_i\\ 0 & D_i^{(2)}\end{pmatrix}$, then it is equivalent to the group of matrices which is obtained by putting $X_i = 0$).

Outline of Proof. Again we shall construct a transformation matrix. Let

$$D \equiv \begin{pmatrix}D_1 & X\\ 0 & D_2\end{pmatrix}$$

be a typical reduced matrix, and let

$$D' \equiv \begin{pmatrix}D_1 & 0\\ 0 & D_2\end{pmatrix}$$

be the completely reduced matrix obtained from D by putting $X = 0$. Then $S = \sum_D D^{-1}D'$ will transform D into D', because if D_0 is any matrix of the reduced group,

$$\begin{aligned} D_0 S &= D_0 \sum_D D^{-1}D' = \sum_D D_0 D^{-1}D' \\ &= \sum_D (DD_0^{-1})^{-1} D' \\ &= \Big[\sum_{DD_0^{-1}} (DD_0^{-1})^{-1}(D'D_0'^{-1})\Big] D_0' \\ &= SD_0'. \end{aligned}$$

Hence, $D_0S = SD_0'$; and inspection of the form of S shows that it is non-singular, so $S^{-1}D_0S = D_0'$.

Therefore, reducibility and complete reducibility are identical requirements for finite matrix groups.

Corollary. If the only matrices which commute with a matrix group are scalar matrices, then the matrix group is irreducible.

We can now state a criterion for reducibility.

Theorem. A matrix group $\Gamma = \{D_1, \ldots, D_\gamma\}$ is irreducible if and only if

$$\frac{1}{\gamma} \sum_{i=1}^{\gamma} |\chi(D_i)|^2 = 1$$

or, if and only if

$$\frac{1}{\gamma} \sum_{i=1}^{r} r_i |\chi_i|^2 = 1,$$

where χ_i is the value of the character for the ith class.

Example. For the matrix quaternion group we have for the sum

$$\tfrac{1}{8}[1 \times 2^2 + 1 \times (-2)^2 + 6 \times 0^2] = 1,$$

so it is irreducible.

An important requirement on the dimension of an irreducible matrix group is the following:

Theorem. The dimension d of an irreducible matrix group must be a divisor of its order γ.

Thus, for the matrix quaternion group, $d = 2$ and $\gamma = 8$ so $\gamma/d = 4$.

Theorem. If $\Gamma = \{D_1, \ldots, D_\gamma\}$ is an irreducible matrix group, then

$$\sum_{i=1}^{\gamma} D_i = 0$$

and hence

$$\sum_{i=1}^{r} r_i \chi_i = 0.$$

This can easily be verified for the matrix quaternion group.

Theorem. Every irreducible abelian group is 1-dimensional, and hence cyclic.

Another occasionally useful result on irreducible matrix groups, which is known as Burnside's theorem, is the following.

Theorem. If $\Gamma = \{D_1, \ldots, D_\gamma\}$ is an irreducible matrix group of dimension d, then there exists no nonzero, d-dimensional square matrix D such that

$$\operatorname{tr}(DD_i) = 0$$

for all i.

Let us now classify matrix groups according to their reality.

Definition. A matrix group is
(1) of the *first kind* (or an integer matrix group) if it is equivalent to a group of real matrices (in which case it is equivalent to its complex conjugate, and also to a group of orthogonal matrices),
(2) of the *second kind* (or a half-integer matrix group) if it is equivalent to its complex conjugate (in the same order, $D_i^* = S^{-1}D_iS$), but not to a real group,
(3) of the *third kind* if it is not equivalent to its complex conjugate (i.e., there does not exist S such that $D_i^* = S^{-1}D_iS$).

Theorem. If $\Gamma = \{D_1, \ldots, D_\gamma\}$ is an irreducible matrix group, then

$$\frac{1}{\gamma}\sum_{i=1}^{\gamma}\chi(D_i^2) = \begin{cases} 1 \text{ if and only if } \Gamma \text{ is of first kind} \\ -1 \text{ if and only if } \Gamma \text{ is of second kind} \\ 0 \text{ if and only if } \Gamma \text{ is of third kind.} \end{cases}$$

Example. For the quaternion matrix group, the sum on the left becomes

$$\tfrac{1}{8}(2 \times 2 - 6 \times 2) = -1,$$

so the group is of the second kind.

Since matrix groups of the first or second kind are equivalent to their complex conjugates, it follows that their characters must be real functions. Further, it follows from our theorems on the equivalence of matrices that every matrix of a group of second kind is equivalent to a real matrix (but the same transformation matrix need not transform every matrix of the group to real form). On the other hand, characters of groups of the third kind must be complex functions. Again, groups of odd order are peculiar, because all irreducible ones must be of the third kind (except for the trivial group of order one).

Theorem. The dimension of an irreducible matrix group of second kind must be even.

It is well known that time reversal in quantum mechanics is intimately connected with complex conjugation, and it is occasionally useful in group theory to introduce a time reversal operator. If Γ is a matrix group of first or second kind, then a unitary matrix U such that $\Gamma^* = U\Gamma U^{-1}$ is called a *time reversal operator* associated with the matrix group Γ.

Let us call a matrix group *integral* if it is equivalent to a matrix group in which all matrices are integral, and *rational* if it is equivalent to a matrix group in which every matrix element is a rational number.

Theorem. Every rational matrix group is an integral matrix group.
Further, we are led to the following obvious conjecture:
Conjecture. A matrix group Γ is integral if Γ satisfies the three conditions.

(1) Γ is of first kind,
(2) Γ has integral character,
(3) Γ is irreducible.

A result on the imprimitivity of matrix groups is the following. A matrix group is imprimitive if it contains a normal abelian subgroup which is not contained in the center.

Let us conclude our study of matrix groups with a listing of some further properties of characters. The first property is shown by an equation for the product of two values of the character of a matrix group:

$$\chi(D_1)\chi(D_2) = \frac{d}{\gamma}\sum_{i=1}^{\gamma} \chi(D_1 D_i^{-1} D_2 D_i).$$

Finally, if we indicate the matrix group to which a character belongs by a right-handed superscript, we have

$$\begin{aligned} \chi^{(\Gamma^*)} &= \chi^{(\Gamma)*} \\ \chi^{(\Gamma^t)} &= \chi^{(\Gamma)*} \\ \chi^{(\Gamma^\dagger)} &= \chi^{(\Gamma)} \\ \chi^{(\Gamma_1 \oplus \Gamma_2)} &= \chi^{(\Gamma_1)} + \chi^{(\Gamma_2)} \\ \chi^{(\Gamma_1 \otimes \Gamma_2)} &= \chi^{(\Gamma_1)}\, \chi^{(\Gamma_2)}. \end{aligned}$$

The characters of $\Gamma_{(k)}$ and $\Gamma_{[k]}$ can be computed from the character of Γ together with the multiplication table of Γ by using the equations of Chapter I for the traces of $D_{(k)}$ and $D_{[k]}$. Thus, for example

$$\chi^{(\Gamma_{(2)})}(D) \equiv \operatorname{tr}(D_{(2)}) = \tfrac{1}{2}\chi^{(\Gamma)}(D^2) + \tfrac{1}{2}[\chi^{(\Gamma)}(D)]^2 .$$

2. The Key Theorem of Representation Theory

Let us now get down to the meat of this chapter, representations.

Definition. A *representation* Γ of a group G is a matrix group homomorph of G, together with a specification of the homomorphism.*

Example. The matrix quaternion group which has been considered several times previously is isomorphic to the quaternion group under the correspondence $A_i \to D_i$ and is therefore a representation of the quaternion group. Another representation of Q is

* A more general definition of a representation which includes infinite-dimensional representation is as follows. A representation of a group G is a group Γ of nonsingular linear transformations in a vector space (possibly infinite-dimensional) such that G is homomorphic to Γ. If $\Gamma_1 = \{D^{(1)}(A)\}$ and $\Gamma_2 = \{D^{(2)}(A)\}$ are two representations of G defined in the vector spaces V_1 and V_2, they are said to be equivalent if there exists a one-to-one linear correspondence T between the elements of V_1 and V_2 ($TV_1 = V_2$) such that $TD^{(1)}(A) = D^{(2)}(A)T$ for all A in G. Since we shall be primarily interested in finite groups (which have no irreducible infinite-dimensional representations) we shall not pursue this more abstract line of development.

$$\begin{array}{ll} I \to 1 & A_4 \to -1 \\ A_1 \to 1 & A_5 \to -1 \\ A_2 \to 1 & A_6 \to -1 \\ A_3 \to 1 & A_7 \to -1, \end{array}$$

which is a 1-dimensional representation.

Let us call a representation *faithful* (or *true*) if the matrix group of the representation is isomorphic to the original group. Thus, the matrix quaternion group is a faithful representation of Q, whereas the 1-dimensional representation given above is an unfaithful representation of Q. From our study of homomorphisms we know that every representation of a group G will be a faithful representation of some quotient group of G. Hence, we can speak of the *kernel* of a representation, and this will be the set of elements of G which is mapped on the identity matrix of the representation. It will therefore also be the set of all elements for which the value of the character is equal to the dimension of the representation. For example, the kernel of the above 1-dimensional representation is the normal subgroup I, A_1, A_2, and A_3. More or less conversely, we can say that every representation of a homomorph of G is a representation of G. This follows directly from the transitivity property of homomorphisms; i.e., if $G \to G'$ and $G' \to \Gamma$, then $G \to \Gamma$.

In a representation Γ of a group G, associated with every element A of G is a matrix D of Γ, which will subsequently be denoted by $D(A)$. Thus we could also define a representation to be a function from a group onto a matrix group which preserves group multiplication.

As one might expect, the results on matrix groups which have been previously discussed also apply to representations. One modification, however, should be made when applying the theorems on matrix groups to representations; viz., instead of averaging over distinct matrices of the matrix group, we now average over all elements of the original group. To be more specific, the equation

$$\sum_{i=1}^{\gamma} D_i = 0$$

becomes

$$\sum_{i=1}^{g} D(A_i) = 0,$$

where G is now taken to be of order g, and Γ may be of some smaller order γ (which must still be a divisor of g). Likewise, the equation

$$\frac{1}{\gamma}\sum_{i=1}^{\gamma} \chi(D_i^2) = \pm 1 \text{ or } 0$$

becomes

$$\frac{1}{g}\sum_{i=1}^{g} \chi(D^2(A_i)) = \pm 1 \text{ or } 0$$

or

$$\frac{1}{g}\sum_{i=1}^{g}\chi(A_i^2) = \pm 1 \text{ or } 0;$$

and

$$\frac{1}{\gamma}\sum_{i=1}^{r} r_i|\chi_i|^2 = 1$$

becomes

$$\frac{1}{g}\sum_{i=1}^{r} r_i|\chi_i|^2 = 1,$$

where now r_i is the order of the ith class of G, and r is the number of classes of G. This simple transcription of formulas from matrix groups to representations is possible because in a homomorphism the number of elements mapped on an element of the homomorph is the same for all elements of the homomorph.

We might at this point state a theorem due to Ito on the dimension of any irreducible representation of a group, which is somewhat sharper than the one we stated in connection with matrix groups.

Theorem. The dimension d of any irreducible representation of a group G must be a divisor of the index of each of the maximal normal abelian subgroups of G (where by a maximal normal abelian subgroup is meant a normal abelian subgroup which is not a proper subgroup of any other normal abelian subgroup).

For example, Q has five normal abelian subgroups, of which three are maximal. The three maximal ones are all of order four, and therefore have index 2. Hence, every irreducible representation of Q must have dimension 1 or 2.

One may wonder what groups can be profitably treated by means of representation theory. To elucidate this point let us first show that every group has a representation, and in fact, a faithful representation. Obviously, if we map every element of a group on the number 1 we get a representation, but this representation is *trivial*, and will be so referred to subsequently. To get a faithful representation of a group we can proceed as follows. Let $G = \{A_1,\ldots,A_g\}$ be a group, and let A_i be some element of G. Now consider the set of elements $\{(A_iA_1),\ldots,(A_iA_g)\}$. Each element A_iA_j of this set is some group element, hence, multiplying the set $\{A_1,\ldots,A_g\}$ through by A_i simply reorders the elements. If, therefore, we consider the group elements $A_1,\ldots,A_g$ arranged in a column matrix, then we can write down a g-dimensional permutation matrix $D^t(A_i)$ which will reorder the elements in the same way as multiplication by A_i. The correspondence $A_i \to D(A_i)$ is the desired representation. The representation is faithful because no two elements can produce the same reordering.

Example. Consider the cyclic group of order three, $C_3 = \{I, A, A^2\}$. Then

$$\{II, IA, IA^2\} = \{I, A, A^2\}$$
$$\{AI, A^2, AA^2\} = \{A, A^2, I\}$$
$$\{A^2I, A^2A, A^2A^2\} = \{A^2, I, A\}.$$

Hence

$$I \to \begin{pmatrix} 1 & 0 & 0 \\ 0 & 1 & 0 \\ 0 & 0 & 1 \end{pmatrix} \qquad A \to \begin{pmatrix} 0 & 0 & 1 \\ 1 & 0 & 0 \\ 0 & 1 & 0 \end{pmatrix} \qquad A^2 \to \begin{pmatrix} 0 & 1 & 0 \\ 0 & 0 & 1 \\ 1 & 0 & 0 \end{pmatrix}.$$

The above constructed, faithful, g-dimensional permutation representation is called the *regular* representation of the group. The trace of $D(A_i)$ is equal to the number of elements left fixed by A_i, but $A_i A = A$ implies $A_i = I$, so the only A_i which leaves any elements fixed is the identity, and it leaves them all fixed. Hence, the character of the regular representation is zero except for the identity element, for which it has the value g. In brief,

$$\chi^{(reg)}(A) = g\delta(I, A).$$

To investigate further the range of applicability of representation theory to abstract groups, let us state the key theorem of representation theory* (remembering that r designates the number of classes of a group).

Theorem. Every group has exactly r inequivalent irreducible representations, and if Γ_p and Γ_q are any two of these, then the matrix elements satisfy the orthogonality relations

$$\sum_{A \in G} [D^{(p)}(A)^{-1}]_{ij} [D^{(q)}(A)]_{kl} = \frac{g}{d_p} \delta_{i,l} \delta_{j,k} \delta_{p,q},$$

where $\sum_{A \in G}$ means the sum over all elements of G,

$$d_p = \text{dimension of } \Gamma_p,$$

$$\delta_{p,q} = \begin{cases} 0 \text{ if } \Gamma_p \neq \Gamma_q, \\ 1 \text{ if } \Gamma_p = \Gamma_q, \end{cases}$$

and the equation does not apply if Γ_p is equivalent to but not identical with Γ_q.

Since g/d is always an integer, it follows that the right side of the orthogonality relation is always a nonnegative integer.

Example. We have already considered two irreducible representations of Q. Let us take Γ_p to be the 1-dimensional representation, and Γ_q the 2-dimensional. Further, let us choose the (k, l)th matrix element of Γ_q to be the upper right. The left side of the orthogonality equation then becomes

$$(0 + 0 + 0 + 0 - 1 + 1 + i - i) = 0.$$

---

* See Appendix II for a proof.

Since every representation is either irreducible or completely reducible into irreducible ones, it follows that all representations of a group are determined (up to equivalence) once the irreducible representations are known. Consequently, the irreducible representations will be the center of attraction for us. Furthermore, these are all finite-dimensional, which is why we have considered finite-dimensional matrices. To reiterate, it is from the preceding key theorem that representation theory derives its power.

Note. (1) If $\Gamma_p \cdot\not\equiv\cdot \Gamma_q$, then the orthogonality relation can be written

$$\sum_{A\epsilon G} D_{ij}^{(p)-1}(A)\, D_{kl}^{(q)}(A) = 0.$$

(2) If Γ_p and Γ_q are unitary, then the orthogonality relation can be written

$$\sum_{A\epsilon G} D_{ij}^{(p)*}(A)\, D_{kl}^{(q)}(A) = \frac{g}{d}\delta_{ik}\,\delta_{jl}\,\delta_{pq}.$$

The question naturally arises as to how to construct the inequivalent, irreducible representations of a group. An interesting result bearing on this equation has been obtained by Brauer. It states that every irreducible representation of a group of order g can be written in the field* of the gth roots of unity. That is, any irreducible representation of a group is equivalent to an irreducible representation in which every matrix element is a number in the field generated by the gth roots of unity. Although the irreducible representations of many of the groups of mathematical physics have been tabulated (see Appendix I), there is no satisfactory method for deriving them in general. Nonetheless, we shall have a few more words to say about this later.

3. Character Tables

Let us now discuss the characters of the irreducible representations of a group (which will subsequently be distinguished by the label *primitive*). Since there are exactly r inequivalent, irreducible representations of a group, and the characters of two representations are equal if and only if the representations are equivalent, it follows that a group has exactly r unequal primitive characters. Also, each character is a class function and has, therefore, at most r different values. Hence, we can arrange the values of the primitive characters of a group in a square $r \times r$ table which is called the *character table* of the group. Letting $\chi_i^{(p)}$ be the value of the character of the pth irreducible representation for the ith class, we can write the table as follows:

---

* Consult any book on modern algebra for a discussion of fields.

	C_1	C_2	C_3		C_r
	1	r_2	r_3		r_r
Γ_1	1	1	1	. . . . .	1
Γ_2	d_2	$\chi_2^{(2)}$	$\chi_3^{(2)}$	. . . . .	$\chi_r^{(2)}$
Γ_3	d_3	$\chi_2^{(3)}$	$\chi_3^{(3)}$	. . . . .	$\chi_r^{(3)}$
	.				
	.				
Γ_r	d_r	$\chi_2^{(r)}$	$\chi_3^{(r)}$	. . . . .	$\chi_r^{(r)}$

The values of the character of Γ_p appear in the pth row, and the values of the r primitive characters for the ith class appear in the ith column. Since the trivial representation always occurs, we have put it in the first row, and since the character of the identity matrix is the dimension of the representation, we have indicated that in the first column.

Example. Q has the following character table:

	C_1	C_2	C_3	C_4	C_5
	1	1	2	2	2
Γ_1	1	1	1	1	1
Γ_2	1	1	1	−1	−1
Γ_3	1	1	−1	1	−1
Γ_4	1	1	−1	−1	1
Γ_5	2	−2	0	0	0

so all of the irreducible representations of Q are of dimension 1 or 2 as expected. Furthermore, the values of the 1-dimensional characters are also the matrices of the representations. The 2-dimensional representation is the one we have been using all along. However, we could deduce directly from the character table that the matrix of Γ_5 belonging to the class C_2 is $-I$.

The term "character table" implies that the character table characterizes a group much as does the multiplication table. Actually, however, a character table does not completely characterize a group. For example, Q and D_4 have the same character table, while on the other hand, tables exist which satisfy all the requirements known for a character table except that they do not belong to any groups.

Not only the matrix elements of the irreducible representation of a group but also the characters satisfy orthogonality relations.

Theorem. $$\sum_{i=1}^{r} r_i \chi_i^{(p)*} \chi_i^{(q)} = g\,\delta_{p,q} \qquad \text{(row orthog.)}$$

$$\sum_{p=1}^{r} \chi_i^{(p)*} \chi_j^{(p)} = \frac{g}{r_i}\delta_{ij} \qquad \text{(column orthog.),}$$

where now $\delta_{p,q} = 1$ if $\Gamma_p \cdot\!\equiv\!\cdot \Gamma_q$ and otherwise $\delta_{p,q} = 0$.

The first equation follows directly from the orthogonality relations for matrix elements by putting $j = i$ and $l = k$ and summing over i and k to get traces. This equation expresses an orthogonality property of the rows of the character table. The second equation expresses an orthogonality property of the columns of the character table, and follows directly from the first.

By means of the orthogonality relations for characters we can now investigate the problem of expressing any representation (up to equivalence) as a direct sum of irreducible representations, or, in other words, the complete reduction of an arbitrary representation.

Theorem. If Γ is an arbitrary representation of G with character χ, and $\{\Gamma_p\}$ $(p = 1,\ldots,r)$ are the irreducible representations of G, then $\Gamma \cdot\!\equiv\!\cdot \sum_{p=1}^{r} c^p \Gamma_p$, where the sum is a direct sum and where

$$c^p = \frac{1}{g} \sum_{i=1}^{r} r_i \chi_i^{(p)*} \chi_i.$$

Outline of Proof. Either Γ is irreducible (in which case one c^p is one and the others zero) or it is completely reducible, and therefore equivalent to a direct sum of irreducible representations. If $\Gamma \cdot\!\equiv\!\cdot \sum_{p=1}^{r} c^p \Gamma_p$, then $\chi_i = \sum_{p=1}^{r} c^p \chi_i^{(p)}$, where the sum is now an ordinary sum. Multiplying the equation by $r_i \chi_i^{(q)*}$ and summing over i we get

$$\sum_{i=1}^{r} r_i \chi_i^{(q)*} \chi_i = \sum_{p=1}^{r} c^p \sum_{i=1}^{r} r_i \chi_i^{(q)*} \chi_i^{(p)}.$$

Using the row orthogonality relation to replace the last sum, we have

$$\sum_{i=1}^{r} r_i \chi_i^{(q)*} \chi_i = \sum_{p=1}^{r} c^p g\, \delta_{p,q} = g c^q.$$

Thus, by means of the character table, we can now determine the number of times each irreducible representation occurs in a given representation, knowing only the character of the given representation. However, finding a transformation matrix which will reduce a given representation is a much more difficult problem.

Example. C_3 has the character table

	1	1	1
Γ_1	1	1	1
Γ_2	1	ϵ	ϵ^*
Γ_3	1	ϵ^*	ϵ

$$\epsilon = \exp\left[\tfrac{2}{3}\pi i\right] = -\tfrac{1}{2} + \tfrac{1}{2} i \sqrt{3}\,\cdot$$

The previously determined regular representation has the character

$$\chi^{(reg)} = (3, 0, 0).$$

Writing

$$\Gamma_{(reg)} = c_1 \Gamma_1 \oplus c_2 \Gamma_2 \oplus c_3 \Gamma_3$$

and solving for c_1 we have

$$c_1 = \tfrac{1}{3} \sum_{i=1}^{r} r_i \chi_i^{(1)*} \chi_i^{(reg)} = \tfrac{1}{3} \sum_{i=1}^{r} r_i \chi_i^{(reg)}$$
$$= \tfrac{3}{3} = 1.$$

Similarly, $c_2 = c_3 = 1$.

Let us apply this method to the regular representation of an arbitrary group. The character is $\chi^{(reg)} = (g, 0, 0, 0, \ldots, 0)$. Hence, $c^p = \frac{1}{g} d_p g = d_p$. Thus, the number of times the regular representation contains each irreducible representation is equal to the dimension of the irreducible representation. But

$$\chi^{(reg)}(I) = \sum_{p=1}^{r} d_p \chi^{(p)}(I) = \sum_{p=1}^{r} d_p^{\,2}$$

and

$$\chi^{(reg)}(I) = g.$$

Theorem. $$\sum_{p=1}^{r} d_p^{\,2} = g.$$

When this equation has a unique solution in terms of positive integers the dimensions of the irreducible representations of a group are easily found; otherwise, more elaborate methods are necessary.

Example. For Q, $g = 8$ and $r = 5$. Hence,

$$d_1^{\,2} + d_2^{\,2} + d_3^{\,2} + d_4^{\,2} + d_5^{\,2} = 8$$

and this equation has only one solution (except for the order) in terms of positive integers, $d_1 = d_2 = d_3 = d_4 = 1$ $d_5 = 2$, which agrees with the character table for Q. On the other hand, the previously discussed Dirac group has $g = 32$ $r = 17$. But

$$32 = 12 \times 1^2 + 5 \times 2^2 = 16 \times 1^2 + 1 \times 4^2.$$

Hence, in this case the dimensions can not be determined in this way.

We can also determine the total number of inequivalent representations of a given dimension d of a group. It is simply the number of solutions for $(c^1, \ldots, c^r)$ in terms of nonnegative integers of the equation $d = \sum_{p=1}^{r} c^p d_p$, which is just the reduction formula $\chi = \sum_{p=1}^{r} c^p \chi^{(p)}$ applied to the identity class. Thus Q has eleven inequivalent 2-dimensional representations.

Another useful consequence of the orthogonality relations is the following.

Theorem. Two representations Γ_1 and Γ_2 of a group have no irreducible representation in common if and only if

$$\sum_{i=1}^{r} r_i \chi_i^{(1)*} \chi_i^{(2)} = 0.$$

Let us now state a very useful theorem which connects commutator subgroups and 1-dimensional representations.

Theorem. The number of 1-dimensional representations of a group is equal to the index g/h_c of the commutator subgroup (and is therefore a divisor of the order of the group).

Example. For Q, $g/h_c = 4$.

Thus, we can directly and unambiguously determine the number of 1-dimensional representations without recourse to the earlier formula for dimensions which does not always uniquely determine them. The g/h_c 1-dimensional representations of G are, incidentally, the representations of the abelian quotient group G/H_c.

Let us now proceed to the derivation of an equation which will enable us to compute character tables.

Let us define the ith *class matrix* $S_i^{(\Gamma)}$ of the representation Γ of a group G to be the sum of all matrices belonging to C_i; i.e.,

$$S_i^{(\Gamma)} \equiv \sum_{A \epsilon C_i} D^{(\Gamma)}(A).$$

Theorem. If Γ_p is an irreducible representation of G, then

(1) $S_i^{(p)} S_j^{(p)} = \sum_{k=1}^{r} h_{ij,k} S_k^{(p)}$

(2) $S_i^{(p)} = \dfrac{r_i \chi_i^{(p)}}{d_p} I.$

The first result follows quite simply from the earlier considerations on class multiplication. To get the second result we note first that $D^{(p)^{-1}}(A)\, S_i^{(p)}\, D^{(p)}(A) = S_i^{(p)}$. Since $[S_i^{(p)}, D^{(p)}(A)] = 0$ for all A in G it follows that $S_i^{(p)}$ must be a scalar matrix, $S_i^{(p)} = \lambda_i^{(p)} I$. But $\operatorname{tr}(S_i^{(p)}) = \sum_{A \epsilon C_i} \operatorname{tr}(D^{(p)}(A)) = r_i \chi_i^{(p)}$. Hence, $\lambda_i^{(p)} d_p = r_i \chi_i^{(p)}$.

Using this theorem we can immediately derive the equation which is basic to the computation of character tables.

Theorem. If Γ is any irreducible representation of a group G, and χ is the corresponding primitive character, then χ must satisfy the following equation:

$$r_i r_j \chi_i \chi_j = d \sum_{k=1}^{r} h_{ij,k} r_k \chi_k.$$

Proof. Substituting (2) of the preceding theorem in (1) we have

$$\left(\frac{r_i \chi_i}{d}\right) I \left(\frac{r_j \chi_j}{d}\right) I = \sum_{k=1}^{r} h_{ij,k} \left(\frac{r_k \chi_k}{d}\right) I.$$

Cancelling out I, and multiplying by d^2 we get the described result.

4. Computation of Character Tables

Two methods will be discussed here.

(A)

This method is based on the two equations

$$\sum_{p=1}^{r} d_p^{\,2} = g$$

$$r_i r_j \chi_i^{(p)} \chi_j^{(p)} = d_p \sum_{k=1}^{r} h_{ij,k} r_k \chi_k^{(p)}.$$

This method therefore requires (as does the second method also) the determination from the multiplication table of the quantities g, r_i, r, and $h_{ij,k}$. The method is applicable only if the first equation has a unique solution (although other equations could be used to determine the dimensions). In that case the only unknown in the second equation is the character. Since the second equation is quadratic, it may have redundant solutions. These, however, can frequently be eliminated by using other requirements such as the irreducibility criterion for a representation $\frac{1}{g} \sum_{i=1}^{r} r_i |\chi_i|^2 = 1$.

Example. We have already applied the first equation to determine the dimensions of the irreducible representations of Q, and found

$$d_1 = d_2 = d_3 = d_4 = 1; \; d_5 = 2.$$

Using the previously determined values of $h_{ij,k}$ for Q we get for the second set of equations

$$\chi_1^2 = d\chi_1$$
$$\chi_1 \chi_2 = d\chi_2$$
$$\vdots$$
$$\chi_1 \chi_5 = d\chi_5$$
$$\chi_2^2 = d\chi_1$$
$$\chi_2 \chi_3^2 = d\chi_3$$
$$\vdots$$

$$\chi_2\chi_5 = d\chi_5$$
$$2\chi_3{}^2 = d(\chi_1 + \chi_2)$$
$$\chi_3\chi_4 = d\chi_5$$
$$\chi_3\chi_5 = d\chi_4$$
$$2\chi_4{}^2 = d(\chi_1 + \chi_2)$$
$$\chi_4\chi_5 = d\chi_3$$
$$2\chi_5{}^2 = d(\chi_1 + \chi_2).$$

The first five equations, which have χ_1 on the left, are simply identities. Let us determine the character of the 2-dimensional irreducible representation. Putting $d = 2$ and omitting the identities, we get

$$\begin{array}{lll} \chi_2{}^2 = 4 & & \\ \chi_2\chi_3 = 2\chi_3 & \chi_3{}^2 = 2 + \chi_2 & \\ \cdot & \chi_3\chi_4 = 2\chi_5 & \chi_4{}^2 = 2 + \chi_2 \\ \cdot & & \chi_4\chi_5 = 2\chi_3 \\ \cdot & & \\ \chi_2\chi_5 = 2\chi_5 & \chi_3\chi_5 = 2\chi_4 & \chi_5{}^2 = 2 + \chi_2. \end{array}$$

The first equation implies $\chi_2 = \pm 2$. This set of equations has several solutions, but $1 = \frac{1}{g}\sum_{i=1}^{r} r_i|\chi_i|^2 = \frac{1}{8}(2^2 + 2^2 + 2\,|\chi_3|^2 + 2\,|\chi_4|^2 + 2\,|\chi_5|^2)$ implies $\chi_3 = \chi_4 = \chi_5 = 0$. Furthermore, $\sum_{i=1}^{r} r_i\chi_i = 0$ implies $\chi_2 = -2$. Hence, in this case we are able to compute the character without examining in detail all of the solutions of the set of equations for χ.

(B)

The second method is complete and unambiguous, but in consequence it is also tedious. This method is essentially an eigenvalue problem and is based on the two equations

$$r_i r_j \chi_i \chi_j = d \sum_{k=1}^{r} h_{ij,k} r_k \chi_k$$

and

$$\frac{1}{g}\sum_{i=1}^{r} r_i|\chi_i|^2 = 1.$$

Let us now derive the desired characteristic equation from the first equation. Let $\{y_1,\ldots,y_r\}$ be a set of r unspecified variables. Further, let

$$\psi_i = r_i\chi_i \qquad\qquad l = \frac{1}{d}\sum_{i=1}^{r} \psi_i y_i$$

$$L_{jk} = \sum_{i=1}^{r} h_{ij,k} y_i.$$

Then, by multiplying the first basic equation for χ by y_i, summing over i, and substituting the above abbreviations, we obtain

$$\sum_{k=1}^{r} L_{jk}\psi_k = l\psi_j,$$

or in matrix notation:

$$L\psi = l\psi.$$

This is the desired eigenvalue problem, and

$$|L - lI| = 0$$

is the desired characteristic equation. Let $\{l_1, \ldots, l_r\}$ be the r roots of the characteristic equation, and write it in the form

$$(l - l_1)(l - l_2)\ldots(l - l_r) = 0.$$

But we already know what the roots are, namely,

$$l_p = \frac{1}{d_p}\sum_{i=1}^{r} \psi_i^{(p)} y_i = \frac{1}{d_p}\sum_{i=1}^{r} r_i \chi_i^{(p)} y_i.$$

Hence, the characteristic equation can be written in the factored form

$$\left(l - \frac{1}{d_1}\sum_{i=1}^{r} r_i\chi_i^{(1)}y_i\right)\left(l - \frac{1}{d_2}\sum_{i=1}^{r} r_i\chi_i^{(2)}y_i\right)\ldots\left(l - \frac{1}{d_r}\sum_{i=1}^{r} r_i\chi_i^{(r)}y.\right) = 0.$$

Thus, if we compute the characteristic equation $|L - lI| = 0$, and then factor it in the above form, we can simply read off the values of $\dfrac{\chi_i^{(p)}}{d_p}$ for all irreducible representations Γ_p (by dividing the coefficients of the variable y_i by r_i). To obtain the characters themselves, however, we must still evaluate the dimensions d_p. This can be accomplished with the aid of the second basic equation

$$\frac{1}{g}\sum_{i=1}^{r} r_i |\chi_i^{(p)}|^2 = 1,$$

which can be written

$$1 = \frac{|\chi_1^{(p)}|^2}{g}\sum_{i=1}^{r} r_i \left|\frac{\chi_i^{(p)}}{\chi_1^{(p)}}\right|^2 = \frac{d_p{}^2}{g}\sum_{i=1}^{r} r_i \left|\frac{\chi_i^{(p)}}{d_p}\right|^2 .$$

Hence, knowing $\dfrac{\chi_i^{(p)}}{d_p}$ we can solve for d_p by means of the equation

$$d_p = g^{\frac{1}{2}}\left\{\sum_{i=1}^{r} r_i \left|\frac{\chi_i^{(p)}}{d_p}\right|^2\right\}^{-\frac{1}{2}}$$

The positive root is taken because d_p is always positive.

Example. Again, making use of the previously determined class multiplication coefficients $h_{ij,k}$ for Q, we obtain for the matrix L

$$L = \begin{pmatrix} y_1 & y_2 & y_3 & y_4 & y_5 \\ y_2 & y_1 & y_3 & y_4 & y_5 \\ 2y_3 & 2y_3 & y_1 + y_2 & 2y_5 & 2y_4 \\ 2y_4 & 2y_4 & 2y_5 & y_1 + y_2 & 2y_3 \\ 2y_5 & 2y_5 & 2y_4 & 2y_3 & y_1 + y_2 \end{pmatrix} .$$

The characteristic polynomial of L can then be factored in the form

$$|L - lI| = -(l - l_1)(l - l_2)...(l - l_5),$$

where

$$\begin{aligned} l_1 &= y_1 + y_2 + 2y_3 + 2y_4 + 2y_5 \\ l_2 &= y_1 + y_2 + 2y_3 - 2y_4 - 2y_5 \\ l_3 &= y_1 + y_2 - 2y_3 + 2y_4 - 2y_5 \\ l_4 &= y_1 + y_2 - 2y_3 - 2y_4 + 2y_5 \\ l_5 &= y_1 - y_2 \quad . \end{aligned}$$

Hence for $\frac{\chi_i^{(p)}}{d_p}$ we obtain

$$\frac{\chi^{(1)}}{d_1} = (1,1,1,1,1) \qquad \frac{\chi^{(2)}}{d_2} = (1,1,1,-1,-1)$$

$$\frac{\chi^{(3)}}{d_3} = (1,1,-1,1,-1) \qquad \frac{\chi^{(4)}}{d_4} = (1,1,-1,-1,1)$$

$$\frac{\chi^{(5)}}{d_5} = (1,-1,0,0,0).$$

Solving for the dimensions, we obtain:

$$d_1 = \sqrt{\frac{8}{1^2 + 1^2 + 2 \times 1^2 + 2 \times 1^2 + 2 \times 1^2}} = \sqrt{\frac{8}{8}} = \sqrt{1} = 1$$

$$d_2 = 1 \qquad d_3 = 1 \qquad d_4 = 1 \qquad d_5 = 2.$$

Hence, for the characters we obtain

$$\chi^{(1)} = (1,1,1,1,1) \qquad \chi^{(2)} = (1,1,1,-1,-1)$$

$$\chi^{(3)} = (1,1,-1,1,-1) \qquad \chi^{(4)} = (1,1,-1,-1,1)$$

$$\chi^{(5)} = (2,-2,0,0,0).$$

5. Properties of Character Tables

Let us now list some miscellaneous properties of character tables.

Theorem. (1) If $\chi_i^{(p)}$ is complex, then there exists a class C_j such that $\chi_j^{(p)} = \chi_i^{(p)*}$ (namely the inverse class of C_i, $C_j = C_{i'}$).

(2) If $\chi^{(p)}$ is a complex-valued function, then another row of the character table is $\chi^{(p)*}$.

(3) The determinant of the character table (considered as a matrix X) is given by

$$\det(X) = \epsilon\left\{\frac{g^r}{r_1 r_2 \ldots r_r}\right\}^{\frac{1}{2}} \qquad \epsilon = \pm 1, \pm i.$$

(4) Det (X) is real or imaginary according as the number of irreducible representations of the third kind is twice an even number or twice an odd number.

(5) Every row of a character table which belongs to a representation of dimension > 1 has a zero entry.

(6) If a character table has only one row belonging to a given dimension, then every entry in that row must be an integer.

(7) If a character table has only one column belonging to a given order (of a class), then every entry in that column must be an integer.

(8) If a character table has only one row belonging to a given dimension, then every entry in that row must be zero except those entries which belong to classes contained in the commutator subgroup.

(9) A class C_i consists of commutators if and only if

$$\sum_{p=1}^{r} \frac{\chi_i^{(p)}}{d_p} \neq 0.$$

(10) Let $\chi^{(1)},\ldots,\chi^{g/h_c}$ be the 1-dimensional representations, and let $\chi^{(I)} \equiv \sum_{p=1}^{g/h_c} \chi^{(p)}$. Then $\chi_i^{(I)}$ is nonzero if and only if $C_i \subseteq H_c$. Hence H_c can be determined from the character table, and therefore the character table is also useful in determining the solvability of a group.

(11) The 1-dimensional (or *linear*) characters form a group, the *character group*, under multiplication, and this group is isomorphic to the quotient group G/H_c.

(12) If C_i and C_j are two distinct classes, then the character table has at least one row such that $\chi_i \neq \chi_j$.

(13) The classes for which the character of a particular row has the value $d = \chi_i$ constitute the kernel of that representation.

(14) The number of square roots of any element of class C_i is given by

$$\zeta_i = \sum_{p=1}^{r} \beta_p \chi_i^{(p)}$$

$$\begin{aligned} \text{where } \beta_p &= 1 \text{ if } \Gamma_p \text{ is of first kind} \\ &= -1 \text{ if } \Gamma_p \text{ is of second kind} \\ &= 0 \text{ if } \Gamma_p \text{ is of third kind.} \end{aligned}$$

(15) If G has even order then at least two rows of the character table must belong to irreducible representations of the first kind.

(16) The number of rows with real entries only is equal to the number of ambivalent classes r_a of the group ($r_a = 1$ for groups of odd order).

(17) Let $R(\chi)$ be the real part of the character χ, let $C_{i'}$ be the class inverse to C_i, and let $\Gamma_{p'}$ be the representation conjugate to Γ_p, $\Gamma_{p'} = \Gamma_p{}^*$. Then

$$\sum_{p=1}^{r} R(\chi_i^{(p)})\, R(\chi_j^{(p)}) = 0 \quad \text{if } j \neq i,\ \ j \neq i'$$

$$= \frac{g}{2r_i} \quad \text{if } j = i \neq i'$$

$$\sum_{i=1}^{r} r_i R(\chi_i^{(p)})\, R(\chi_i^{(q)}) = 0 \quad \text{if } p \neq q,\ \ p \neq q'$$

$$= \frac{g}{2} \quad \text{if } p = q \neq q'.$$

(18) $\sum_{p=1}^{r} d_p \chi_i^{(p)} = 0 \qquad i = 2,3,\ldots,r.$

If we define the character vector of a group belonging to a particular representation Γ to be the r-dimensional vector with components

$$\left(\frac{d_\Gamma}{\sqrt{g}}, \sqrt{\frac{r_2}{g}}\,\chi_2^{(\Gamma)},\ldots, \sqrt{\frac{r_r}{g}}\,\chi_r^{(\Gamma)}\right),$$

then we see that every character vector lies in an r-dimensional vector space, and (from the orthogonality relations) that the r primitive character vectors form an orthonormal basis of this space. Furthermore, every class function can be considered to be a vector in this space if its values are written out in component form as $(f_1, f_2, \ldots, f_r)$. Thus every class function vector is a linear combination of primitive character vectors. The matrix elements of the irreducible representations of a group can be similarly treated, this treatment being called the Peter-Weyl theorem.

Theorem. Let us choose the inequivalent irreducible representations of a group G to be all unitary, and define $U_{p,ij}$ to be the g-dimensional vector whose components are

$$\left(\sqrt{\frac{d_p}{g}}\, D_{ij}^{(p)}(I), \sqrt{\frac{d_p}{g}}\, D_{ij}^{(p)}(A_1),\ldots, \sqrt{\frac{d_d}{g}}\, D_{ij}^{(p)}(A_{g-1})\right).$$

Then

(1) there are g vectors $U_{p,ij}$ ($i,j = 1,\ldots,d_p$; $p = 1,\ldots,r$)

(2) the g vectors $U_{p,ij}$ are orthonormal,

(3) every function $f(A)$ on the group G, when expressed as a g-dimensional vector in the form $f(I), f(A_1), \ldots, f(A_{g-1})$, can be expressed as a linear combination of the g vectors $U_{p,ij}$.

The first part of the theorem follows from the fact that for a given p, (i,j) has $d_p{}^2$ values, and $\sum_{p=1}^{r} d_p{}^2 = g$. The orthonormality of the vectors $U_{p,ij}$ follows directly from the key orthogonality equation for matrix elements of irreducible representations.

If we are given any representation of a group, then we can construct from it a representation of dimension 1 by replacing each matrix by its determinant. Thus, this process when applied to the irreducible representation Γ_5 of Q yields Γ_1. Furthermore, those elements of G whose determinant is one in a particular representation form a normal subgroup of G whose quotient group is cyclic.

We can now state a simple criterion for determining whether or not an arbitrary (reducible or irreducible) representation is of first kind or not.

Theorem. A representation Γ is equivalent to a real representation if and only if each irreducible component of the second kind occurs an even number of times, and the irreducible components of third kind occur in complex conjugate pairs.

With the help of this theorem we can determine the reality class of any representation. Thus, Γ is of second kind if and only if χ is real and Γ is not of first kind; and Γ is of third kind if and only if χ is not real.

A miscellaneous but useful theorem on characters is the following:

Theorem. Let $P(x)$ be any polynomial in a single variable with integral coefficients, let Γ be any representation of a group G, and let χ be the corresponding character. Then the number

$$\sum_{A \epsilon G} P(\chi(A))$$

is divisible by g.

Example. Let $P(x) = 3x^2 - 5$ and let Γ be the representation Γ_5 of Q. Then $\sum_{A \epsilon Q} P(\chi(A)) = (3 \times 2^2 - 5) + (3 \times 2^2 - 5) - 6 \times 5 = -16$, which is divisible by $g = 8$.

We can now derive a useful consequence of this theorem by considering a representation Γ for which the character χ has only integral values and defining $P(x) \equiv (x - \chi_2)(x - \chi_3)\ldots(x - \chi_t)$, where only the t distinct values of the character are used. Clearly, P has integral coefficients so we must have $\sum_{A \epsilon G} P(\chi(A))$ divisible by g. But $\sum_{A \epsilon G} P(\chi(A)) = kP(\chi_1)$ where k is the order of the kernel of Γ.

Corollary. Let Γ be any d-dimensional representation with an integer-valued character, and let k be the order of the kernel of Γ. Then $k(d - \chi_2)(d - \chi_3)\ldots(d - \chi_t)$, where only distinct values of the character are used, is divisible by g.

6. Faithful Representations

Let us now briefly consider faithful versus unfaithful representations. We already know that the kernel of any representation Γ is the set of all classes C_i such that $\chi_i^{(\Gamma)} = d_\Gamma$. We also know that every group has a faithful representation (the regular representation), but not every group has a faithful irreducible representation (e.g., D_2). Every cyclic group C_n does, however, have a faithful irreducible representation (viz., the mapping of the generator of C_n onto $e^{2\pi i/n}$). Also, we can say that every nontrivial irreducible representation of a group is faithful if and only if the group is simple. Further, every representation which contains a faithful representation as a component must be faithful. Let us now state two theorems on faithful irreducible representations which are due to Burnside and Weisner, respectively.

Theorem. A group G has a faithful irreducible representation if it does not have two minimal normal subgroups whose orders are powers of the same prime.

Example. Q has only one minimal normal subgroup and therefore has a faithful irreducible representation, viz., Γ_5.

Theorem. G has no faithful irreducible representations if and only if G contains a subgroup H such that

(1) order (H) = a power of some prime p,

(2) H is generated by the minimal normal subgroups of G whose orders are powers of p,

(3) every subgroup of H of index p contains a normal subgroup different from the identity.

Example. Q has only one minimal normal subgroup; and since H must be generated by this subgroup, it must be the subgroup itself. Hence, order $(H) = 2$, and $p = 2$. However, condition (3) is not fulfilled because the identity element is a subgroup of H of index 2. Hence, Q does not fulfill the conditions and must therefore have a faithful irreducible representation, as it does.

One final interesting theorem on faithful irreducible representations is the following, which makes use of the fact that the inner Kronecker product of two representations of a group is also a representation.

Theorem. If Γ is a faithful irreducible representation, then every irreducible representation of G will occur as a component of some (inner) Kronecker power of Γ.

Example. For Q,

$$\Gamma_5 \otimes \Gamma_5 \cdot\equiv\cdot \Gamma_1 \oplus \Gamma_2 \oplus \Gamma_3 \oplus \Gamma_4.$$

7. Kronecker Products

The preceding theorem and example lead us naturally into a further study of inner Kronecker products of irreducible representations of a group. Since any representation can be decomposed into irreducible representations, we can define the *coefficients of composition* $\gamma_{ij,k}$ of a group G by means of the equation

$$\Gamma_i \otimes \Gamma_j = \sum_{k=1}^{r} \gamma_{ij,k} \Gamma_k,$$

where Γ_i, Γ_j, and Γ_k are all irreducible representations of G. Since the character of the Kronecker product is the product of the characters, we have

$$\chi^{(i)}\chi^{(j)} = \sum_{k=1}^{r} \gamma_{ij,k} \chi^{(k)},$$

from which we can solve for the γ's in terms of the χ's by multiplying the equation by $\chi^{(k')*}$, summing over classes, and using the row orthogonality relation for characters. One obtains

$$\gamma_{ij,k} = \frac{1}{g} \sum_{l=1}^{r} r_l \chi_l^{(i)} \chi_l^{(j)} \chi_l^{(k)*}.$$

Here we have solved for the γ's in terms of the χ's, but the reverse is also possible (much as for the $h_{ij,k}$'s) although we shall not carry out the development here. Let us now list some properties of the γ's (letting $\Gamma_{i'} = \Gamma_i^*$).

Theorem. (1) $\gamma_{ij,k} = \gamma_{ji,k} = \gamma_{i'k,j} = \gamma_{j'k,i} = \gamma_{i'j',k'} = \gamma_{ik',j'} = \gamma_{jk',i'}$.

(2) Let $\beta_{ijlm} \equiv \sum_{k=1}^{r} \gamma_{ij,k} \gamma_{kl,m}$. Then β_{ijlm} is unaltered by any permutation of i, j, l.

(3) $\sum_{k=1}^{r} \gamma_{ij,k}^2 = g \sum_{k=1}^{r} \frac{1}{r_k}$.

(4) $\gamma_{ij,1} = \delta_{ij'}$.

(5) $\gamma_{1j,k} = \gamma_{j1,k} = \delta_{jk}$.

(6) $\sum_{k=1}^{r} \gamma_{ij,k}^2 = \sum_{k=1}^{r} \gamma_{ii',k} \gamma_{jj',k}$.

A theorem stated implicitly by (4) is that $\Gamma_i \otimes \Gamma_j$ contains the trivial representation if and only if $\Gamma \cdot\equiv\cdot \Gamma_i^*$. Let us fire one parting shot at inner Kronecker products.

Theorem. If $q\ (\leqslant r)$ irreducible representations of a group G form a group under inner Kronecker multiplication, then G contains a normal subgroup H such that H is contained in the kernel of each of the q representations, but not in the kernel of any other irreducible representation.

Thus, for the group of 1-dimensional representations of a group, $H = H_c$.

Let us proceed now to a consideration of outer Kronecker products of representations.

Theorem. If G_1 and G_2 are any two groups, and if Γ_1 and Γ_2 are irreducible representations of G_1 and G_2, respectively, then $\Gamma_1 \times \Gamma_2$ is an irreducible representation of $G_1 \times G_2$. Conversely, every irreducible representation of $G_1 \times G_2$ is an outer Kronecker product of an irreducible representation of G_1 with an irreducible representation of G_2.

Thus, considering character tables as matrices, we see that the character table of $G_1 \times G_2$ must be the Kronecker product of the tables of G_1 and G_2.

Example. C_2 has the character table

	1	1
Γ_1	1	1
Γ_2	1	−1

and $D_2 = C_2 \times C_2$, so D_2 must have the character table

	1	1	1	1
Γ_1	1	1	1	1
Γ_2	1	−1	1	−1
Γ_3	1	1	−1	−1
Γ_4	1	−1	−1	1

8. Simply Reducible Groups

Let us for a moment consider symmetrized and antisymmetrized squares of representations, which will tie in very closely with simply reducible groups and with inner Kronecker products. First let us give a representation-theoretic characterization of simply reducible groups (which incidentally, is the one used for infinite groups).

Theorem. A group is simply reducible if and only if

(1) every irreducible representation is equivalent to its complex conjugate (and therefore of first or second kind, so every primitive character is real),

(2) the Kronecker product of any two irreducible representations contains no irreducible representation more than once (so the γ's are all 0 or 1).

Hence, the character table of a group will determine whether or not it is simply reducible, and the multiplication table is not necessary.

If a representation Γ has character χ, then let us for the moment call the character of the symmetrized and antisymmetrized squares of Γ, $\chi^{(2)}$ and $\chi^{[2]}$. Then, from our formulas for the traces of $D_{(k)}$ and $D_{[k]}$ it follows that

$$\chi^{(2)}(A) = \tfrac{1}{2}\chi^2(A) + \tfrac{1}{2}\chi(A^2)$$
$$\chi^{[2]}(A) = \tfrac{1}{2}\chi^2(A) - \tfrac{1}{2}\chi(A^2).$$

Let us call an irreducible representation *even* (*odd*) if it occurs as a component of the symmetrized (antisymmetrized) square of some integer representation or of the antisymmetrized (symmetrized) square of some half-integer representation. In general, an irreducible representation can be both even and odd, or neither.

Theorem. An irreducible representation of a simply reducible group can not be both even and odd.

Example. Consider Q

$$\Gamma_1^{(2)} = \Gamma_2^{(2)} = \Gamma_3^{(2)} = \Gamma_4^{(2)} = \Gamma_1$$
$$\Gamma_5^{(2)} = \Gamma_2 \oplus \Gamma_3 \oplus \Gamma_4 \qquad \Gamma_5^{[2]} = \Gamma_1.$$

Hence, Γ_1 is an even representation (which is always true), and Γ_2, Γ_3, and Γ_4 are odd representations. However, Γ_5 is neither even nor odd.

The fact that the irreducible representation Γ_5 of Q is neither even nor odd could have been deduced from a general theorem and the fact that Γ_5 is a half-integer representation.

Theorem. Both even and odd irreducible representations of a simply reducible group must be integer representations.

One final result on simply reducible groups is the following (the preceding theorem being a consequence of this).

Theorem. The inner Kronecker product of two integer or of two half-integer representations of a simply reducible group contains only integer representations. The inner Kronecker product of an integer and a half-integer representation contains only half-integer representations.

9. Reduction by Idempotents

As has been intimated before, the problem of reducing a representation (i.e., finding the transformation matrix) is generally a difficult one. However, this problem can be partially handled by the method of reduction by idempotents.

Theorem. Let Γ be a d-dimensional representation of the group G, and let $S_i^{(\Gamma)}$ be the ith class matrix belonging to Γ. Then, the r (not necessarily distinct) d-dimensional matrices

$$e_p^{(\Gamma)} \equiv \frac{d_p}{g} \sum_{i=1}^{r} \chi_i^{(p)*} S_i^{(\Gamma)}$$

satisfy the conditions

(1) $\sum_{p=1}^{r} e_p^{(\Gamma)} = I,$

(2) $e_p^{(\Gamma)} e_q^{(\Gamma)} = \delta_{p,q} e_q^{(\Gamma)}$ (e's idempotent),

(3) $[e_p^{(\Gamma)}, D^{(\Gamma)}(A)]_- = 0.$

Instead of proving these simple but elegant relations, let us prove a less elegant result which will expose the basic idea of the theory of idempotents.

Theorem. Suppose $\Gamma = \sum_{p=1}^{r} c^{(p)} \Gamma_p$ is expressed in completely reduced form

$$D^{(\Gamma)} = \begin{pmatrix} D^{(1)} & & & & & & & & \\ & D^{(1)} & & & & & & & \\ & & \ddots & & & & & & \\ & & & D^{(1)} & & & & & \\ & & & & D^{(2)} & & & & \\ & & & & & D^{(2)} & & & \\ & & & & & & \ddots & & \\ & & & & & & & D^{(2)} & \\ & & & & & & & & D^{(3)} \\ & & & & & & & & & \ddots \end{pmatrix}.$$

Then, the pth idempotent matrix $e_p^{(\Gamma)}$ has the form

$$e_p^{(\Gamma)} = \begin{pmatrix} 0 & & & & & & & & & \\ & 0 & & & & & & & & \\ & & \ddots & & & & 0 & & & \\ & & & 0 & & & & & & \\ & & & & I & & & & & \\ & & & & & I & & & & \\ & & & & & & \ddots & & & \\ & & & & & & & I & & \\ & & & & & & & & 0 & \\ & & 0 & & & & & & & \ddots \\ & & & & & & & & & & 0 \end{pmatrix},$$

where each I is a d_p-dimensional unit matrix, there are $c^{(p)}$ of them, and they occur in the positions of $D^{(p)}$ in the complete reduction of $D^{(\Gamma)}$.

Outline of Proof. Since $e_p^{(\Gamma)}$ is a linear combination of $D^{(\Gamma)}$'s, we need only look at one irreducible component of $D^{(\Gamma)}$. Therefore, let us consider the d_q-dimensional idempotent matrix

$$e_p^{(q)} \equiv \frac{d_p}{g} \sum_{i=1}^{r} \chi_i^{(p)*} S_i^{(q)}.$$

belonging to the irreducible representation Γ_q. In this case we know that

$$S_i^{(q)} = \frac{r_i \chi_i^{(q)}}{d_q} I$$

so

$$e_p^{(q)} = \frac{d_p}{g d_q} \left(\sum_{i=1}^{r} r_i \chi_i^{(p)*} \chi_i^{(q)} \right) I.$$

Using the row orthogonality equation, we get

$$e_p^{(q)} = \frac{d_p}{d_q} \delta_{p,q} I = \delta_{p,q} I.$$

From this equation it is clear that $e_p^{(\Gamma)}$ must have the above form.

Using this form of $e_p^{(\Gamma)}$ we can easily prove the three relations of the first theorem on idempotents. Further, we see from this form of the idempotents of the representation Γ that $e_p^{(\Gamma)}$ simply projects every vector of the carrier space of Γ into that subspace which is the carrier space of the component $c^{(p)}\Gamma_p$ of Γ. This is true whether Γ is completely reduced or not.

Hence, we can construct the component $c^{(p)}\Gamma_p$ of Γ in the following way. Let v be any vector in the carrier space V of Γ, and let

$$u^{(p)}(v) = e_p^{(\Gamma)} v.$$

Then $u^{(p)}(v)$ lies in the $c^{(p)}d_p$-dimensional subspace V_p of V, which is the carrier space of $c^{(p)}\Gamma_p$. Further, from the completely reduced form of Γ we see that $D^{(\Gamma)}(A)u^{(p)}(v)$ will also lie in V_p. Therefore, since every vector of V_p is some $u^{(p)}(v)$ we can construct a basis

$$\{u_1^{(p)}, u_2^{(p)}, \ldots, u^{(p)}{}_{c^{(p)}d_p}\}$$

of V_p from $u^{(p)}(v)$'s. Then we know that

$$D^{(\Gamma)}(A) u_i^{(p)} = \sum_{j=1}^{c^{(p)}d_p} d_{ji}(A) u_j^{(p)}$$

(note the order of the subscripts on d). The matrices $d(A) = \|d_{ij}(A)\|$ then form the representation $c^{(p)}\Gamma_p$.

Theorem. Let Γ be a representation of dimension d with carrier space V. Let $c^{(p)}\Gamma_p$ be a component of Γ containing all the equivalent irreducible components Γ_p of Γ(p fixed), and let $e_p^{(\Gamma)}$ be the corresponding idempotent. Let $v_1, \ldots, v_d$ be a basis of V, and let $w_i^{(p)} = e_p^{(\Gamma)} v_i$. Then the set of $c^{(p)}d_p$

orthonormal vectors $\{u_j^{(p)}\}$ obtained from the set $\{w_i^{(p)}\}$ by applying Schmidt's process of orthonormalization is a basis of V_p. Further, if we let u be the column matrix of all $u_j^{(p)}$'s, let v be the column matrix of all v_i's, and let S be the matrix transforming v into u, $u = Sv$. Then the partially reduced form of Γ is $S^{t-1}\Gamma S^t$.

This method of reduction by idempotents leaves us with the problem of reducing a direct sum of equivalent irreducible representations.

Example. Let Γ be the regular representation of C_3. Then

$$e_1^{(reg)} = \frac{1}{3}\begin{pmatrix} 1 & 1 & 1 \\ 1 & 1 & 1 \\ 1 & 1 & 1 \end{pmatrix} \quad e_2^{(reg)} = \frac{1}{3}\begin{pmatrix} 1 & \epsilon^* & \epsilon \\ \epsilon & 1 & \epsilon^* \\ \epsilon^* & \epsilon & 1 \end{pmatrix} \quad e_3^{(reg)} = \frac{1}{3}\begin{pmatrix} 1 & \epsilon & \epsilon^* \\ \epsilon^* & 1 & \epsilon \\ \epsilon & \epsilon^* & 1 \end{pmatrix}.$$

Letting $v = \begin{pmatrix} x \\ y \\ z \end{pmatrix}$ be an arbitrary vector of the carrier space of Γ, we have

$$e_1^{(reg)}v = \frac{1}{3}\begin{pmatrix} x+y+z \\ x+y+z \\ x+y+z \end{pmatrix} \quad e_2^{(reg)}v = \frac{1}{3}\begin{pmatrix} x+\epsilon^*y+\epsilon z \\ \epsilon x+y+\epsilon^*z \\ \epsilon^*x+\epsilon y+z \end{pmatrix} \quad e_3^{(reg)}v = \frac{1}{3}\begin{pmatrix} x+\epsilon y+\epsilon^*z \\ \epsilon^*x+y+\epsilon z \\ \epsilon x+\epsilon^*y+z \end{pmatrix}.$$

Each of these vectors has only one independent component, so the idempotents will completely reduce the regular representation of C_3 into 1-dimensional representations. Let us call these vectors u_1, u_2, and u_3 and call the matrices of the regular representation I, D_1, and D_2. Then

$$\begin{array}{lll} Iu_1 = u_1 & D_1u_1 = u_1 & D_2u_1 = u_1 \\ Iu_2 = u_2 & D_1u_2 = \epsilon^*u_2 & D_2u_2 = \epsilon u_2 \\ Iu_3 = u_3 & D_1u_3 = \epsilon u_3 & D_2u_3 = \epsilon^*u_3. \end{array}$$

Comparison of the three rows above with the three rows of the character table of C_3 shows that u_1, u_2, and u_3 generate the three irreducible representations of C_3.

In this case it was not necessary to consider a basis of V, but let us do so anyway for illustration. Let

$$v_1 = \begin{pmatrix} 1 \\ 0 \\ 0 \end{pmatrix} \qquad v_2 = \begin{pmatrix} 0 \\ 1 \\ 0 \end{pmatrix} \qquad v_3 = \begin{pmatrix} 0 \\ 0 \\ 1 \end{pmatrix}.$$

Then

$$w_1^{(1)} = \frac{1}{3}\begin{pmatrix} 1 \\ 1 \\ 1 \end{pmatrix} \qquad w_2^{(1)} = \frac{1}{3}\begin{pmatrix} 1 \\ 1 \\ 1 \end{pmatrix} \qquad w_3^{(1)} = \frac{1}{3}\begin{pmatrix} 1 \\ 1 \\ 1 \end{pmatrix}$$

$$w_1^{(2)} = \frac{1}{3}\begin{pmatrix} 1 \\ \epsilon \\ \epsilon^* \end{pmatrix} \qquad w_2^{(2)} = \frac{1}{3}\begin{pmatrix} \epsilon^* \\ 1 \\ \epsilon \end{pmatrix} \qquad w_3^{(2)} = \frac{1}{3}\begin{pmatrix} \epsilon \\ \epsilon^* \\ 1 \end{pmatrix}$$

$$w_1^{(3)} = \frac{1}{3}\begin{pmatrix} 1 \\ \epsilon^* \\ \epsilon \end{pmatrix} \qquad w_2^{(3)} = \frac{1}{3}\begin{pmatrix} \epsilon \\ 1 \\ \epsilon^* \end{pmatrix} \qquad w_3^{(3)} = \frac{1}{3}\begin{pmatrix} \epsilon^* \\ \epsilon \\ 1 \end{pmatrix},$$

and we see that

$$w_1^{(1)} = w_2^{(1)} = w_3^{(1)}$$
$$w_2^{(2)} = \epsilon^* w_1^{(2)} \qquad w_3^{(2)} = \epsilon w_1^{(2)}$$
$$w_2^{(3)} = \epsilon w_1^{(3)} \qquad w_3^{(3)} = \epsilon^* w_1^{(3)} \quad .$$

Hence, the only linearly independent vectors we obtain for the three subspaces are $w_1^{(1)}$, $w_1^{(2)}$, and $w_1^{(3)}$ which we can therefore choose to be $u^{(1)}$, $u^{(2)}$, and $u^{(3)}$. The u's are clearly orthonormal. With this choice of u's we see that

$$u^{(1)} = \tfrac{1}{3}(v_1 + v_2 + v_3)$$
$$u^{(2)} = \tfrac{1}{3}(v_1 + \epsilon v_2 + \epsilon^* v_3)$$
$$u^{(3)} = \tfrac{1}{3}(v_1 + \epsilon^* v_2 + \epsilon v_3),$$

or letting u be the column matrix of u-vectors and v that of v-vectors

$$u = Sv,$$

where

$$S = \frac{1}{3}\begin{pmatrix} 1 & 1 & 1 \\ 1 & \epsilon & \epsilon^* \\ 1 & \epsilon^* & \epsilon \end{pmatrix} = S^t.$$

The transformed representation is then given by

$$S^{t-1}DS^t \quad \text{or} \quad S^{-1}DS$$

and we get in this way the same completely reduced form of Γ that we had before.

The problem of finding the irreducible representations of a group can in general be partially solved by using idempotents to reduce partially the regular representation (which contains all irreducible representations). However, one is still left with the problem of reducing representations of the form $c^{(p)}\Gamma_p$.

To reiterate for the sake of emphasis: the idempotent method allows us to find bases for the components $c^{(p)}\Gamma_p$ of Γ.

There is a second idempotent method which allows us to do even more, but which in turn requires more information to begin with. The first idempotent method required us to know the representation Γ and the character table. The second idempotent method requires us to know the irreducible representations also. With the second method we can determine directly the bases of the irreducible components Γ_p of Γ.

The second idempotent method is based on the following theorem which is a direct consequence of the key theorem.

Theorem. Let $G = \{A\}$ be a group whose elements are operators (without specifying what the elements operate on), let $\Gamma = \{D(A)\}$ be an irreducible representation of G, and let

$$\zeta_{ij} \equiv \frac{d}{g} \sum_{A} D_{ij}(A^{-1})A \ .$$

Then

$$\zeta_{ij}\zeta_{kl} = \delta_{il}\zeta_{kj} \ .$$

The quantities ζ_{ii} are therefore idempotent. We shall combine the preceding theorem with the following theorem to obtain the basic theorem of the second method of reduction by idempotents.

Theorem. Let $\Gamma = \{D(A)\}$ be a representation of the group $G = \{A\}$, $\Gamma_p = \{D^{(p)}(A)\}$ be the pth irreducible representation of G, and $\{u_i\}(i = 1,\dots, d_p)$ be d_p linearly independent vectors in the carrier space V of Γ. Then $\{u_i\}$ is a basis for the component Γ_p of Γ, i.e.,

$$D(A)u_i = \sum_{j=1}^{d_p} D_{ji}^{(p)}(A)u_j$$

if and only if

$$\zeta_{ij}^{(p)}u_i = u_j \text{ (no sum over } i),$$

where

$$\zeta_{ij}^{(p)} \equiv \frac{d_p}{g} \sum_{A} D_{ij}^{(p)}(A^{-1})D(A).$$

It will be noted that if Γ_p is 1-dimensional, $\zeta^{(p)} = e_p^{(\Gamma)}$.

By combining these two results we can now prove the main theorem.

Theorem. Let $\Gamma = \{D(A)\}$ be any representation of $G = \{A\}$, Γ_p the pth irreducible representation of G, and v any nonzero vector in the carrier space V of Γ. Then

$$u_i^{(p)} \equiv \zeta_{ii}^{(p)}v \qquad \text{(for one fixed } i)$$
$$u_j^{(p)} \equiv \zeta_{ij}^{(p)}u_i \qquad (j \neq i)$$

is a basis for the component Γ_p.

Outline of Proof. Let us show that the second equation of the preceding theorem is true so that the first will also be. By the definition of u_j, the second equation holds for $j \neq i$. Thus we need only prove it for $j = i$. So, we must prove that $\zeta_{ii}^{(p)}u_i = u_i$ Substituting the definition of u_i we get $\zeta_{ii}^{(p)2}v = \zeta_{ii}^{(p)}v$, which we know is true because $\zeta_{ii}^{(p)}$ is idempotent.

If Γ_p occurs more than once as a component of Γ, then a different v must be chosen for each Γ_p. If Γ_p appears $c^{(p)}$ times, then we can take for the v's any $c^{(p)}$ vectors in the basis of V. Let us now prove some orthogonality relations for the u's.

Theorem. Let $u_{ai}^{(p)}$ be the ith basis vector for the ath component Γ_p of Γ, $\{v_n\}$ be a basis of V,

$$u_{ai}^{(p)} = \sum_{n=1}^{d} a_{ai,n}^{(p)} v_n,$$

and

$$\langle u_{ai}^{(p)} | u_{a'i'}^{(p')} \rangle \equiv \sum_{n=1}^{d} a_{ai,n}^{(p)*} a_{a'i',n}^{(p')}$$

(which is the usual definition of inner product when the basis $\{v_n\}$ is orthonormal). Then, if the u's are normalized $\langle u | u \rangle = 1$, if the representations Γ and Γ_p generated by $\{v_n\}$ and $\{u_{ai}^{(p)}\}$ are unitary, and either identical or inequivalent, then

$$\langle u_{ai}^{(p)} | u_{ai'}^{(p')} \rangle = \delta_{p,p'} \delta_{i,i'}$$

$$\langle u_{ai}^{(p)} | u_{a'i}^{(p)} \rangle = \langle u_{aj}^{(p)} | u_{a'j}^{(p)} \rangle.$$

Outline of Proof. First let us prove that

$$\langle Du_{ai}^{(p)} | Du_{a'i'}^{(p')} \rangle = \langle u_{ai}^{(p)} | u_{a'i'}^{(p')} \rangle.$$

To do this we observe that

$$Du_{ai}^{(p)} = \sum_{n=1}^{d} a_{ai,n}^{(p)} Dv_n = \sum_{n=1}^{d} a_{ai,n}^{(p)} \sum_{m=1}^{d} D_{m,n} v_m$$

$$= \sum_{m=1}^{d} \left(\sum_{n=1}^{d} a_{ai,n}^{(p)} D_{m,n} \right) v_m.$$

Hence

$$\langle Du_{ai}^{(p)} | Du_{a'i'}^{(p')} \rangle = \sum_{m=1}^{d} \left(\sum_{n=1}^{d} a_{ai,n}^{(p)} D_{mn} \right)^* \left(\sum_{n'=1}^{d} a_{a'i',n'}^{(p')} D_{mn'} \right)$$

$$= \sum_{n=1}^{d} \sum_{n'=1}^{d} a_{ai,n}^{(p)*} a_{a'i',n'}^{(p')} \sum_{m=1}^{d} D_{mn}^* D_{mn'}.$$

If D is unitary the last sum is $\delta_{n,n'}$ and the preliminary equation is proved. But

$$Du_{ai}^{(p)} = \sum_{j=1}^{d_p} D_{ji}^{(p)} u_{aj}^{(p)}$$

so the preliminary equation becomes

$$\langle u_{ai}^{(p)} | u_{a'i'}^{(p')} \rangle = \sum_{j,j'=1}^{d_p} D_{ji}^{(p)*} D_{j'i'}^{(p')} \langle u_{aj}^{(p)} | u_{a'j'}^{(p')} \rangle.$$

Since this equation holds for every $D^{(p)}(A)$, we can sum both sides of the equation over all members of the group and use the orthogonality relations to get

$$\langle u_{ai}^{(p)} | u_{a'i'}^{(p')} \rangle = \frac{1}{d_p} \delta_{p,p'} \delta_{i,i'} \sum_{j=1}^{d_p} \langle u_{aj}^{(p)} | u_{a'j}^{(p)} \rangle.$$

Putting $a = a'$ and making use of the normalization of the u's we get the first equation. Putting $p = p'$ and $i = i'$ we get

$$\langle u_{ai}^{(p)} | u_{a'i}^{(p)} \rangle = \frac{g}{d_p} \sum_{j=l}^{d_p} \langle u_{aj}^{(p)} | u_{a'j}^{(p)} \rangle.$$

But since the right side is independent of i, so is the left side, and we get the second equation.

Usually the u's are chosen so $\langle u_{ai}^{(p)} | u_{a'i}^{(p)} \rangle = 0$. If the u's do not come out this way automatically when ζ_{ii} is applied to the basis vectors of V, then the $u_{ai}^{(p)}$'s obtained in this way are orthonormalized by Schmidt's process. This automatically makes all u's belonging to different Γ_p's (fixed p) orthogonal. Furthermore, the u's resulting from the orthonormalization still form bases for the Γ_p's.

The $u_{ai}^{(p)}$'s discussed above might be called symmetry basis vectors and the equations of the preceding theorem are the orthogonality relations for symmetry basis vectors.

10. Groups of Mathematical Physics

Let us now consider some groups which are of particular interest in mathematical physics.

A. Cyclic Groups

Since C_n is abelian, every irreducible representation is of dimension 1, and there are n of them. Let A be a generator of C_n (so order $(A) = n$) and let ϵ be any nth root of unity. Then $A^j \to \epsilon^j$ is a 1-dimensional representation of C_n; and since there are n ϵ's, every 1-dimensional representation is of this form. Hence, if we now let $\epsilon = e^{2\pi i/n}$ be a primitive nth root of unity, we can write the character table of C_n in the form

	1	1	1		1	
Γ_1	1	1	1	...	1	
Γ_2	1	ϵ	ϵ^2	...	ϵ^{n-1}	
Γ_3	1	ϵ^2	ϵ^4	...	ϵ^{2n-2}	
Γ_4	1	ϵ^3	ϵ^6	...	ϵ^{3n-3}	C_n
	⋮	⋮	⋮	...	⋮	
Γ_n	1	ϵ^{n-1}	ϵ^{2n-2}	...	$\epsilon.^{(n-1)^2}$	

B. Dihedral Groups

The cyclic subgroup of D_n generated by the second generator $(A_2{}^n = I)$ is also a normal subgroup of index 2, which is therefore maximal. Hence, every irreducible representation of D_n is of dimension 1 or 2. Furthermore, using the value of h_c given in the previous chapter, we have for the number of 1-dimensional representations

$$g/h_c \equiv \frac{2n}{h_c} = 2 \qquad \text{if } n \text{ is odd}$$

$$= 4 \qquad \text{if } n \text{ is even.}$$

Since the total number of irreducible representations, r, was

$$r = \frac{n+1}{2} + 1 \qquad n \text{ odd}$$

$$= \frac{n}{2} + 3 \qquad n \text{ even,}$$

we have for the number of inequivalent 2-dimensional representations

$$\frac{n-1}{2} \qquad n \text{ odd}$$

$$\frac{n}{2} - 1 \qquad n \text{ even.}$$

The number of irreducible 2-dimensional representations of D_n is exactly equal to the number of classes of order two of D_n which lie in the cyclic normal subgroup generated by A_2. Each such class consists of ${A_2}^j$ and $({A_2}^j)^{-1}$. If n is odd, the only other class contained in the subgroup is I; if n is even, there are two additional classes in the subgroup, I and $A_2^{n/2}$. Finally, if n is odd there is one class of D_n which is not contained in the subgroup and it is of order n. If n is even, there are two classes not in the subgroup, each of order $n/2$ (one class containing elements $A_1 A_2^{2j}$, and the other class containing elements $A_1 A_2^{2j+1}$).

Let us now write down (without derivation) the character tables for D_n for odd and even n. For brevity, let us put $\phi = 2\pi/n$ and $m = (n-1)/2$ for n odd and $m = n/2$ for n even.

n odd

D_n	$C(I)$ 1	$C(A_2)$ 2	$C({A_2}^2)$ 2		$C({A_2}^m)$ 2	$C(A_1)$ n
Γ_1	1	1	1	$\cdots$	1	1
Γ_2	1	1	1	$\cdots$	1	-1
Γ_3	2	$2\cos\phi$	$2\cos 2\phi$	$\cdots$	$2\cos m\phi$	0
Γ_4	2	$2\cos 2\phi$	$2\cos 4\phi$	$\cdots$	$2\cos 2m\phi$	0
$\vdots$	$\vdots$	$\vdots$	$\vdots$	$\cdots$	$\vdots$	$\vdots$
$\Gamma_{\frac{n+3}{2}}$	2	$2\cos n\phi$	$2\cos 2n\phi$	$\cdots$	$2\cos m^2\phi$	0

n even

	$C(I)$	$C(A_2)$	$C(A_2{}^2)$		$C(A_2^{m-1})$	$C(A_2{}^m)$	$C(A_1A_2^{2j})$	$C(A_1A_2^{2j+1})$
	1	2	2		2	1	$n/2$	$n/2$
Γ_1	1	1	1	…	1	1	1	1
Γ_2	1	1	1	…	1	1	-1	-1
Γ_3	1	-1	1	…	$(-1)^{m-1}$	$(-1)^m$	1	-1
Γ_4	1	-1	1	…	$(-1)^{m-1}$	$(-1)^m$	-1	1
Γ_5	2	$2\cos\phi$	$2\cos 2\phi$	…	$2\cos(m-1)\phi$	$2\cos m\phi$	0	0
Γ_6	2	$2\cos 2\phi$	$2\cos 4\phi$	…	$2\cos 2(m-1)\phi$	$2\cos 2m\phi$	0	0
	⋮	⋮	⋮	…	⋮	⋮	⋮	⋮
$\Gamma_{\frac{n+6}{2}}$	2	$2\cos(m-1)\phi$	$2\cos 2(m-1)\phi$	…	$2\cos(m-1)^2\phi$	$2\cos m(m-1)\phi$	0	0

D_n

C. Tetrahedral Group

Since $g = 12$ and $h_c = 4$, the number of 1-dimensional representations must be $g/h_c = 3$. Since $r = 4$ there is only one other irreducible representation, and from the equation $1^2 + 1^2 + 1^2 + d_4{}^2 = 12$ we see that $d_4 = 3$. The classes of T are (using the multiplication table given in connection with semidirect products) $C_1 = I$, $C_2 = \{A_1, A_{10}, A_{11}\}$, $C_3 = \{A_2, A_3, A_4, A_5\}$, and $C_4 = \{A_6, A_7, A_8, A_9\}$. The character table is

	C_1	C_2	C_3	C_4
	1	3	4	4
Γ_1	1	1	1	1
Γ_2	1	1	ϵ	ϵ^*
Γ_3	1	1	ϵ^*	ϵ
Γ_4	3	−1	0	0

T

$$\epsilon = e^{2\pi i/3} = -\frac{1}{2} + \frac{i\sqrt{3}}{2}$$

D. Octahedral Group

The number of 1-dimensional representations is $g/h_c = 24/12 = 2$, and the total number of inequivalent irreducible representations is $r = 5$. Since the order of the center is one, we have $d_p \leqslant \sqrt{24} = 4{\cdot}899$ and hence $d_p \leqslant 4$. From the equation $24 = 1^2 + 1^2 + d_3{}^2 + d_4{}^2 + d_5{}^2$ we get

$$d_3{}^2 + d_4{}^2 + d_5{}^2 = 22.$$

At most, one d_p could be four, say d_5, in which case the equation would become $d_3{}^2 + d_4{}^2 = 6$, which has no solution. Hence, $d_p \neq 4$ and $d_p \leqslant 3$. The unique solution is easily seen to be $d_3 = 2$, $d_4 = d_5 = 3$. The classes of the octahedral group are $C_1 = I$, $C_2 = \{A_6, A_{17}, A_{19}\}$, $C_3 = \{A_1, A_3, A_7, A_8, A_{15}, A_{23}\}$, $C_4 = \{A_5, A_{10}, A_{13}, A_{16}, A_{18}, A_{21}\}$, $C_5 = \{A_2, A_4, A_9, A_{11}, A_{12}, A_{14}, A_{20}, A_{22}\}$. The character table is

	C_1	C_2	C_3	C_4	C_5
	1	3	6	6	8
Γ_1	1	1	1	1	1
Γ_2	1	1	−1	−1	1
Γ_3	2	2	0	0	−1
Γ_4	3	−1	−1	1	0
Γ_5	3	−1	1	−1	0

O

E. Icosahedral Group

The character table is

	C_1	C_2	C_3	C_4	C_5
	1	12	12	15	20
Γ_1	1	1	1	1	1
Γ_2	3	$\frac{1+\sqrt{5}}{2}$	$\frac{1-\sqrt{5}}{2}$	-1	0
Γ_3	3	$\frac{1-\sqrt{5}}{2}$	$\frac{1+\sqrt{5}}{2}$	-1	0
Γ_4	4	-1	-1	0	1
Γ_5	5	0	0	1	-1

$\mathscr{I}$

11. Tensors and Invariants

Let us now clear up a few miscellaneous topics associated with representation theory. Let us first give a definition of a tensor which includes contravariant tensors, covariant tensors, relative tensors, pseudotensors, spinors, undors, and exspinors as special cases. It should be noted first that a tensor is defined with respect to a particular group and may not be a tensor with respect to some other group. Thus a tensor with respect to the 3-dimensional rotation group may not be a tensor with respect to the group of all real nonsingular 3-dimensional matrices (the real general linear group $GL(3, R)$).

Let us consider a space S consisting of a set of points P. By an n-coordinate system C_n in S let us understand an assignment of an n-tuple of real numbers to each point of S such that no two points are assigned the same n-tuple. Two different n-coordinate systems can differ in the way they assign n-tuples to the points as well as in the n-tuples that are used. As n-coordinate transformation from C_n to C_n' is an n-tuple of real functions whose arguments are n-tuples of real numbers such that the value of an n-tuple of functions for an n-tuple of numbers specifying a point in the coordinate system C_n is the n-tuple of numbers specifying the point in the coordinate system C_n'.

Definition. Let S be a space and $\{C_n\}$ be a set of n-coordinate systems of S generated from a single n-coordinate system by a group G of n-coordinate transformations. Further, let $\{f_i(P,C_n)\}$ and $\{a_{ij}(P,C_n,C_n')\}$ be two sets of complex-valued functions such that

$$f_i(P,C_n') = \sum_j a_{ij}(P,C_n,C_n')f_j(P,C_n)$$

for all C_n and C_n' in the set $\{C_n\}$. Any two such sets of functions $\{f_i(P,C_n)\}$ and $\{a_{ij}(P,C_n)\}$ constitute a *tensor* with respect to the group G. The functions $f_i(P,C_n)$ are the components of the tensor, and the functions $a_{ij}(P,C_n)$ are the transformation coefficients of the tensor.

We see that if $f_i(P,C_n) = 0$ for all i then $f_i(P,C_n') = 0$ for all i and all C_n' in the set $\{C_n\}$. The transformation of a tensor is usually interpreted geometrically as an alias transformation. The two ordinary types of spinors are simply tensors which transform under irreducible representations of the 3-dimensional rotation group, or of the proper orthochronous Lorentz group.

Let us now consider invariant theory briefly. Invariants are of importance not only in physics (e.g., the velocity of light being an invariant of special relativity theory) but also in geometry. In fact, F. Klein has defined geometry as the study of properties of a space which are invariant under a group of transformations on the space. Thus congruence is a property of Euclidean space which is invariant under the Euclidean group (i.e., the group of rotations and translations).

Definition. Let Γ be any d-dimensional representation of a group G, and $F(x_1,\ldots,x_d)$ be any function of d complex variables (defined for all values of x_i). Then $F(x_1,\ldots x_d)$ is an *invariant* of Γ if $F(Dx_1,\ldots,Dx_d) = F(x_1,\ldots,x_d)$, for all D in Γ and all values of the x's (where $Dx_i = \sum_{j=1}^{d} D_{ij}\, x_j$).

Example. The group of transformations of the eight thermodynamic variables considered in Chapter II has as one representation the eight permutation transformations of the first four variables, U, H, F, and G. An invariant of this representation is the function

$$F(U,H,F,G) = U + H + F + G.$$

Let us first consider linear invariants, where by a linear invariant is meant a function F of the form

$$F(x_1,\ldots,x_d) = \sum_{i=1}^{d} F_i x_i \qquad (F_i = \text{constant}).$$

The thermodynamic invariant given above is thus a linear invariant. Linear invariants are very closely related to invariant vectors (Chap. I).

Theorem. Let G be any group, let Γ be a d-dimensional representation of G, and let S be any matrix which transforms Γ into unitary form, $S^{-1}DS = U$ (all D in Γ). Then if v is any invariant vector of Γ, and $u \equiv (SS_{\dagger})^{-1}v$, it follows (representing $x_1,\ldots,x_d$ by a column matrix x) that

$$F(x) \equiv u^{\dagger}x$$

is a linear invariant of Γ. Conversely, every linear invariant of Γ can be written in the form

$$F(x) = u^{\dagger}x,$$

and the vector v defined by

$$v \equiv (SS^{\dagger})u$$

is an invariant vector of Γ.

The proof of this is quite simple and straightforward. We see now that we can establish a natural 1-1 correspondence between linear invariants and invariant vectors of a representation Γ. We might then ask how many linearly independent invariant vectors a representation has.

Theorem. The number of linearly independent invariant vectors of a representation Γ is equal to the number of times the trivial representation Γ_1 is contained in Γ. This number is in turn given by the formula

$$c^{(1)} = \frac{1}{g} \sum_{i=1}^{r} r_i \chi_i^{(\Gamma)}.$$

This result follows because, as already pointed out, every invariant subspace of dimension d' of the carrier space of Γ is the carrier space of a completely reduced d'-dimensional component representation of Γ. But each invariant vector of Γ is the basis of a 1-dimensional invariant subspace of $V^{(\Gamma)}$. Hence, each linearly independent invariant vector of Γ is the basis of a carrier space of a 1-dimensional component of Γ. Since the vectors are invariant, each of these 1-dimensional representations must be the trivial representation.

There still remains the problem of constructing invariant vectors.

Theorem. Let v be any vector of the carrier space of Γ, and let

$$D = \frac{1}{g} \sum_{A \in G} D(A).$$

Then Dv is an invariant vector of Γ, and conversely, every invariant vector of Γ is of this form (for some v).

Outline of Proof.

$$D(B)(Dv) = \frac{1}{g} D(B) \sum_{A} D(A)v = \frac{1}{g} \sum_{A} D(B)D(A)v = \frac{1}{g} \sum_{A'} D(A')v = Dv,$$

so Dv is invariant. Conversely, if u is invariant, then $Du = u$.

We can get higher degree invariants in a similar way. Instead of considering $x_1, \ldots, x_d$ let us consider the $\binom{d+k-1}{k}$ products $x_1{}^k, x_2{}^k, \ldots, x_d{}^k, x_1{}^{k-1}x_2, \ldots$ of degree k. If we put these products in a column matrix $x_{(k)}$, then we can write all homogeneous kth degree invariants in the form $F(x) = u_{(k)}^{+} x_{(k)}$, where $v_{(k)} = (S_{(k)} S_{(k)}^{+}) u_{(k)}$ is an invariant vector of the kth symmetrized Kronecker power $\Gamma_{(k)}$ of Γ.

12. Representations Generated by Functions

While we are considering the effects of groups on functions, let us show how an operator which operates on functions can be associated with each matrix of a d-dimensional representation $\Gamma = \{D(A)\}$. We shall simply define a linear operator $\mathscr{D}(A)$ on functions of d complex variables as follows:

$$\mathscr{D}(A)F(x) \equiv F(D^{-1}(A)x).$$

Then $\mathscr{D}(A)\mathscr{D}(B) = \mathscr{D}(AB)$§. If we let $x' = D(A)x$ and $F' = \mathscr{D}(A)F$, then the definition says that $F'(x') = F(x)$.

If we restrict ourselves to representations Γ composed of real matrices so that we can also restrict ourselves to real x's, and if we consider only functions $F(x)$, which are square-integrable over some range of x, then these F's form a vector space whose dimension is infinite (a function space or Hilbert space). If F_1 and F_2 are two such functions, or vectors, then we can define an inner (or scalar) product by

$$\langle F_1 | F_2 \rangle \equiv \int F_1^*(x) F_2(x) dx.$$

We can also define the symbol

$$\langle F_1 | \mathscr{D} | F_2 \rangle \equiv \int F_1^*(x) \mathscr{D} F_2(x) dx.$$

The adjoint $\mathscr{D}^\dagger$ of the operator $\mathscr{D}$ is defined by the equation

$$\langle F_1 | \mathscr{D} | F_2 \rangle^* = \langle F_2 | \mathscr{D}^\dagger | F_1 \rangle$$

which must hold for all F_1 and F_2. The operator $\mathscr{D}$ is then said to be unitary if $\mathscr{D}^\dagger = \mathscr{D}^{-1}$ and Hermitian if $\mathscr{D}^\dagger = \mathscr{D}$.

We can now easily see that $\Gamma_\infty \equiv \{\mathscr{D}(A)\}$ is an infinite dimensional representation, and that if the matrices D of Γ are orthogonal then the operators $\mathscr{D}$ of Γ_∞ must be unitary. Also, Γ_∞ must be reducible.

An important concept which is closely related to the representations of a group in function space is that of a tensor operator.

Definition. Let $G = \{A\}$ be a group, $\Gamma = \{D(A)\}$ be an orthogonal d-dimensional representation of G, and $\Gamma_\infty = \{\mathscr{D}(A)\}$ be the corresponding unitary representation in function space. If $\mathscr{O} = \{\mathscr{O}_1, \ldots, \mathscr{O}_d\}$ is a set of d operators in the Hilbert space, then $\mathscr{O}$ is a *tensor operator* relative to Γ if

$$\mathscr{D}(A)\mathscr{O}_i\mathscr{D}(A^{-1}) = \sum_{j=1}^{d} D_{ji}(A)\mathscr{O}_j$$

(for all A in G)‡. $\mathscr{O}$ is irreducible if Γ is irreducible.

---

§ $\mathscr{D}(AB)F(x) = F(D^{-1}(AB)x)$ and $F_B(x) \equiv \mathscr{D}(B)F(x) = F(D^{-1}(B)x)$,
so $\mathscr{D}(A)F_B(x) = F_B(D^{-1}(A)x) = F(D^{-1}(B)D^{-1}(A)x) = F([D(A)D(B)]^{-1}x)$
or $\mathscr{D}(A)\mathscr{D}(B)F(x) = F(D^{-1}(AB)x) = \mathscr{D}(AB)F(x)$.

‡ More generally, if $\Gamma = \{D(A)\}$ and $\Gamma' = \{\mathscr{D}(A)\}$ are any two representations of G, if d is the dimension of Γ, and if $\mathscr{O} = \{\mathscr{O}_1, \ldots, \mathscr{O}_d\}$ is a set of d operators in the carrier space of Γ' such that

$$\mathscr{D}(A)\mathscr{O}_i\mathscr{D}(A^{-1}) = \sum_{j=1}^{d} D_{ji}(A)\mathscr{O}_j$$

(for all A in G), then $\mathscr{O}$ is a tensor operator relative to Γ and Γ'.

Let us continue the study of the relation between groups and functions. Let us denote a point of a space (not necessarily a vector space) by q, and consider a *space* S as being simply a collection (either finite or infinite) of points q, i.e., $S = \{q\}$. It will not be necessary for our purposes to specify a metric (or distance function) in S, or to specify neighborhoods. By a *transformation* on S let us mean any function $T(q)$ which is defined for all q in S and whose value is a point in S, i.e., $T(q)$ is in S. In short, the domain of a transformation T on S is the entire space S, and the range of T lies in S. Let us call a transformation T *one-to-one* if $q_1 \neq q_2$, implies that $T(q_1) \neq T(q_2)$, and vice versa. Thus, if T is a one-to-one transformation, and $Q = T(q)$, then we can define a one-to-one transformation T^{-1} by the equation $q = T^{-1}(Q)$. The entire preceding discussion is simply a generalization of the usual theory of vector spaces and matrices.

Example. Let us take the space S to be the set of all atoms of some particular molecule, so each point q of S is an atom. Then any interchange of the atoms is a one-to-one alibi transformation on the space.

By the product of two one-to-one transformations T_1 and T_2 let us mean the function $T_1 T_2$ defined by $(T_1 T_2)(q) = T_1[T_2(q)]$.

Definition. A *transformation group* on a space S is a set $\{T\}$ of one-to-one transformations on S which form a group under multiplication.

Example. Again let S be the set of all atoms of a molecule. Then the set of all interchanges which interchange only atoms of the same kind is a transformation group on S.

Definition. A transformation group G on S is called *transitive* if any point of S can be transformed into any other point of S by a transformation belonging to G.

By a *function* $F(q)$ on S let us mean a single-valued function whose domain is S and whose range is in the field of complex numbers.

Example. Choosing S as above, $F(q) \equiv m(q)$, where $m(q)$ is the mass of atom q, is a function on S.

Definition. Let $\{F_1(q),..., F_d(q)\}$ be a set of d functions on S, and let $G = \{T\}$ be a group of transformations on S. If

$$F_i(T^{-1}q) = \sum_{j=1}^{d} D_{ji}(T) F_j(x) \qquad (i = 1,..., d)$$

where the D's form a representation Γ of G, then the functions $\{F_i(x)\}$ are said to *generate* the representation Γ.

Example. Let S be the set of two identical atoms of a homonuclear diatomic molecule. Let $G = C_2 = \{I, T\}$, where T is the interchange of the two atoms. Further, let us choose an axis (say the x-axis) through the two atoms with the origin at the center of mass midway between them. Then, if we choose $F_1(q)$ to be the x-coordinate of atom q, and $F_2(q) \equiv - F_1(q)$, we have

$$F_1(I^{-1}q) = F_1(Iq) = F_1(q), \quad F_1(T^{-1}q) = F_1(Tq) = F_2(q),$$
$$F_2(Iq) = F_2(q), \quad \text{and} \quad F_2(Tq) = F_1(q).$$

Hence, $F_1(q)$ and $F_2(q)$ generate the representation $I \to \begin{pmatrix} 1 & 0 \\ 0 & 1 \end{pmatrix}$, $T \to \begin{pmatrix} 0 & 1 \\ 1 & 0 \end{pmatrix}$ which is the regular representation of C_2, and is of first kind.

Let us now suppose that an inner product $\langle F_i|F_j\rangle$ can be defined for the functions on S which has the usual properties. Thus if S is a Euclidean space, then $\langle F_i|F_j\rangle = \int F_i^*(x)F_j(x)dx$, and if S contains only a finite number of points, $\langle F_i|F_j\rangle = \sum_q F_i^*(q)F_j(q)$.

Now let us state the theorem which is the main objective of this long discussion, and which is essentially a time reversal theorem.

Theorem. Let $S = \{q\}$ be a space, let $G = \{T\}$ be a transformation group on S, and let $\{F_1(q),\ldots, F_d(q)\}$ be a set of orthonormal functions on S which generate a representation $\Gamma = \{D(T)\}$ of G. If $\{F_1^*(q),\ldots, F_d^*(q)\}$ depend linearly on $\{F_1(q),\ldots, F_d(q)\}$, then Γ must be of the first kind.

Outline of Proof. By assumption, there exist complex (or real) numbers U_{ij} such that $F_i^*(q) = \sum_{j=1}^{d} U_{ij}F_j(q)$. Then $U_{ij} = \langle F_j|F_i^*\rangle$, and

$$(UU^\dagger)_{ik} = \sum_{j=1}^{d} \langle F_k^*|F_j\rangle\langle F_j|F_i^*\rangle.$$

But

$$F_k^* = \sum_{j=1}^{d} \langle F_j|F_k^*\rangle F_j$$

so

$$\langle F_k^*|F_i^*\rangle = \sum_{j,l} \langle F_j|F_k^*\rangle^*\langle F_l|F_i^*\rangle\langle F_j|F_l\rangle$$
$$= \sum_{j} \langle F_k^*|F_j\rangle\langle F_j|F_i^*\rangle.$$

Hence, $(UU^\dagger)_{ik} = \langle F_k^*|F_i^*\rangle = \langle F_k|F_i\rangle^* = \delta_{ik}$. Thus U is unitary. Let us put $F(q) = ||F_i(q)||$ so we have $F^*(q) = UF(q)$. Taking the complex conjugate of both sides we have $U^*F^*(q) = F(q)$, and multiplying by $U^{*-1} = U^t$ we get $F^*(q) = U^tF(q)$. Hence, if U transforms F into F^* so does U^t. Applying the equation $F^* = UF$ at the point $T^{-1}q$ we have $F^*(T^{-1}q) = UF(T^{-1}q)$, or $[D^tF(q)]^* = UD^tF(q)$, or $D^\dagger F^* = UD^tF$. Substituting $F^* = U^tF$ on the left side we get $(D^\dagger U^t - UD^t)F = 0$. In order for F to be composed of d linearly independent functions we must have $(D^\dagger U^t - UD^t) = 0$, i.e. $D^* = U^{-1}DU$. Hence $\Gamma^* \cdot\!\equiv\!\cdot\, \Gamma$ and Γ must either be of first or second kind. In case Γ is not a direct sum of irreducible unitary representations, we can transform the F's by a nonsingular linear transformation into a new set of F's which will generate a Γ' which is a direct sum of irreducible unitary representations ($\Gamma' \cdot\!\equiv\!\cdot\, \Gamma$). Then $\Gamma'^* = U'^{-1}\Gamma'U'$ and if Γ' is of second kind, U' must be skew symmetric. But $F'^* = U'F'$ and $F'^* = U'^tF' = -U'F'$. Hence, $U'F' = -U'F'$ and therefore $U'F' = 0$. But this implies that $F' = 0$ and therefore $F = 0$, contrary to assumption. Hence, Γ can not be of second kind. Thus, Γ must be of first kind.

It follows that if Γ is of second or third kind, then the F^*'s can not all depend linearly on the F's.

Example. In the preceding example F_1 and F_2 are orthogonal, and normalized if the unit of length is defined to be the distance from the center of mass to an atom. Since $F_i^* = F_i$ the F's should generate a representation of first kind, as indeed they do.

It should be observed that in the preceding theorem it was assumed that every F_i^* depends linearly on the F_j's. However, this is not necessary if Γ is irreducible.

Corollary. Let $\{F_1(q),\ldots, F_d(q)\}$ be an orthonormal set of functions on S which generate an irreducible representation Γ of the transformation group $G = \{T\}$. If any of the complex conjugate functions $\{F_1^*(q),\ldots, F_d^*(q)\}$ depends linearly on $\{F_1(q),\ldots, F_d(q)\}$, then they all do, and Γ is of the first kind.

Outline of Proof. Let us collect the functions $\{F_1^*,\ldots {}^*F_\delta^*\}$ which depend linearly on F into the column matrix f^*, and the remaining F^*'s into the column matrix g^*. By assumption f^* depends linearly on F, or on f and g, so we can write

$$f^* = V_{ff}f + V_{fg}g,$$

where V_{ff} is a square matrix and V_{fg} is a rectangular matrix. By taking the complex conjugate of both sides and substituting the above expression for f^* we get

$$f = V_{ff}^*f^* + V_{fg}^*g^* = V_{ff}^*(V_{ff}f + V_{fg}g) + V_{fg}^*g^*,$$

or

$$V_{fg}^*g^* = (1 - V_{ff}^*V_{ff})f - V^*V_{fg}g.$$

Consequently, if $V_{fg}^* \neq 0$ some functions of g^* will depend linearly on F, contrary to assumption. Hence, $V_{fg} = 0$, and from the original equation for f^*,

$$f^* = V_{ff}f$$

(and V_{ff} must be nonsingular in order for the functions of f to be linearly independent). Let us partition each matrix D of Γ into blocks which operate on f and g.

$$D = \begin{pmatrix} D_{ff} & D_{fg} \\ D_{gf} & D_{gg} \end{pmatrix},$$

so $F' = DF$ implies $f' = D_{ff}f + D_{fg}g$. By taking the complex conjugate of both sides and substituting for f^* we obtain $f' = V_{ff}^{-1}D_{ff}^*V_{ff}f + V_{ff}^{-1}D_{fg}^*g^*$.

By subtracting these two equations we get

$$D_{fg}^* g^* = (V_{ff} D_{ff} - D_{ff}^* V_{ff}) f + V_{ff} D_{fg} g.$$

Again, in order for g^* to be linearly independent of f and g we must have $D_{fg} = 0$. But $D_{fg} = 0$ implies Γ is reduced, contrary to assumption. Hence, our original splitting of F^* into f^* and g^* is impossible, and either all F_i^*'s depend linearly on F or none do. Since we have assumed that some do, it follows that all must. Then by the preceding theorem it follows that Γ must be of first kind.

It follows that if Γ is of the second or third kind, and irreducible, then none of the F^*'s can depend linearly on the F's.

13. Subduced Representations

Let us conclude this chapter with two remarks about subgroups. Let G be a group, H a subgroup of G, and Γ a representation of G. If we consider only those matrices of Γ which are images of elements of H, then we see that these matrices form a representation $\Gamma^{(s)}$ of H of the same dimension as Γ. We shall subsequently refer to $\Gamma^{(s)}$ as the representation of H which is *subduced* by the representation Γ of G. Usually the term induced is applied here, but "induced" will be reserved for another process (more or less the inverse) in this book.

Let G be any group, H any subgroup, and G/H the quotient group. Further, let Γ be any representation of G/H. Then since G/H is homomorphic to Γ, and G is homomorphic to G/H, it follows that G is homomorphic to Γ. Hence, from any representation Γ of G/H we get by this inverse process a representation of G, which we shall say is *engendered* by Γ. If Γ is irreducible, then so is the engendered representation of G.

Conversely, since every irreducible representation of G/H engenders an irreducible representation of G, it follows that every irreducible representation of G/H is just one of the irreducible representations of G which contains H in its kernel. Hence, the character table of G/H can be constructed from that of G if one knows how the classes of G are distributed among the classes of G/H.

In Chapter V the relations between representations of groups and their subgroups will be discussed further.

BIBLIOGRAPHY

Auld, B. A. (1952). Applications of Group Theory in the Study of Symmetrical Waveguide Junctions. Stanford Univ. Microwave Lab. Rep. 157 Palo Alto, Calif.

Barriol, J. (1947). "Application of the Theory of Groups to the Study of Molecular and Crystalline Vibrations." Masson, Paris.

Bhagavantam, S., and Venkatarayudu, T. (1951). "Theory of Groups and its Application to Physical Problems." Andhra Univ. Waltair, India.

Blichfeldt, H. F. (1917). "Finite Collineation Groups." Univ. of Chicago Press, Chicago.

Boerner, H. (1955). "Representations of Groups." Springer-Verlag, Berlin.

Brauer, R., and Nesbitt, C. (1937). "On the Modular Representations of Groups of Finite Order." Univ. of Toronto Press, Toronto.

Burnside, W. (1911). "Theory of Groups of Finite Order." Cambridge Univ. Press, London and New York.

Corson, E. M. (1951). "Perturbation Methods in the Quantum Mechanics of n-Electron Systems." Hafner, New York.

Dickson, L. E. (1901). "Linear Groups." B. G. Teubner, Leipzig.

Dickson, L. E. (1926). "Modern Algebraic Theories." B. H. Sanborn, New York.

Eyring, H., Walter, J., and Kimball, G. E. (1944). "Quantum Chemistry." John Wiley & Sons, New York.

Falk, G. (1955). Algebra. "Encyclopedia of Physics," Vol. 2, p. 1. Springer-Verlag, Berlin.

Frame, J. S. (1933). The Theory of Tables of Group Characteristics. Ph.D. Dissertation. Harvard Univ., Cambridge, Massachusetts.

Hamermesh, M. Group Theory and its Application to Physical Problems (Notes). Argonne Natl. Lab., Lemont, Illinois.

Higman, B. (1955). "Applied Group-Theoretic and Matrix Methods." Clarendon Press, Oxford.

Inui, T., and Yanagawa, S. (1950). "The Application of Group Representations to Atoms and Molecules" (in Japanese). Japan.

Koster, G. F. (1956). Notes on Group Theory. Mass. Inst. Technol. Solid-state and Molecular Theory Technical Rep. No. 8, Cambridge, Massachusetts.

Landau, L., and Lifschitz, E. (1948). "Quantum Mechanics." Ogiz, Moscow.

Littlewood, D. E. (1950). "The Theory of Group Characters." Clarendon Press, Oxford.

Ludwig, G. (1954). "The Foundations of Quantum Mechanics." Springer-Verlag, Berlin.

Margenau, H., and Murphy, G. M. (1943). "The Mathematics of Physics and Chemistry." D. Van Nostrand, New York.

McIntosh, H. V. (1955). Seminar in Group Theory (notes). Aberdeen Proving Ground, Aberdeen, Maryland.

Murnaghan, F. D. (1938). "The Theory of Group Representations." Johns Hopkins Press, Baltimore, Maryland.

Murnaghan, F. D. (1955). Matrix Groups (Notes). Haverford College, Haverford, Penna.

Schur, J. (1936). "The Algebraic Foundations of the Representation Theory of Groups." Gebr. Frey & Kratz, Zürich.

Speiser, A. (1956). "Theory of Groups of Finite Order," 4th ed. Birkhäuser, Basel.

van der Waerden, B. L. (1949). "Modern Algebra." Frederick Ungar, New York.

van der Waerden, B. L. (1932). "The Group Theoretic Method in Quantum Mechanics." Springer, Berlin.

Venkatarayudu, T. (1954). Applications of Group Theory to Physical Problems (Notes). New York Univ., New York.

Weyl, H. (1931). "The Theory of Groups and Quantum Mechanics." Methuen & Co., London.

Wigner, E. P. (1931). "Group Theory and its Application to the Quantum Mechanics of Atomic Spectra." Friedr. Vieweg & Sohn Akt.-Ges., Braunschweig.

Wigner, E. P. (1951). On the Matrices which reduce the Kronecker Products of S.R. Groups (Notes). Princeton Univ., Princeton, New Jersey.

Wilson, E. B., Decius, J. C., and Cross, P. C. (1955). "Molecular Vibrations." McGraw-Hill, New York.

Chapter IV

APPLICATIONS

We now have the machinery necessary to apply group theory to problems of physics. It should be emphasized that group theory is primarily valuable in mathematical physics for analyzing the effects of known geometrical symmetry on physical systems. The first example to be treated, annihilation and creation operators, is an exception; but the second example, molecular vibrations, will illustrate the effect of geometrical symmetry and its analysis by means of group theory very well. It might also be mentioned that the reason classical analysis (i.e., calculus) is inadequate and unnatural for investigating effects of symmetry (particularly when only a finite number of symmetries is present) is that symmetry is a condition "in the large" whereas classical analysis is primarily a theory "in the small."

1. Fermion Annihilation and Creation Operators (continued from Chapter II)

By now it should be obvious that we should try to get an explicit matrix form for the γ operators (70, 101) via a representation of the group of γ's. Since each γ is to be a different operator, the representation giving the γ's must be faithful. An obvious possibility for such a representation is the regular representation. However, the regular representation is reducible, so that any linear equations involving annihilation and creation operators could be split up into linearly independent sets if the regular representation were used. Such a system of equations might then describe a "compound" system, whereas one normally wants to consider a "simple" system. In other words, an annihilation operator might annihilate several kinds of particles whereas one normally wants it to annihilate only one kind. Also, in the case $n = 4$ when the γ's are coefficients in the Dirac equation, if the γ's are reducible then the Dirac equation can be split into linearly independent equations. This splitting seems philosophically undesirable if the Dirac equation is to describe a single kind of particle.

Without further discussion of the philosophical aspects, let us require the representation to be irreducible. We must now investigate the possible irreducible representations of the group of γ's. Since $H_c = \{\pm 1\}$ is the only minimal normal subgroup, we know by Burnside's theorem that there must be at least one faithful irreducible representation of $G(n)$. Since the γ's do not commute with each other it follows that no 1-dimensional representation (which is cyclic) can be faithful. But the number of 1-dimensional representations is $g/h_c = 2^n$, whereas the total number of inequivalent irreducible representations is $r = 2^n + 1$. Hence, there is one irreducible representation $\Gamma(n)$ which is not 1-dimensional, and which is therefore faithful. From $g = \sum_{p=1}^{r} d_p{}^2$ we get for the dimension of Γ

$$d = 2^{n/2} = 2^m. \tag{4:1.1}$$

Since $\Gamma(n)$ is the only irreducible representation of dimension 2^m, we know that the character χ must be integral and must be zero for all classes not contained in $H_c = \{\pm 1\}$. Hence, χ has only two nonzero values: $\chi(1)$ and $\chi(-1)$. But $\chi(1) = d = 2^m$ and $\chi(1) + \chi(-1) = 0$ so

$$\chi(-1) = -\chi(1) = -2^m$$

and

$$\chi = (2^m, -2^m, 0, 0, 0, \ldots, 0). \tag{4:1.2}$$

We can also determine the reality class of $\Gamma(n)$ quite easily, because the square of every element is $\pm I$, so

$$\frac{1}{g} \sum_{A \in G} \chi(A^2) = \frac{1}{g}[\zeta(1)\chi(1) + \zeta(-1)\chi(-1)] \tag{4:1.3}$$

$$= \frac{d}{g}[\zeta(1) - \zeta(-1)] .$$

But as shown in Chapter II, equation (2:18),

$$\zeta(1) = 2^n + i^{\frac{1}{2}n(\frac{1}{2}n-1)}\, 2^{\frac{1}{2}n},$$

and since $\zeta(1) + \zeta(-1) = g = 2 \times 2^n$ we have

$$\zeta(-1) = g - \zeta(1) = 2^n - i^{\frac{1}{2}n(\frac{1}{2}n-1)}\, 2^{\frac{1}{2}n}$$

and

$$\frac{1}{g} \sum_{A} \chi(A^2) = \frac{2d}{g}\, 2^{\frac{1}{2}n} i^{\frac{1}{2}n(\frac{1}{2}n-1)} \tag{4:1.4}$$

$$= i^{\frac{1}{2}n(\frac{1}{2}n-1)} . \tag{4:1.5}$$

Hence, Γ is of first or second kind according as $\frac{1}{2}n(\frac{1}{2}n - 1)$ is a multiple of 4 or not. Thus $\Gamma(2)$ is real, $\Gamma(4)$ is of second kind, etc. However, because of this alternation of reality character with n, no limit is approached as n becomes infinite (the case of most physical interest other than $n = 4$).

Since any representation of $G(n)$ which has the correct character will be $\Gamma(n)$, and since an explicit form is already well known, let us simply write it down without derivation. Let us define three matrices

$$\sigma_1 = \begin{pmatrix} 0 & 1 \\ 1 & 0 \end{pmatrix} \qquad \sigma_2 = \begin{pmatrix} 0 & -i \\ i & 0 \end{pmatrix} \qquad \sigma_3 = \begin{pmatrix} 1 & 0 \\ 0 & -1 \end{pmatrix} \tag{4:1.6}$$

which are the well-known Pauli matrices, and which have the properties

$$[\sigma_i, \sigma_j]_+ = 2\delta_{ij} \tag{4:1.6a}$$

$$\sigma_1 \sigma_2 = i\sigma_3 \quad \text{(cycl.)} \tag{4:1.6b}$$

$$\sigma_j^\dagger = \sigma_j \quad . \tag{4:1.6c}$$

The representation $\Gamma(n)$ can now be written explicitly as

$$1 \to I(n) \tag{4:1.7a}$$

$$-1 \to -I(n) \tag{4:1.7b}$$

$$q_j \to \sigma_3 \otimes \sigma_3 \otimes \ldots \sigma_3 \otimes \sigma_1 \otimes I \otimes I \otimes \ldots \otimes I \tag{4:1.7c}$$

$$p_j \to \sigma_3 \otimes \sigma_3 \otimes \ldots \sigma_3 \otimes \sigma_2 \otimes I \otimes I \otimes \ldots \otimes I, \tag{4:1.7d}$$

where $I(n)$ is the $2^{n/2}$-dimensional, identity matrix σ_1 is in the jth position in q_j, σ_2 is in the jth position in p_j, and each Kronecker product contains $m = n/2$ matrices. The matrices representing the other group elements can then be obtained by multiplying these matrices.

Since

$$a_j = \tfrac{1}{2}(q_j + ip_j) \tag{4:1.8a}$$

$$b_j = \tfrac{1}{2}(q_j - ip_j), \tag{4:1.8b}$$

we obtain for the matrices representing the a's and b's

$$a_j \to \sigma_3 \otimes \ldots \otimes \sigma_3 \otimes \begin{pmatrix} 0 & 1 \\ 0 & 0 \end{pmatrix} \otimes I \otimes \ldots \otimes I \tag{4:1.9a}$$

$$b_j \to \sigma_3 \otimes \ldots \otimes \sigma_3 \otimes \begin{pmatrix} 0 & 0 \\ 1 & 0 \end{pmatrix} \otimes I \otimes \ldots \otimes I, \tag{4:1.9b}$$

and we see that in this representation

$$b_j = a_j^\dagger \tag{4:1.10}$$

which is true for any representation $\Gamma(n)$ that is related to this one by a unitary equivalence transformation. Also we see that in this representation the a's and b's are real.

The reason for calling these operators annihilation operators can be seen fairly easily. Consider a system consisting of several identical noninteracting fermions in a box. Let us suppose that there are m different one-particle states (i.e., different energy, different spin, etc.) for the fermions. Then the state of the total system can be specified by specifying the number of fermions in each one-particle state. However, the Pauli exclusion principle tells us that the number of fermions in any one-particle state must be either zero or one. Instead of specifying the state of the system by a set of m zeros and ones, we can specify it by a set of m 2-dimensional column matrices as follows. A filled one-particle state is represented by the matrix $\begin{pmatrix}0\\1\end{pmatrix}$ and an empty one-particle state by the matrix $\begin{pmatrix}1\\0\end{pmatrix}$. The state of the total system is then specified by the 2^m-dimensional column matrix which is the ordered Kronecker product of the m appropriate 2-dimensional column matrices. Using this matrix representation of states and our matrix representation of a's and b's we see that if state j is filled, a_j will empty it (with perhaps a change of sign) whereas if it is empty, b_j will fill it.

Let us define a new operator.

$$N_j = b_j a_j \tag{4:1.11}$$

From the anticommutation rules (2:12) for a and b it follows that

$$N_j^2 = N_j \tag{4:1.12}$$

so that the eigenvalues of N must all be either zero or one. We might therefore expect the eigenvalue of N_j belonging to a particular state of the system to be the number of fermions in state j. From Eq. (4:1.9) we get for the matrix representation of N.

$$N_j = I \otimes I \otimes \ldots \otimes I \otimes \begin{pmatrix}0 & 0\\0 & 1\end{pmatrix} \otimes I \otimes \ldots \otimes I, \tag{4:1.13}$$

from which we see that in this representation our conjecture is true.

Since the number of fermions in a one-particle state is physically observable, it follows (from a postulate of quantum mechanics) that the N_j's must be hermitian operators. If then we require the matrix representing N_j to be hermitian, it follows that the matrix must also be diagonalizable by a unitary matrix. But this means that N_j can be obtained from a representation which is unitarily equivalent to the one we have written down, and therefore that any hermitian N_j can be written in the form

$$N_j = b_j a_j \tag{4:1.14a}$$

where

$$b_j = a_j^\dagger. \tag{4:1.14b}$$

Thus a hermitian N can always be obtained from a unitary representation satisfying (4:1.14b).

Finally, let us take a look at $G(2) = D_4$, and $\Gamma(2)$.

$$q \to \sigma_1$$
$$p \to \sigma_2,$$

and $\Gamma(2)$ is the group $\{\pm 1, \pm \sigma_1, \pm \sigma_2, \pm i\sigma_3\}$ of order eight. If we let

$$S = \begin{pmatrix}1 & -i\\1 & i\end{pmatrix},$$

then

$$q \to S^{-1}\sigma_1 S = \sigma_3 \tag{4:1.15a}$$

$$p \to S^{-1}\sigma_2 S = \sigma_1 \tag{4:1.15b}$$

is an equivalent real representation for which

$$a \to \frac{i}{2}(\sigma_1 - i\sigma_3) = \frac{1}{2}\begin{pmatrix} 1 & i \\ i & -1 \end{pmatrix} \tag{4:1.16a}$$

$$b \to -\frac{i}{2}(\sigma_1 + i\sigma_3) = \frac{1}{2}\begin{pmatrix} 1 & -i \\ -i & -1 \end{pmatrix} \tag{4:1.16b}$$

$$N \to \frac{1}{2}\begin{pmatrix} 1 & i \\ -i & 1 \end{pmatrix} \tag{4:1.16c}$$

are all complex. This representation of D_4 is the one obtained by considering D_4 as the 2-dimensional orthogonal symmetry group of a square. We shall return to this later in considering the irreducible representation of space groups.

Now let us conclude with a few remarks about the Dirac equation. The γ's of the Dirac equation belong to the group $G(4)$ and therefore are 4-dimensional. Consequently, the Hamiltonian H is a 4-dimensional matrix and in order for the equation to make sense, the function $\psi(x,y,z,t)$ must be a 4-dimensional column matrix

$$\psi(x,y,z,t) = \begin{pmatrix} \psi_1(x,y,z,t) \\ \psi_2(x,y,z,t) \\ \psi_3(x,y,z,t) \\ \psi_4(x,y,z,t) \end{pmatrix}.$$

2. Molecular Vibrations (Classical)

We shall consider a classical mechanical system of point particles for which the kinetic and potential energies can be expressed in the form

$$2T = \sum_{i,j} \dot{q}_i a_{ij} \dot{q}_j \tag{4:2.1a}$$

$$2V = \sum_{i,j} q_i b_{ij} q_j, \tag{4:2.1b}$$

where the q's are generalized coordinates and the a's and b's are constants which are independent of time and of the q's, and all quantities are assumed real. Letting

$$A = ||a_{ij}|| \qquad B = ||b_{ij}|| \tag{4:2.2}$$

and letting q be the column matrix of q's we can write (4:2.1) in the form

$$2T = \dot{q}^t A \dot{q} \tag{4:2.3a}$$

$$2V = q^t B q. \tag{4:2.3b}$$

By observing that

$$\dot{q}_i a_{ij} \dot{q}_j + \dot{q}_j a_{ji} \dot{q}_i = \dot{q}_i \left(\frac{a_{ij} + a_{ji}}{2} \right) \dot{q}_j + \dot{q}_j \left(\frac{a_{ij} + a_{ji}}{2} \right) \dot{q}_i$$

and that the coefficients of $\dot{q}_i \dot{q}_j$ and $\dot{q}_j \dot{q}_i$ are equal in the last expression we see that we can choose A and B symmetric

$$A^t = A \qquad B^t = B. \tag{4:2.4}$$

Furthermore, since kinetic energy is never negative and is zero only when all velocities are zero, it follows that A must be a positive definite matrix. By the last theorem of Chapter I we know that there must exist a real non-singular matrix S_0 such that

$$S_0{}^t A S_0 = I \tag{4:2.5a}$$

$$S_0{}^t B S_0 = \Lambda, \tag{4:2.5b}$$

where Λ is a diagonal matrix.

Let us now consider the equations of motion of the system. For the Lagrangian we have

$$2L \equiv 2T - 2V = \dot{q}^t A \dot{q} + q^t B q \tag{4:2.6}$$

so the equation of motion

$$\frac{d}{dt}\left(\frac{\partial L}{\partial \dot{q}_i}\right) - \frac{\partial L}{\partial q_i} = 0 \tag{4·2.7}$$

becomes

$$A\ddot{q} + Bq = 0. \tag{4:2.8}$$

If we define a normal mode of motion to be a motion of the system

$$q(t) = q_0 e^{-i\omega t}, \tag{4:2.9}$$

then by substituting (4:2.9) in (4:2.8) we find

$$(B - \omega^2 A) q_0 = 0 \tag{4:2.10}$$

so that if q_0 is not to be identically zero we must have

$$|B - \omega^2 A| = 0. \tag{4:2.11}$$

The equation

$$|B - \lambda A| = 0 \tag{4:2.12}$$

is called the secular equation of the system, and the roots λ are the squares of the various possible frequencies of oscillation of the system.

$$\lambda = \omega^2 = 4\pi^2 \nu^2. \tag{4:2.13}$$

If d is the dimension of A and B there can be at most d different frequencies $|\omega|$. If λ is negative then the corresponding normal mode is not oscillatory, but q either increases or decreases exponentially with time. If $\lambda = 0$ then q is a linear function of time. If we know a root $\lambda = \omega^2$ of the secular equation, then we can go back to equation (4:2.10) and solve for q_0 (except for a normalization factor usually).

Suppose that we perform a linear transformation of coordinates

$$q' = S^{-1}q. \tag{4:2.14}$$

Then if we define

$$A' = S^tAS \tag{4:2.15a}$$

$$B' = S^tBS, \tag{4:2.15b}$$

we can write the kinetic and potential energies in the form

$$2T = \dot{q}'^tA'\dot{q}' \tag{4:2.16a}$$

$$2V = q'^tB'q' \tag{4:2.16b}$$

and the equation of motion in the form

$$A'\ddot{q}' + B'q' = 0, \tag{4:2.17}$$

so the secular equation in the new coordinates becomes

$$|B' - \lambda A'| = 0. \tag{4:2.18}$$

Furthermore, the secular equations in the two coordinate systems have the same roots because

$$|B' - \lambda A'| = |S^t(B - \lambda A)S| = |S^t||B - \lambda A||S| = |S||S^t||B - \lambda A|$$
$$= |S|^2|B - \lambda A|$$

and $|S| \neq 0$ so

$$|B' - \lambda A'| = 0 \text{ if and only if } |B - \lambda A| = 0.$$

If in particular we choose $S = S_0$ we find that

$$A' = I \tag{4:2.19a}$$

$$B' = \Lambda \tag{4:2.19b}$$

$$2T = \dot{q}'^t\dot{q}' \tag{4:2.19c}$$

$$2V = q'^t\Lambda q' \tag{4:2.19d}$$

$$|\Lambda - \lambda I| = 0. \tag{4:2.19e}$$

Thus we see that the squares of the normal mode frequencies are just the eigenvalues of the diagonal matrix $\Lambda = S_0{}^tBS_0$. Also, in the new coordinate system defined by S_0 the equation of motion is

$$\ddot{q}' + \Lambda q' = 0, \tag{4:2.20}$$

which is just the equation of a harmonic oscillator (actually a set of harmonic oscillator equations). For this reason we shall refer to this theory as vibration theory. The general solution is

$$q_j'(t) = \alpha_j e^{-i\omega_j t} + \beta_j e^{i\omega_j t}. \tag{4:2.21}$$

Any generalized coordinate which satisfies a harmonic oscillator equation and which therefore always varies with time according to a single frequency (as $q_j'(t)$ in (4:2.21)) is called a normal coordinate. We shall, however, only consider normal coordinates which are linear combinations of the originally chosen coordinates. The transformation S_0 thus transforms all coordinates into normal coordinates. We see also that when all coordinates are normal the matrices A and B are diagonal. This means that there is no coupling between the equations of motion for normal coordinates. We can in fact use this condition as a definition of a set of normal coordinates.

If $q(t) = q_0 e^{-i\omega_j t}$ is a normal mode belonging to frequency ω_j, and $q_j'(t) = \alpha_j e^{-i\omega_j t} + \beta_j e^{i\omega_j t}$ is a normal coordinate belonging to ω_j, then by choosing $\beta_j = 0$ and $\alpha_j = 1$ we can write $q(t) = q_0\, q_j'(t)$. That is, each coordinate $q_k(t)$ is proportional to the normal coordinate $q_j'(t)$, and all other normal coordinates can be chosen zero. Hence, a normal mode can also be defined as a motion in which a single normal coordinate is nonzero (and its β is zero).

Example. Two Coupled Harmonic Oscillators.

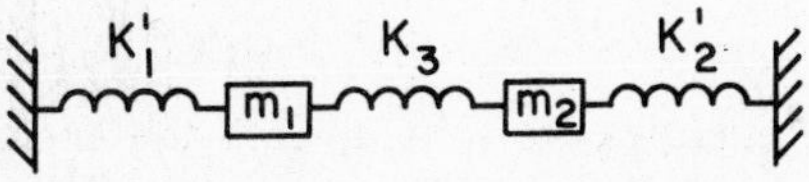

Let x_1 be the displacement of the mass m_1 to the right of its equilibrium position, and x_2 the same for m_2. Assuming Hooke's law for the three springs we have

$$2T = m_1 \dot{x}_1^2 + m_2 \dot{x}_2^2 \tag{4:2.22a}$$

$$2V = K_1' x_1^2 + K_2' x_2^2 + K_3 (x_1 - x_2)^2 = K_1 x_1^2 + K_2 x_2^2 - 2K_3 x_1 x_2 \tag{4:2.22b}$$

where

$$K_1 = K_1' + K_3 \qquad K_2 = K_2' + K_3. \tag{4:2.22c}$$

Thus

$$x = \begin{pmatrix} x_1 \\ x_2 \end{pmatrix} \qquad A = \begin{pmatrix} m_1 & 0 \\ 0 & m_2 \end{pmatrix} \qquad B = \begin{pmatrix} K_1 & -K_3 \\ -K_3 & K_2 \end{pmatrix}. \tag{4:2.23}$$

The matrix S_0 can be chosen to be

$$S_0 = \begin{pmatrix} \dfrac{1}{\sqrt{m_1}} \cos\theta & \dfrac{1}{\sqrt{m_1}} \sin\theta \\ -\dfrac{1}{\sqrt{m_2}} \sin\theta & \dfrac{1}{\sqrt{m_2}} \cos\theta \end{pmatrix}, \tag{4:2.24a}$$

where

$$\tan 2\theta = \frac{2K_3/\sqrt{(m_1 m_2)}}{m/K_1 - K_2(m_2)} \,. \tag{4:2.24b}$$

Then the normal coordinates are

$$\begin{pmatrix} q_1' \\ q_2' \end{pmatrix} = S_0^{-1} \begin{pmatrix} x_1 \\ x_2 \end{pmatrix},$$

or

$$q_1' = \sqrt{m_1} \cos\theta\, x_1 - \sqrt{m_2} \sin\theta\, x_2 \tag{4:2.25a}$$

$$q_2' = \sqrt{m_1} \sin\theta\, x_1 + \sqrt{m_2} \cos\theta\, x_2, \tag{4:2.25b}$$

and Λ is

$$\Lambda \equiv S_0{}^t B S_0 = \begin{pmatrix} \lambda_1 & 0 \\ 0 & \lambda_2 \end{pmatrix}, \tag{4:2.26a}$$

where

$$\lambda_1 = \omega_1{}^2 = \frac{K_1}{m_1} \cos^2\theta + \frac{K_2}{m_2} \sin^2\theta + \frac{K_3}{\sqrt{(m_1 m_2)}} \sin 2\theta \tag{4:2.26b}$$

$$\lambda_2 = \omega_2{}^2 = \frac{K_1}{m_1} \sin^2\theta + \frac{K_2}{m_2} \cos^2\theta - \frac{K_3}{\sqrt{(m_1 m_2)}} \sin 2\theta. \tag{4:2.26c}$$

The energies are therefore given by

$$2T = \dot{q}_1{}^2 + \dot{q}_2{}^2 \tag{4:2.27a}$$

$$2V = \omega_1{}^2 q_1{}^2 + \omega_2{}^2 q_2{}^2 \tag{4:2.27b}$$

and we see that the energies are split up into the energies associated with the individual normal coordinates. The equations of motion in displacement coordinates are

$$m_1 \ddot{x}_1 + K_1 x_1 - K_3 x_2 = 0 \tag{4:2.28a}$$

$$m_2 \ddot{x}_2 + K_2 x_2 - K_3 x_1 = 0, \tag{4:2.28b}$$

and in normal coordinates they are

$$\ddot{q}_1 + \omega_1{}^2 q_1 = 0 \tag{4:2.29a}$$

$$\ddot{q}_2 + \omega_2{}^2 q_2 = 0. \tag{4:2.29b}$$

Thus we see that the equations (4:2.27) are coupled through the K_3 terms, but the equations (4:2.28) are uncoupled.

Now that we have laid the foundation of vibration theory we can proceed to the consideration of the effects of symmetry of the vibrating system (113, 114, 119, 132, 153, 174, 184, 187, 194). The two problems of primary interest in vibration theory are the determination of the possible normal mode frequencies and the determination of the normal coordinates in terms of the coordinates with which the problem is initially formulated. The determination of the frequencies requires "only" the solution of the secular equation $|B - \lambda A| = 0$, whereas the determination of the normal coordinates requires the determination of the transformation matrix S_0, a much more difficult problem. In fact, if one knows S_0 one can immediately find the frequencies by simply computing $\Lambda = S_0{}^t B S_0$. Both the frequency problem and the normal coordinate problem in general require a complete and detailed knowledge of all masses and force constants; i.e., of the matrices A and B. However, if the system possesses some symmetry one can partially solve both of the above problems without a detailed knowledge of A and B.

We shall now see how symmetry considerations alone will allow us to

(1) put an upper bound (frequently less than d) on the number of possible frequencies $|\omega|$

(2) put a lower bound (frequently greater than one) on the degeneracy of each frequency $|\omega|$

(3) put an upper bound on the number of constants required to specify T and V

(4) partially factor the secular equation

(5) construct coordinates in terms of which the matrices A and B are reduced (but not necessarily diagonalized).

By a configuration of the system let us mean a value of q. By assumption, $V = V(q)$. Suppose we can find a nonsingular matrix $\bar{D}$ of the same dimension as q such that $V(\bar{D}q) = V(q)$, for every configuration q. In other words, the configurations q and $\bar{D}q$ (which may be complex) have the same potential energy. This symmetry is frequently obvious, but the construction of $\bar{D}$ will be discussed in detail later. Since

$$2V(q) = q^t B q$$

$$2V(\bar{D}q) = (\bar{D}q)^t B(\bar{D}q) = q^t \bar{D}^t B \bar{D} q$$

and since $V(q) = V(\bar{D}q)$ is assumed to hold for all q, it follows that

$$\bar{D}^t B \bar{D} = B. \tag{4:2.30}$$

Obviously $\bar{D} = I$ always works, but if a nontrivial $\bar{D}$ can be found then an entire nontrivial group can be found because

$$V(\bar{D}^2 q) = V(\bar{D}[\bar{D}q]) = V(\bar{D}q) = V(q)$$

and by replacing q by $\bar{D}^{-1}q$ in $V(q) = V(\bar{D}q)$,

$$V(\bar{D}^{-1}q) = V(q).$$

Thus the group generated by $\bar{D}$ leaves V invariant. Of course, there may be many other matrices leaving V invariant, and it is of advantage to find as many as possible, as will be seen shortly. We must also assume that $T\bar{D}(\dot{q}) = T(\dot{q})$ for every $\dot{q}$.

Equation (4:2.30) above restricts the possible form of B (if any nontrivial $\bar{D}$'s are known). The restrictions thus imposed on B can be explicitly determined by writing out this matrix equation in detail. However, group theory will provide a "simpler" more systematic method of inferring the consequences of (4:2.30).

Let us designate the group of $\bar{D}$'s by $\bar{\Gamma}$, and let us consider first the case in which $\bar{\Gamma}$ is irreducible. Let us write (4:2.30) in the form

$$B\bar{D} = \bar{D}^{t-1}B \qquad (\text{each } \bar{D}\epsilon\bar{\Gamma}). \tag{4:2.31}$$

But if $\bar{\Gamma}$ is irreducible, so is $\bar{\Gamma}^t$. Hence, by Schur's lemma, B must be either a zero matrix or a nonsingular matrix. If $B = 0$ the problem is trivial so let us consider the case $|B| \neq 0$.

Taking $\bar{\Gamma}$ as irreducible, and $|B| \neq 0$, let us transform $\bar{\Gamma}$ into unitary form

$$\bar{D}_0 = T^{-1}\bar{D}T \qquad \bar{D}_0{}^\dagger\bar{D}_0 = I \qquad B_0 = T^tBT$$

so (4:2.31) becomes

$$B_0\bar{D}_0 = \bar{D}_0{}^*B_0 \tag{4:2.32a}$$

or

$$\bar{D}_0{}^* = B_0\bar{D}_0B_0^{-1}. \tag{4:2.32b}$$

Thus $\bar{\Gamma} \cdot\equiv\cdot \bar{\Gamma}^*$ so $\bar{\Gamma}$ must be of first or second kind. If $\bar{\Gamma}$ is of first kind we can assume $\bar{D}_0$ orthogonal so $\bar{D}_0{}^* = \bar{D}_0$ and B_0 commutes with $\{\bar{D}_0\}$. In this case B_0 and hence B must be scalar matrices. Similarly, A must be a scalar matrix so $B - \lambda A$ is also a scalar matrix and can therefore have only one root. Thus if $\bar{\Gamma}$ is irreducible and of first kind, the system can have only one normal frequency whose degeneracy is d. The secular equation must be completely factored to begin with since $B - \lambda A$ is a scalar matrix, and consequently all coordinates must be normal coordinates. Also, only one constant apiece is required to specify A and B. If $\bar{\Gamma}$ is of second kind, let U be a unitary matrix such that

$$\bar{D}_0{}^* = UD_0U^{-1}. \tag{4:2.33}$$

Since $\{\bar{D}_0\}$ and $\{\bar{D}_0{}^*\}$ are both unitary we know that there is such a matrix. We know further that $B_0 = \alpha U$, where α is a number. From the definition of B_0 and the fact that B is symmetric we see that $B_0{}^t = B_0$. But since $\bar{\Gamma}$ is of second kind we know that $U^t = -U$. Since these three equations

$$B_0 = \alpha U \qquad B_0{}^t = B_0 \qquad U^t = -U$$

are incompatible, it follows that $\bar{\Gamma}$ can not be of second kind. Hence, if $\bar{\Gamma}$ is irreducible it must be of first kind, and A and B must be scalar matrices. Unfortunately, $\bar{\Gamma}$ is not ordinarily irreducible. It is true, however, that $\bar{\Gamma}$ is normally of first kind. It should be observed that no detailed information about the form of A and B was needed.

Taking $\bar{\Gamma}$ as completely reducible into two irreducible representations, Γ_1 and Γ_2, let us assume that a coordinate transformation has been performed so that $\bar{\Gamma}$ is in completely reduced unitary form, and that the component Γ_p's of first kind are in real form. Then

$$\bar{D} = \begin{pmatrix} D^{(1)} & 0 \\ 0 & D^{(2)} \end{pmatrix}$$

and if we block off B in the same way,

$$B = \begin{pmatrix} B_{11} & B_{12} \\ B_{21} & B_{22} \end{pmatrix}$$

and write (4:2.31) in the form

$$B\bar{D} = \bar{D}^* B \tag{4:2.34}$$

(4:2.31) becomes, in terms of the submatrices

$$B_{11} D^{(1)} = D^{(1)*} B_{11} \tag{4:2.35a}$$

$$B_{22} D^{(2)} = D^{(2)*} B_{22} \tag{4:2.35b}$$

$$B_{12} D^{(2)} = D^{(1)*} B_{12} \tag{4:2.35c}$$

$$B_{21} D^{(1)} = D^{(2)*} B_{21}. \tag{4:2.35d}$$

Let us now consider the two possible cases $\Gamma_2 \cdot\not\equiv\cdot \Gamma_1^*$, and $\Gamma_2 \cdot\equiv\cdot \Gamma_1^*$. In the first case we see immediately from Schur's lemma and equations (4:2.35) that $B_{12} = 0$ and $B_{21} = 0$, and that B_{11} and B_{22} must be scalar matrices (possibly zero). Hence, $B_{11} = \beta_{11} I$, $B_{22} = \beta_{22} I$, and

$$B = \begin{pmatrix} \beta_{11} I & 0 \\ 0 & \beta_{22} I \end{pmatrix}. \tag{4:2.36a}$$

The matrix A must have the same form,

$$A = \begin{pmatrix} \alpha_{11} I & 0 \\ 0 & \alpha_{22} I \end{pmatrix}, \tag{4:2.36b}$$

so

$$B - \lambda A = \begin{pmatrix} (\beta_{11} - \lambda\alpha_{11}) I & 0 \\ 0 & (\beta_{22} - \lambda\alpha_{22}) I \end{pmatrix} \tag{4:2.36c}$$

and

$$|B - \lambda A| = (\beta_{11} - \lambda\alpha_{11})^{d_1} (\beta_{22} - \lambda\alpha_{22})^{d_2}. \tag{4:2.36d}$$

Hence, $\Gamma = \Gamma_1 \oplus \Gamma_2$ and $\Gamma_2 \cdot\not\equiv\cdot \Gamma_1^*$ imply that the system has at most two distinct frequencies, and that the degeneracy of each is at least the dimension of the corresponding irreducible representation. The reason the phrase "at least" is used is that the two roots of the secular equation may be equal even though the symmetry of the problem does not require them to be. This might happen by a particular choice of masses and force constants and is referred to as *accidental degeneracy*. In short, accidental degeneracy is a degeneracy not required by symmetry. Of course, a degeneracy may appear to be accidental because some elements of symmetry were accidentally omitted from $\bar{\Gamma}$. The number of constants required to specify A and B is two (possible complex) apiece, or four real constants. If a coordinate system is used in which $\bar{\Gamma}$ is not completely reduced, then the matrix elements of A and B in this coordinate system can be expressed in terms of the two independent constants per matrix by means of the matrix which transforms $\bar{\Gamma}$ into completely reduced form. If $\Gamma_2 \cdot\equiv\cdot \Gamma_1{}^*$ we can assume the coordinate transformation performed so that $\Gamma_2 = \Gamma_1{}^*$. The equations (4:2.35) then become

$$B_{11} D^{(1)} = D^{(2)} B_{11} \tag{4:2.37a}$$
$$B_{22} D^{(2)} = D^{(1)} B_{22} \tag{4:2.37b}$$
$$B_{12} D^{(2)} = D^{(2)} B_{12} \tag{4:2.37c}$$
$$B_{21} D^{(1)} = D^{(1)} B_{21}. \tag{4:2.37d}$$

From the last two equations we see that B_{12} and B_{21} are scalar matrices, $B_{12} = \beta_{12} I$ and $B_{21} = \beta_{21} I$. Since B is symmetric we have also $\beta_{21} = \beta_{12}$. From the fact that Γ_1 and Γ_2 are unitary we know that $B_{11} = \beta_{11} U_1$ and $B_{22} = \beta_{22} U_2$, where U_1 and U_2 are unitary. Also we can choose $U_2 = U_1^{-1}$. Again, however, if Γ_1 were of the second kind, U would be skew symmetric, whereas $B_{11}^t = B_{11}$. Hence, Γ_1 and Γ_2 must be of first kind, and U_1 and U_2 can be chosen as the identity matrix if Γ_1 and Γ_2 have been transformed to orthogonal form. Therefore,

$$B = \begin{pmatrix} \beta_{11} I & \beta_{12} I \\ \beta_{12} I & \beta_{22} I \end{pmatrix} \tag{4:2.38a}$$

$$A = \begin{pmatrix} \alpha_{11} I & \alpha_{12} I \\ \alpha_{12} I & \alpha_{22} I \end{pmatrix} \tag{4:2.38b}$$

$$B - \lambda A = \begin{pmatrix} (\beta_{11} - \lambda\alpha_{11}) I & (\beta_{12} - \lambda\alpha_{12}) I \\ (\beta_{12} - \lambda\alpha_{12}) I & (\beta_{22} - \lambda\alpha_{22}) I \end{pmatrix} \tag{4:2.38c}$$

$$d_1 = d_2 = d \tag{4:2.38d}$$

$$|B - \lambda A| = \begin{vmatrix} \beta_{11} - \lambda\alpha_{11} & \beta_{12} - \lambda\alpha_{12} \\ B_{12} - \lambda\alpha_{12} & \beta_{22} - \lambda\alpha_{22} \end{vmatrix}^d . \tag{4:2.38e}$$

Again we see that there are at most two frequencies and that the degeneracy of each is at least d. The secular equation this time is factored into quadratic factors, and the number of constants required to specify A and B is three apiece.

Taking $\bar{\Gamma}$ as orthogonal and completely reducible into an arbitrary number of irreducible components of first kind, let us suppose $\bar{\Gamma}$ completely reduced with each irreducible component in orthogonal form. Equation (4:2.31) then becomes

$$B\bar{D} = \bar{D}B, \tag{4:2.39a}$$

where

$$\bar{D} = \begin{pmatrix} D^{(1)} & & & \\ & D^{(2)} & & \\ & & \cdot & \\ & & & \cdot \\ & & & & \cdot \end{pmatrix}, \tag{4:2.39b}$$

and

$$D^{(p)t} = D^{(p)-1} \quad , \quad \bar{D}^t = \bar{D}^{-1} \,. \tag{4:2.39c}$$

Let us also suppose that all equivalent irreducible components of $\bar{\Gamma}$ are equal and that these equal components are grouped together in the completely reduced form of $\bar{D}$. This grouping can always be accomplished by means of an equivalence transformation by a permutation matrix. Thus

$$\bar{D} = \begin{pmatrix} D^{(1)} & & & & & & \\ & D^{(1)} & & & & & \\ & & \ddots & & & & \\ & & & D^{(2)} & & & \\ & & & & D^{(2)} & & \\ & & & & & \ddots & \\ & & & & & & D^{(r)} \end{pmatrix}. \tag{4:2.40}$$

By again breaking up B into blocks, using (4:2.39a) with (4:2.40), and applying Schur's lemma we find that B must have the form

$$B = \begin{pmatrix} B^{(1)} & & & \\ & B^{(2)} & & \\ & & \cdot & \\ & & & \cdot \\ & & & & \cdot \end{pmatrix}, \tag{4:2.41}$$

where $B^{(p)}$ is a submatrix the size of the corresponding block of all $D^{(p)}$'s in (4:2.40). Also, $B^{(p)}$ must have the form

$$B^{(p)} = \begin{pmatrix} \beta_{11}^{(p)} I & \beta_{12}^{(p)} I & \cdots \\ \beta_{12}^{(p)} I & \beta_{22}^{(p)} I & \cdots \end{pmatrix} \tag{4:2.42a}$$

$$= \beta^{(p)} \otimes I = B^{(p)t}, \tag{4:2.42b}$$

where

$$\dim (I) = d_p \tag{4:2.42c}$$

$$\dim (\beta^p) = c^{(p)} \tag{4:2.42d}$$

$$\beta^{(p)t} = \beta^{(p)}, \tag{4:2.42e}$$

and $c^{(p)}$ is the number of times Γ_p occurs in $\bar{\Gamma}$. Similarly,

$$A = \begin{pmatrix} A^{(1)} & & & \\ & A^{(2)} & & \\ & & \cdot & \\ & & & \cdot \\ & & & & \cdot \end{pmatrix} \tag{4:2.42f}$$

$$A^{(p)} = \alpha^{(p)} \otimes I. \tag{4:2.42g}$$

Hence,

$$|B - \lambda A| = |\beta^{(1)} - \lambda\alpha^{(1)}|^{d_1} |\beta^{(2)} - \lambda\alpha^{(2)}|^{d_2} \ldots \tag{4:2.42h}$$

Again we see that the number of different frequencies is at most equal to the number of irreducible components of $\bar{\Gamma}$, and that the degeneracy of each frequency is at least equal to the dimension of the corresponding irreducible component of $\bar{\Gamma}$. Since $\bar{\Gamma}$ can be reduced by a real transformation, we can assume that the transformed B is real, so the number of real constants required to specify A and B is

$$\tfrac{1}{2} \sum_{p=1}^{r} c^{(p)}(c^{(p)} + 1)$$

apiece. Also, we see that if a particular irreducible component Γ_p of $\bar{\Gamma}$ occurs only once that $A^{(p)}$ and $B^{(p)}$ are diagonal so the corresponding symmetry coordinates are normal coordinates.

The actual carrying out of the preceding group theoretic method of factoring the secular equation requires the complete reduction of $\bar{\Gamma}$. If the character table of $\bar{\Gamma}$ is known then the irreducible components of $\bar{\Gamma}$ and the number of times each occurs can be easily determined by the use of characters. The determination of a transformation matrix which will completely reduce $\bar{\Gamma}$ is more difficult, and usually can be performed most easily by means of one of the idempotent methods. The coordinates in which $\bar{\Gamma}$ is completely reduced are called symmetry coordinates.

Let us now consider the relation of symmetry coordinates to normal coordinates. To do this, let us first consider two sets of normal coordinates $Q(1)$ and $Q(2)$. In normal coordinates

$$A = I \qquad B = \Lambda = \begin{pmatrix} \Lambda_1 & & & & \\ & \Lambda_2 & & & \\ & & \Lambda_3 & & \\ & & & \cdot & \\ & & & & \cdot \\ & & & & & \cdot \end{pmatrix} \tag{4:2.43}$$

where each Λ_i is a scalar matrix, and $i \neq j$ implies $\Lambda_i \neq \Lambda_j$. If $Q(2) = R^{-1}Q(1)$ then in accordance with (4:2.15)

$$R^tR = I \qquad R^t\Lambda R = \Lambda. \tag{4:2.44}$$

By use of the first equation, the second can be written

$$[R, \Lambda]_- = 0 \tag{4:2.45}$$

By breaking up R into block form and applying the above equation we see that R can have nonzero blocks only on the diagonal

$$R = \begin{pmatrix} S_1 & & & & & \\ & S_2 & & & & \\ & & S_3 & & & \\ & & & \cdot & & \\ & & & & \cdot & \\ & & & & & \cdot \end{pmatrix} \tag{4:2.46}$$

This is the most general form of transformation matrix carrying one normal coordinate system into another and leaving the order of eigenvalues of Λ as in (4:2.43).

Now let q be a set of symmetry coordinates, and assume $\bar{\Gamma}$ contains irreducible components of the first kind only which are orthogonal in the q-system. Then in this coordinate system (4:2.42g, b)

$$A^{(p)} = \alpha^{(p)} \otimes I \qquad B^{(p)} = \beta^{(p)} \otimes I$$

and

$$\bar{D} = \sum_{p=1}^{r} c^{(p)} D^{(p)}. \tag{4:2.47}$$

If $\bar{\Gamma}$ before transformation to reduced form is real we can assume the transformation to be real so that $\alpha^{(p)}$ and $\beta^{(p)}$ must be real. Since also

$$\alpha^{(p)t} = \alpha^{(p)} \qquad \beta^{(p)t} = \beta^{(p)} \tag{4:2.48}$$

and α is positive definite, there is a real nonsingular matrix S_p such that

$$S_p^t \alpha^{(p)} S_p = I \qquad S_p^t \beta^{(p)} S_p = b^{(p)} \tag{4:2.49}$$

where $b^{(p)}$ is diagonal. Hence

$$(S_p \otimes I)^t A^{(p)} (S_p \otimes I) = I \qquad (S_p \otimes I)^t B^{(p)} (S_p \otimes I) = \Lambda_p \tag{4:2.50}$$

(if the rows of the Kronecker products are appropriately ordered). Hence, letting

$$S = \sum_{p=1}^{r} S_p \otimes I \tag{4:2.51}$$

we see that

$$Q \equiv S^{-1} q \tag{4:2.52}$$

is a normal coordinate system. But also by careful inspection of the forms of the matrices one can see that

$$S^{-1}\bar{D}S = \bar{D}. \tag{4:2.53}$$

Hence, in the normal coordinates Q, $\bar{\Gamma}$ is completely reduced into irreducible components; therefore the normal coordinates Q are symmetry coordinates. Furthermore, the general transformation matrix R of (4:2.46) just transforms each irreducible component of $\bar{\Gamma}$ into an equivalent irreducible component. Hence, all normal coordinate systems for which Λ has the form (4:2.43) are symmetry coordinate systems. But this includes all normal coordinate systems (except for normalization constants) if the coordinates are just numbered appropriately. Hence, all normal coordinate systems are symmetry coordinate systems.

The fact that normal coordinates of different frequencies could not transform together could have been derived directly from the equation of motion. If Q_j is a normal coordinate, then $\ddot{Q}_j + \omega_j{}^2 Q_j = 0$, and if $Q_j' = \sum_i \bar{D}_{ji} Q_i$ is the transformed normal coordinate then $\ddot{Q}_j' + \omega_j'^2 Q_j' = 0$. But if Q's of several frequencies are mixed in Q_j' this is impossible.

From now on let us designate symmetry coordinates by Q.

Let us say a word here about the omission of symmetry elements from $\bar{\Gamma}$. If some elements are inadvertently omitted from $\bar{\Gamma}$ then the subgroup $\bar{\Delta}$ may be reducible into irreducible components of smaller dimension than those of $\bar{\Gamma}$. Use of $\bar{\Delta}$ would thus overestimate the possible number of frequencies and underestimate the degeneracy of each.

We can also state the preceding results on the form of A and B in terms of symmetry coordinates. In order to state the theorem we shall need a more precise notation for the symmetry coordinates. Consider $\bar{\Gamma}$ in the completely reduced form (4:2.40) and let Q be the corresponding column matrix of symmetry coordinates. By $Q_{\alpha i}^{(p)}$ let us mean that symmetry coordinate of Q which belongs to the ith row of the αth Γ_p block in $\bar{\Gamma}$. We can now state the theorem.

Theorem. Let Q be a set of symmetry coordinates in which $\bar{\Gamma}$ is completely reduced into irreducible unitary components, and in which the irreducible components are either identical or inequivalent. Also let

$$2V = Q^t B Q = 2 \sum_{pp'\alpha\alpha' ii'} V_{\alpha\alpha' ii'}^{pp'},$$

where

$$2V_{\alpha\alpha' ii'}^{pp'} = Q_{\alpha i}^{p} B_{\alpha\alpha' ii'}^{pp'} Q_{\alpha' i'}^{p'}.$$

Then $V_{\alpha\alpha' ii'}^{pp'}$ is zero unless $\Gamma_{p'} = \Gamma_p{}^*$ and $i = i'$.

We can see this easily by considering $V(Q)$ and $V(\bar{D}Q)$. We know that

$$V_{\alpha\alpha' ii'}^{pp'}(Q) = V_{\alpha\alpha' ii'}^{pp'}(\bar{D}Q) = \frac{1}{g} \sum_{D} V_{\alpha\alpha' ii'}^{pp'}(\bar{D}Q).$$

But

$$2V^{pp'}_{aa'ii'} = (\bar{D}Q)^p_{ai} B^{pp'}_{aa'ii'} (\bar{D}Q)^{p'}_{a'i'} = \sum_{j,j'} D^{(p)}_{ij} D^{(p')}_{i'j'} Q^{(p)}_{aj} B^{pp'}_{aa'ii'} Q^{(p')}_{a'i'}$$

so

$$\frac{2}{g} \sum_{\bar{D}} V^{pp'}_{aa'ii'}(\bar{D}Q) = \sum_{jj'} \left(\frac{1}{g} \sum_{D} D^{(p)}_{ij} D^{(p')}_{i'j'} \right) Q^{(p)}_{aj} B^{pp'}_{aa'ii'} Q^{(p')}_{a'j'}. \tag{4:2.54}$$

But by the key orthogonality theorem

$$\frac{1}{g} \sum_{D} D^{(p)}_{ij} D^{(p')}_{i'j'} = \frac{1}{d_p} \delta_{p*p'} \delta_{ii'} \delta_{jj'} \tag{4:2.55}$$

so

$$2V^{pp'}_{aa'ii'}(Q) = \frac{2}{g} \sum_{\bar{D}} V^{pp'}_{aa'ii'}(\bar{D}Q) = \delta_{p*p'} \delta_{ii'} \left[B^{pp'}_{aa'ii'} \frac{1}{d_p} \sum_{j} Q^{(p)}_{aj} Q^{(p')}_{a'j'} \right]. \tag{4:2.56}$$

Also of interest are some orthogonality relations involving symmetry coordinates. Essentially the same relations were stated and proved in the treatment of the second idempotent method; we shall omit the proofs here. Let Q be a set of symmetry coordinates as in the preceding theorem, let q be the initially chosen coordinates, and let $\eta^p_{ai,j}$ be the transformation coefficients. Then

$$Q^{(p)}_{ai} = \sum_j \eta^{(p)}_{ai,j} q_j. \tag{4:2.57}$$

The inner (or scalar) product of two symmetry coordinates can then be defined by

$$\langle Q^{(p)}_{ai} | Q^{(p')}_{a'i'} \rangle \equiv \sum_j \eta^{(p)*}_{ai,j} \eta^{(p')}_{a'i',j}. \tag{4:2.58}$$

If $\bar{\Gamma}$ before transformation to reduced form is unitary, then

$$\langle Q^{(p)}_{ai} | Q^{(p')}_{ai'} \rangle = \delta_{p,p'} \delta_{i,i'} \tag{4:2.59a}$$

$$\langle Q^{(p)}_{ai} | Q^{(p)}_{a'i} \rangle = \langle Q^{(p)}_{aj} | Q^{(p)}_{a'j} \rangle. \tag{4:2.59b}$$

Let us now illustrate the rather lengthy foregoing theory with a very simple example.

Example. Two Coupled Harmonic Oscillators of Equal Masses with Identical End Springs

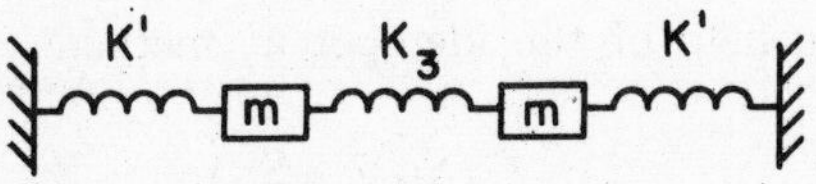

We now restrict the general problem of two coupled oscillators by the assumptions that $m_1 = m_2 = m$ and $K_1' = K_2' = K'$. We now have

$$2T = m(\dot{x}_1^2 + \dot{x}_2^2) \tag{4:2.60a}$$

$$2V = K(x_1^2 + x_2^2) - 2K_3 x_1 x_2 \tag{4:2.60b}$$

where

$$K = K' + K_3. \tag{4:2.60c}$$

When the oscillators are in equilibrium position ($x_1 = x_2 = 0$) the system is symmetrical about the center. Thus the operation of inversion is a symmetry element of the equilibrium configuration. If we let the distance from the center to one of the equilibrium positions be a, then the inversion transformation for a nonequilibrium configuration is

$$x_1' = -2a + x_1 \tag{4:2.61a}$$

$$x_2' = 2a + x_2. \tag{4:2.61b}$$

First of all, however, this is not a homogeneous transformation of the x's, and second of all it does not leave V invariant (i.e., $V(x_1', x_2') \neq V(x_1, x_2)$). Hence (4:2.61) is not a $\bar{D}$. However, we can use (4:2.61) as a cue for deriving a $\bar{D}$. Instead of simply reflecting the masses through the center, let us perform this reflection and then interchange the masses. Or, in other words, let us reflect the displacements of the masses, but not the masses themselves. This transformation is

$$x_1' = -x_2 \tag{4:2.62a}$$

$$x_2' = -x_1 \tag{4:2.62b}$$

which is homogeneous. Also, it is evident that T and V are invariant under this transformation, so that

$$\bar{D} = \begin{pmatrix} 0 & -1 \\ -1 & 0 \end{pmatrix}. \tag{4:2.63}$$

Since $\bar{D}^2 = 1$ we see that $\bar{\Gamma}$ is isomorphic to C_2. Also, since $\chi^{(\bar{\Gamma})} = (2, 0)$ it is apparent that $\bar{\Gamma} \cdot\!\equiv\!\cdot \Gamma_1 \oplus \Gamma_2$ so that there can be two distinct frequencies, and symmetry in this case does not reduce the possible number of frequencies. Hence, we want to find a 2×2 matrix S such that

$$S^{-1}\begin{pmatrix} 0 & -1 \\ -1 & 0 \end{pmatrix} S = \begin{pmatrix} 1 & 0 \\ 0 & -1 \end{pmatrix}. \tag{4:2.64}$$

In this case the problem is so simple that we can determine S directly from (4:2.64) without the help of the idempotent methods. The most general form of S^{-1} is

$$S^{-1} = \begin{pmatrix} S_{11} & -S_{11} \\ S_{21} & S_{21} \end{pmatrix} \tag{4:2.65a}$$

so

$$\begin{pmatrix} Q_1 \\ Q_2 \end{pmatrix} = S^{-1}\begin{pmatrix} x_1 \\ x_2 \end{pmatrix} = \begin{pmatrix} S_{11}(x_1 - x_2) \\ S_{21}(x_1 + x_2) \end{pmatrix}. \tag{4:2.65b}$$

From (4:2.60) we have

$$A = \begin{pmatrix} m & 0 \\ 0 & m \end{pmatrix} \qquad B = \begin{pmatrix} K & -K_3 \\ -K_3 & K \end{pmatrix} \tag{4:2.66}$$

so

$$S^tAS = \begin{pmatrix} \dfrac{m}{2S_{11}^2} & 0 \\ 0 & \dfrac{m}{2S_{21}^2} \end{pmatrix} \tag{4:2.67a}$$

$$S^tBS = \begin{pmatrix} \dfrac{K+K_3}{2S_{11}^2} & 0 \\ 0 & \dfrac{K-K_3}{2S_{21}^2} \end{pmatrix}. \tag{4:2.67b}$$

By choosing $S_{11} = S_{21} = \sqrt{(\frac{1}{2}m)}$ we find

$$S^tAS = I \tag{4:2.68a}$$

$$S^tBS = \begin{pmatrix} \dfrac{K+K_3}{m} & 0 \\ 0 & \dfrac{K-K_3}{m} \end{pmatrix} \tag{4:2.68b}$$

$$Q_1 = \sqrt{(\tfrac{1}{2}m)}\,(x_1 - x_2) \tag{4:2.68c}$$

$$Q_2 = \sqrt{(\tfrac{1}{2}m)}\,(x_1 + x_2) \tag{4:2.68d}$$

$$\omega_1{}^2 = \frac{K+K_3}{m} \tag{4:2.68e}$$

$$\omega_2{}^2 = \frac{K-K_3}{m}\,. \tag{4:2.68f}$$

If we want to normalize the symmetry coordinates we can choose

$$Q_1 = \frac{x_1 - x_2}{\sqrt{2}} \tag{4:2.69a}$$

$$Q_2 = \frac{x_1 + x_2}{\sqrt{2}}. \tag{4:2.69b}$$

It should be noted that the symmetry coordinates in this case are also normal coordinates. The first symmetry mode

$$Q_1 \neq 0 \qquad Q_2 = 0$$

is one in which

$$x_2 = -x_1 \tag{4:2.70a}$$

and the second symmetry mode is one in which

$$x_2 = x_1. \tag{4:2.70b}$$

Thus in the first mode the masses move equally toward or away from each other, and in the second mode they move with each other.

So far we have said nothing about molecules, but it is now time to do so. First, let us assume that the potential energies of all molecules to be considered are invariant under all rotations and translations; or, in other words, the potential energy of a molecule should not depend on where it is or how it is oriented in space. The potential energy can then be expressed in terms of "internal" coordinates of the molecule such as changes of bond lengths and bond angles. Let us also assume that the molecule has a single equilibrium position. Then the total energy $H = T + V$ of the molecule when expressed in appropriate coordinates can be shown to be approximately the sum of a translational part, a rotational part, and a vibrational part.§ Actually, this splitting is only necessary in the kinetic energy because the potential energy is already purely vibrational because of the preceding assumption. To define what the proper coordinates are let us introduce a Cartesian coordinate frame F whose origin is at the center of mass of the molecule in its equilibrium configuration and whose axes are parallel to three orthogonal eigenvectors of the inertial matrix of the molecule in its equilibrium configuration. The inertial matrix J is defined by

$$J_{kl} = \sum_{\mu} m_\mu (r^{(\mu)2}\delta_{kl} - x_k^{(\mu)} x_l^{(\mu)}), \qquad (4:2.71)$$

where the index μ numbers the atoms of the molecule, the sum is over all atoms of the molecule, $r^{(\mu)}$ is the distance from the origin to the equilibrium position of the μth atom, and $x_k^{(\mu)}$ is the kth Cartesian coordinate of the μth atom relative to an arbitrary Cartesian frame with origin at the center of mass of the equilibrium molecule. The proper coordinates of an N-atomic molecule are then the three Cartesian coordinates of the origin of F relative to some fixed Cartesian frame F_0, the three Euler angles of F relative to F_0, and $3N - 6$ internal coordinates.

Since the problem of the motion of a molecule can be split into the above three parts, we shall concern ourselves only with the vibration part, and shall describe all molecules in the above-defined Cartesian frame F. Instead of using $3N-6$ internal coordinates, however, we can instead use the $3N$ Cartesian displacement coordinates of the N-atoms from their respective equilibrium positions. In this case, however, not all of the coordinates are independent, and the following relations among them can be shown to hold:

$$\sum_{\mu=1}^{N} m_\mu \mathbf{r}_\mu = \mathbf{0} \qquad (4:2.72a)$$

§ See Wilson, E. B., Decius J. C., and Cross, P. C., "Molecular Vibrations," McGraw-Hill, New York, 1955, for a proof.

$$\sum_{\mu=1}^{N} m_\mu \mathbf{a}_\mu \times \mathbf{r}_\mu = \mathbf{0}, \tag{4:2.72b}$$

where $\mathbf{r}_\mu$ is the displacement vector from the equilibrium position of the μth atom to its actual position, and $\mathbf{a}_\mu$ is the vector from the origin of F to the equilibrium position of the μth atom. Equations (4:2.72) are approximately the conditions that the molecule have no linear or angular momentum relative to the frame F.

So far we have no connection between molecular energies and the quadratic forms of T and V assumed earlier for vibration problems. If we use Cartesian displacement coordinates in the frame F, then the vibrational kinetic energy T is simply

$$2T = \sum_{\mu=1}^{N} m_\mu \dot{\mathbf{r}}_\mu^{\,2}. \tag{4:2.73a}$$

The potential energy V is not so simple. However, if we assume that V can be expanded in a Taylor series in the displacement coordinates, we have

$$2V = \sum_{\mu,\nu=1}^{N} \mathbf{r}_\mu{}^t B^{\mu\nu} \mathbf{r}_\nu + \ldots, \tag{4.2.74}$$

where $B^{\mu\nu}$ is a symmetric 3-dimensional matrix, and $B^{\mu\nu} = B^{\nu\mu}$. The constant term has been omitted because we can choose $V = 0$ when all $\mathbf{r}_\mu$ are zero; the first order terms have been omitted because by definition $\mathbf{r}_\mu = \mathbf{0}$ (all μ) is the equilibrium configuration so we must have

$$[\nabla_{\mathbf{r}_\mu} V]_{\mathbf{r}_\mu = \mathbf{0}} = \mathbf{0}. \tag{4:2.75}$$

If we now make the very important assumption that the vibrations are small, then we can drop the third and higher order terms in (4:2.74). With this assumption we have

$$2V = \sum_{\mu,\nu=1}^{N} \mathbf{r}_\mu{}' B^{\mu\nu} \mathbf{r}_\nu. \tag{4:2.73b}$$

The equations (4:2.73a) and (4:2.73b) show that with the aid of some plausible assumptions the kinetic and potential vibrational energies of a molecule can be given the desired bilinear form when expressed in terms of Cartesian displacement coordinates. Since the Cartesian displacement coordinates are small, however, it is usually possible to express internal coordinates approximately linearly in terms of Cartesian displacement coordinates, and therefore to give T and V the desired bilinear forms in terms of internal coordinates.

Let us for the present use Cartesian displacement coordinates, and investigate further the effects of the assumption that V depends only on the interaction distances. If $\boldsymbol{\tau}$ is any real 3-dimensional vector, then we should have

$$V(\mathbf{r}_\mu + \boldsymbol{\tau}) = V(\mathbf{r}_\mu), \tag{4:2.76}$$

since an equal translation of all atoms preserves interatomic distances. Let us write V in the form

$$2V = r^t B r, \tag{4:2.77}$$

where r is the $3N$-dimensional column matrix of all r_μ's and B is the symmetric square matrix of all $B^{\mu\nu}$'s. Then, letting τ be a $3N$-dimensional column matrix consisting of N identical 3-dimensional τ's, we can write (4:2.76) in the form

$$r^t B\tau + \tau^t B r + \tau^t B\tau = 0, \tag{4:2.78}$$

and since $(\tau^t B r) = (r^t B \tau)^t = r^t B\tau$, we have, by choosing τ small and neglecting $\tau^t B \tau$,

$$r^t B\tau = 0. \tag{4:2.79}$$

Since this must hold for all r, we have

$$B\tau = 0, \tag{4:2.80}$$

and since τ contains three arbitrary constants we see that B has three linearly independent eigenvectors belonging to eigenvalue zero. We can treat the rotational invariance similarly. If we rotate all of the equilibrium position vectors $\mathbf{a}_\mu$ by the same rotation matrix R, but leave the actual atomic position fixed, then the interatomic distance will remain unchanged, and so will V. A little geometrical consideration shows that the displacement vectors from the new equilibrium positions are given by

$$\mathbf{r}_\mu' = (I - R)\mathbf{a}_\mu + \mathbf{r}_\mu, \tag{4:2.81}$$

so

$$V((I - R)\mathbf{a}_\mu + \mathbf{r}_\mu) = V(\mathbf{r}_\mu). \tag{4:2.82}$$

If we let a be the $3N$-dimensional column matrix of $\mathbf{a}_\mu$'s, and R be a direct sum of N identical R's, then we can write (4:2.82) as

$$[(I - R)a]^t B r + r^t B[(I - R)a] + [(I - R)a]^t B[(I - R)a] = 0.$$

If we make the rotation small, then $R \cong I$, and we can drop the last term as a second-order term and obtain

$$B[(I - R)a] = 0. \tag{4:2.83}$$

Since R contains three arbitrary constants, so does the vector $(I - R)a$ (except when the $\mathbf{a}_\mu$'s are parallel, this being the case of a linear molecule). By slightly more detailed considerations of the forms of τ and $(I - R)a$ one can see that this set of vectors contains six linearly independent vectors. Hence, the assumed translation-rotation invariance of V implies that B has the eigenvalue zero, and that the degeneracy of the zero eigenvalue is at least six. Hence, Λ has six zero eigenvalues, and the system has six normal modes of zero frequency.

By slightly more detailed considerations§ it can be shown that the six normal coordinates belonging to zero frequency are

$$(1-3) \qquad \sum_{\mu=1}^{N} m_\mu \mathbf{r}_\mu \tag{4:2.84a}$$

$$(4-6) \qquad \sum_{\mu=1}^{N} m_\mu \mathbf{a}_\mu \times \mathbf{r}_\mu. \tag{4:2.84b}$$

It will be noted that these normal coordinates are just the quantities which, in (4:2.72), we required to be zero.

The remaining problem of the construction of the $\bar{D}$'s can be solved in essentially the same way as for two identical coupled oscillators. Let us define the symmetry group $\Gamma = \{D\}$ of a molecule to be the set of all alibi orthogonal transformations in the frame F whose only effect on the equilibrium molecule is to permute identical atoms. The reason for restricting consideration to orthogonal matrices is that we want the equilibrium positions to remain fixed (although the atoms occupying them may be changed by a transformation), and in particular we do not want the distances between equilibrium positions changed as would happen if nonorthogonal transformations were used. It should also be pointed out that in principle any finite subgroup of the 3-dimensional orthogonal group could be a molecular symmetry group, although in practice not all of them are used. To construct $\bar{\Gamma}$ from Γ, or $\bar{D}$ from D, we simply define $\bar{D}$ to be the transformation obtained by applying D to the nonequilibrium molecule and then permuting the atoms back to the neighborhoods of their original equilibrium positions. Symbolically, $\bar{D} = P^{-1}D$ (which does not yet appear to be a matrix). If the effect of D on the equilibrium configuration is to transform atom i into atom j, then $\bar{D}$ transforms the displacements of the atoms (leaving the atoms in their equilibrium neighborhoods) as follows: The $\bar{D}$-transformed displacement $\mathbf{r}_j'$ of atom j is $D\mathbf{r}_i$; i.e., $\mathbf{r}_j' = D\mathbf{r}_i$. Let

$$v = \begin{pmatrix} \mathbf{r}_1 \\ \mathbf{r}_2 \\ \vdots \end{pmatrix}$$

be the column matrix of displacement vectors, and let P be the N-dimensional permutation matrix which takes $\mathbf{r}_i$ into $\mathbf{r}_j$ (i.e., which permutes the displacement vectors in v in the same way D permutes the atoms of the

§ See Wilson, E. B., Decius, J. C., and Cross, P. C., "Molecular Vibrations," McGraw-Hill, New York, 1955.

equilibrium molecule). Then, if we multiply each displacement vector of the permuted column matrix by D we obtain a new column matrix

$$v' = \begin{pmatrix} \mathbf{r}_1' \\ \mathbf{r}_2' \\ \vdots \end{pmatrix}$$

which is $\bar{D}v$. If we call the permutation matrix P, then $\bar{D} = P \otimes D$ (with proper ordering of the rows of the Kronecker product). But, from the definition of P it is clear that $D_1 D_2 = D_3$ implies $P_1 P_2 = P_3$. Hence $\bar{D}_1 \bar{D}_2 = (P_1 \otimes D_1)(P_2 \otimes D_2) = P_1 P_2 \otimes D_1 D_2 = P_2 \otimes D_3 = \bar{D}_3$, so $\bar{\Gamma}$ is a representation of Γ. Also,

$$\bar{D}^t = (P \otimes D)^t = P^t \otimes D^t = P^{-1} \otimes D^{-1} = \bar{D}^{-1},$$

so $\bar{\Gamma}$ is orthogonal. Finally, it should be borne in mind that $\bar{D}$ is always to be a linear homogeneous transformation.

Example. For a homonuclear triatomic molecule whose equilibrium configuration is an equilateral triangle, one D is a counterclockwise rotation in the plane of the molecule through 120°. If we choose the z-axis perpendicular to the plane of the equilibrium molecule, then

$$D = \begin{pmatrix} -\frac{1}{2} & -\frac{1}{2}\sqrt{3} & 0 \\ \frac{1}{2}\sqrt{3} & \frac{1}{2} & 0 \\ 0 & 0 & 1 \end{pmatrix}$$

and if the atoms are numbered counterclockwise,

$$P = \begin{pmatrix} 0 & 0 & 1 \\ 1 & 0 & 0 \\ 0 & 1 & 0 \end{pmatrix}$$

so

$$\bar{D} = \begin{pmatrix} 0 & 0 & D \\ D & 0 & 0 \\ 0 & D & 0 \end{pmatrix}.$$

Now let us see why T and V are invariant under $\bar{D}$. The effect of $\bar{D}$ is to exchange displacements among identical atoms and to change the directions of these displacements. Since the same transformation holds for all times, $\bar{D}$ has the same effect on velocities. However, $2T = \sum_{\mu=1}^{N} m_\mu \dot{\mathbf{r}}_\mu^{\,2}$, so T does not depend on the direction of $\mathbf{r}_\mu$, nor does it depend on how a set of velocities is assigned to a set of atoms of equal mass. Now let us consider the potential energy. Since D is an orthogonal transformation it leaves all interatomic distances unchanged and therefore leaves the potential energy invariant. However, D does not cause a homogeneous transformation of Cartesian displacement coordinates and for that reason is not acceptable as a $\bar{D}$. However, when the atoms are permuted among each other after the operation D, only identical atoms are interchanged so the potential energy is still not changed. Because the atoms end up in their equilibrium neighborhoods, the resulting transformation $\bar{D} = P \otimes D$ is homogeneous in r-space. Each transformed displacement vector $\mathbf{r}_\mu{}'$ is just D operating on some other displacement vector $\mathbf{r}_\nu$.

Example. H_2O

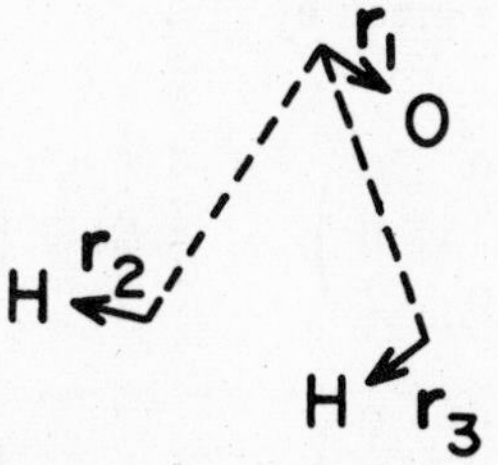

The equilibrium configuration is indicated with dotted lines and a set of possible displacement vectors with arrows. The symmetry group Γ of H_2O consists of four elements. If we choose the frame F as prescribed,

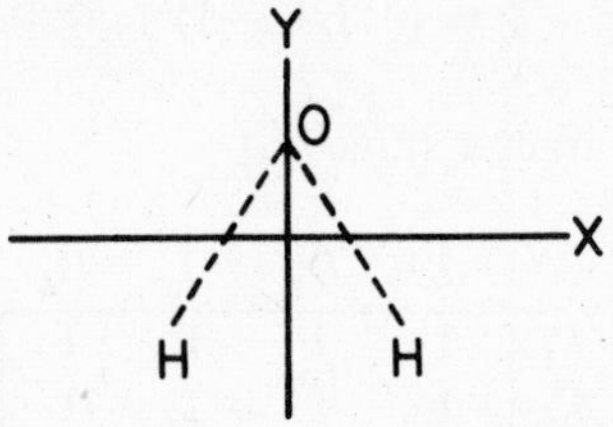

then the four elements of Γ are: (1) the identity transformation, (2) the reflection through the XY-plane, (3) the reflection through the YZ-plane, and (4) the 180° rotation about the Y-axis. The corresponding matrices of Γ are

$$I = \begin{pmatrix} 1 & & \\ & 1 & \\ & & 1 \end{pmatrix} \qquad D_2 = \begin{pmatrix} 1 & & \\ & 1 & \\ & & -1 \end{pmatrix}$$

$$D_3 = \begin{pmatrix} -1 & & \\ & 1 & \\ & & 1 \end{pmatrix} \qquad D_4 = \begin{pmatrix} -1 & & \\ & 1 & \\ & & -1 \end{pmatrix}. \tag{4:2.85}$$

Since the square of each matrix is the identity, it follows that this group must be isomorphic to the dihedral group D_2. Since Γ is abelian it has only 1-dimensional irreducible representations. Since also the degeneracy of a frequency is equal to the dimension of the corresponding irreducible component of the representation $\bar{\Gamma}$, it follows that in this case the symmetry never requires any degeneracy greater than one. Consequently the number of possible frequencies is also not reduced by symmetry in this case. Nevertheless, the water molecule will illustrate several facets of the problem.

Suppose the matrices $\bar{D}$ of $\bar{\Gamma}$ transform the 9-dimensional column matrix $v = \begin{pmatrix} \mathbf{r}_1 \\ \mathbf{r}_2 \\ \mathbf{r}_3 \end{pmatrix}$. Then the $\bar{D}$'s are given by

$$\bar{I} = \begin{pmatrix} I & 0 & 0 \\ 0 & I & 0 \\ 0 & 0 & I \end{pmatrix} \qquad \bar{D}_2 = \begin{pmatrix} D_2 & 0 & 0 \\ 0 & D_2 & 0 \\ 0 & 0 & D_2 \end{pmatrix} \tag{4:2.86}$$

$$\bar{D}_3 = \begin{pmatrix} D_3 & 0 & 0 \\ 0 & 0 & D_3 \\ 0 & D_3 & 0 \end{pmatrix} \qquad \bar{D}_4 = \begin{pmatrix} D_4 & 0 & 0 \\ 0 & 0 & D_4 \\ 0 & D_4 & 0 \end{pmatrix}$$

where each submatrix is 3-dimensional. The character $\bar{\chi}$ of $\bar{\Gamma}$ is therefore

$$\bar{\chi} = (9, 3, 1, -1) \tag{4:2.87}$$

so that by use of the character table

	I	D_2	D_3	D_4
Γ_1	1	1	1	1
Γ_2	1	1	−1	−1
Γ_3	1	−1	1	−1
Γ_4	1	−1	−1	1

we obtain

$$\bar{\Gamma} \cdot\!\equiv\!\cdot\, 3\Gamma_1 \oplus 3\Gamma_2 \oplus 2\Gamma_3 \oplus \Gamma_4. \tag{4:2.88}$$

For the idempotents ζ (or e) we have

$$\zeta^{(p)} = \tfrac{1}{4} \sum_{i=1}^{4} \chi_i^{(p)} \bar{D}_i, \tag{4:2.89}$$

so

$$4\zeta^{(1)} = \begin{pmatrix} \begin{pmatrix} 0 & & \\ & 4 & \\ & & 0 \end{pmatrix} & 0 & 0 \\ 0 & \begin{pmatrix} 2 & & \\ & 2 & \\ & & 0 \end{pmatrix} & \begin{pmatrix} -2 & & \\ & 2 & \\ & & 0 \end{pmatrix} \\ 0 & \begin{pmatrix} -2 & & \\ & 2 & \\ & & 0 \end{pmatrix} & \begin{pmatrix} 2 & & \\ & 2 & \\ & & 0 \end{pmatrix} \end{pmatrix} \tag{4:2.90a}$$

$$4\zeta^{(2)} = \begin{pmatrix} \begin{pmatrix} 4 & & \\ & 0 & \\ & & 0 \end{pmatrix} & 0 & 0 \\ 0 & \begin{pmatrix} 2 & & \\ & 2 & \\ & & 0 \end{pmatrix} & \begin{pmatrix} 2 & & \\ & -2 & \\ & & 0 \end{pmatrix} \\ 0 & \begin{pmatrix} 2 & & \\ & -2 & \\ & & 0 \end{pmatrix} & \begin{pmatrix} 2 & & \\ & 2 & \\ & & 0 \end{pmatrix} \end{pmatrix} \tag{4:2.90b}$$

$$4\zeta^{(3)} = \begin{pmatrix} \begin{pmatrix} 0 & & \\ & 0 & \\ & & 4 \end{pmatrix} & 0 & 0 \\ 0 & \begin{pmatrix} 0 & & \\ & 0 & \\ & & 2 \end{pmatrix} & \begin{pmatrix} 0 & & \\ & 0 & \\ & & 2 \end{pmatrix} \\ 0 & \begin{pmatrix} 0 & & \\ & 0 & \\ & & 2 \end{pmatrix} & \begin{pmatrix} 0 & & \\ & 0 & \\ & & 2 \end{pmatrix} \end{pmatrix} \tag{4:2.90c}$$

$$4\zeta^{(4)} = \begin{pmatrix} 0 & 0 & 0 \\ 0 & \begin{pmatrix} 0 & & \\ & 0 & \\ & & 2 \end{pmatrix} & \begin{pmatrix} 0 & & \\ & 0 & \\ & & -2 \end{pmatrix} \\ 0 & \begin{pmatrix} 0 & & \\ & 0 & \\ & & -2 \end{pmatrix} & \begin{pmatrix} 0 & & \\ & 0 & \\ & & 2 \end{pmatrix} \end{pmatrix}. \tag{4:2.90d}$$

For $\zeta^{(p)}v$ we obtain

$$4\zeta^{(1)}v = \begin{pmatrix} 0 \\ 4y_1 \\ 0 \\ 2x_2 - 2x_3 \\ 2y_2 + 2y_3 \\ 0 \\ -2x_2 + 2x_3 \\ 2y_2 + 2y_3 \\ 0 \end{pmatrix} \tag{4:2.91a}$$

$$4\zeta^{(2)}v = \begin{pmatrix} 4x_1 \\ 0 \\ 0 \\ 2x_2 + 2x_3 \\ 2y_2 - 2y_3 \\ 0 \\ 2x_2 + 2x_3 \\ -2y_2 + 2y_3 \\ 0 \end{pmatrix} \tag{4:2.91b}$$

$$4\zeta^{(3)}v = \begin{pmatrix} 0 \\ 0 \\ 4z_1 \\ 0 \\ 0 \\ 2z_2 + 2z_3 \\ 0 \\ 0 \\ 2z_2 + 2z_3 \end{pmatrix} \tag{4:2.91c}$$

$$4\zeta^{(4)}v = \begin{pmatrix} 0 \\ 0 \\ 0 \\ 0 \\ 0 \\ 2z_2 - 2z_3 \\ 0 \\ 0 \\ -2z_2 + 2z_3 \end{pmatrix} \tag{4:2.91d}$$

The set of all vectors $\zeta^{(1)}v$ is the 3-dimensional carrier space of $3\Gamma_1$. Since $\bar{D}\zeta^{(1)}v$ is just $\zeta^{(1)}v$ it follows that each component of $\zeta^{(1)}v$ is a scalar and therefore a symmetry coordinate. Hence y_1, $x_2 - x_3$, and $y_2 + y_3$ are the linearly independent symmetry coordinates belonging to Γ_1. In general, if

$$v = \begin{pmatrix} x_1 \\ y_1 \\ \cdot \\ \cdot \\ \cdot \end{pmatrix} \qquad w_{ij}^{(p)} = \zeta_{ij}^{(p)} v = \begin{pmatrix} Q_{ij,1}^{(p)} \\ Q_{ij,2}^{(p)} \\ \cdot \\ \cdot \\ \cdot \end{pmatrix} \text{ and } w_{ij}^{(p)\prime} \equiv \bar{D} w_{ij}^{(p)},$$

then $Q_{ij,n}^{(p)\prime} = \sum_k D_{kj}^{(p)} Q_{ik,n}^{(p)}$. We could also find a transformation matrix completely reducing $\bar{\Gamma}$, but we do not need to. We thus have

Irreducible Component of $\bar{\Gamma}$	*Corresponding Symmetry Coordinates*
Γ_1	$y_1,\ x_2 - x_3,\ y_2 + y_3$
Γ_2	$x_1,\ x_2 + x_3,\ y_2 - y_3$
Γ_3	$z_1,\ z_2 + z_3$
Γ_4	$z_2 - z_3$

The six zero-frequency normal coordinates are

$$Mx_1 + m(x_2 + x_3) \tag{4:2.92a}$$

$$My_1 + m(y_2 + y_3) \tag{4:2.92b}$$

$$Mz_1 + m(z_2 + z_3) \tag{4:2.92c}$$

$$2z_1 - z_2 - z_3 \tag{4:2.92d}$$

$$z_2 - z_3 \tag{4:2.92e}$$

$$(2x_1 - x_2 - x_3) + \left(1 + \frac{2m}{M}\right)\left(\tan\frac{\phi}{2}\right)(y_2 - y_3), \tag{4:2.92f}$$

where M is the mass of the oxygen atom, m is the mass of the hydrogen atom, and ϕ is the angle between the two OH bonds in the equilibrium configuration. It will be seen that the first zero-frequency normal coordinate is a linear combination of symmetry coordinates belonging to Γ_2, so it also belongs to Γ_2. The representations to which the six zero-frequency normal coordinates belong are thus Γ_2, Γ_1, Γ_3, Γ_3, Γ_4, and Γ_2, respectively. There must be only three linearly independent symmetry coordinates left. These are (without normalization)

Γ_p	Q
Γ_1	$x_2 - x_3$
Γ_1	$2my_1 - M(y_2 + y_3)$
Γ_2	$2mx_1 - M(x_2 + x_3) - M(\cot\frac{1}{2}\phi)(y_2 - y_3)$

where the Q's have been made orthogonal to the zero-frequency normal coordinates.

Let us now view the problem from the point of view of internal coordinates. As our three internal coordinates, let us choose the increases of length, r_{12}

and r_{13}, of the two OH bonds from their equilibrium value l, and the change α of the angle between these bonds from its equilibrium value ϕ. Some elementary geometric considerations show that for small displacements

$$r_{12} = (x_1 - x_2)\sin\tfrac{1}{2}\phi + (y_1 - y_2)\cos\tfrac{1}{2}\phi \tag{4:2.93a}$$

$$r_{13} = -(x_1 - x_3)\sin\tfrac{1}{2}\phi + (y_1 - y_3)\cos\tfrac{1}{2}\phi \tag{4:2.93b}$$

$$\alpha = -(x_2 - x_3)\frac{\cos\frac{1}{2}\phi}{l} - (2y_1 - y_2 - y_3)\frac{\sin\frac{1}{2}\phi}{l}. \tag{4:2.93c}$$

If we want to express the vibrational kinetic energy T in terms of internal coordinates, we can solve the three equations (4:2.93), together with the six equations obtained by putting the zero-frequency normal coordinates (4:2.92) equal to zero, for the Cartesian displacement coordinates in terms of the internal coordinates, and then substitute in the equation

$$2T = M\dot{\mathbf{r}}_1^2 + m(\dot{\mathbf{r}}_2^2 + \dot{\mathbf{r}}_3^2). \tag{4:2.94}$$

For the Cartesian displacement coordinates we obtain

$$z_1 = z_2 = z_3 = 0 \tag{4:2.95a}$$

$$x_1 = \frac{m\sin\frac{1}{2}\phi}{M + 2m\sin^2\frac{1}{2}\phi}(r_{12} - r_{13}) \tag{4:2.95b}$$

$$x_2 = \frac{M(\sin\frac{1}{2}\phi)(r_{13} - r_{12})}{2M + 4m\sin^2\frac{1}{2}\phi} - \frac{2l\alpha\cos^2\frac{1}{2}\phi + (r_{12} + r_{13})\sin\phi}{4\cos\frac{1}{2}\phi} \tag{4:2.95c}$$

$$x_3 = -\frac{M}{m}x_1 - x_2 \tag{4:2.95d}$$

$$y_1 = \frac{m}{M + 2m}[(r_{12} + r_{13})\cos\tfrac{1}{2}\phi - l\alpha\sin\tfrac{1}{2}\phi] \tag{4:2.95e}$$

$$y_2 = -\frac{My_1}{2m} - \frac{M(r_{12} - r_{13})\cos\frac{1}{2}\phi}{2M + 4m\sin^2\frac{1}{2}\phi} \tag{4:2.95f}$$

$$y_3 = -\frac{M}{m}y_1 - y_2. \tag{4:2.95g}$$

The kinetic energy can now be expressed in internal coordinates by substituting (4:2.95) in (4:2.94). Actually, however, this procedure is extremely laborious and a better method of obtaining normal frequencies is available.

Before considering the kinetic energy further let us consider the 3-dimensional $\bar{\Gamma}_{\text{int}}$ generated by the three internal coordinates. If the $\bar{D}$'s operate on $v = \begin{pmatrix} r_{12} \\ r_{13} \\ \alpha \end{pmatrix}$ then from (4:2.93) and (4:2.86) we obtain

$$\bar{I} = \begin{pmatrix} 1 & 0 & 0 \\ 0 & 1 & 0 \\ 0 & 0 & 1 \end{pmatrix} \qquad \bar{D}_2 = \begin{pmatrix} 1 & 0 & 0 \\ 0 & 1 & 0 \\ 0 & 0 & 1 \end{pmatrix} \tag{4:2.96}$$

$$\bar{D}_3 = \begin{pmatrix} 0 & 1 & 0 \\ 1 & 0 & 0 \\ 0 & 0 & 1 \end{pmatrix} \qquad \bar{D}_4 = \begin{pmatrix} 0 & 1 & 0 \\ 1 & 0 & 0 \\ 0 & 0 & 1 \end{pmatrix},$$

so

$$\bar{\chi}_{\text{int}} = (3, 3, 1, 1) \tag{4:2.97}$$

and

$$\bar{\Gamma}_{\text{int}} \cdot\!\equiv\!\cdot\, 2\Gamma_1 \oplus \Gamma_2, \tag{4:2.98}$$

which is equivalent to the representation generated by the three nonzero-frequency symmetry coordinates. The $\bar{D}$'s could also have been obtained directly by geometrical consideration of the transformations. The ζ's (or e's) are given by

$$4\zeta^{(1)} = \begin{pmatrix} 2 & 2 & 0 \\ 2 & 2 & 0 \\ 0 & 0 & 4 \end{pmatrix} \qquad 4\zeta^{(2)} = \begin{pmatrix} 2 & -2 & 0 \\ -2 & 2 & 0 \\ 0 & 0 & 0 \end{pmatrix} \tag{4:2.99}$$

and the ζv's are given by

$$4\zeta^{(1)}v = \begin{pmatrix} 2r_{12} + 2r_{13} \\ 2r_{12} + 2r_{13} \\ 4\alpha \end{pmatrix} \qquad 4\zeta^{(2)}v = \begin{pmatrix} 2r_{12} - 2r_{13} \\ 2r_{12} - 2r_{13} \\ 0 \end{pmatrix} \tag{4:2.100}$$

so the symmetry coordinates belonging to Γ_1 are $(r_{12} + r_{13})$ and α, and the one belonging to Γ_2 is $(r_{12} - r_{13})$. Using the general formula given earlier we see that four constants apiece are required to specify T and V. This can also be seen directly from the fact that no cross terms between symmetry coordinates belonging to different irreducible components (i.e., different species of symmetry coordinates) can occur. We also see that use of the symmetry coordinates will factor the secular equation into a quadratic and a linear factor.

Let us now return to the kinetic energy. If P is the rectangular matrix transforming the mass-normalized Cartesian displacement coordinates $\sqrt{m_\mu}\,\mathbf{r}_\mu$ into the linearly independent internal coordinates (see (4:2.93)), then the kinetic energy matrix A in internal coordinates can be shown to be given by

$$A = (PP^\dagger)^{-1}. \tag{4:2.101}$$

To calculate the normal frequencies we need only the matrix

$$G \equiv PP^\dagger, \tag{4:2.102}$$

because if we designate the potential energy matrix B in internal coordinates by F, then the secular equation can be written

$$|FG - \lambda I| = 0 \tag{4:2.103a}$$

or

$$|GF - \lambda I| = 0 \tag{4:2.103b}$$

(since FG and GF always have the same eigenvalues). From (4:2.93) we find for G

$$G = \begin{pmatrix} a & b & c \\ b & a & c \\ c & c & d \end{pmatrix}, \tag{4:2.104a}$$

where

$$a = \frac{1}{m} + \frac{1}{M} \tag{4:2.104b}$$

$$b = \frac{\cos\phi}{M} \tag{4:2.104c}$$

$$c = -\frac{\sin\phi}{Ml} \tag{4:2.104d}$$

$$d = \frac{2}{l^2}(a - b). \tag{4:2.104e}$$

By evaluating $G^{-1} = A$, the kinetic energy can be written out explicitly.

Let us consider a simple, approximate potential energy function V of the form

$$2V = F_r(r_{12}^2 + r_{13}^2) + F_a \alpha^2, \tag{4:2.105}$$

where F_r and F_a are force constants, all cross terms are omitted, and the same stretching constant F_r is used for both OH bonds. The F-matrix is then diagonal

$$F = \begin{pmatrix} F_r & & \\ & F_r & \\ & & F_a \end{pmatrix}. \tag{4:2.106}$$

If we let

$$Q_1 = \alpha \tag{4:2.107a}$$

$$Q_2 = \frac{r_{12} + r_{13}}{\sqrt{2}} \tag{4:2.107b}$$

$$Q_3 = \frac{r_{12} - r_{13}}{\sqrt{2}}, \tag{4:2.107c}$$

then V can be written in the form

$$2V = F_a Q_1^2 + F_r(Q_2^2 + Q_3^2). \tag{4:2.108}$$

If we now write down the secular equation $|FG - \lambda I| = 0$ in internal coordinates (this problem is simple enough that we do not need to use symmetry coordinates) and solve for the three roots λ we obtain

$$\lambda_{\pm}^{(1)} = \tfrac{1}{2}[dF_a + (a+b)F_r \pm \sqrt{\{[dF_a - (a+b)F_r]^2 + 8c^2F_aF_r\}}] \quad (4{:}2.109a)$$

$$\lambda^{(2)} = (a-b)F_r. \quad (4{:}2.109b)$$

If we assign to the physical parameters of the water molecule the following values:

$$l = 0{\cdot}96\ \mathring{A}$$
$$\phi = 105°$$
$$M = 26{\cdot}72 \times 10^{-24}\text{g}$$
$$m = 1{\cdot}684 \times 10^{-24}\text{g}$$
$$F_r = 7{\cdot}76 \times 10^5 \text{ dyne-cm}^{-1}$$
$$F_a = 6{\cdot}36 \times 10^{-12} \text{ dyne-cm},$$

we obtain for the λ's, ω's, ν's, and wave numbers $k = \nu/c$

	1+	1−	2	
λ	$4{\cdot}83 \times 10^{29}$	$0{\cdot}881 \times 10^{29}$	$4{\cdot}97 \times 10^{29}$	sec^{-2}
ω	$6{\cdot}95 \times 10^{14}$	$2{\cdot}97 \times 10^{14}$	$7{\cdot}05 \times 10^{14}$	sec^{-1}
ν	$1{\cdot}11 \times 10^{14}$	$0{\cdot}473 \times 10^{14}$	$1{\cdot}12 \times 10^{14}$	sec^{-1}
k	3690	1580	3740	cm^{-1}

The experimentally determined values of the normal wave numbers are

	1+	1−	2	
k	3652	1595	3756	cm^{-1}

and it is seen that the calculated values are not in bad agreement. Actually of course, the force constants are frequently determined from experiment, although they can be calculated theoretically.

A more complicated molecule which demonstrates more decisively the power of the group-theoretic method is BF_3. The symmetry group is $D_3 \times C_2$ which is nonabelian, and there are six internal coordinates so $\bar{\Gamma}_{\text{int.}}$ is 6-dimensional. Since $\bar{\Gamma}_{\text{int.}}$ decomposes into two distinct 1-dimensional representations and one 2-dimensional representation (occurring twice), it follows that there can be at most four distinct frequencies, and that two of them are at least doubly degenerate. In symmetry coordinates the sixth-degree secular equation factors into two linear factors and two quadratic factors so it can be solved in closed form. The number of constants required for T and V is at most five apiece.

Finally, let us consider one other general aspect of the group-theoretic treatment of molecules presented here. In order to determine the number of possible distinct frequencies and the degeneracy of each we need only the character $\bar{\chi}_{\text{int.}}$ of $\bar{\Gamma}_{\text{int.}}$. This can be obtained without first finding the symmetry coordinates and zero-frequency normal coordinates, as follows. In Cartesian displacement coordinates we can always write $\bar{D}$ as a matrix whose elements are the matrix D and zero submatrices of the same dimension, see (4:2.86). But the number of D's occurring on the diagonal of $\bar{D}$ is just the number $N(D)$ of atoms in the equilibrium molecule left fixed by D. Hence

$$\bar{\chi}(D) = N(D)\chi(D). \tag{4:2.110}$$

If we now subtract from $\bar{\chi}$ that part of the character due to the transformations of the zero-frequency normal coordinates we will obtain $\bar{\chi}_{\text{int.}}$. The linear momentum zero-frequency normal coordinates transform like a 3-dimensional vector, and therefore contribute the character $\chi(D)$. The angular momentum zero-frequency coordinates transform like the three independent components of the second rank skew symmetric tensor $\sum_{\mu=1}^{N} a_i^{(\mu)} x_j^{(\mu)} - a_j^{(\mu)} x_i^{(\mu)}$, (i.e., like an axial vector) and therefore contribute the character (see Chapter I on antisymmetrized Kronecker products) $\frac{1}{2}[\chi^2(D) - \chi(D^2)] = |D|\chi(D)$, where $|D| = \det(D)$. Hence,

$$\bar{\chi}_{\text{int.}}(D) = [N(D) - 1 - |D|]\chi(D). \tag{4:2.111}$$

Example. $H_2 0$

$$\begin{array}{llll} N(I) = 3 & N(D_2) = 3 & N(D_3) = 1 & N(D_4) = 1 \\ |I| = 1 & |D_2| = -1 & |D_3| = -1 & |D_4| = 1. \end{array}$$

The values of the bracket expression $[N(D) - 1 - |D|]$ for the four matrices are: 1, 3, 1, and -1. Since $\chi = (3, 1, 1, -1)$ we have $\bar{\chi}_{\text{int.}} = (3, 3, 1, 1)$ in agreement with the result obtained earlier.

3. Symmetric Waveguide Junctions

Let us consider a system consisting of several waveguides joined in a sourceless "black box," or junction, and let us restrict ourselves to rectangular, circular, or coaxial guides. Further, let us assume that the system is lossless, i.e., no electromagnetic energy is dissipated as heat or is in any other way lost from the electromagnetic system. By a normal mode of a waveguide let us mean any propagating wave which varies sinusoidally with time at each point. A waveguide will then possess an infinite number of possible normal modes, and an uncountably infinite number of possible frequencies. Also, every possible mode (propagating wave) of a waveguide can be expressed as a linear combination of normal modes. In fact, a complete linearly independent set of normal modes can be chosen such that for each mode either the electric vector at every point is perpendicular to the direction of propagation (T.E. mode), or the magnetic vector at every point is perpendicular to the direction of propagation (T.M. mode). Further, there is some minimum possible normal mode frequency; the corresponding normal modes ear called the fundamental (or dominant) modes. The number of linearly independent fundamental modes for rectangular, square, circular, and coaxial guides are: one, two, two, and one. For simplicity of notation we shall restrict consideration to fundamental modes. We shall also assume that the junction is linear. This means that any incoming wave in any guide is broken up by the junction into a set of outgoing waves in the various connected guides, and that an increase of the amplitude of any incoming wave by a factor K will cause an increase of the amplitude of each of the corresponding scattered waves by the same factor K. As usual, a complex formalism will be used which is formally equivalent to the real equations describing the actual physical situation. To describe the scattering caused by the junction we shall introduce one complex number "a_i" for each linearly independent incident fundamental mode, and one complex number "b_i" for each linearly independent outgoing fundamental mode. The complex numbers a_i and b_i represent the amplitudes and phases of the corresponding waves and can be operationally defined through measurements of time-averaged powers (although we shall not do so here). If we let "a" be the column matrix of a_i's and "b" be the column matrix of b_i's, in the same order, then because of the linearity of the junction we can write

$$b = Sa, \tag{4:3.1}$$

where S is a square matrix (the scattering matrix). Because of the assumed losslessness of the system it can be shown that S must be unitary. If the system is assumed to be reciprocal then it follows that $S^t = S$. For simplicity we shall only consider S-matrices such that

$$SS^\dagger = I \tag{4:3.1a}$$

$$S^t = S. \tag{4:3.1b}$$

If every guide is rectangular (and not square) or coax, then the dimension of S is equal to the number of guides; otherwise the dimension of S is greater than the number of guides. If all guides are square or circular, the dimension of S is twice the number of guides; this is the maximum dimension of S. It should also be noted that S depends only on the geometry of the system.

The group-theoretic treatment of this problem, (103), will be very similar to the group-theoretic treatment of the vibration problem. We shall construct matrices $\bar{D}$ such that

$$S\bar{D} = \bar{D}S, \tag{4:3.2}$$

and we shall investigate the consequences of (4:3.2) on the possible form of S.

Again, this could be done without group theory, but can be done more systematically and simply with group theory. Since, again, if any two $\bar{D}$'s satisfy (4:3.2), their product must also satisfy (4:3.2), we can always extend a set of nonsingular $\bar{D}$'s to a group. Since $\bar{D}$ will turn out to be always orthogonal, we can in fact take over the results of the third analysis of B in the preceding section, if we also assume that $\bar{\Gamma} = \{\bar{D}\}$ contains irreducible components of first kind only. In this case we know that the number of different eigenvalues of S is equal to the number of irreducible components of $\bar{\Gamma}$ (if there is no accidental degeneracy), and that the degeneracy of each eigenvalue of S is equal to the dimension of the corresponding irreducible component of $\bar{\Gamma}$. Since $\bar{\Gamma}$ is orthogonal we can completely reduce it by an orthogonal transformation, and thereby leave S symmetrical. The number of complex constants required to specify S is therefore less than $\frac{1}{2}\sum_{p=1}^{r} c^{(p)}(c^{(p)}+1)$ (where $\bar{\Gamma} = \sum_{p=1}^{r} c^{(p)}\Gamma_p$) because S is not only symmetric but also unitary. The transformed S we know must have the form

$$S = \begin{pmatrix} S^{(1)} & & & \\ & S^{(2)} & & \\ & & \cdot & \\ & & & \cdot \\ & & & & \cdot \end{pmatrix}, \tag{4:3.3a}$$

where

$$S^{(p)} = \sigma^{(p)} \otimes I \tag{4:3.3b}$$

$$\dim(\sigma^{(p)}) = c^{(p)} \tag{4:3.3c}$$

$$\sigma^{(p)}\sigma^{(p)\dagger} = I \tag{4:3.3d}$$

$$\dim(I) = d_p \text{ in } (4{:}3.3\text{b}). \tag{4:3.3e}$$

The eigenvectors of S are useful for matching the junction, and can usually be found much more easily from the transformed form of S, (4:3.3a) than from the original form. A matrix transforming $\bar{\Gamma}$ to completely reduced form and S to the form (4:3.3a) can be found by one of the idempotent methods.

Let us now discuss the construction of $\bar{D}$'s. Let us define the symmetry group, $\Gamma = \{D\}$, of the junction to be the group of all orthogonal transformations (about some center of the junction) which simply interchange identical guides of the junction (i.e., the symmetry operations of the junction transform it into itself). If we apply a symmetry transformation to the junction and guides but not to the waves in the system we get the same physical situation back. We also assume that the positive reference directions associated with the fundamental modes of the guides are transformed with the guides. Because of the change of reference directions the a's will change.

Let us consider how the a's belonging to a guide will transform under a rotation about the axis of that guide. If the guide is rectangular (not square), then there is only one "a" and only one possible rotation—a 180° rotation. In that case

$$a' = -a. \tag{4:3.4a}$$

If the guide is coaxial there is only one "a," and it is an invariant under all rotations and reflections. If the guide is square or circular there are two "a's." In this case let us choose the a_1-direction to the right and the a_2-direction up when looking down the axis of the guide toward the junction. Under a counterclockwise rotation of the system through θ we have

$$\begin{pmatrix} a_1' \\ a_2' \end{pmatrix} = \begin{pmatrix} \cos\theta & \sin\theta \\ -\sin\theta & \cos\theta \end{pmatrix} \begin{pmatrix} a_1 \\ a_2 \end{pmatrix} \tag{4:3.4b}$$

i.e., a_1 and a_2 transform like the components of a 2-dimensional vector. Let us consider reflections. In the case of a rectangular guide the plane of reflection can be either parallel to the reference direction or perpendicular to it. In the first case

$$a' = a \tag{4:3.4c}$$

and in the second case

$$a' = -a. \tag{4:3.4d}$$

In the case of the square or circular guide, a_1 and a_2 again transform like a vector.

If the a's change guides under a transformation they will transform as above regarding any rotation of the reference directions of the new guide with respect to the old, and the new a's will be renumbered so as to belong to the new guide.

The above-described rules for the transformation of the column matrix "a" under the symmetry transformations of the junction define the matrices $\bar{D}$, that is,

$$a' = \bar{D}a. \tag{4:3.5a}$$

Also, it can be easily seen by essentially the same arguments that

$$b' = \bar{D}b. \tag{4:3.5b}$$

From the rules given for the construction of $\bar{D}$ it can also be easily seen that $\bar{D}$ is either a pseudopermutation matrix or a pseudopermutation matrix in which some ones have been replaced by 2-dimensional orthogonal submatrices. Therefore the $\bar{D}$'s, and hence $\bar{\Gamma}$, are orthogonal. Also, it is clear that $\bar{\Gamma}$ is a representation of Γ.

Since the transformed junction is identical with the original junction we have

$$S' = S, \tag{4:3.6}$$

but

$$b' = S'a' = Sa' \tag{4:3.7}$$

so from (4:3.5) we find

$$b = \bar{D}^{-1}S\bar{D}a. \tag{4:3.8}$$

Since also

$$b = Sa, \tag{4:3.1}$$

and since these two equations hold for all a, we have

$$\bar{D}^{-1}S\bar{D} = S \tag{4:3.9}$$

or

$$S\bar{D} = \bar{D}S. \tag{4:3.2}$$

Example. 3-arm junction.

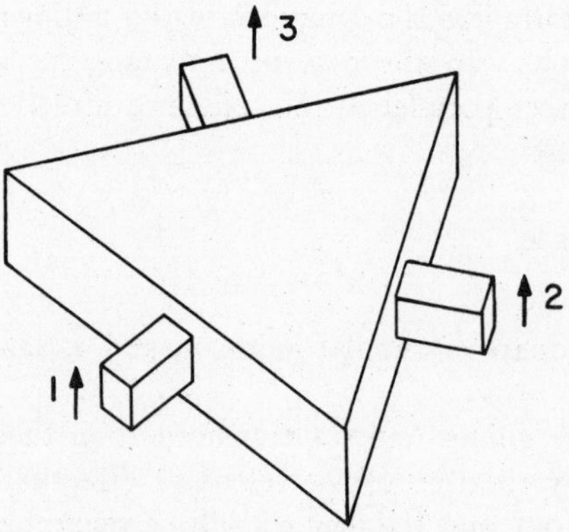

Consider a triangular junction with three identical horizontal rectangular guides coming in at angles of 120° to each other. This system has the symmetry of an equilateral triangle. The symmetry group Γ of the junction is $D_3 \times C_2$. The C_2 enters because of the possibility of reflection through the horizontal plane. If we assume that all three positive reference directions are vertically up, then the $\bar{D}$ for the reflection through the horizontal plane is $-I$. Since $-I$ satisfies (4:3.2) for any S, we see that the reflection does not restrict S at all. Hence, we can drop this reflection and take Γ to be D_3.

Now let us consider the 120° rotation which takes 1 into 2. The corresponding $\bar{D}$ is $\left(\text{with } a = \begin{pmatrix} a_1 \\ a_2 \\ a_3 \end{pmatrix}\right)$

$$\bar{D}_1 = \begin{pmatrix} 0 & 1 & 0 \\ 0 & 0 & 1 \\ 1 & 0 & 0 \end{pmatrix}. \tag{4:3.10}$$

If we consider the reflection through the vertical plane containing the axis of 2 we obtain

$$\bar{D}_2 = \begin{pmatrix} 0 & 0 & 1 \\ 0 & 1 & 0 \\ 1 & 0 & 0 \end{pmatrix}. \tag{4:3.11}$$

These two matrices generate $\bar{\Gamma}$. The classes are: $C_1 = I$; $C_2 = \bar{D}_1, \bar{D}_1^2$; $C_3 = \bar{D}_2, \bar{D}_1 \bar{D}_2, \bar{D}_1^2 \bar{D}_2$. The character is $\bar{\chi} = (3, 0, 1)$, and from the character table

	C_1	C_2	C_3
	1	2	3
Γ_1	1	1	1
Γ_2	1	1	-1
Γ_3	2	-1	0

we find $\bar{\Gamma} = \Gamma_1 \oplus \Gamma_3$. Therefore we can conclude that S has two eigenvalues, one of degeneracy two. We also see that (neglecting the unitarity condition on S) S can be specified by two complex constants. If an orthogonal coordinate transformation is performed which completely reduces $\bar{\Gamma}$, then S must be transformed into the form

$$S' = \begin{pmatrix} \sigma_1 & 0 & 0 \\ 0 & \sigma_3 & 0 \\ 0 & 0 & \sigma_3 \end{pmatrix}. \tag{4:3.12}$$

By means of the first idempotent method we easily find that the orthogonal matrix

$$0 = \begin{pmatrix} \frac{1}{\sqrt{3}} & \frac{1}{\sqrt{3}} & \frac{1}{\sqrt{3}} \\ \frac{2}{\sqrt{6}} & -\frac{1}{\sqrt{6}} & -\frac{1}{\sqrt{6}} \\ 0 & \frac{1}{\sqrt{2}} & -\frac{1}{\sqrt{2}} \end{pmatrix} \tag{4:3.13}$$

completely reduces $\bar{\Gamma}$; i.e., $\bar{\Gamma}' = 0\bar{\Gamma}0^t$ is completely reduced. For $S = 0^t S' 0$ we find

$$S = \begin{pmatrix} \alpha & \beta & \beta \\ \beta & \alpha & \beta \\ \beta & \beta & \alpha \end{pmatrix}, \tag{4:3.14}$$

where

$$\alpha = \tfrac{1}{3}(\sigma_1 + 2\sigma_3) \tag{4:3.14a}$$

$$\beta = \tfrac{1}{3}(\sigma_1 - \sigma_3). \tag{4:3.14b}$$

We now have the general form of S. If we choose for the three eigenvectors of S'

$$v_1' = \begin{pmatrix} 1 \\ 0 \\ 0 \end{pmatrix} \qquad v_2' = \begin{pmatrix} 0 \\ 1 \\ 0 \end{pmatrix} \qquad v_3' = \begin{pmatrix} 0 \\ 0 \\ 1 \end{pmatrix}, \qquad (4:3.15a)$$

then for the corresponding eigenvectors $v_i = 0^t v_i'$ of S we get

$$v_1 = \frac{1}{\sqrt{3}}\begin{pmatrix} 1 \\ 1 \\ 1 \end{pmatrix} \qquad v_2 = \frac{1}{\sqrt{6}}\begin{pmatrix} 2 \\ -1 \\ -1 \end{pmatrix} \qquad v_3 = \frac{1}{\sqrt{2}}\begin{pmatrix} 0 \\ 1 \\ -1 \end{pmatrix} \qquad (4:3.15b)$$

So we now know also the eigenvectors of S. However, group theory does not give us the values of the eigenvalues of S (although we know from the unitarity of S that they must have unit magnitude). We must know more about the system to evaluate the two eigenvalues. Since σ_1 and σ_3 are of unit magnitude we see that one real constant apiece will specify each, and hence that two real constants will specify S. Physically it is fairly evident that one reflection coefficient and one transmission coefficient will specify S.

4. Crystallographic Point Groups

The crystallographic point groups (13, 59, 115, 155, 156) are usually derived by geometric considerations, but in this section we shall see how they can be derived by purely group-theoretic arguments (although not all of the details of the derivation will be carried out). We shall treat only the 3-dimensional groups, but the 2-dimensional groups can be handled in the same way.

Let us call a linear combination of vectors of a vector space integral if every coefficient of the combination is an integer (i.e., a real, whole number). We can then define a 3-dimensional lattice to be the set of all integral linear combinations of three linearly independent vectors of a 3-dimensional real vector space. The three linearly independent vectors which generate a lattice are called the lattice basis vectors. Since any three linearly independent vectors will generate a lattice it is clear that a variety of lattices is possible. On the other hand, it may be possible to generate a single lattice with several different sets of lattice basis vectors.

Let us say that a set of 3-dimensional matrices leaves a 3-dimensional lattice invariant if the effect of any matrix of the set on any vector of the lattice is to transform the vector into another vector belonging to the same lattice. We can then define a 3-dimensional crystallographic point group to be any subgroup of the 3-dimensional orthogonal group O(3) which leaves some 3-dimensional lattice invariant. By definition, therefore, a crystallographic point group is a matrix group. The abstract group which is isomorphic to a point group we shall refer to as the abstract point group; we shall find that there are 18 nonisomorphic abstract point groups. The point group is therefore a faithful orthogonal representation of the abstract point group. Clearly a linear transformation of the coordinate system of the vector space will simply transform an orthogonal representation of an abstract point group into an equivalent representation. Therefore, we shall say that two point groups are the same if and only if they are equivalent with respect to a real transformation. However, we could just as well have omitted the reality condition on the transformation, because if two point groups (which are real!) are equivalent at all, they are equivalent with respect to a real transformation. Also we might note that if two orthogonal point groups are equivalent, then they are equivalent with respect to an orthogonal transformation. Of course, if two point groups are equivalent their abstract point groups must be isomorphic, but the converse is not true. We shall find that there are 32 inequivalent point groups; these are the usual 32 point groups.

Let us now derive an important property of point groups. Let us consider a particular point group which leaves a particular lattice invariant. If we choose the lattice basis vectors as the basis vectors of the vector space, then the matrix elements of the lattice vectors will all be integers. In fact, the lattice will consist of all integral column matrices. Since a matrix of the point group will transform any integral column matrix into another integral column matrix, it follows that the matrices of the point group must be integral. Hence, we find that every point group must be equivalent to an integral matrix group. This means also that the character of a point group must be integral.

Let us say that a point group is of the first kind if it contains only rotations, and is otherwise of the second kind (not to be confused with reality classifications). Let us now show that the subgroup of rotations of a point group of second kind has index 2 (and is therefore normal). Let H be the subgroup, AH one coset, BH another coset, h any element of H, and $h' = B^{-1}Ah$. Since A and B can not be in H we see that $|A| = |B| = -1$, and hence $|h'| = 1$. Thus h' is an element of H and Bh' is an element of BH. But $Bh' = Ah$ so BH and AH have an element in common. Therefore $BH = AH$ and H can have only one coset.

We see also that the rotational subgroup H of a point group G of second kind must itself be a point group, because if G leaves a lattice invariant, H must certainly leave the same lattice invariant.

Let us now consider point groups of the first kind. The trace of a 3-dimensional rotation matrix is $(1 + 2\cos\theta)$, where θ is the angle of rotation. Hence, for a rotation of a point group of the first kind we must have

$$1 + 2\cos\theta = \text{integer}, \tag{4:4.1a}$$

or

$$\cos\theta = \text{half integer}. \tag{4:4.1b}$$

But this means

$$\cos\theta = 0, \pm\tfrac{1}{2}, \pm 1, \tag{4:4.1c}$$

so

$$\theta = 0, 60°, 90°, 120°, 180°. \tag{4:4.1d}$$

Thus only five angles of rotation are possible for elements of a point group of first kind. Consequently only five values for the order of an element are possible, namely, 1, 2, 3, 4, and 6.

Let $\chi_1, \chi_2, \ldots, \chi_t$ be the distinct values of the character of a point group. Then the order g of the point group must be a divisor of the product $[(\chi_1 - \chi_2)(\chi_1 - \chi_3)\ldots(\chi_1 - \chi_t)]$. This follows from the easily proved fact that every point group must be finite, and the theorem that g is a divisor of $\sum_A P(\chi(A))$ if $P(z)$ is a polynomial with integral coefficients. Putting

$$P(z) = (z - \chi_2)(z - \chi_3)\ldots(z - \chi_t) \tag{4:4.2}$$

and remembering that the χ_i's of a point group are integral, we see that this $P(z)$ has integral coefficients. But (since $\chi_1 = \chi(I)$)

$$\sum_A P(\chi(A)) = P(\chi_1) = (\chi_1 - \chi_2)(\chi_1 - \chi_3)\ldots(\chi_1 - \chi_t). \tag{4:4.3}$$

Hence, the desired result is proved.

Since we know all possible values of the character of a point group of first kind, namely, $0, \pm 1, 2, 3$, we can compute the largest possible value which the foregoing product can assume for a point group of first kind. This value is

$$(3 - 0)(3 - 1)(3 + 1)(3 - 2) = 24. \tag{4:4.4}$$

Therefore, the order of every point group of first kind must be a divisor of 24. The possible values are

$$g = 1, 2, 3, 4, 6, 8, 12, 24. \tag{4:4.5}$$

At this point we could make use of the known finite subgroups of the rotation group: C_n, D_n, T, 0, and $\mathscr{I}$. However, since these subgroups can not be derived by group-theoretic methods, we shall not make use of them.

Reference to the table giving the number of nonisomorphic groups of each order shows that there are 32 of orders 1, 2, 3, 4, 6, 8, 12, and 24. These are not the usual 32 crystallographic groups, but we can separate from these 32 groups the nonisomorphic abstract point groups of first kind. This we can do in the following way. First we discard all groups having elements of any order other than 1, 2, 3, 4, or 6. Then we select from the remaining groups those which possess at least one representation Γ satisfying the following conditions:

(1) Γ must be 3-dimensional
(2) Γ must be real
(3) Γ must be faithful
(4) $\chi^{(\Gamma)}$ must assume only the values $0, \pm 1, 2, 3$
(5) the determinant of every matrix of Γ must be one.

These criteria can all be applied to a group by use of the multiplication table and character table alone. The determinant of a 3-dimensional matrix D of Γ can be so evaluated by virtue of the fact that

$$\det(D) = \operatorname{tr}(D_{[3]}) = \tfrac{1}{6}(T_1{}^3 - 3T_1T_2 + 2T_3), \qquad (4{:}4.6)$$

where $T_j = \operatorname{tr}(D^j)$ (see Chapter I on antisymmetrized Kronecker powers).

As an illustration of this procedure let us apply it to the groups of order eight. The five nonisomorphic groups of order eight are: Q, D_4, C_8, $C_4 \times C_2$, $D_2 \times C_2$, the first two of which are nonabelian. We can immediately eliminate C_8 because it has an element of order eight. From the character table

	1	1	2	2	2	
Γ_1	1	1	1	1	1	
Γ_2	1	1	1	−1	−1	
Γ_3	1	1	−1	1	−1	Q
Γ_4	1	1	−1	−1	1	
Γ_5	2	−2	0	0	0	

of Q we see that any representation composed of three 1-dimensional representations will have $\chi_1 = \chi_2 = 3$ so $D_1 = D_2 = I$ and the representation will be unfaithful. But if a 3-dimensional representation contains Γ_5 it can not be real (since Γ_5 is of second kind). Hence Q is out. The group $C_4 \times C_2$ requires more detailed consideration; its character table is

	C_1	C_2	C_3	C_4	C_5	C_6	C_7	C_8	
	1	1	1	1	1	1	1	1	
Γ_1	1	1	1	1	1	1	1	1	
Γ_2	1	−1	1	−1	1	−1	1	−1	
Γ_3	1	i	−1	$-i$	1	i	−1	$-i$	
Γ_4	1	$-i$	−1	i	1	$-i$	−1	i	$C_4 \times C_2$
Γ_5	1	1	1	1	−1	−1	−1	−1	
Γ_6	1	−1	1	−1	−1	1	−1	1	
Γ_7	1	i	−1	$-i$	−1	$-i$	1	i	
Γ_8	1	$-i$	−1	i	−1	i	1	$-i$	

The three 1-dimensional representations composing an acceptable 3-dimensional representation Γ can not all come from the first four because we would have $\chi_5^{(\Gamma)} = 3$, so Γ would be unfaithful (C_5 would be in the kernel of Γ). Likewise the three components can not all come from the last four because we would have $\chi_5^{(\Gamma)} = -3$, which is prohibited. Thus the three 1-dimensional components must be split among the two sets of four with two in one and one in the other. We can not have two from the first set because then we would have $\det(D_5) = -1$. If Γ contains two from the second set they must either be Γ_5 and Γ_6 or Γ_7 and Γ_8 in order for Γ to be real. In the first case $\chi_3^{(\Gamma)} = 3$, and in the second case $\chi_7^{(\Gamma)} = 3$, so these possibilities are ruled out. Hence, $C_4 \times C_2$ is out. The character table for $D_2 \times C_2$ is

	C_1	C_2	C_3	C_4	C_5	C_6	C_7	C_8	
	1	1	1	1	1	1	1	1	
Γ_1	1	1	1	1	1	1	1	1	
Γ_2	1	1	−1	−1	1	1	−1	−1	
Γ_3	1	−1	1	−1	1	−1	1	−1	
Γ_4	1	−1	−1	1	1	−1	−1	1	$D_2 \times C_2$
Γ_5	1	1	1	1	−1	−1	−1	−1	
Γ_6	1	1	−1	−1	−1	−1	1	1	
Γ_7	1	−1	1	−1	−1	1	−1	1	
Γ_8	1	−1	−1	1	−1	1	1	−1	

This group can be analyzed in very much the same way as $C_4 \times C_2$ and can also be ruled out. We are left with only the dihedral group D_4, which, as we shall see, is acceptable.

The group D_4 has the same character table as Q, but because the multiplication tables are different the irreducible 2-dimensional representation of D_4 is real rather than of second kind. Consequently, as can be seen easily from the character table, any of the 1-dimensional representations of D_4 can be added to Γ_5 to give a real faithful representation. The multiplication table is

1	2	3	4	5	6	7	8	
2	1	4	3	6	5	8	7	
3	4	2	1	7	8	6	5	
4	3	1	2	8	7	5	6	
5	6	8	7	1	2	4	3	D_4
6	5	7	8	2	1	3	4	
7	8	5	6	3	4	1	2	
8	7	6	5	4	3	2	1	

The classes are

$$C_1 = A_1; \quad C_2 = A_2; \quad C_3 = A_3, A_4; \quad C_4 = A_5, A_6; \quad C_5 = A_7, A_8;$$

and the character table is

	C_1	C_2	C_3	C_4	C_5	
	1	1	2	2	2	
Γ_1	1	1	1	1	1	
Γ_2	1	1	1	−1	−1	
Γ_3	1	1	−1	1	−1	D_4
Γ_4	1	1	−1	−1	1	
Γ_5	2	−2	0	0	0	

Consider $\Gamma = \Gamma_1 \oplus \Gamma_5$ which has the character $\chi^{(\Gamma)} = (3,-1,1,1,1)$. Then $\det(D_5) = (1/6)(1^3 - 3 \times 1 \times 3 + 2 \times 1) = -6/6 = -1$, so $\Gamma_1 \oplus \Gamma_5$ is out. Similarly, $\Gamma_3 \oplus \Gamma_5$ has $\det(D_5) = -1$, and $\Gamma_4 \oplus \Gamma_5$ has $\det(D_7) = -1$. Hence, only $\Gamma_2 \oplus \Gamma_5$ remains, and this representation satisfies all the requirements. This point group is called D_4, the same as the abstract point group.

Applying this technique to all 32 nonisomorphic abstract groups we find that 11 of them satisfy the requirements of point groups of the first kind. These 11 nonisomorphic abstract point groups of the first kind are: $C_1, C_2, C_3, C_4, D_2, C_6, D_3, D_4, D_6, T$, and 0.

Let us consider now the abstract point groups of second kind. Since the subgroup of rotations of a point group of second kind has index 2, it follows that the possible orders of point groups of second kind are twice those of first kind. Thus the possible orders are

$$g = 2, 4, 6, 8, 12, 24, 48. \tag{4:4.7}$$

The table of groups (Chapter I) shows that there are 96 nonisomorphic groups of these orders. Let us for convenience divide point groups of the second kind into those which contain the inversion $-I$, and those which do not.

If we consider a group G containing the inversion, and let H be the subgroup of rotations, then we can write (using a set-theoretic sum)

$$G = H + (-I)H \tag{4:4.8}$$

as a coset decomposition of G. Since H is a normal subgroup it is easily seen that

$$G = H \times C_2 \tag{4:4.9}$$

(where equals means "isomorphic to"). Since H is a point group of first kind we can now get all abstract point groups of second kind belonging to point groups containing the inversion. There are 11 such nonisomorphic abstract point groups, and they are

$$C_1 \times C_2 = C_2, \quad C_2 \times C_2 = D_2, \quad C_3 \times C_2 = C_6, \quad C_4 \times C_2,$$
$$D_2 \times C_2, \quad C_6 \times C_2, \quad D_3 \times C_2 = D_6, \quad D_4 \times C_2, \quad D_6 \times C_2, \quad T \times C_2,$$

and $0 \times C_2$. Four of these were abstract point groups of first kind, so only seven are new. These are $C_4 \times C_2$, $D_2 \times C_2$, $C_6 \times C_2$, $D_4 \times C_2$, $D_6 \times C_2$, $T \times C_2$ and $0 \times C_2$. We now have a total of 18 non-isomorphic point groups.

Let G be a point group of second kind without inversion, H the subgroup of all rotations, and K the coset of H. Then

$$G = H + K \tag{4:4.10}$$

Let us define a new set G' by replacing each element of K by its negative, so

$$G' \equiv H + (-K). \tag{4:4.11}$$

If k is an element of K then $\det(-k) = 1$, so $-k$ is a rotation. Also, $-k$ is not in H because if it were, $(-k)(k^{-1}) = -I$ would be in G, which it is not. Hence all elements of G' are distinct. Further, G' is a group which is isomorphic to G under the correspondence $h \leftrightarrow h\ k \leftrightarrow -k(h \in H)$. Also, if k leaves a lattice invariant, so does $-k$, so that G' is also a point group. Hence we can conclude that every point group of second kind which does not contain the inversion is isomorphic to a point group of first kind. Therefore this set of point groups contributes no new abstract point groups.

We can now conclude that there are 18 nonisomorphic abstract point groups. These are C_1, C_2, C_3, C_4, D_2, C_6, D_3, D_4, $C_4 \times C_2$, $D_2 \times C_2$, D_6, T, $C_6 \times C_2$, $D_4 \times C_2$, D, $D_6 \times C_2$, $T \times C_2$, and $0 \times C_2$. Thus every divisor of 48 is the order of at least one point group. Also, the character table of every point group can be easily written down from the previously given character tables of the groups C_n, D_n, T, and O. Since these groups all have order less than 60 they are all solvable. Also it may be noted that only two have odd order, C_1 and C_3. Also, every irreducible representation of dimension greater than one of these 18 abstract point groups is real.

So far we have only the abstract point groups and not the point groups themselves. We can find the characters of the point groups from the characters of the abstract point groups by simply constructing the characters of all representations which (1) are 3-dimensional, (2) are real, (3) are faithful, and (4) have integral characters. We must also identify two representations if they differ only by an ordering of the matrices (plus perhaps an equivalence transformation). The reason for this is that a point group is defined as a matrix group in which order does not matter, and not as a representation.

Let us illustrate the procedure by considering the dihedral group D_4 (see the character table given earlier). We already know that $\Gamma_2 \oplus \Gamma_5$ is a point group of first kind. The only other faithful 3-dimensional representations are $\Gamma_1 \oplus \Gamma_5$, $\Gamma_3 \oplus \Gamma_5$, and $\Gamma_4 \oplus \Gamma_5$, which have the characters $(3, -1, 1, 1, 1)$, $(3, -1, -1, 1, -1)$ and $(3, -1, -1, -1, 1)$. These characters satisfy all of the above requirements. Clearly $\Gamma_1 \oplus \Gamma_5$ is different from the other point groups, but since the characters of $\Gamma_3 \oplus \Gamma_5$ and $\Gamma_4 \oplus \Gamma_5$ have the same values (except for order) these two point groups may be the same. In fact, we can easily verify that the following correspondence is an automorphism of D_4:

$$\begin{array}{cccc} 1 \to 1 & 2 \to 2 & 3 \to 3 & 4 \to 4 \\ 5 \to 8 & 6 \to 7 & 7 \to 5 & 8 \to 6. \end{array}$$

Consequently, we can renumber the matrices of $\Gamma_3 \oplus \Gamma_5$ according to this scheme and still have a representation of D_4. But the character of the renumbered representation is just the character of $\Gamma_4 \oplus \Gamma_5$; hence, $\Gamma_3 \oplus \Gamma_5$

and $\Gamma_4 \oplus \Gamma_5$ differ from each other only by the ordering of the matrices (i.e., by an automorphism) and are therefore the same point group. Consequently there are only three different point groups which are isomorphic to D_4. These are $D_4 = \Gamma_2 \oplus \Gamma_5$, $C_{4v} = \Gamma_1 \oplus \Gamma_5$, and $D_{2v} = \Gamma_3 \oplus \Gamma_5$.

Proceeding in this way we find that there are 32 nonequivalent point groups. Following is a table of abstract point groups together with the corresponding point groups of various kinds.

Order	*Abstract Point Group*	*First Kind*	*Second Kind with Inversion*	*Second Kind without Inversion*
1	C_1	C_1		
2	C_2	C_2	S_2	S_1
3	C_3	C_3		
4	C_4	C_4		S_4
4	D_2	D_2	C_{2h}	C_{2v}
6	C_6	C_6	S_6	C_{3h}
6	D_3	D_3		C_{3v}
8	D_4	D_4		C_{4v}, D_{2v}
8	$C_4 \times C_2$		C_{4h}	
8	$D_2 \times C_2$		D_{2h}	
12	D_6	D_6	D_{3v}	C_{6v}, D_{3h}
12	T	T		
12	$C_6 \times C_2$		C_{6h}	
16	$D_4 \times C_2$		D_{4h}	
24	O	O		T_v
24	$D_6 \times C_2$		D_{6h}	
24	$T \times C_2$		T_h	
48	$O \times C_2$		O_h	

(a point group is of first kind if all elements are rotations, and of second kind otherwise).

Following are some alternative symbols for the 32 point groups:

$C_1 = A = 1C$; $C_2 = B = 2C$; $S_2 = \bar{C}_2 = C_i = c_1 = a = 1Ci$;
$S_1 = S = C_{1h} = C_S = \bar{C}_1 = c_2 = b = 2c$;
$C_3 = E = 3C$; $C_4 = D = 4C$; $S_4 = \bar{C}_2 = c_4 = d = 4c$;
$D_2 = V = Q = C = 2D$; $C_{2h} = \Gamma_2 = B_a = 2Ci$; $C_{2v} = \delta_2 = c = 2e$;
$C_6 = F = 6C$; $S_6 = \bar{C}_3 = C3_i = \Gamma_3 = e = 3Ci$; $C_{3h} = S_3 = c_6 = f = 6c$;
$D_3 = EB = 3D$; $C_{3v} = \delta_3 = E_b = 3e$; $D_4 = DB = 4D$;
$C_{4v} = \delta_4 = D_b = 4e$; $D_{2v} = D_{2d} = V_d = Q_d = d_4 = dB = 4d$;
$C_{4h} = \Gamma_4 = D_a = 4Ci$; $D_{2h} = V_h = Q_h = \Delta = C_a = 2Di$;
$D_6 = FB = 6D$; $D_{3v} = D_{3i} = D_{3d} = \Delta_3 = 3B = 3Di$;

$C_{6v} = \delta_6 = F_b = 6e$; $D_{3h} = d_6 = fB = 6d$;
$C_{6h} = \Gamma_6 = F_a = 6Ci$; $D_{4h} = \Delta_4 = de = 4Di$; $T_v = T_d = \theta = T_b = Te$;
$D_{6h} = \Delta_6 = fC = 6Di$; $T_h = \Theta = T_a = Ti$; $O_h = \Omega = O_a = Oi$.

Next we give a table of generating matrices of the 32 point groups together with the number of irreducible components of each.

Point Group	*Generators*	*Number of Irreducible Components*
C_1	$\begin{pmatrix} 1 & 0 & 0 \\ 0 & 1 & 0 \\ 0 & 0 & 1 \end{pmatrix}$	3
C_2	$\begin{pmatrix} 1 & 0 & 0 \\ 0 & -1 & 0 \\ 0 & 0 & -1 \end{pmatrix}$	3
S_2	$\begin{pmatrix} -1 & 0 & 0 \\ 0 & -1 & 0 \\ 0 & 0 & -1 \end{pmatrix}$	3
S_1	$\begin{pmatrix} -1 & 0 & 0 \\ 0 & 1 & 0 \\ 0 & 0 & 1 \end{pmatrix}$	3
C_3	$\begin{pmatrix} 1 & 0 & 0 \\ 0 & -\frac{1}{2} & -\frac{1}{2}\sqrt{3} \\ 0 & \frac{1}{2}\sqrt{3} & -\frac{1}{2} \end{pmatrix}$	3
C_4	$\begin{pmatrix} 1 & 0 & 0 \\ 0 & 0 & -1 \\ 0 & 1 & 0 \end{pmatrix}$	3
S_4	$\begin{pmatrix} -1 & 0 & 0 \\ 0 & 0 & -1 \\ 0 & 1 & 0 \end{pmatrix}$	3
D_2	$\begin{pmatrix} 1 & 0 & 0 \\ 0 & -1 & 0 \\ 0 & 0 & -1 \end{pmatrix} \begin{pmatrix} -1 & 0 & 0 \\ 0 & 1 & 0 \\ 0 & 0 & -1 \end{pmatrix}$	3
C_{2h}	$\begin{pmatrix} -1 & 0 & 0 \\ 0 & -1 & 0 \\ 0 & 0 & -1 \end{pmatrix} \begin{pmatrix} -1 & 0 & 0 \\ 0 & 1 & 0 \\ 0 & 0 & 1 \end{pmatrix}$	3
C_{2v}	$\begin{pmatrix} 1 & 0 & 0 \\ 0 & -1 & 0 \\ 0 & 0 & -1 \end{pmatrix} \begin{pmatrix} 1 & 0 & 0 \\ 0 & -1 & 0 \\ 0 & 0 & 1 \end{pmatrix}$	3

Point Group	*Generators*	*Number of Irreducible Components*
C_6	$\begin{pmatrix} 1 & 0 & 0 \\ 0 & \frac{1}{2} & -\frac{1}{2}\sqrt{3} \\ 0 & \frac{1}{2}\sqrt{3} & \frac{1}{2} \end{pmatrix}$	3
S_6	$\begin{pmatrix} -1 & 0 & 0 \\ 0 & \frac{1}{2} & -\frac{1}{2}\sqrt{3} \\ 0 & \frac{1}{2}\sqrt{3} & \frac{1}{2} \end{pmatrix}$	3
C_{3h}	$\begin{pmatrix} -1 & 0 & 0 \\ 0 & -\frac{1}{2} & -\frac{1}{2}\sqrt{3} \\ 0 & \frac{1}{2}\sqrt{3} & -\frac{1}{2} \end{pmatrix}$	3
D_3	$\begin{pmatrix} 1 & 0 & 0 \\ 0 & -\frac{1}{2} & -\frac{1}{2}\sqrt{3} \\ 0 & \frac{1}{2}\sqrt{3} & -\frac{1}{2} \end{pmatrix} \begin{pmatrix} -1 & 0 & 0 \\ 0 & 1 & 0 \\ 0 & 0 & -1 \end{pmatrix}$	2
C_{3v}	$\begin{pmatrix} 1 & 0 & 0 \\ 0 & -\frac{1}{2} & -\frac{1}{2}\sqrt{3} \\ 0 & \frac{1}{2}\sqrt{3} & -\frac{1}{2} \end{pmatrix} \begin{pmatrix} 1 & 0 & 0 \\ 0 & -1 & 0 \\ 0 & 0 & 1 \end{pmatrix}$	2
D_4	$\begin{pmatrix} 1 & 0 & 0 \\ 0 & 0 & -1 \\ 0 & 1 & 0 \end{pmatrix} \begin{pmatrix} -1 & 0 & 0 \\ 0 & -1 & 0 \\ 0 & 0 & 1 \end{pmatrix}$	2
C_{4v}	$\begin{pmatrix} 1 & 0 & 0 \\ 0 & 0 & -1 \\ 0 & 1 & 0 \end{pmatrix} \begin{pmatrix} 1 & 0 & 0 \\ 0 & -1 & 0 \\ 0 & 0 & 1 \end{pmatrix}$	2
D_{2v}	$\begin{pmatrix} -1 & 0 & 0 \\ 0 & 0 & -1 \\ 0 & 1 & 0 \end{pmatrix} \begin{pmatrix} 1 & 0 & 0 \\ 0 & -1 & 0 \\ 0 & 0 & 1 \end{pmatrix}$	2
C_{4h}	$\begin{pmatrix} 1 & 0 & 0 \\ 0 & 0 & -1 \\ 0 & 1 & 0 \end{pmatrix} \begin{pmatrix} -1 & 0 & 0 \\ 0 & 1 & 0 \\ 0 & 0 & 1 \end{pmatrix}$	3
D_{2h}	$\begin{pmatrix} 1 & 0 & 0 \\ 0 & -1 & 0 \\ 0 & 0 & -1 \end{pmatrix} \begin{pmatrix} -1 & 0 & 0 \\ 0 & 1 & 0 \\ 0 & 0 & -1 \end{pmatrix} \begin{pmatrix} -1 & 0 & 0 \\ 0 & -1 & 0 \\ 0 & 0 & -1 \end{pmatrix}$	3
D_6	$\begin{pmatrix} 1 & 0 & 0 \\ 0 & \frac{1}{2} & -\frac{1}{2}\sqrt{3} \\ 0 & \frac{1}{2}\sqrt{3} & \frac{1}{2} \end{pmatrix} \begin{pmatrix} -1 & 0 & 0 \\ 0 & -1 & 0 \\ 0 & 0 & 1 \end{pmatrix}$	2
D_{3v}	$\begin{pmatrix} -1 & 0 & 0 \\ 0 & \frac{1}{2} & -\frac{1}{2}\sqrt{3} \\ 0 & \frac{1}{2}\sqrt{3} & \frac{1}{2} \end{pmatrix} \begin{pmatrix} 1 & 0 & 0 \\ 0 & -1 & 0 \\ 0 & 0 & 1 \end{pmatrix}$	2

Point Group	*Generators*	*Number of Irreducible Components*
C_{6v}	$\begin{pmatrix} 1 & 0 & 0 \\ 0 & \frac{1}{2} & -\frac{1}{2}\sqrt{3} \\ 0 & \frac{1}{2}\sqrt{3} & \frac{1}{2} \end{pmatrix} \begin{pmatrix} 1 & 0 & 0 \\ 0 & -1 & 0 \\ 0 & 0 & 1 \end{pmatrix}$	2
D_{3h}	$\begin{pmatrix} -1 & 0 & 0 \\ 0 & -\frac{1}{2} & -\frac{1}{2}\sqrt{3} \\ 0 & \frac{1}{2}\sqrt{3} & -\frac{1}{2} \end{pmatrix} \begin{pmatrix} -1 & 0 & 0 \\ 0 & 1 & 0 \\ 0 & 0 & -1 \end{pmatrix}$	2
T	$\begin{pmatrix} 1 & 0 & 0 \\ 0 & -1 & 0 \\ 0 & 0 & -1 \end{pmatrix} \begin{pmatrix} 0 & 0 & 1 \\ 1 & 0 & 0 \\ 0 & 1 & 0 \end{pmatrix}$	1
C_{6h}	$\begin{pmatrix} 1 & 0 & 0 \\ 0 & \frac{1}{2} & -\frac{1}{2}\sqrt{3} \\ 0 & \frac{1}{2}\sqrt{3} & \frac{1}{2} \end{pmatrix} \begin{pmatrix} -1 & 0 & 0 \\ 0 & 1 & 0 \\ 0 & 0 & 1 \end{pmatrix}$	3
D_{4h}	$\begin{pmatrix} 1 & 0 & 0 \\ 0 & 0 & -1 \\ 0 & 1 & 0 \end{pmatrix} \begin{pmatrix} -1 & 0 & 0 \\ 0 & -1 & 0 \\ 0 & 0 & -1 \end{pmatrix}$	2
O	$\begin{pmatrix} 1 & 0 & 0 \\ 0 & 0 & 1 \\ 0 & -1 & 0 \end{pmatrix} \begin{pmatrix} 0 & 0 & 1 \\ 1 & 0 & 0 \\ 0 & 1 & 0 \end{pmatrix}$	1
T_v	$\begin{pmatrix} 1 & 0 & 0 \\ 0 & 0 & -1 \\ 0 & -1 & 0 \end{pmatrix} \begin{pmatrix} 1 & 0 & 0 \\ 0 & -1 & 0 \\ 0 & 0 & -1 \end{pmatrix} \begin{pmatrix} 0 & 0 & 1 \\ 1 & 0 & 0 \\ 0 & 1 & 0 \end{pmatrix}$	1
D_{6h}	$\begin{pmatrix} 1 & 0 & 0 \\ 0 & \frac{1}{2} & -\frac{1}{2}\sqrt{3} \\ 0 & \frac{1}{2}\sqrt{3} & \frac{1}{2} \end{pmatrix} \begin{pmatrix} -1 & 0 & 0 \\ 0 & 1 & 0 \\ 0 & 0 & 1 \end{pmatrix} \begin{pmatrix} 1 & 0 & 0 \\ 0 & -1 & 0 \\ 0 & 0 & 1 \end{pmatrix}$	2
T_h	$\begin{pmatrix} -1 & 0 & 0 \\ 0 & 1 & 0 \\ 0 & 0 & 1 \end{pmatrix} \begin{pmatrix} 1 & 0 & 0 \\ 0 & -1 & 0 \\ 0 & 0 & -1 \end{pmatrix} \begin{pmatrix} 0 & 0 & 1 \\ 1 & 0 & 0 \\ 0 & 1 & 0 \end{pmatrix}$	1
O_h	$\begin{pmatrix} 1 & 0 & 0 \\ 0 & 0 & 1 \\ 0 & -1 & 0 \end{pmatrix} \begin{pmatrix} 0 & 0 & 1 \\ 1 & 0 & 0 \\ 0 & 1 & 0 \end{pmatrix} \begin{pmatrix} -1 & 0 & 0 \\ 0 & -1 & 0 \\ 0 & 0 & -1 \end{pmatrix}$	1

From the matrices of a point group one can deduce a geometrical interpretation of the group. For example, D_4 is generated by a 90° rotation around the x-axis plus a 180° rotation around the z-axis.

The careful reader will have noted that we have not proved that any of the above 32 groups is a point group; all we have proved is that there are no other point groups. To prove that these actually are point groups we must show that each one really does leave some lattice invariant. We will do this in a later section on lattices.

Let L be any 3-dimensional lattice, and let G be the set of all 3-dimensional orthogonal matrices which leave L invariant. Then G is a point group, and it is called the holohedry of L. It turns out that only seven of the 32 point groups can be holohedry of any lattice. These seven are S_2, C_{2h}, D_{2h}, D_{3v}, D_{4h}, D_{6h}, and O_h. Since every point group is a subgroup of at least one of these seven holohedry, we can classify the point groups into seven crystallographic systems. More precisely, we associate with each holohedry all point groups which are subgroups of it but of no holohedry of lower order.

System	*Number of Point Groups*	*Point Groups*
Triclinic	2	S_2, C_1
Monoclinic	3	C_{2h}, C_2, S_1
Rhombic	3	D_{2h}, D_2, C_{2v}
Trigonal	5	D_{3v}, D_3, C_{3v}, S_6, C_3
Tetragonal	7	D_{4h}, C_{4h}, D_{2v}, C_{4v}, D_4, S_4, C_4
Hexagonal	7	D_{6h}, C_{6h}, D_{3h}, C_{6v}, D_6, C_{3h}, C_6
Cubic	5	O_h, T_h, T_v, O, T

The crystal systems also have alternative names: triclinic = anorthic, rhombic = orthorhombic = viergruppe, trigonal = rhombohedral, tetragonal = quadratic, cubic = tesseral = regular = isometric.

Example. Let us find the point group of a simple crystal, and for ease of visualization let us choose a 2-dimensional crystal. Graphite is known to crystallize in a layer structure, so let us choose one such layer as our 2-dimensional crystal. The carbon atoms of such a layer are arranged in a hexagonal array. By a Bravais lattice of a crystal let us mean a lattice which partitions the crystal into identical parallelogram-shaped regions, and which is not a sublattice of any lattice that performs such a partition. The parallelogram-shaped regions are called Bravais unit cells (in three dimensions they are parallelopipeds). A unit cell is clearly just a fundamental region of a lattice, if the lattice is considered as a transformation group of translations (some detailed consideration of the boundary points of the unit cell is also required). From the illustration on the next page it will be seen that 2-dimensional graphite has two carbon atoms per unit cell.

If the length of a hexagon side is called s ($s = 1{\cdot}42\mathring{A}$) then the unit cell sides have length $s\sqrt{3}$. The angles of the unit cell are 60° and 120°. By inspection it can now be seen that a 60° rotation about a lattice point (vertex of a unit cell) carries every lattice point into another lattice point (but not cell sides into cell sides). Also, a reflection through a line through the lattice

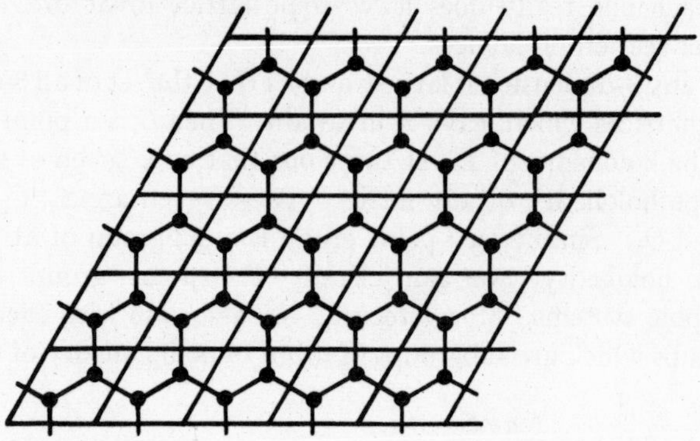

point and perpendicular to a hexagon side or through a hexagon vertex carries lattice points into lattice points. These transformations also carry atoms into atoms. Consequently the point group is the symmetry group of the hexagon D_6. However, the matrices of this D_6 are 2-dimensional so it is not the same as the 3-dimensional point group D_6, although the two are isomorphic. The 2-dimensional D_6 is just the 2-dimensional component of the 3-dimensional D_6. The generators are:

$$\begin{pmatrix} \frac{1}{2} & -\frac{1}{2}\sqrt{3} \\ \frac{1}{2}\sqrt{3} & \frac{1}{2} \end{pmatrix} \begin{pmatrix} -1 & 0 \\ 0 & 1 \end{pmatrix}$$

In this case it was implicitly assumed that the point group of a crystal is the set of all orthogonal transformations about a lattice point which transform not only the lattice into itself but also the crystal into itself. This definition of point groups is valid, however, only for certain "simple" types of crystals (see Section **13** where the more general definition in terms of space groups will be given).

It might be noted that the point group of any kind of crystal can in principle be determined by optical goniometer measurements. Since these are external macroscopic measurements, point group symmetry is sometimes referred to as macroscopic symmetry.

Finally, some tables will be given. As will be discussed in Section **6**, the 3-dimensional rotation group $R(3)$ has exactly one faithful irreducible representation of each odd dimension from one to infinity (excluding infinity). If we designate the irreducible $(2l + 1) -$ dimensional representation by Γ_l, then since every point group of the first kind is a subgroup of $R(3)$, it follows that Γ_l will subduce a representation of every point group which contains only rotations. The problem then is to decompose such a subduced representation of a point group into irreducible representations of the point group. Let us designate the representation of a point group subduced by Γ_l by Γ_l also, and the irreducible representations of the point groups by $\Delta_1, \Delta_2, \ldots, \Delta_r$ (with the same numbering as in the character tables in Chapter III). The reductions for the nonabelian point groups are as follows.

D_3:

	C_1 1	C_2 2	C_3 3
Δ_1	1	1	1
Δ_2	1	1	-1
Δ_3	2	-1	0

$$\Gamma_0 = \Delta_1$$
$$\Gamma_1 = \Delta_2 \oplus \Delta_3$$
$$\Gamma_2 = \Delta_1 \oplus 2\Delta_3$$
$$\Gamma_3 = \Delta_1 \oplus 2\Delta_2 \oplus 2\Delta_3$$
$$\Gamma_4 = 2\Delta_1 \oplus \Delta_2 \oplus 3\Delta_3$$
$$\Gamma_5 = \Delta_1 \oplus 2\Delta_2 \oplus 4\Delta_3$$
$$\Gamma_l = \Gamma_{l-6} \oplus 2(\Delta_1 \oplus \Delta_2 \oplus 2\Delta_3) \ (l = 6, 7, 8, \ldots)$$

D_4:
$$\Gamma_0 = \Delta_1$$
$$\Gamma_1 = \Delta_2 \oplus \Delta_5$$
$$\Gamma_2 = \Delta_1 \oplus \Delta_3 \oplus \Delta_4 \oplus \Delta_5$$
$$\Gamma_3 = \Delta_2 \oplus \Delta_3 \oplus \Delta_4 \oplus 2\Delta_5$$
$$\Gamma_{4\lambda+k} = \Gamma_k + \lambda(\Delta_1 \oplus \Delta_2 \oplus \Delta_3 \oplus \Delta_4 \oplus 2\Delta_5) \begin{pmatrix} k = 0, 1, 2, 3 \\ \lambda = 0, 1, 2, \ldots \end{pmatrix}$$

D_6:

	C_1 1	C_2 1	C_3 2	C_4 2	C_5 3	C_6 3
Δ_1	1	1	1	1	1	1
Δ_2	1	1	1	1	-1	-1
Δ_3	1	-1	1	-1	1	-1
Δ_4	1	-1	1	-1	-1	1
Δ_5	2	2	-1	-1	0	0
Δ_6	2	-2	-1	1	0	0

$$\Gamma_0 = \Delta_1$$
$$\Gamma_1 = \Delta_2 \oplus \Delta_6$$
$$\Gamma_2 = \Delta_1 \oplus \Delta_5 \oplus \Delta_6$$
$$\Gamma_3 = \Delta_2 \oplus \Delta_3 \oplus \Delta_4 \oplus \Delta_5 \oplus \Delta_6$$
$$\Gamma_4 = \Delta_1 \oplus \Delta_3 \oplus \Delta_4 \oplus 2\Delta_5 \oplus \Delta_6$$
$$\Gamma_5 = \Delta_2 \oplus \Delta_3 \oplus \Delta_4 \oplus 2\Delta_5 \oplus 2\Delta_6$$
$$\Gamma_{6\lambda+k} = \Gamma_k \oplus \lambda(\Delta_1 \oplus \Delta_2 \oplus \Delta_3 \oplus \Delta_4 \oplus 2\Delta_5 \oplus 2\Delta_6) \begin{pmatrix} k = 0, \ldots, 5 \\ \lambda = 0, 1, 2, \ldots \end{pmatrix}$$

$$T\colon\quad \begin{aligned} &\Gamma_0 = \Delta_1\\ &\Gamma_1 = \Delta_4\\ &\Gamma_2 = \Delta_2 \oplus \Delta_3 \oplus \Delta_4\\ &\Gamma_3 = \Delta_1 \oplus 2\Delta_4\\ &\Gamma_4 = \Delta_1 \oplus \Delta_2 \oplus \Delta_3 \oplus 2\Delta_4\\ &\Gamma_5 = \Delta_2 \oplus \Delta_3 \oplus 3\Delta_4\\ &\Gamma_{6\lambda+k} = \Gamma_k \oplus \lambda(\Delta_1 \oplus \Delta_2 \oplus \Delta_3 \oplus 3\Delta_4) \begin{pmatrix} k = 0,\ldots,5 \\ \lambda = 0,1,2,\ldots \end{pmatrix} \end{aligned}$$

$$O\colon\quad \begin{aligned} &\Gamma_0 = \Delta_1\\ &\Gamma_1 = \Delta_5\\ &\Gamma_2 = \Delta_3 \oplus \Delta_4\\ &\Gamma_3 = \Delta_2 \oplus \Delta_4 \oplus \Delta_5\\ &\Gamma_4 = \Delta_1 \oplus \Delta_3 \oplus \Delta_4 \oplus \Delta_5\\ &\Gamma_5 = \Delta_3 \oplus \Delta_4 \oplus 2\Delta_5\\ &\Gamma_{5+k'} \oplus \Gamma_{6-k'} = \Delta_1 \oplus \Delta_2 \oplus 2\Delta_3 \oplus 3\Delta_4 \oplus 3\Delta_5 \; (k' = 1,\ldots,6)\\ &\Gamma_{12\lambda+k} = \Gamma_k \oplus \lambda(\Delta_1 \oplus \Delta_2 \oplus 2\Delta_3 \oplus 3\Delta_4 \oplus 3\Delta_5 \begin{pmatrix} k = 0,\ldots,11 \\ \lambda = 0,1,2,\ldots \end{pmatrix}. \end{aligned}$$

5. Proportionality Tensors in Crystals

Frequently two physical observables in a crystal are related by a proportionality "tensor," as for example the electric field strength vector $\mathbf{E}(\mathbf{r}, t)$ and the electric displacement vector $\mathbf{D}(\mathbf{r}, t)$ are related by the dielectric tensor (or dyadic)

$$\mathbf{D}(\mathbf{r}, t) = \epsilon(\mathbf{r}, t)\cdot\mathbf{E}(\mathbf{r}, t). \tag{4:5.1}$$

If the crystal is homogeneous then ϵ is independent of $\mathbf{r}$.

In general, let $S(\mathbf{r}, t)$ be an n-component observable which is linearly related to an m-component observable $\sigma(\mathbf{r}, t)$ at each space-time point $(\mathbf{r}, t)$ by a set of mn coefficients $C(\mathbf{r}, t)$. Let us assume that C is independent of $\mathbf{r}$, and consider $S(\mathbf{r}, t)$ and $\sigma(\mathbf{r}, t)$ to be written as column matrices so we have

$$S(\mathbf{r}, t) = C(t)\sigma(\mathbf{r}, t), \tag{4:5.2}$$

where $C(t)$ is an n by m matrix. Since the time dependence of these quantities will not interest us we shall omit the argument t from now on.

The problem which will be treated in this Section (16, 63, 65, 87, 95, 152, 167, 176) is that of determining how the symmetry of a crystal restricts the possible number of independent components of a proportionality "tensor" C. By the number of independent components of C we shall mean the number of constants required to specify C. In the absence of any further knowledge about C the number of independent components will be mn. In many cases, however, C possesses some symmetry properties which are independent of the symmetry of the crystal. Thus the dielectric tensor is always symmetric, $\epsilon^t = \epsilon$.

As a preliminary, let us investigate the effect of linear (alias) coordinate transformations on C. Let

$$\mathbf{r}' = T\mathbf{r} \tag{4:5.3}$$

and assume $S(\mathbf{r})$ and $\sigma(\mathbf{r})$ are tensors so

$$S'(\mathbf{r}') = PS(\mathbf{r}) \tag{4:5.3a}$$

$$\sigma'(\mathbf{r}') = R\sigma(\mathbf{r}). \tag{4:5.3b}$$

By assumption

$$S'(\mathbf{r}') = C'\sigma'(\mathbf{r}'), \tag{4:5.4}$$

so we obtain

$$C' = PCR^{-1}. \tag{4:5.5}$$

Since this is a linear transformation of C, we see that C really is a tensor. If we put the elements of C in a column matrix γ (in suitable order), then (4:5.5) can be written

$$\gamma' = Q\gamma, \tag{4:5.6}$$

where

$$Q = P \otimes R^{-1t}. \tag{4:5.6a}$$

The matrices $Q(T)$ form a representation Γ of the group G of 3-dimensional matrices T. If some symmetry of C is known at the beginning, then we shall select the independent components and call the corresponding column matrix γ_0. From (4:5.6) we can find the transformation matrix Q_0 of γ_0

$$\gamma_0' = Q_0\gamma_0. \tag{4:5.7}$$

The Q_0's form a representation Γ_0 of G.

We can now consider the effect of crystal symmetry on γ_0. If G is the point group of the crystal then for a large class of proportionality tensors we will have

$$\gamma_0' = \gamma_0 \tag{4:5.8}$$

for all T in G. In this case γ_0 will be an invariant vector of Γ_0. But the number of linearly independent invariant vectors of Γ_0 is just equal to the number of times Γ_0 contains the trivial representation. Since every invariant vector is a linear combination of such a set of independent invariant vectors, it follows that the number of constants required to specify any invariant vector is just equal to the number of times Γ_0 contains the trivial representation. Hence, if we let N_0 be the number of independent components of γ_0, we have

$$N_0 = \frac{1}{g}\sum_{i=1}^{r} r_i \chi_i^{(\Gamma_0)}, \tag{4:5.9}$$

where g is the order of the point group G, and $\chi^{(\Gamma_0)}$ is the character of the representation Γ_0. If C possesses no inherent symmetry, then

$$\Gamma_0 = \Gamma = \{P \otimes R^{-1t}\}.$$

Example. Let us consider a crystal such as hydrogen peroxide, H_2O_2, which has the point group D_4, and compute the maximum number of independent components of the dielectric tensor ϵ. The dielectric tensor ϵ is a symmetric second-order tensor, so the independent components generate the representation of the point group D_4 which is the symmetrized Kronecker square of D_4. Referring to the character table of D_4 in the preceding section, we see that we want the character of the symmetrized Kronecker square of $\Gamma_2 \oplus \Gamma_5$. Using the formula

$$\text{tr}\,(D_{(2)}) = \tfrac{1}{2}[\text{tr}\,(D^2) + \text{tr}^2\,(D)] \tag{4:5.10}$$

of Chapter I for the symmetrized Kronecker squares together with the multiplication table for D_4, we find that the character of $(\Gamma_2 \oplus \Gamma_5)_{(2)}$ is $\chi = (6, 2, 0, 2, 2)$. Hence

$$N_0 = \tfrac{1}{8}(1 \times 6 + 1 \times 2 + 2 \times 0 + 2 \times 2 + 2 \times 2) = \tfrac{16}{8} = 2,$$

so the dielectric tensor can be specified by two constants.

Example. Let us now compute the number of independent components of the elasticity tensor of hydrogen peroxide.

The elasticity tensor connects the stress and strain tensors, both of which are symmetric second rank tensors. Hence these tensors transform according to the symmetrized square of $\Gamma_2 \oplus \Gamma_5$. Thus $P = R = T_{(2)}$. But the elasticity tensor is symmetric so it transforms according to the symmetrized square of $T_{(2)}$. Hence, the representation generated by the elasticity tensor is the symmetrized square of the representation generated by the dielectric tensor. Proceeding as before we find the character to be $\chi = (21, 5, 1, 5, 5)$ so

$$N_0 = \tfrac{1}{8}(21 + 5 + 2 + 10 + 10) = \tfrac{48}{8} = 6.$$

Thus the elasticity tensor can be specified by six constants.

Some proportionality tensors, such as the gyration tensor, are not invariant vectors, but are pseudoinvariant vectors; i.e., an orthogonal transformation of determinant minus one changes the sign. In this case

$$N_0 = \frac{1}{g} \sum_{i=1}^{r} r_i |T_i| \chi_i^{(\Gamma_0)}, \tag{4:5.11}$$

where $|T_i|$ is the determinant of any matrix of the point group in the class C_i. This can be found from the character of the point group by means of the formula of Chapter I for antisymmetrized Kronecker powers, together with the equation

$$|D| = \mathrm{tr}\,(D_{[d]}), \qquad (4{:}5.12)$$

where d is the dimension of D.

6. The Three-Dimensional Rotation Group

Unfortunately, in applications of group theory it is very difficult to separate finite from infinite groups completely in any satisfactory way. Consequently we shall occasionally need to know something about the 3-dimensional rotation group, and for that reason we shall give here a brief summary of its properties (without any derivations).

(1) $R(3)$ is not abelian.

(2) $R(3)$ has an uncountably infinite number of classes.

(3) Two rotations are in the same class if and only if the magnitudes of their rotation angles are the same.

(4) $R(3)$ is simple, unsolvable, and simply reducible.

(5) $R(3)$ has a countably infinite number of irreducible representations.

(6) $R(3)$ has exactly one irreducible representation of every dimension from one to infinity.

(7) If a representation of $R(3)$ is reducible it is completely reducible.

(8) Every irreducible representation of $R(3)$ is of first or second kind according as the dimension is odd or even.

(9) Every irreducible representation of the first kind is either even or odd according as the dimension is equal to one plus a multiple of four or not; i.e., if $d = 2l + 1$ then Γ is even if l is even and odd if l is odd.

(10) If we let Γ_j be the irreducible representation of dimension $d_j = 2j + 1$ (j = integer or half-integer), then the character is given by

$$\chi_j(\theta) = \frac{\sin\,(j+\frac{1}{2})\theta}{\sin\frac{1}{2}\theta} \quad (\theta = \text{angle of rotation}).$$

(11)
$$\frac{1}{4\pi}\int_0^{4\pi} \chi_j(\theta)\chi_k(\theta)\sin^2\tfrac{1}{2}\theta\, d\theta = \delta_{j,k}$$

(12) If Γ is an arbitrary representation of $R(3)$ with character $\chi(\theta)$, and if $\Gamma \cdot\!\equiv\!\cdot \sum_j c^{(j)}\Gamma_j$, then

$$c^{j)} = \frac{1}{4\pi}\int_0^{4\pi} \sin\,(j+\tfrac{1}{2})\theta \sin\tfrac{1}{2}\theta\,\chi(\theta)d\theta.$$

(13) The orthogonality relations for representation matrices expressed in terms of Euler angles are

$$\int_0^{2\pi} d\alpha \int_0^{\pi} d\beta \sin\beta \int_0^{2\pi} d\gamma\, D_{ij}^{(p)-1}(\alpha,\beta,\gamma) D_{kl}^{(q)}(\alpha,\beta,\gamma) = \frac{8\pi^2}{2p+1}\delta_{il}\delta_{jk}\delta_{pq}.$$

(14) Γ_j is the $2j$th symmetrized Kronecker power of $\Gamma_{1/2}$: $\Gamma_j = [\Gamma_{1/2}]_{(2j)}$

(15) $\Gamma_{1/2}$ is the group of all 2-dimensional, unitary, unimodular matrices.

(16) $\Gamma_{1/2}$ is two-to-one homomorphic to $R(3)$ (the kernel being the two matrices I and $-I$) and is therefore not a representation in the sense in which we have been using the word until now. However, $R(3)$ is a representation of $\Gamma_{1/2}$ in our previous sense of the word. To distinguish $\Gamma_{1/2}$ from an ordinary representation it is sometimes called a spin representation or a two-valued representation.

(17) All of the irreducible even-dimensional representations of $R(3)$ are spin representations (one-to-two). All of the irreducible odd-dimensional representations are faithful ordinary representations.

(18) The spin representation $\Gamma_{1/2}$ is given explicitly in terms of Euler angles by

$$R(\alpha,\beta,\gamma) \to \pm D^{(1/2)}(\alpha,\beta,\gamma) = \pm \begin{pmatrix} e^{\frac{1}{2}i(\alpha+\gamma)}\cos\frac{\beta}{2} & e^{\frac{1}{2}i(\alpha-\gamma)}\sin\frac{\beta}{2} \\ -e^{-\frac{1}{2}i(\alpha-\gamma)}\sin\frac{\beta}{2} & e^{-\frac{1}{2}i(\alpha+\gamma)}\cos\frac{\beta}{2} \end{pmatrix},$$

where the rotation matrix $R(\alpha,\beta,\gamma)$ is written out explicitly in Chapter I.

(19) A time reversal matrix U for the representation $\Gamma_{1/2}$ of $R(3)$ is the matrix $U = \begin{pmatrix} 0 & -i \\ i & 0 \end{pmatrix}$

$$D^{(1/2)}(R)^* = UD^{(1/2)}(R)U^{-1}.$$

The matrix U is also the Pauli spin matrix σ_y. If a real time reversal matrix is desired then $i\sigma_y$ can be chosen instead.

(20) The matrix elements of the matrices of the irreducible representations Γ_j can be simply expressed in terms of the Jacobi polynomials. Let

$$P_n^{(a,b)}(x) \equiv \frac{(-1)^n}{2^n n!}(1-x)^{-a}(1+x)^{-b}\frac{d^n}{dx^n}[(1-x)^{a+n}(1+x)^{b+n}].$$

Then $R(\alpha,\beta,\gamma) \to D^{(j)}(\alpha,\beta,\gamma)$ where $R(\alpha,\beta,\gamma)$ is defined in Chapter I,

$$D_{mm'}^{(j)}(\alpha,\beta,\gamma) = \left[\frac{(j+m)!(j-m)!}{(j+m')!(j-m')!}\right]^{\frac{1}{2}} e^{i(m\alpha+m'\gamma)}[\cos\tfrac{1}{2}\beta]^{m+m'}[\sin\tfrac{1}{2}\beta]^{m-m'}$$

$$\cdot\, P_{j-m}^{(m-m',\, m+m')}(\cos\beta) \qquad j = 0, \tfrac{1}{2}, 1, \tfrac{3}{2}, \ldots$$

and the rows and columns are numbered from j to $-j$ (i.e.; $m = j, j-1, j-2, \ldots, -j$; $m' = j, j-1, j-2, \ldots, -j$). If j is a half-odd-integer then $R(\alpha,\beta,\gamma) \to \pm D^{(j)}(\alpha,\beta,\gamma)$. The representations so defined are unitary.

(21) The representations for integral j defined in (20) are generated by the surface spherical harmonics $\mathscr{Y}_{j,m}(\theta, \phi)$. Let

$$P_j^m(x) \equiv (1 - x^2)^{\frac{1}{2}|m|} \frac{d^{|m|}}{dx^{|m|}} P_j(x) \quad j = 0, 1, 2, \ldots; \; m = -j, \ldots, j$$

where $P_j(x)$ is the Legendre polynomial of degree j. Let

$$Y_{jm}(\theta, \phi) \equiv \left[\frac{2j+1}{4\pi} \frac{(j-|m|)!}{(j+|m|)!}\right]^{\frac{1}{2}} P_j^m(\cos\theta) e^{im\phi}$$

$$\mathscr{Y}_{jm}(\theta, \phi) \equiv (-1)^m Y_{jm}(\theta, \phi) \text{ if } m \geqslant 0$$

$$\equiv Y_{jm}(\theta, \phi) \text{ if } m < 0.$$

Finally, let

$$\mathbf{r}' = R^{-1}(\alpha, \beta, \gamma)\mathbf{r} \text{ (alibi transformation)}$$
$$\mathbf{r} = (r, \theta, \phi)$$
$$\mathbf{r}' = (r, \theta', \phi').$$

Then

$$\mathscr{Y}_{l,m}(\theta', \phi') = \sum_{m'=-l}^{l} D^{(l)}_{m'm}(\alpha, \beta, \gamma) \, \mathscr{Y}_{lm'}(\theta, \phi).$$

(22)
$$\Gamma_j \otimes \Gamma_{j'} = \sum_{J=|j-j'|}^{j+j'} \Gamma_J.$$

This is the famous Clebsch-Gordan formula.

(23)
$$[\Gamma_{1/2}]_N = \sum_{j=(\frac{1}{2}N)-[\frac{1}{2}N]}^{\frac{1}{2}N} c_j^N \Gamma_j,$$

where $[N/2]$ is the largest integer which does not exceed $N/2$, and

$$c_j^N = c_{j+\frac{1}{2}}^{N-1} + c_{j-\frac{1}{2}}^{N-1} = \binom{N}{\frac{1}{2}N - j} - \binom{N}{\frac{1}{2}N - j - 1}.$$

The 3-dimensional orthogonal group $O(3)$ is isomorphic to $R(3) \times C_2$. An irreducible representation of $O(3)$ in which $-I \to I$ is said to have even parity, and one in which $-I \to -I$ is said to have odd parity. Also, if $\mathscr{I}$ is the inversion operator, then

$$\mathscr{I} Y_{l,m}(\theta, \phi) = Y_{l,m}(\pi - \theta, \pi + \phi) = (-1)^l Y_{l,m}(\theta, \phi).$$

(24) The Clebsch-Gordan (or Wigner, or vector addition, or vector coupling) coefficients $C^{abc}_{\alpha\beta\gamma}$ are real numbers which are defined for nonnegative integral and half-integral values of a, b, c, and for positive and negative integral and half-integral values of α, β, γ. The arguments a, b, c, α, β, γ must, however, satisfy the following conditions in order for $C^{abc}_{\alpha\beta\gamma}$ to be defined.

$$\begin{aligned} a + b + c &= \text{integer} \\ a + b - c &\geqslant 0 \\ a - b + c &\geqslant 0 \\ -a + b + c &\geqslant 0 \\ |\alpha| &\leqslant a \\ |\beta| &\leqslant b \\ |\gamma| &\leqslant c \\ a + \alpha &= \text{integer} \\ b + \beta &= \text{integer} \\ c + \gamma &= \text{integer}. \end{aligned}$$

The coefficients can be defined through either of the following two equations.

$$C^{abc}_{\alpha\beta\gamma} = \delta_{\alpha+\beta,\gamma} \sqrt{\frac{(c+a-b)!(c-a+b)!(a+b-c)!(c+\gamma)!(c-\gamma)!(2c+1)}{(c+a+b+1)!(a-\alpha)!(a+\alpha)!(b-\beta)!(b+\beta)!}}$$

$$\cdot \sum_k (-1)^{k+b+\beta} \frac{(c+b+\alpha-k)!(a-\alpha+k)!}{(c-a+b-k)!(c+\gamma-k)!k!(k+a-b-\gamma)!} \cdot$$

The sum is over-all integral values of k which do not make the argument of any factorial negative.

$$C^{abc}_{\alpha\beta\gamma} = \delta_{\alpha+\beta,\gamma} \sqrt{\frac{(a+b-c)!(c+a-b)!(c+b-a)!(2c+1)}{(c+a+b+1)!}}$$

$$\cdot \sum_k (-1)^k \frac{\sqrt{(a+\alpha)!(a-\alpha)!(b+\beta)!(b-\beta)!(c+\gamma)!(c-\gamma)!}}{k!(a+b-c-k)!(a-\alpha-k)!(b+\beta-k)!(c-b+\alpha+k)!(c-a-\beta+k)!}$$

The sum is as before.

(25) The symmetry properties of the Clebsch-Gordan coefficients are as follows:

$$\begin{aligned} C^{abc}_{\alpha\beta\gamma} &= (-1)^{a+b-c} C^{abc}_{-\alpha,-\beta,-\gamma} \\ &= C^{bac}_{-\beta,-\alpha,-\gamma} \\ &= (-1)^{a+b-c} C^{bac}_{\beta\alpha\gamma} \\ &= \sqrt{\frac{2c+1}{2a+1}} (-1)^{a-\alpha+c-\gamma} C^{cba}_{\gamma,-\beta,\alpha} \\ &= \sqrt{\frac{2c+1}{2a+1}} (-1)^{b+\beta} C^{cba}_{-\gamma,\beta,-\alpha} \\ &= \sqrt{\frac{2c+1}{2a+1}} (-1)^{c-\gamma+a-\alpha} C^{bca}_{\beta,-\alpha-\gamma} \\ &= \sqrt{\frac{2c+1}{2b+1}} (-1)^{a-\alpha} C^{acb}_{\alpha,-\gamma,-\beta} \\ &= \sqrt{\frac{2c+1}{2b+1}} (-1)^{a-\alpha} C^{cab}_{\gamma,-\alpha,\beta} \quad . \end{aligned}$$

The orthogonality properties are as follows:

$$\sum_{\alpha=-a}^{a} \sum_{\beta=-b}^{b} C^{abc}_{\alpha\beta\gamma} C^{abc'}_{\alpha\beta\gamma'} = \delta_{cc'} \delta_{\gamma\gamma'}$$

$$\sum_{c=|a-b|}^{a+b} \sum_{\gamma=-c}^{c} C^{abc}_{\alpha\beta\gamma} C^{abc}_{\alpha'\beta'\gamma} = \delta_{\alpha\alpha'} \delta_{\beta\beta'}$$

$$\sum_{\gamma=-c}^{c} \sum_{\beta=-b}^{b} C^{abc}_{\alpha\beta\gamma} C^{a'bc}_{\alpha'\beta\gamma} = \frac{2c+1}{2a+1} \delta_{aa'} \delta_{\alpha\alpha'} .$$

(26) The Racah coefficients $W(a\,b\,c\,d;\,e\,f)$ are real numbers defined for integral and half-integral values of the arguments satisfying

$$\begin{aligned} a + b + e &= \text{integer} \\ c + d + e &= \text{integer} \\ a + c + f &= \text{integer} \\ b + d + f &= \text{integer} \end{aligned}$$

The Racah coefficients $W(abcd;\,ef)$ are defined in terms of Clebsch-Gordan coefficients by the equation

$$W(abcd;\,ef) = \frac{1}{\sqrt{(2e+1)(2f+1)}} \sum_{\alpha=-a}^{a} \sum_{\beta=-b}^{b} C^{abe}_{\alpha\beta} C^{edc}_{\alpha+\beta,\gamma-\alpha-\beta} C^{bdf}_{\beta,\gamma-\alpha-\beta} C^{afc}_{\alpha,\gamma-\alpha}$$

where

$$C^{abc}_{\alpha\beta} \equiv C^{abc}_{\alpha\beta,\alpha+\beta}$$

$$-c \leqslant \gamma \leqslant c$$

and the sum is independent of γ.

(27) The Wigner j-symbols for the 3-dimensional rotation group are defined as follows. The three-j-symbol is

$$\begin{pmatrix} a\,b\,c \\ \alpha\beta\gamma \end{pmatrix} \equiv (-1)^{a-b-\gamma}(2c+1)^{-\frac{1}{2}} C^{abc}_{\alpha\beta,\gamma-} .$$

The one-j-symbol is

$$\begin{pmatrix} a \\ \alpha\beta \end{pmatrix} \equiv (2a+1)^{\frac{1}{2}} \begin{pmatrix} a o a \\ \alpha o \beta \end{pmatrix} = (-1)^{a+\alpha} \delta_{\alpha,-\beta}.$$

The six-j-symbol is

$$\begin{Bmatrix} abc \\ def \end{Bmatrix} \equiv (-1)^{a+b+d+e} W(abed;\,cf).$$

The nine-j-symbol is

$$\begin{Bmatrix} abc \\ def \\ ghi \end{Bmatrix} \equiv \sum_{k} (-1)^{2k}(2k+1) \begin{Bmatrix} adg \\ hik \end{Bmatrix} \begin{Bmatrix} beh \\ dkf \end{Bmatrix} \begin{Bmatrix} cfi \\ kab \end{Bmatrix}.$$

The twelve-j-symbol is

$$\begin{Bmatrix} abcd \\ efgh \\ ijkl \end{Bmatrix} \equiv (-1)^{c+g+i+h} \sum_m (-1)^{2m}(2m+1) \begin{Bmatrix} abc \\ efg \\ ijm \end{Bmatrix} \begin{Bmatrix} kcd \\ glm \end{Bmatrix} \begin{Bmatrix} kih \\ jlm \end{Bmatrix}.$$

(28) The fundamental significance of the Clebsch-Gordan coefficients is that the $[(2j_1+1)(2j_2+1)]^2$ coefficients $C^{j_1 j_2 j}_{m_1 m_2 m}$($j_1, j_2$ fixed) are the elements of a $(2j_1+1)(2j_2+1)$-dimensional unitary matrix which will reduce the Kronecker product $\Gamma_{j_1} \otimes \Gamma_{j_2}$ of two irreducible representations Γ_{j_1} and Γ_{j_2} of the 3-dimensional rotation group $R(3)$. A more precise statement is as follows. Let every irreducible representation occurring in the Clebsch-Gordan equation

$$\Gamma_{j_1} \otimes \Gamma_{j_2} \cdot\!\equiv\!\cdot \sum_{j=|j_1-j_2|}^{j_1+j_2} \Gamma_j$$

have the form given in (20). Let the rows of $\Gamma_{j_1} \otimes \Gamma_{j_2}$ be numbered by the ordered pair m_1, m_2 and the columns by the ordered pair m_1', m_2'. Finally, let

$$S_{m_1'm_2',jm} \equiv C^{j_1 j_2 j}_{m_1' m_2' m}\ .$$

Then

$$S^{-1}[D^{(j_1)}(R) \otimes D^{(j_2)}(R)]S = \sum_{j=|j_1-j_2|}^{j_1+j_2} D^{(j)}(R)$$

where the sum on the right side of the equation is a direct sum. Consequently, the functions $Z_{jm}(\theta_1 \phi_1 \theta_2 \phi_2)$ defined by

$$Z_{jm}(\theta_1 \phi_1 \theta_2 \phi_2) \equiv \sum_{m_1=-j_1}^{j_1} \sum_{m_2=-j_2}^{j_2} C^{j_1 j_2 j}_{m_1 m_2 m} \mathscr{Y}_{j_1 m_1}(\theta_1 \phi_1) \mathscr{Y}_{j_2 m_2}(\theta_2 \phi_2)$$

generate the irreducible representation Γ_j of $R(3)$.

(29) Let us consider an infinitesimal rotation R and express it as a product of infinitesimal rotations about the x-, y-, and z-axes.

$$R = R_x(\omega_x) R_y(\omega_y) R_x(\omega_x).$$

By expanding each matrix element in a power series in the angles $\omega_x, \omega_y, \omega_z$, and retaining only first-order terms, one finds

$$R = I + i\boldsymbol{\omega}\cdot\mathbf{J}$$

where

$$\boldsymbol{\omega} = (\omega_x, \omega_y, \omega_z)$$
$$\mathbf{J} = (J_x, J_y, J_z)$$
J_x, J_y, J_z are square matrices
$$[J_x, J_y]_- = iJ_z(\text{cycl.}).$$

If $R \to D(R)$ is any representation of the 3-dimensional rotation group $R(3)$, then

$$D(R) = D(R_x)D(R_y)D(R_z)$$

and for an infinitesimal rotation, one obtains, by expanding matrix elements as before

$$D(R) = D(I) + i\boldsymbol{\omega}\cdot D(\mathbf{J})$$

where

$$[D(J_x), D(J_y)]_- = iD(J_z)(\text{cycl.}).$$

The matrices $D(J_x)$, $D(J_y)$, $D(J_z)$ are called the *infinitesimal transformations* of the representation $R \to D(R)$ of the group, and are easily seen to be hermitian when the representation is unitary. Let us denote the infinitesimal transformations of the irreducible representation Γ_j by $J_x^{(j)}$, $J_y^{(j)}$, and $J_z^{(j)}$. Also, let us define (for any representation)

$$J_\pm = J_x \pm iJ_y.$$

Then the representation Γ_j can always be put in a form such that

$$J_z^{(j)} = \begin{pmatrix} j & 0 & 0 & 0 & \cdots & 0 \\ 0 & j-1 & 0 & 0 & \cdots & 0 \\ 0 & 0 & j-2 & 0 & \cdots & 0 \\ \vdots & \vdots & \vdots & \vdots & & \vdots \\ 0 & 0 & 0 & 0 & \cdots & -j \end{pmatrix}$$

$$J_+^{(j)} = \begin{pmatrix} 0 & \sqrt{1\cdot 2j} & 0 & 0 & \cdots & 0 \\ 0 & 0 & \sqrt{2\cdot(2j-1)} & 0 & \cdots & 0 \\ 0 & 0 & 0 & \sqrt{3\cdot(2j-2)} & \cdots & 0 \\ \vdots & \vdots & \vdots & \vdots & & \vdots \\ 0 & 0 & 0 & 0 & \cdots & \sqrt{2j\cdot 1} \\ 0 & 0 & 0 & 0 & \cdots & 0 \end{pmatrix}$$

$$J_-^{(j)} = J_+^{(j)t}.$$

Note that

$$\mathbf{J}^{(\frac{1}{2})} = \tfrac{1}{2}\boldsymbol{\sigma}$$

where $\boldsymbol{\sigma} = (\sigma_x, \sigma_y, \sigma_z)$ and

$$\sigma_x = \begin{pmatrix} 0 & 1 \\ 1 & 0 \end{pmatrix} \qquad \sigma_y = \begin{pmatrix} 0 & -i \\ i & 0 \end{pmatrix} \qquad \sigma_z = \begin{pmatrix} 1 & 0 \\ 0 & -1 \end{pmatrix}$$

are the Pauli spin matrices.

The irreducible representations defined in (20) yield these infinitesimal representations. If a representation is irreducible, so is the set of infinitesimal transformations. Consequently, since the matrix

$$J^2 \equiv J_x^2 + J_y^2 + J_z^2$$

commutes with J_x, J_y, and J_z, it must, in an irreducible representation, be a scalar matrix. In Γ_j

$$J^2 = j(j+1)I.$$

The $(2j_1 + 1)(2j_2 + 1)$-dimensional unitary matrix defined in terms of Clebsch-Gordan coefficients in (28) also satisfies

$$S^{-1}(J_x^{(j_1)} \otimes I_{j_2} + I_{j_1} \otimes J_x^{(j_2)})S = \sum_{j=|j_1-j_2|}^{j_1+j_2} J_x^{(j)} \quad \text{(cycl.)}$$

where the sum on the right is a direct sum.

If

$$\mathcal{J}_x \equiv i \sin\phi \frac{\partial}{\partial\theta} + i\cos\phi\cot\theta\frac{\partial}{\partial\phi}$$

$$\mathcal{J}_y \equiv -i\cos\phi\frac{\partial}{\partial\theta} + i\sin\phi\cot\theta\frac{\partial}{\partial\phi}$$

$$\mathcal{J}_z \equiv -i\frac{\partial}{\partial\phi}$$

$$\mathcal{J}_\pm \equiv \mathcal{J}_x \pm i\mathcal{J}_y = e^{\pm i\phi}\left(\pm\frac{\partial}{\partial\theta} + i\cot\theta\frac{\partial}{\partial\phi}\right)$$

$$\mathcal{J}^2 \equiv \mathcal{J}_x^2 + \mathcal{J}_y^2 + \mathcal{J}_z^2 = -\frac{1}{\sin\theta}\frac{\partial}{\partial\theta}\sin\theta\frac{\partial}{\partial\theta} - \frac{1}{\sin^2\theta}\frac{\partial^2}{\partial\phi^2}$$

then

$$[\mathcal{J}_x, \mathcal{J}_y]_- = i\mathcal{J}_z \text{(cycl.)}$$

so $\mathcal{J}_x$, $\mathcal{J}_y$, $\mathcal{J}_z$ are infinitesimal rotation operators in function space. Furthermore

$$\mathcal{J}^2\mathcal{Y}_{jm}(\theta,\phi) = j(j+1)\mathcal{Y}_{jm}(\theta,\phi)$$

$$\mathcal{J}_z\mathcal{Y}_{jm}(\theta,\phi) = m\mathcal{Y}_{jm}(\theta,\phi)$$

$$\mathcal{J}_\pm\mathcal{Y}_{jm}(\theta,\phi) = \sqrt{(j \mp m)(j \pm m + 1)}\,\mathcal{Y}_{j,m\pm 1}(\theta,\phi).$$

Infinitesimal rotation operators expressed in terms of Euler angles can also be constructed. Let $\mathcal{J}(\alpha,\beta,\gamma)$ be defined by

$$\mathcal{J}_x \equiv -i\left(\cos\alpha\cot\beta\frac{\partial}{\partial\alpha} + \sin\alpha\frac{\partial}{\partial\beta} - \frac{\cos\alpha}{\sin\beta}\frac{\partial}{\partial\gamma}\right)$$

$$\mathcal{J}_y \equiv -i\left(\sin\alpha\cot\beta\frac{\partial}{\partial\alpha} - \cos\alpha\frac{\partial}{\partial\beta} - \frac{\sin\alpha}{\sin\beta}\frac{\partial}{\partial\gamma}\right)$$

$$\mathcal{J}_z \equiv -i\frac{\partial}{\partial\alpha}$$

and let $\mathcal{J}'(\alpha,\beta,\gamma)$ be defined by

$$\mathcal{J}_x'(\alpha,\beta,\gamma) \equiv -\mathcal{J}_x(\gamma,\beta,\alpha)$$
$$\mathcal{J}_y'(\alpha,\beta,\gamma) \equiv -\mathcal{J}_y(\gamma,\beta,\alpha)$$
$$\mathcal{J}_z'(\alpha,\beta,\gamma) \equiv \mathcal{J}_z(\gamma,\beta,\alpha).$$

Then

$$[\mathscr{J}_x, \mathscr{J}_y]_- = i\mathscr{J}_z(\text{cycl.}) \qquad [\mathscr{J}_x', \mathscr{J}_y']_- = i\mathscr{J}_z'(\text{cycl.})$$
$$[\mathscr{J}_k, \mathscr{J}_l']_- = 0 \ \ (k, l = 1, 2, 3).$$

If we let

$$\mathscr{J}_\pm \equiv \mathscr{J}_x \pm i\mathscr{J}_y$$
$$\mathscr{J}^2 \equiv \mathscr{J}_x^2 + \mathscr{J}_y^2 + \mathscr{J}_z^2$$

and if we let $D^{(j)}_{mm'}(\alpha, \beta, \gamma)$ be the function defined in (20), then

$$\mathscr{J}^2 = \mathscr{J}'^2 = -\frac{\partial^2}{\partial\beta^2} - \cot\beta\frac{\partial}{\partial\beta} - \frac{1}{\sin^2\beta}\left(\frac{\partial^2}{\partial\alpha^2} + \frac{\partial^2}{\partial\gamma^2}\right) + \frac{2\cos\beta}{\sin^2\beta}\frac{\partial^2}{\partial\alpha\partial\gamma}$$

and, omitting arguments of $D^{(j)}_{mm'}(\alpha, \beta, \gamma)$

$$\mathscr{J}^2 D^{(j)}_{mm'} = j(j+1)D^{(j)}_{mm'} = \mathscr{J}'^2 D^{(j)}_{mm'}$$

$$\mathscr{J}_z D^{(j)}_{mm'} = mD^{(j)}_{mm'} \qquad \mathscr{J}_z' D^{(j)}_{mm'} = m' D^{(j)}_{mm'}$$

$$\mathscr{J}_\pm D^{(j)}_{mm'} = \sqrt{(j \pm m + 1)(j \mp m)}\, D^{(j)}_{m\pm 1, m'}$$
$$\mathscr{J}'_\pm D^{(j)}_{mm'} = \sqrt{(j \pm m' + 1)(j \mp m')}\, D^{(j)}_{mm'\pm 1}.$$

Consequently, the $(2j + 1)$ matrix elements $D^{(j)}_{mm'}$ (j, m' fixed) generate the irreducible representation Γ_j of $R(3)$, and so do the $(2j + 1)$ matrix elements $D^{(j)}_{mm'}$ with j and m fixed.

Two other useful differential forms of infinitesimal rotation operators can be constructed. The first is expressed in terms of two independent variables u and v.

$$\mathscr{J}_x \equiv \frac{1}{2}\left(v\frac{\partial}{\partial u} + u\frac{\partial}{\partial v}\right)$$

$$\mathscr{J}_y \equiv \frac{i}{2}\left(v\frac{\partial}{\partial u} - u\frac{\partial}{\partial v}\right)$$

$$\mathscr{J}_z \equiv \frac{1}{2}\left(u\frac{\partial}{\partial u} - v\frac{\partial}{\partial v}\right)$$

$$\mathscr{J}_\pm \equiv \mathscr{J}_x \pm i\mathscr{J}_y$$

$$\mathscr{J}_+ = u\frac{\partial}{\partial v}$$

$$\mathscr{J}_- = v\frac{\partial}{\partial u}$$

$$[\mathscr{J}_x, \mathscr{J}_y]_- = i\mathscr{J}_z\ (\text{cycl.})$$

$$\mathscr{J}^2 \equiv \mathscr{J}_x^2 + \mathscr{J}_y^2 + \mathscr{J}_z^2.$$

If

$$\phi_{jm}(u, v) \equiv \frac{u^{j+m}v^{j-m}}{\sqrt{(j+m)!(j-m)!}}$$

then

$$\mathscr{J}^2\phi_{jm} = j(j+1)\phi_{jm}$$

$$\mathscr{J}_z\phi_{jm} = m\phi_{jm}$$

$$\mathscr{J}_\pm\phi_{jm} = \sqrt{(j \mp m)(j \pm m + 1)}\,\phi_{j,m\pm 1}.$$

The second form is expressed in terms of three independent variables x, y, z.

$$\mathscr{J}_x \equiv i\left(z\frac{\partial}{\partial y} - y\frac{\partial}{\partial z}\right)$$

$$\mathscr{J}_y \equiv i\left(x\frac{\partial}{\partial z} - z\frac{\partial}{\partial x}\right)$$

$$\mathscr{J}_z \equiv i\left(y\frac{\partial}{\partial x} - x\frac{\partial}{\partial y}\right)$$

$$[\mathscr{J}_x, \mathscr{J}_y]_- = i\mathscr{J}_z(\text{cycl.}).$$

The commutation relations

$$[\mathscr{J}_x, \mathscr{J}_y]_- = i\mathscr{J}_z(\text{cycl.})$$

are, of course, the relations satisfied by quantum mechanical angular momentum operators (using units with $\hbar = 1$). Consequently, angular momentum operators are infinitesimal rotation operators.

(30) Tensor operators were discussed in Chapter III, Section 12. The basic equation was

$$\mathscr{D}(A)\mathscr{O}_i\mathscr{D}(A^{-1}) = \sum_{j=1}^{d} D_{ji}(A)\mathscr{O}_j$$

where $d = \dim D$. If for the rotation group $R(3)$ we let

$$\mathscr{D} = \mathscr{I} + i\boldsymbol{\omega}\cdot\mathscr{J}$$

$$D = I + i\boldsymbol{\omega}\cdot\mathbf{J}$$

we find

$$[\mathscr{J}, \mathscr{O}_l]_- = \sum_{k=1}^{d} \mathbf{J}_{kl}\mathscr{O}_k.$$

The tensor operator is irreducible when $D(A) = D^{(j)}(A)$, $\mathbf{J} = \mathbf{J}^{(j)}$. In this case, by numbering the rows of $\mathbf{J}^{(j)}$ by the eigenvalues of J_z, we have

$$[\mathscr{J}, \mathscr{O}_m^{(j)}]_- = \sum_{m'=-j}^{j} \mathbf{J}_{m'm}^{(j)}\mathscr{O}_{m'}$$

so, using the $\mathbf{J}^{(j)}$ of (29)

$$[\mathscr{J}_z, \mathcal{O}^{(j)}_m]_- = m\,\mathcal{O}^{(j)}_m$$

$$[\mathscr{J}_\pm, \mathcal{O}^{(j)}_m]_- = \sqrt{(j \mp m)(j \pm m + 1)}\,\mathcal{O}^{(j)}_{m\pm 1}.$$

If $\mathcal{O}^{(j_1)}(1)$ and $\mathcal{O}^{(j_2)}(2)$ are two irreducible tensor operators in two vector spaces, then the product operator defined by

$$\mathcal{O}^{(j)}_m(j_1, j_2) \equiv \sum_{m_1=-j_1}^{j_1} \sum_{m_2=-j_2}^{j_2} C^{j_1 j_2 j}_{m_1 m_2 m}\,\mathcal{O}^{(j_1)}_{m_1}(1)\,\mathcal{O}^{(j_2)}_{m_2}(2)$$

is an irreducible tensor operator in the product space. The scalar product of two irreducible tensor operators $\mathcal{O}^{(j)}(1)$ and $\mathcal{Q}^{(j)}(2)$ is defined by the equation

$$\mathcal{O}^{(j)}(1)\cdot\mathcal{Q}^{(j)}(2) \equiv \sum_{m=-j}^{j} (-1)^m \mathcal{O}^{(j)}_m(1)\,\mathcal{Q}^{(j)}_{-m}(2)$$

and is a scalar operator.

(31) We can now state some properties of Clebsch-Gordan coefficients, Racah coefficients, and Wigner nine-j-symbols which are useful in connection with tensor operators. First, let us consider an irreducible tensor operator in a Hilbert space $\mathfrak{h}$ (normally a space of solutions of a Schrödinger equation), and let $|j, m\rangle$ be an orthonormal set of vectors (or functions) in $\mathfrak{h}$ generating the irreducible representation Γ_j of $R(3)$, with the vectors also being eigenvectors of $\mathscr{J}_z$ belonging to the eigenvalue m; i.e., (neglecting the possibility that more than one set of vectors may generate Γ)

$$\langle jm|\mathscr{J}_z|j'm'\rangle = m\delta_{jj'}\delta_{mm'}$$

$$\langle jm|\mathscr{J}_\pm|j'm'\rangle = \sqrt{(j \pm m)(j \mp m + 1)}\,\delta_{jj'}\delta_{m,m'\pm 1}.$$

Then

$$\langle j'm'|\mathcal{O}^{(j)}_m|j''m''\rangle = \frac{(-1)^{j''-m''}}{\sqrt{(2j+1)}} A(jj'j'')\,C^{j'j''j}_{m',-m'',m}$$

where $A\,(j, j', j'')$ is a number which depends on the numbers j, j', j'' and on the operator $\mathcal{O}^{(j)}$, but not on the numbers m, m', and m''.

In a quantum mechanical problem, this equation separates the physical and geometrical parts of the matrix element $\langle j'm'|\mathcal{O}^{(j)}_m|j''m''\rangle$. The function $A(j, j', j'')$ is usually written in the form $\langle j'||\mathcal{O}^{(j)}||j''\rangle$ and called the *reduced matrix element.*

Now consider tensor operators $\mathcal{O}^{(j)}$ and $\mathcal{Q}^{(j)}$ operating in the same space. Then

$$\langle j'm'|\mathcal{O}^{(j)}\cdot\mathcal{Q}^{(j)}|j''m''\rangle$$
$$= \frac{1}{2j+1}\,\delta_{j'j''}\delta_{m'm''} \sum_{j'''} (-1)^{j'-j'''} \langle j'||\mathcal{O}^{(j)}||j'''\rangle\langle j'''||\mathcal{Q}^{(j)}||j''\rangle.$$

If $\mathcal{O}^{(J)}$ and $\mathcal{Q}^{(J)}$ operate in different spaces and if $|j_1 j_2 jm\rangle$ (j_1, j_2, j fixed) is a set of $(2j+1)$ orthonormal vectors in the product space generating Γ_j and formed by taking linear combinations of vectors $|j_1 m_1\rangle \otimes |j_2 m_2\rangle$ using Clebsch-Gordan coefficients, then

$$\langle j_1 j_2 jm|\mathcal{O}^{(J)}\cdot\mathcal{Q}^{(J)}|j_1' j_2' j' m'\rangle = \delta_{jj'}\delta_{mm'}(-1)^{j_1+j_2'+j} \cdot\langle j_1||\mathcal{O}^{(J)}||j_1'\rangle\langle j_2||\mathcal{Q}^{(J)}||j_2'\rangle W(j_1 j_2 j_1' j_2'; jJ).$$

The reduced matrix element of the tensor product of two tensor operators in the same space

$$\mathcal{O}_m^{(j)}(j', j'') \equiv \sum_{m'=-j'}^{j'} \sum_{m''=-j''}^{j''} C_{m'm''m}^{j'j''j}\, \mathcal{O}_{m'}^{(j')}\mathcal{Q}_{m''}^{(j'')}$$

can be expressed in terms of reduced matrix elements of the individual tensor operators by the equation

$$\langle j'||\mathcal{O}^{(j)}(j_1, j_2)||j''\rangle = (-1)^{j+j_1+j_2+2j'+2j''}\sqrt{2j+1} \cdot\sum_{j'''} W(j_1 j_2 j'' j'; jj''')\langle j'||\mathcal{O}^{(j_1)}||j'''\rangle\langle j'''||\mathcal{Q}^{(j_2)}||j''\rangle.$$

For the reduced matrix element of the tensor product of two tensor operators in different spaces

$$\mathcal{O}_M^{(J)}(J_1, J_2) \equiv \sum_{M_1=-J_1}^{J_1} \sum_{M_2=-J_2}^{J_2} C_{M_1 M_2 M}^{J_1 J_2 J}\, \mathcal{O}_{M_1}^{(J_1)}(1)\mathcal{O}_{M_2}^{(J_2)}(2)$$

we have

$$\langle j_1' j_2' J'||\mathcal{O}^{(J)}(J_1, J_2)||j_1'' j_2'' J''\rangle = \sqrt{(2J'+1)(2J''+1)(2J+1)} \cdot\begin{Bmatrix} j_1' j_1'' J_1 \\ j_2' j_2'' J_2 \\ J' J'' J \end{Bmatrix}\langle j_1'||\mathcal{O}^{(J_1)}(1)||j_1''\rangle\langle j_2'||\mathcal{O}^{(J_2)}(2)||j_2''\rangle.$$

Finally, let us say a few words about the 2-dimensional rotation and orthogonal groups, $R(2)$ and $O(2)$. The group $R(2)$ is abelian, so its irreducible representations are all 1-dimensional. They are*:

$$\Gamma_m\colon R(\theta) = \begin{pmatrix} \cos\theta & -\sin\theta \\ \sin\theta & \cos\theta \end{pmatrix} \to e^{im\theta} \ (m = 0, \pm 1, \pm 2, \ldots).$$

$O(2)$ is not abelian and has only two 1-dimensional irreducible representations, the rest being 2-dimensional. Every element of $O(2)$ can be written in the form

$$R(\theta) = \begin{pmatrix} \cos\theta & -\sin\theta \\ \sin\theta & \cos\theta \end{pmatrix}$$

*Let $G=\{x\}$ be the additive group of real numbers and let H be the additive group of integers. Then $G/H = R(2)$. Consequently from the ordinary irreducible representations $x \to e^{i\lambda x}$ (λ real) of G one can obtain multivalued representations of $R(2)$.

or

$$S(\theta) = \begin{pmatrix} \cos\theta & \sin\theta \\ \sin\theta & -\cos\theta \end{pmatrix}$$

where $|R| = 1$ and $|S| = -1$. One 1-dimensional representation is the trivial one, and the other is $R(\theta) \to 1$, $S(\theta) \to -1$. The 2-dimensional representations are:

$$\Gamma_m: \quad R(\theta) \to \begin{pmatrix} e^{-im\theta} & 0 \\ 0 & e^{im\theta} \end{pmatrix} \quad (m = 1, 2, 3, \ldots)$$

$$S(\theta) \to \begin{pmatrix} 0 & e^{-im\theta} \\ e^{im\theta} & 0 \end{pmatrix},$$

which have characters $\chi^{(m)}(R(\theta)) = 2\cos m\theta$ and $\chi^{(m)}(S(\theta)) = 0$.

7. Double Point Groups

The existence of double point groups (**14, 142**) arises from the existence of two-valued representations of the 3-dimensional rotation group. Let us consider a two-to-one homomorphism of the group of 2-dimensional, unitary, unimodular matrices onto the 3-dimensional rotation group. If P is a point group containing only rotations, then the set ${}^{(d)}P$ of all unitary, unimodular matrices which are mapped onto P by the homomorphism is a group which is called the double group of P. Since the homomorphism is two-to-one, the order of ${}^{(d)}P$ is twice the order of P. Since there is more than one homomorphism from the 2-dimensional, unitary, unimodular, group onto $R(3)$ we can find more than one double point group belonging to P. However, since all irreducible 2-dimensional representations of $R(3)$ are equivalent, it follows that all double point groups of P are equivalent and therefore isomorphic. We could also get double point groups of any even dimension by using the other irreducible two-valued representations of $R(3)$. Since these would all be isomorphic to the 2-dimensional double point groups, however, we would obtain no new (nonisomorphic) groups in this way. Let us define ${}^{(d)}P$ to be the abstract double point group so that there will be just one ${}^{(d)}P$ for each P which contains only rotations.

Since no new double groups are obtained from the point groups containing reflections, and since the double groups are of importance primarily in crystal physics, we shall consider only the 11 nonisomorphic crystallographic point groups, which contain only rotations; i.e., C_1, C_2, C_3, C_4, D_2, C_6, D_3, D_4, D_6, T, and 0.

Obviously ${}^{(d)}C_1 = C_2$, since there is only one group of order two (by equal here we mean isomorphic). Further, ${}^{(d)}C_2$ must be either C_4 or D_2, and since D_2 has no faithful 2-dimensional representations (as seen from the character table) it follows that ${}^{(d)}C_2 = C_4$. If A generates the cyclic group C_n, so $A^n = I$, then the representation of C_n subduced by a spin representation of $R(3)$ has the property that $A \to \pm B$ where $B^{2n} = I$. The result is that ${}^{(d)}C_n = C_{2n}$. By writing out the matrices explicitly one finds that ${}^{(d)}D_2 = Q$. It will be noted from the last example that the double group of an abelian group is not necessarily abelian, and that the number of classes of a double group is not necessarily twice the number of the point group.

The point group D_3 leads to the group of order 12 which we have not previously encountered, the five groups of order 12 being C_{12}, $C_6 \times C_2$, D_6, T, and ${}^{(d)}D_3$. Let us consider ${}^{(d)}D_3$ in more detail. From the table of generators given in Section (4) of this Chapter, we find that D_3 is generated by the two matrices

$$A_1 = \begin{pmatrix} 1 & 0 & 0 \\ 0 & -\frac{1}{2} & -\frac{1}{2}\sqrt{3} \\ 0 & \frac{1}{2}\sqrt{3} & -\frac{1}{2} \end{pmatrix} \qquad A_2 = \begin{pmatrix} -1 & 0 & 0 \\ 0 & 1 & 0 \\ 0 & 0 & -1 \end{pmatrix}$$

The multiplication table for D_3 is

I	1	2	3	4	5
1	3	4	I	5	2
2	5	I	4	3	1
3	I	5	1	2	4
4	2	1	5	I	3
5	4	3	2	1	I

D_3

and the three classes are $C_1 = I$; $C_2 = A_1, A_3$; $C_3 = A_2, A_4, A_5$. The character table is

	C_1	C_2	C_3
Γ_1	1	1	1
Γ_2	1	1	−1
Γ_3	2	−1	0

D_3 .

By using the explicit formula given in Section 6 for the 2-dimensional spin representation of $R(3)$ we find

$$A_1 \to \pm B_1 \qquad A_2 \to \pm B_2,$$

where

$$B_1 = \begin{pmatrix} -\dfrac{1}{2} & \dfrac{i}{2}\sqrt{3} \\ \dfrac{i}{2}\sqrt{3} & -\dfrac{1}{2} \end{pmatrix} \qquad B_2 = \begin{pmatrix} 0 & 1 \\ -1 & 0 \end{pmatrix}.$$

If we put

$$R = -I$$

$$C_j = -B_j = RB_j$$

we have for the multiplication table of ${}^{(d)}D_3$

I	B_1	B_2	B_3	B_4	B_5	R	C_1	C_2	C_3	C_4	C_5
B_1	B_3	B_4	I	B_5	B_2	C_1	C_3	C_4	R	C_5	C_2
B_2	B_5	R	B_4	C_3	C_1	C_2	C_5	I	C_4	B_3	B_1
B_3	I	B_5	B_1	B_2	B_4	C_3	R	C_5	C_1	C_2	C_4
B_4	B_2	C_1	B_5	R	C_3	C_4	C_2	B_1	C_5	I	B_3
B_5	B_4	C_3	B_2	C_1	R	C_5	C_4	B_3	C_2	B_1	I
R	C_1	C_2	C_3	C_4	C_5	I	B_1	B_2	B_3	B_4	B_5
C_1	C_3	C_4	R	C_5	C_2	B_1	B_3	B_4	I	B_5	B_2
C_2	C_5	I	C_4	B_3	B_1	B_2	B_5	R	B_4	C_3	C_1
C_3	R	C_5	C_1	C_2	C_4	B_3	I	B_5	B_1	B_2	B_4
C_4	C_2	B_1	C_5	I	B_3	B_4	B_2	C_1	B_5	R	C_3
C_5	C_4	B_3	C_2	B_1	I	B_5	B_4	C_3	B_2	C_1	R

${}^{(d)}D_3$

The six classes are: $C_1 = I$; $C_1' = R$; $C_2 = B_1, B_3$; $C_2' = C_1, C_3$; $C_3 = B_2, B_4, B_5$; $C_3' = C_2, C_4, C_5$. The commutator subgroup is $H_c = \{I, B_1, B_3\}$ and a maximal normal abelian subgroup is $\{I, R, B_1, B_3, C_1, C_3\}$. Consequently ${}^{(d)}D_3$ must have four 1-dimensional representations, and no irreducible representations of dimension greater than two. There must therefore be two irreducible 2-dimensional representations. Since the first four classes are ambivalent it follows also that four of the rows of the character table must be real. Since the spin representation itself is irreducible and has a real character it follows that the character of the other irreducible 2-dimensional representation must also be real (because complex ones occur in conjugate pairs). Hence, the two complex characters must be 1-dimensional. The character table is

	C_1	C_1'	C_2	C_2'	C_3	C_3'
	1	1	2	2	3	3
Γ_1	1	1	1	1	1	1
Γ_2	1	1	1	1	-1	-1
Γ_3	1	-1	1	-1	i	$-i$
Γ_4	1	-1	1	-1	$-i$	i
Γ_5	2	2	-1	-1	0	0
Γ_6	2	-2	-1	1	0	0

${}^{(d)}D_3$

The remaining groups D_4, D_6, T, and O will be discussed more briefly.

${}^{(d)}D_4$: The defining relations are

$$A^4 = B^2 = R \qquad R^2 = I \qquad ABA = B,$$

where R commutes with all elements. The seven classes are: $C_1 = I$; $C_1' = R$; $C_2 = A^2, A^6$; $C_3 = A, A^7$; $C_3' = A^3, A^5$; $C_4 = B, A^2B, A^4B, A^6B$; $C_5 = AB, A^3B, A^7B$. The character table is

	C_1	C_1'	C_2	C_3	C_3'	C_4	C_5	
	1	1	2	2	2	4	4	
Γ_1	1	1	1	1	1	1	1	
Γ_2	1	1	1	1	1	−1	−1	
Γ_3	1	1	1	−1	−1	1	−1	
Γ_4	1	1	1	−1	−1	−1	1	$^{(d)}D_4$
Γ_5	2	2	−2	0	0	0	0	
Γ_6	2	−2	0	$\sqrt{2}$	$-\sqrt{2}$	0	0	
Γ_7	2	−2	0	$-\sqrt{2}$	$\sqrt{2}$	0	0	

$^{(d)}D_6$: The defining relations are

$$A^6 = B^2 = R \qquad R^2 = I \qquad ABA = B,$$

where R again commutes with all elements. The nine classes are: $C_1 = I$; $C_1' = R$; $C_2 = A^3, A^9$; $C_3 = A^2, A^{10}$; $C_3' = A^4, A^8$; $C_4 = A, A^{11}$; $C_4' = A^5, A^7$; $C_5 = B, A^2B, A^4B, A^6B, A^8B, A^{10}B$; $C_6 = AB, A^3B, A^5B, A^7B, A^9B, A^{11}B$. The character table is

	C_1	C_1'	C_2	C_3	C_3'	C_4	C_4'	C_5	C_6	
	1	1	2	2	2	2	2	6	6	
Γ_1	1	1	1	1	1	1	1	1	1	
Γ_2	1	1	1	1	1	1	1	−1	−1	
Γ_3	1	1	−1	1	1	−1	−1	1	−1	
Γ_4	1	1	−1	1	1	−1	−1	−1	1	
Γ_5	2	2	2	−1	−1	−1	−1	0	0	$^{(d)}D_6$
Γ_6	2	2	−2	−1	−1	1	1	0	0	
Γ_7	2	−2	0	1	−1	$\sqrt{3}$	$-\sqrt{3}$	0	0	
Γ_8	2	−2	0	1	−1	$-\sqrt{3}$	$\sqrt{3}$	0	0	
Γ_9	2	−2	0	−2	2	0	0	0	0	

$^{(d)}T$: The defining relations are

$$A^3 = B^2 = R \qquad R^2 = I \qquad (AB)^2 = RBA^2,$$

where R again commutes with all elements. The seven classes are: $C_1 = I$; $C_1' = R$; $C_2 = B, A^3B, ABA^2, ABA^5, A^2BA, A^2BA^4$; $C_3 = A, AB, BA, A^2B^5$; $C_3' = A^4, A^4B, BA^4, A^2BA^2$; $C_4 = A^2, A^5B, BA^5, ABA^4$; $C_4' = A^5, A^2B, BA^2, ABA$. The character table is

	C_1	C_1'	C_2	C_3	C_3'	C_4	C_4'	
	1	1	6	4	4	4	4	
Γ_1	1	1	1	1	1	1	1	
Γ_2	1	1	1	ω	ω	ω^2	ω^2	
Γ_3	1	1	1	ω^2	ω^2	ω	ω	
Γ_4	2	-2	0	1	-1	-1	1	$^{(d)}T$
Γ_5	2	-2	0	ω	$-\omega$	$-\omega^2$	ω^2	
Γ_6	2	-2	0	ω^2	$-\omega^2$	$-\omega$	ω	
Γ_7	3	3	-1	0	0	0	0	

where $\omega = e^{2\pi i/3} = -\frac{1}{2} + \frac{i}{2}\sqrt{3}$.

$^{(d)}O$: The defining relations are

$$A^4 = B^2 = R, \qquad R^2 = I \qquad AB^2A = B \qquad ABA = BA^2B,$$

and R again commutes with A and B. The eight classes are: $C_1 = I$; $C_1' = R$; $C_2 = A^2, (AB)^2, (BA)^2, RA^2, R(AB)^2, R(BA)^2$; $C_3 = A, AB, BA, A^3B^2, B^2A^3, RA^3$; $C_3' = A^3, RA, RAB, RBA, RA^3B^2, RB^2A^3$; $C_4 = AB^2, B^2A, BAB, (BA)^2A, ABA^2, A^2BA, RAB^2, RB^2A, RBAB, R(BA)^2A, RABA^2, RA^2BA$; $C_5 = B, A^2B, BA^2, A^2B^2, B^2A^2, RB^2, RA^2BA^2, ABA$; $C_5' = B^2, A^2BA^2, RB, RA^2B, RBA^2, RA^2B^2, RB^2A^2, RABA$.

The character table is

	C_1	C_1'	C_2	C_3	C_3'	C_4	C_5	C_5'	
	1	1	6	6	6	12	8	8	
Γ_1	1	1	1	1	1	1	1	1	
Γ_2	1	1	1	-1	-1	-1	1	1	
Γ_3	2	2	2	0	0	0	-1	-1	
Γ_4	2	-2	0	$\sqrt{2}$	$-\sqrt{2}$	0	-1	1	$^{(d)}O$
Γ_5	2	-2	0	$-\sqrt{2}$	$\sqrt{2}$	0	-1	1	
Γ_6	3	3	-1	-1	-1	1	0	0	
Γ_7	3	3	-1	1	1	-1	0	0	
Γ_8	4	-4	0	0	0	0	1	-1	

If one considers the two-valued representation of a point group subduced by a two-valued representation of the 3-dimensional rotation group as a single-valued representation of the double point group, then one can reduce such a representation with respect to the irreducible representations of the double point group. It will be noted from the character tables just presented that some classes of a point group "split" into two classes in the double group; i.e., if one considers the matrices of a two-valued representation of $R(3)$ which correspond to the elements of a single class of a point group, then one finds that these matrices form two classes in the double group. This splitting is indicated by using the same subscript for two classes of the double group and distinguishing them by primes. It will further be noted that some characters (e.g., Γ_5 for ${}^{(d)}D_3$) have the same value for C_i and C_i'; i.e., the splitting of a class does not split the character. The characters for which this is not true (e.g., Γ_6 for ${}^{(d)}D_3$) are called "new" characters. These new representations are two-valued representations of the original point group.

Let us now designate by Γ_j the $(2j+1)$-dimensional representation of a double point group ${}^{(d)}P$ subduced by the $(2j+1)$-dimensional two-valued representation of $R(3)$. It is easily seen that Γ_j is composed only of new representations of ${}^{(d)}P$, because $\chi_i^{(j)} = -\chi_{i'}^{(j)}$ so that if we designate the irreducible representations and characters of ${}^{(d)}P$ by Δ_k and $\phi^{(k)}$ we have

$$c^k = \frac{1}{g}\sum_i r_i \phi_i^{(k)*}\chi_i^{(j)} + \frac{1}{g}\sum_{i'} r_{i'}\phi_{i'}^{(k)*}\chi_{i'}^{(j)} = 0$$

if every class of P splits in ${}^{(d)}P$ and Δ_k is not a new representation. To show that c^k is zero even when some classes do not split let us consider such a class. If $R(\theta)$ is an element of such a class of P, then the traces of the two corresponding elements of ${}^{(d)}P$ (using the 2-dimensional spin representation) are $\pm\cos(\frac{1}{2}\theta)$. These two elements can therefore belong to the same class only if $\cos(\frac{1}{2}\theta) = 0$, or $\theta = \pi$ or 3π. Since the character of Γ_j is

$$\chi^{(j)}(\theta) = \frac{\sin(j+\frac{1}{2})\theta}{\sin\frac{1}{2}\theta},$$

we see that $\chi^{(j)}$ will be zero for any class which does not split. Hence, the above sum for c^k is again over splitting classes only so that c^k is again zero.

Let us now write down some useful tables for the decompositions of Γ_j in terms of new representations for the nonabelian double point groups. Since the double point group of D_2 is Q, which has only one new representation (the 2-dimensional one Δ_5) it is clear that $\Gamma_j = (j+\frac{1}{2})\Delta_5$. The other noncyclic groups are more complicated. Designating the irreducible representations of the double groups by Δ instead of Γ and numbering them as in the preceding character tables we have

$${}^{d}D_3:\quad \begin{aligned} &\Gamma_{1/2} = \Delta_6 \\ &\Gamma_{3/2} = \Delta_3 \oplus \Delta_4 \oplus \Delta_6 \\ &\Gamma_{5/2} = \Delta_3 \oplus \Delta_4 \oplus 2\Delta_6 \\ &\Gamma_j = \Gamma_{j-3} \oplus \Gamma_{5/2} \qquad (j = 7/2, 9/2, 11/2, \ldots) \end{aligned}$$

$${}^{d}D_4:\quad \begin{aligned} &\Gamma_{1/2} = \Delta_6 \\ &\Gamma_{3/2} = \Delta_6 \oplus \Delta_7 \\ &\Gamma_{5/2} = \Delta_6 \oplus 2\Delta_7 \\ &\Gamma_{7/2} = 2\Delta_6 \oplus 2\Delta_7 \\ &\Gamma_{4\lambda+j} = 2\lambda\Gamma_{3/2} \oplus \Gamma_j \qquad \begin{pmatrix} \lambda = 0, 1, 2, \ldots \\ j = 1/2, 3/2, 5/2, \ldots \end{pmatrix} \end{aligned}$$

$$
\begin{aligned}
{}^dD_6\text{:}\quad & \Gamma_{1/2} = \Delta_7 \\
& \Gamma_{3/2} = \Delta_7 \oplus \Delta_9 \\
& \Gamma_{5/2} = \Delta_7 \oplus \Delta_8 \oplus \Delta_9 \\
& \Gamma_{7/2} = \Delta_7 \oplus 2\Delta_8 \oplus \Delta_9 \\
& \Gamma_{9/2} = \Delta_7 \oplus 2\Delta_8 \oplus 2\Delta_9 \\
& \Gamma_{11/2} = 2\Delta_7 \oplus 2\Delta_8 \oplus 2\Delta_9 \\
& \Gamma_{6\lambda+j} = 2\lambda\Gamma_{5/2} \oplus \Gamma \qquad \begin{pmatrix} \lambda = 0, 1, 2, \ldots \\ j = 1/2, \ldots, 11/2 \end{pmatrix}
\end{aligned}
$$

$$
\begin{aligned}
{}^dT\text{:}\quad & \Gamma_{1/2} = \Delta_4 \\
& \Gamma_{3/2} = \Delta_5 \oplus \Delta_6 \\
& \Gamma_{5/2} = \Delta_4 \oplus \Delta_5 \oplus \Delta_6 \\
& \Gamma_j = \Gamma_{j-3} \oplus \Gamma_{5/2} \qquad (j = 7/2, 9/2, 11/2, \ldots)
\end{aligned}
$$

$$
\begin{aligned}
{}^dO\text{:}\quad & \Gamma_{1/2} = \Delta_4 \\
& \Gamma_{3/2} = \Delta_8 \\
& \Gamma_{5/2} = \Delta_5 \oplus \Delta_8 \\
& \Gamma_{7/2} = \Delta_4 \oplus \Delta_5 \oplus \Delta_8 \\
& \Gamma_{9/2} = \Delta_4 \oplus 2\Delta_8 \\
& \Gamma_{11/2} = \Delta_4 \oplus \Delta_5 \oplus 2\Delta_8 \\
& \Gamma_{12\lambda+j} = 2\lambda\Gamma_{11/2} \oplus \Gamma_j \qquad \begin{pmatrix} \lambda = 0, 1, 2, \ldots \\ j = 1/2, \ldots, 23/2 \end{pmatrix} \\
& \Gamma_{6+j} = \Gamma_{11/2} \oplus \Gamma_j' \qquad (j = 1/2, \ldots, 11/2)
\end{aligned}
$$

where Γ_j' is the same as Γ_j except that Δ_4 and Δ_5 are interchanged.

So far nothing has been said about how these double groups are applied. However, as might be surmised, they are important in treating the energy levels of spinning electrons in the electric fields in crystals. A more detailed discussion of term splitting in crystals will, however, be reserved until the theory of atomic structure has been presented

8. Nonrelativistic Wave Equations

We shall now consider the effect of symmetry on quantum mechanical wave functions and energy levels. We shall consider both the time-independent Schrodinger wave equation for spinless particles and the time-independent Pauli wave equation for spin 1/2 particles.

Let us consider a system of N spinless particles and assume that the system has a time-independent classical Hamiltonian $H(\mathbf{r}_1, \ldots, \mathbf{r}_N; \mathbf{p}_1, \ldots, \mathbf{p}_N)$. If the arguments of H are properly ordered, then the quantum mechanical Hamiltonian will be the operator

$$H(\mathbf{r}_1, \ldots, \mathbf{r}_N; -i\hbar\, \boldsymbol{\nabla}_1, \ldots, -i\hbar\, \boldsymbol{\nabla}_N),$$

where $\hbar = 1{\cdot}0544 \times 10^{-27}$ erg-sec is the Dirac constant $(=h/2\pi)$. If

$\psi(\mathbf{r}_1,\ldots,\mathbf{r}_N,t)$ is the wave function describing the system, then ψ must satisfy the time-dependent Schrodinger wave equation

$$H(\mathbf{r}_1,\ldots,\mathbf{r}_N;\ -i\hbar\nabla_1,\ldots,\ -i\hbar\nabla_N)\psi(\mathbf{r}_1,\ldots,\mathbf{r}_N,t) = i\hbar\,\frac{\partial\psi(\mathbf{r}_1,\ldots,\mathbf{r}_N,t)}{\partial t}\,. \qquad (4{:}8.1)$$

If ψ is of the form

$$\Psi(\mathbf{r}_1,\ldots,\mathbf{r}_N,t) = \phi(\mathbf{r}_1,\ldots,\mathbf{r}_N)e^{-\frac{i}{\hbar}Et} \qquad (4{:}8.2)$$

(where E is a number), then ϕ satisfies the time-independent Schrodinger wave equation

$$H(\mathbf{r}_1,\ldots,\mathbf{r}_N;-i\hbar\nabla_1,\ldots,-i\hbar\nabla_N)\phi(\mathbf{r}_1,\ldots,\mathbf{r}_N) = E\phi(\mathbf{r}_1,\ldots,\mathbf{r}_N) \qquad (4{:}8.3)$$

The time-independent wave equation (4:8.3) is a linear partial differential equation (usually of second order) in which the independent variables are $\mathbf{r}_1,\ldots,\mathbf{r}_N$, and the single dependent variable is the wave function $\phi(\mathbf{r}_1,\ldots,\mathbf{r}_N)$. From the required hermiticity of H it easily follows that E must be a real number. Furthermore, boundary conditions on ϕ usually exclude some real numbers as possibilities for E. The allowed values of E are called the eigenvalues of H, and the ϕ's are called eigenfunctions. The eigenvalues $\{E\}$ are the possible energies of the system, and the eigenfunctions $\{\phi\}$ belonging to a single energy level E describe (except for time variation) the various possible states of the system with energy E. The degeneracy of an energy level E is the number of linearly independent eigenfunctions ϕ belonging to E. The level E is said to be nondegenerate if the degeneracy is one; i.e., if every ϕ belonging to E is at constant times a fixed eigenfunction ϕ_0. Also from the hermiticity of H it follows that two eigenfunctions belonging to different eigenvalues must be orthogonal.

Let us return to the problem of symmetry and consider a linear inhomogeneous coordinate transformation S which has a unique inverse (where $\mathbf{r}$ is now the $3N$-dimensional coordinate vector)

$$\mathbf{r}' = S\mathbf{r} = D\mathbf{r} + \mathbf{c} \qquad (4{:}8.4)$$

where D is a nonsingular square matrix and $\mathbf{c}$ is a column matrix, so

$$\mathbf{r} = S^{-1}\mathbf{r}' = D^{-1}\mathbf{r} - D^{-1}\,\mathbf{c}. \qquad (4{:}8.4a)$$

The gradient transforms according to the equation

$$\nabla' = D^{-1t}\nabla. \qquad (4{:}8.5)$$

If we consider the time-independent Schrodinger wave equation

$$H(\mathbf{r}, -i\hbar\nabla)\phi(\mathbf{r}) = E\phi(\mathbf{r}) \qquad (4{:}8.6)$$

and substitute the transformed variables, we have

$$H(D\mathbf{r} + \mathbf{c}, -i\hbar\, D^{-1t}\boldsymbol{\nabla})\phi(D\mathbf{r} + \mathbf{c}) = E\phi(D\mathbf{r} + \mathbf{c}). \tag{4:8.7}$$

If the transformed Hamiltonian is the same as the original, i.e., if

$$H(D\mathbf{r} + \mathbf{c}, -i\hbar\, D^{-1t}\boldsymbol{\nabla}) = H(\mathbf{r}, -i\hbar\boldsymbol{\nabla}), \tag{4:8.8}$$

then we know from (4:8.7) that not only $\phi(\mathbf{r})$ but also $\mathscr{S}^{-1}\phi(\mathbf{r}) = \phi(S\mathbf{r})$ is a solution of the wave equation belonging to the energy E.

We can now state our main conclusion. Suppose $\{\phi_1, \ldots, \phi_d\}$ is a complete set of d linearly independent eigenfunctions belonging to the energy E. Then if S is a linear coordinate transformation which leaves the Hamiltonian H invariant, it follows that

$$\mathscr{S}\phi_i(\mathbf{r}) = \phi_i(S^{-1}\mathbf{r}) = \sum_{j=1}^{d} D_{ji}^{(E)}(S)\phi_j(\mathbf{r})\ . \tag{4:8.9}$$

It is easily seen that the set of all symmetries S of the Hamiltonian H must be a group G, so that the set of d-dimensional matrices $D^{(E)}(S)$ must be a d-dimensional representation Γ_E of G. In brief then, the eigenfunctions belonging to a given energy eigenvalue generate a representation of the symmetry group of the Hamiltonian.

Usually Γ_E will be irreducible so that the degeneracy of each energy level must be the dimension of some irreducible representation of the symmetry group G. If there is no symmetry then $G = C_1 = I$ and the one irreducible representation has dimension one so every energy level is non-degenerate. Consequently, speaking loosely, one can say that as the symmetry increases the possible degeneracy increases. If Γ_E is reducible one says that the energy level is accidentally degenerate.

Normally, the Hamiltonian will be of the form

$$H(\mathbf{r}, -i\hbar\boldsymbol{\nabla}) = T(-i\hbar\boldsymbol{\nabla}) + V(\mathbf{r}) \tag{4:8.10}$$

where the kinetic energy T has the form

$$T(-i\hbar\boldsymbol{\nabla}) = -\frac{\hbar^2}{2}\sum_{k=1}^{N}\frac{1}{m_k}\nabla_k^{\,2}. \tag{4:8.10a}$$

Using (4:8.5) one easily finds that T is invariant under all orthogonal transformations and under all translations, i.e., under the Euclidean group. Hence, if one considers only symmetry groups which are subgroups of the Euclidean group (as is frequently the case) then one only needs to consider the symmetry of the potential energy V.

Example. Hydrogen Atom

More specifically, let us consider a spinless point charge $-e$ of mass m in a Coulomb field produced by a fixed charge Ze. The kinetic and potential energies are then

$$T = -\frac{\hbar^2}{2m}\nabla^2 \tag{4:8.11a}$$

$$V = -\frac{Ze^2}{r} \tag{4:8.11b}$$

so the symmetry group of the Hamiltonian is the full 3-dimensional orthogonal group. The time-independent wave equation is

$$-\frac{\hbar^2}{2m}\nabla^2\phi - \frac{Ze^2}{r}\phi = E\phi, \tag{4:8.12}$$

which has as a complete orthonormal set of eigenfunctions (for bound states)

$$\phi_{n,l,m}(r,\theta,\phi) = N_{n,l}e^{-\rho/2}\rho^l L_{n+l}^{2l+1}(\rho)Y_{l,m}(\theta,\phi), \tag{4:8.13}$$

where spherical coordinates are used, where

$$n = 1, 2, 3, \ldots, \infty \tag{4:8.13a}$$

$$l = 0, 1, 2, \ldots, n-1 \tag{4:8.13b}$$

$$m = -l, -l+1, \cdots, l-1, l \tag{4:8.13c}$$

$$N_{n,l} = -\left\{\left(\frac{2Z}{na_0}\right)^3 \frac{(n-l-1)!}{2n[(n+l)!]^3}\right\}^{1/2} \tag{4:8.13d}$$

$$\rho = \frac{2Z}{na_0}r \tag{4:8.13e}$$

$$a_0 = \frac{\hbar^2}{me^2} \tag{4:8.13f}$$

where

$$L_{n+l}^{2l+1}(\rho) = -\sum_{k=0}^{n-l-1} \frac{[(n+l)!]^2(-\rho)^k}{k!(n-l-k-1)!(2l+k+1)!} \tag{4:8.13g}$$

is the associated Laguerre polynomial, and where $Y_{l,m}(\theta,\phi)$ is the spherical harmonic defined in Section 6 of this Chapter. The energy eigenvalues depend on the parameter n (the principal quantum number), but not on the parameters l and m (the azimuthal or orbital angular momentum quantum number and the magnetic quantum number). The energy is

$$E_n = -\frac{Z^2e^2}{2a_0}\frac{1}{n^2} \tag{4:8.14}$$

so by referring to (4:8.13) and (4:8.13a-c) we see that the degeneracy of E_n is

$$d_n = n^2. \tag{4:8.15}$$

Since the $2l+1$ eigenfunctions $\{\phi_{n,l,-l}; \phi_{n,l,-l+1}; \ldots; \phi_{n,l,l}\}$ generate an irreducible representation of $O(3)$ (because all angular dependence is contained in the Y's) and since the energy does not depend on l, we see that the energy levels are accidentally degenerate. By altering the radial dependence of the field slightly (but leaving it spherically symmetric) we could remove the accidental degeneracy.

Example. Stark Effect

If we put a hydrogen atom in a uniform electric field **F** (along the z-axis say) then the potential energy is changed to

$$V = -\frac{Ze^2}{r} + FeZ \tag{4:8.16}$$

so the symmetry group is now the group of all rotation-reflections about the Z-axis; i.e., the symmetry group is the 2-dimensional orthogonal group $O(2)$. Since $O(2)$ has only 1- and 2-dimensional irreducible representations (see Section 6 of this Chapter) we see that an energy level of a hydrogen atom in an electric field will be either nondegenerate or doubly degenerate (if there is no accidental degeneracy). This means that every energy level of the free atom with $n > 1$ must split into several levels when the atom is placed in an electric field. The magnitude of the splitting depends, of course, on the strength of the field.

We can discuss the splitting in some more detail and can in fact find the number of levels into which any given level splits. Let us first forget about the accidental degeneracy. Suppose the level E splits into several levels $E_1, E_2, \ldots$ and that the degeneracy of E_1 is d_1, of E_2 is d_2, etc. Then the d_1 wave functions belonging to E_1 generate an irreducible representation of 0(2) as do the d_2 belonging to E_2, etc. In the limiting case of a zero field the irreducible representations of 0(2) generated by the eigenfunctions belonging to the split levels must add up to the representation of 0(2) subduced by the irreducible representation of 0(3) belonging to E. Hence to find the number of levels into which a level E splits in a weak field we simply need to reduce the representation of 0(2) subduced by the irreducible representation of 0(3) belonging to E. The irreducible representation Γ_l of 0(3) generated by $Y_{l,m}(\theta, \phi)(m = -l, \ldots, l)$ has the character $\dfrac{\sin (l + \frac{1}{2})\theta}{\sin \frac{1}{2}\theta}$ for the rotation around the Z-axis

$$\begin{pmatrix} \cos\theta & -\sin\theta & 0 \\ \sin\theta & \cos\theta & 0 \\ 0 & 0 & 1 \end{pmatrix}$$

and the character 1 for the rotation-reflection about the Z-axis

$$\begin{pmatrix} \cos\theta & \sin\theta & 0 \\ \sin\theta & -\cos\theta & 0 \\ 0 & 0 & 1 \end{pmatrix}$$

The character of the rotation-reflection can be obtained by writing it as

$$\begin{pmatrix} -1 & 0 & 0 \\ 0 & -1 & 0 \\ 0 & 0 & -1 \end{pmatrix} \begin{pmatrix} -\cos\theta & -\sin\theta & 0 \\ -\sin\theta & \cos\theta & 0 \\ 0 & 0 & -1 \end{pmatrix},$$

where the second matrix is a rotation through π since the determinant is positive and the trace is -1. Since the effect of the inversion on $Y_{l,m}$ is to multiply it by $(-1)^l$, the character of the rotation-reflection is

$$(-1)^l \frac{\sin (l + \frac{1}{2})\pi}{\sin \frac{1}{2}\pi} = (-1)^l(-1)^l = 1.$$

Since

$$\frac{\sin (l + \frac{1}{2})\theta}{\sin \frac{1}{2}\theta} = 1 + 2 \sum_{k=1}^{l} \cos k\theta, \tag{4:8.17}$$

it easily follows that

$$\Gamma_l = \Delta_{\text{triv}} + \sum_{k=1}^{l} \Delta_k, \tag{4:8.18}$$

where the irreducible representations of 0(2) have been denoted by Δ_k (see Section 6 of this Chapter). Since the decomposition (4:8.18) contains $(l + 1)$ terms we see that the set of $(2l + 1)$ eigenfunctions belonging to Γ_l will split into $(l + 1)$ levels. However, because of accidental degeneracy the level E_n of the hydrogen atom contains all l-values from zero to $n - 1$, so the number of levels into which E_n splits is

$$\sum_{l=0}^{n-1} (l + 1) = \tfrac{1}{2}n(n + 1). \tag{4:8.19}$$

Of these $\frac{1}{2}n(n + 1)$ levels, n are nondegenerate and $\frac{1}{2}n(n - 1)$ are doubly degenerate.

Now let us briefly consider a system of particles which have total spin angular momentum $\frac{1}{2}\hbar\sqrt{3}$ and spin 1/2. The wave function for a single such particle is now a two-component column matrix

$$\Phi(\mathbf{r}) = \begin{pmatrix} \phi_+(\mathbf{r}) \\ \phi_-(\mathbf{r}) \end{pmatrix} \tag{4:8.20}$$

in order to take account of the two possible orientations of the Z-component of spin, and the Hamiltonian is a function of $\mathbf{r}$, $\boldsymbol{\nabla}$, and $\boldsymbol{\sigma}$, where

$$\sigma_x = \begin{pmatrix} 0 & 1 \\ 1 & 0 \end{pmatrix} \qquad \sigma_y = \begin{pmatrix} 0 & -i \\ i & 0 \end{pmatrix} \qquad \sigma_z = \begin{pmatrix} 1 & 0 \\ 0 & -1 \end{pmatrix} \tag{4:8.21}$$

These are the Pauli spin matrices and satisfy the relations

$$\sigma_x \sigma_y = i_k \sigma \text{ (cycl.)} \tag{4:8.21a}$$

$$[\sigma_x, \sigma_y]_+ = 0 \text{ (cycl.)} \tag{4:8.21b}$$

$$\sigma_x^2 = 1 \text{ (cycl.)}, \tag{4:8.21c}$$

where (cycl.) means that the relations hold under the cyclic permutations of indices $x \to y$, $y \to z$, $z \to x$ and $z \to y$, $y \to x$, $x \to z$. The time-independent Pauli wave equation

$$H(\mathbf{r}, -i\hbar \nabla, \boldsymbol{\sigma}) \begin{pmatrix} \phi_+(\mathbf{r}) \\ \phi_-(\mathbf{r}) \end{pmatrix} = E \begin{pmatrix} \phi_+(\mathbf{r}) \\ \phi_-(\mathbf{r}) \end{pmatrix}$$

becomes, after a coordinate rotation

$$H(R\mathbf{r}, -i\hbar R \nabla, U^{-1}\boldsymbol{\sigma}U)U^{-1} \begin{pmatrix} \phi_+(R\mathbf{r}) \\ \phi_-(R\mathbf{r}) \end{pmatrix} = EU^{-1} \begin{pmatrix} \phi_+(R\mathbf{r}) \\ \phi_-(R\mathbf{r}) \end{pmatrix} \tag{4:8.22}$$

if we assume that

$$U^{-1}H(R\mathbf{r}, -i\hbar R \nabla, \boldsymbol{\sigma})U = H(R\mathbf{r}, -i\hbar R \nabla, U^{-1}\boldsymbol{\sigma}U), \tag{4:8.23}$$

where

$$U = D^{(1/2)}(R) \tag{4:8.24}$$

is the 2-dimensional spin representation of $R(3)$ written out explicitly in Section 6 of this Chapter. Thus, the spin representation of the 3-dimensional rotation group is used to describe the transformation of a spin-dependent wave equation under a coordinate rotation. An orthogonal coordinate transformation is also permissible since it can be represented by a spin transformation, but more general transformations can not be represented in spin space. If

$$H(R\mathbf{r}, -i\hbar R^t \nabla, U^{-1}\boldsymbol{\sigma}U) = H(\mathbf{r}, -i\hbar \nabla, \boldsymbol{\sigma}), \tag{4:8.25}$$

then it follows that

$$U^{-1} \begin{pmatrix} \phi_+(R\mathbf{r}) \\ \phi_-(R\mathbf{r}) \end{pmatrix} = U^{-1}\mathscr{R}^{-1} \begin{pmatrix} \phi_+(\mathbf{r}) \\ \phi_-(\mathbf{r}) \end{pmatrix} = \mathscr{O}^{-1} \begin{pmatrix} \phi_+(\mathbf{r}) \\ \phi_-(\mathbf{r}) \end{pmatrix} \tag{4:8.26}$$

where

$$\mathscr{O} = U\mathscr{R}$$

must also be an eigenvector of $H(\mathbf{r}, -i\hbar \nabla, \boldsymbol{\sigma})$ belonging to the energy level E if

$$\begin{pmatrix} \phi_+(\mathbf{r}) \\ \phi_-(\mathbf{r}) \end{pmatrix}$$

belongs to the energy level E.

Actually we can consider transformations in coordinate space and spin space quite separately if we desire. Thus if $S\mathbf{r} = D\mathbf{r} + \mathbf{c}$ is any linear inhomogeneous transformation in coordinate space and T is any linear homogeneous transformation in spin space, then

$$T^{-1}\begin{pmatrix}\phi_+(S\mathbf{r})\\ \phi_-(S\mathbf{r})\end{pmatrix} \tag{4:8.27}$$

will be an eigenvector of $H(\mathbf{r}, -i\hbar\nabla, \boldsymbol{\sigma})$ belonging to energy E if the untransformed wave function is an eigenvector and if

$$H(S\mathbf{r}, -i\hbar D^{-1t}\nabla, T^{-1}\boldsymbol{\sigma}T) = H(\mathbf{r}, -i\hbar\,\nabla, \boldsymbol{\sigma}). \tag{4:8.28}$$

It has again been implicitly assumed that

$$T^{-1}H(\mathbf{r}, -i\hbar\,\nabla, \boldsymbol{\sigma})T = H(\mathbf{r}, -i\hbar\,\nabla, T^{-1}\boldsymbol{\sigma}T). \tag{4:8.29}$$

Therefore if $\Phi_1(\mathbf{r}),\ldots, \Phi_d(\mathbf{r})$ is a complete linearly independent set of eigenvectors of H belonging to energy E we know that

$$(\mathscr{S}T)\Phi_i(\mathbf{r}) = T\Phi_i(S^{-1}\mathbf{r}) = \sum_{j=1}^{d} D_{ji}(S, T)\Phi_j(\mathbf{r}). \tag{4:8.30}$$

As usual the set of d-dimensional matrices $\{D(S, T)\}$ is a d-dimensional representation of the symmetry group $G = \{(S, T)\}$.

The invariance condition (4:8.23) for rotations can be simplified by virtue of the relation

$$U^{-1}\boldsymbol{\sigma}U = R\boldsymbol{\sigma} \tag{4:8.31}$$

which follows directly from the definition of U in terms of R and which means for example that

$$U^{-1}\sigma_x U = R_{11}\,\sigma_x + R_{12}\,\sigma_y + R_{13}\,\sigma_z.$$

The condition (4:8.23) can therefore be written

$$H(R\mathbf{r}, -i\hbar R\,\nabla, R\boldsymbol{\sigma}) = H(\mathbf{r}, -i\hbar\,\nabla, \boldsymbol{\sigma}). \tag{4:8.32}$$

In particular we see that if $\mathbf{G}(\mathbf{r})$ is any vector in coordinate space, then

$$\mathbf{G}(\mathbf{r})\cdot\boldsymbol{\sigma} \tag{4:8.33}$$

will be a scalar under all rotations because

$$\mathbf{G}'(\mathbf{r}')\cdot\boldsymbol{\sigma}' = [R\mathbf{G}(\mathbf{r})]\cdot[R\boldsymbol{\sigma}] = \mathbf{G}(\mathbf{r})\cdot\boldsymbol{\sigma}.$$

This is the kind of term that normally enters the Hamiltonian. Thus the Hamiltonian for a single spinning electron in both an electrostatic field and a magnetostatic field is

$$H = \frac{1}{2m}\left(-i\hbar\,\nabla + \frac{e}{c}\mathbf{A}(\mathbf{r})\right)^2 + \frac{e\hbar}{2mc}\mathbf{H}(\mathbf{r})\cdot\boldsymbol{\sigma} - \frac{e\hbar}{4m^2c^2}[\mathbf{F}(\mathbf{r}) \times \mathbf{H}(\mathbf{r})]\cdot\boldsymbol{\sigma}, \tag{4:8.34}$$

where e is the negative of the actual charge, $\mathbf{A}$ is the vector potential, $\mathbf{H} = \nabla \times \mathbf{A}$, $\mathbf{H}$ is the magnetic field strength, and $\mathbf{F}$ is the electric field strength. The last term is the Thomas spin-orbit interaction.

If the system consists of N particles, then the wave function is a

2^N-dimensional vector in the Kronecker product of N spin spaces, and the 2^N-dimensional spin matrices are also Kronecker products of N spin matrices. In considering rotational invariance one transforms all coordinates and spins simultaneously. Again, however, one can consider invariance of the Hamiltonian under distinct transformations of every coordinate and every spin. Generally one would like to find every mathematical symmetry transformation whether its physical meaning is immediately obvious or not. However, the physically obvious symmetries are of course the easy ones to find. Again the linearly independent eigenvectors belonging to a single energy level generate a representation of the symmetry group. More explicitly, in the N-particle case

$$H = H(\mathbf{r}_1,..., \mathbf{r}_N; -i\hbar\,\nabla_1,..., -i\hbar\,\nabla_N; \boldsymbol{\sigma}_1,..., \boldsymbol{\sigma}_N) \tag{4:8.35}$$

and one looks for a set of coordinate and spin transformations $S_1,...,S_N$; $T_1,..., T_N$ such that the transformed H is equal to the original H, i.e.,

$$\begin{aligned} H(S_1\mathbf{r}_1,...,S_N\mathbf{r}_N; -i\hbar\, D_1^{-1t}\nabla_1,..., -i\hbar\, D_N^{-1t}\nabla_N; T_1^{-1}\boldsymbol{\sigma}_1 T_1,..., T_N^{-1}\boldsymbol{\sigma}_N T_N) \\ = H(\mathbf{r}_1,..., \mathbf{r}_N; -i\hbar\,\nabla_1,..., -i\hbar\,\nabla_N; \boldsymbol{\sigma}_1,..., \boldsymbol{\sigma}_N). \end{aligned} \tag{4:8.36}$$

The σ's are now 2^N-dimensional

$$\boldsymbol{\sigma}_j = I \otimes I \otimes ... \otimes I \otimes \boldsymbol{\sigma} \otimes I \otimes ... \otimes I, \tag{4:8.37}$$

where the $(N-1)$ I's are 2-dimensional unit matrices, and the 2-dimensional spin matrix $\boldsymbol{\sigma}$ is in the jth position. The T's must also be 2^N-dimensional as must the eigenvectors $\Phi(\mathbf{r}_1,..., \mathbf{r}_N)$. If $\{\Phi_1,..., \Phi_d\}$ is a complete linearly independent set of eigenvectors belonging to H we again have for a symmetry transformation

$$\begin{aligned} (\mathscr{S}_1...\mathscr{S}_N T_1...T_N)\Phi_i(\mathbf{r}_1,..., \mathbf{r}_N) = T_1...T_N\,\Phi_i(S_1^{-1}\mathbf{r}_1,..., S_N^{-1}\mathbf{r}_N) \\ = \sum_{j=1}^{d} D_{ji}(S_1,...,S_N; T_1,..., T_N)\Phi_j(\mathbf{r}_1,..., \mathbf{r}_N), \end{aligned} \tag{4:8.38}$$

where the D's form a d-dimensional representation of the symmetry group.

The similarity of this theory to the classical theory of molecular vibrations where we looked for matrices $\bar{D}$ such that $T(\bar{D}\dot{q}) = T(\dot{q})$, and $V(\bar{D}q) = V(q)$ should be noted.

Finally, let us consider a rather different type of symmetry which is sometimes called time-reversal symmetry (188). Let us consider only real Hamiltonians

$$H^* = H. \tag{4:8.39}$$

The Hamiltonian is generally real for a system of spinless particles not in a magnetic field. From the time-independent wave equation $H\phi = E\phi$ and the fact that E must be real, we see by conjugation that $H\phi^* = E\phi^*$, so that

ϕ^* must also be an eigenvector of H belonging to E (ϕ^* is called the time-reversed ϕ). Let $\{\phi_1, \ldots, \phi_d\}$ be a linearly independent set of eigenvectors belonging to E and generating the irreducible representation Γ_E of the symmetry group of H. If the complex conjugate of any eigenvector of this set depends linearly on the set, then we know that Γ_E must be of the first kind. Conversely, if Γ_E is not of the first kind, then the conjugates of the eigenvectors of the set $\{\phi_1, \ldots, \phi_d\}$ must all be linearly independent of the set so that the level E must be accidentally degenerate. In short then, if an energy level belonging to a real Hamiltonian has an irreducible representation Γ_e of second or third kind, then E is accidentally degenerate.

Similar considerations can be made for a spin-dependent Hamiltonian even though it is not real. In many such Hamiltonians there is only one type of term which is either complex or spin-dependent, and this type of term has the form

$$i\mathbf{Q}\cdot\boldsymbol{\sigma}, \tag{4:8.40}$$

where $\mathbf{Q}$ is a real vector operator. The complex conjugate of such a term is $-i\mathbf{Q}\cdot\boldsymbol{\sigma}^*$, so that from the identity

$$\sigma_y \boldsymbol{\sigma}^* \sigma_y = -\boldsymbol{\sigma} \tag{4:8.41}$$

we see that

$$\begin{aligned} \sigma_y(i\mathbf{Q}\cdot\boldsymbol{\sigma})^*\sigma_y &= \sigma_y(-i\mathbf{Q}\cdot\boldsymbol{\sigma}^*)\sigma_y \\ &= -i\mathbf{Q}\cdot\sigma_y\boldsymbol{\sigma}^*\sigma_y \\ &= (i\mathbf{Q}\cdot\boldsymbol{\sigma}). \end{aligned} \tag{4:8.42}$$

Since the remaining terms of such a Hamiltonian are real and commute with σ_y we see that for a one-particle system

$$\sigma_y H^* \sigma_y = H. \tag{4:8.43}$$

Consequently by taking the complex conjugate of the time independent wave equation and multiplying by σ_y we obtain

$$H(\sigma_y \Phi^*) = E(\sigma_y \Phi^*). \tag{4:8.44}$$

Therefore, if Φ is an eigenvector of an H satisfying (4:8.43), which belongs to E, so is $\sigma_y \Phi^*$. We note that the state represented by $\sigma_y \Phi^*$ is the time-reversed state of Φ, and that σ_y is the time-reversal operator for the spin representation $\Gamma_{1/2}$ of $R(3)$. For an N-particle system one replaces the one-particle time-reversal matrix σ_y in (4:8.43,4) by the N-particle time-reversal matrix $\sigma_y \otimes \sigma_y \otimes \ldots \otimes \sigma_y = \sigma_{1y}\sigma_{2y}\ldots\sigma_{Ny}$ (where each term contains N factors).

Let us briefly state some easily provable results about accidental degeneracy due to time reversal symmetry. If $\{\Phi_1(\mathbf{r}), \ldots, \Phi_d(\mathbf{r})\}$ is a linearly independent set of degenerate eigenvectors which generate an irreducible representation Γ_E of the symmetry group G of H, if G is a subgroup of $R(3)$ (or $O(3)$), and if the time-reversed state of any state of this set is linearly dependent on the set then Γ_E must be of the first kind if the number of particles is even and of the second kind if the number of particles is odd. Conversely, if Γ_E does not satisfy this requirement the level E must be accidentally degenerate.

These results can be extended to the case in which the symmetry group G is a subgroup of the Euclidean group (inhomogeneous orthogonal group) because the subgroup T of pure translations is a normal subgroup so one can obtain a spin representation by letting each coset RT of T be represented by $D^{(1/2)}(R)$.

9. Stationary Perturbation Theory

For very few quantum mechanical systems and for almost none of practical interest is the wave equation solvable exactly in terms of known functions. Consequently, approximation methods are frequently used. The most commonly used approximation method is the Rayleigh-Schrödinger perturbation theory.

Before proceeding to perturbation theory proper, let us make some preliminary symmetry considerations regarding eigenfunction expansions. Let H_0 be the Hamiltonian of a system for which the time-independent wave equation is exactly solvable, and let H be the Hamiltonian of some other system described by the same independent variables for which the wave equation is not exactly solvable. Since the linearly independent eigenfunctions $\{\phi_m^{(0)}\}$ of H_0 usually form a complete system (in some sense) we shall assume that the linearly independent eigenfunctions $\{\phi_n\}$ of H are expandable in terms of those of H_0:

$$\phi_n = \mathbf{S}_m a_{nm} \phi_m^{(0)} , \tag{4:9.1}$$

where the symbol $\mathbf{S}$ denotes either a summation or an integration or both, depending on whether the index m varies discretely, continuously, or both; and the coefficients a_{nm} are as yet unknown.

Let us first consider the case in which every eigenvalue of both H_0 and H is non-degenerate, and H_0 possesses the symmetry group $G_0 = \{A\}$ (see the preceding Section). Let the operator in function space corresponding to A be $\mathscr{A}$. Then if $\phi_m^{(0)}$ is an eigenfunction of H_0 belonging to energy $E_m^{(0)}$, so is $\mathscr{A}\phi_m^{(0)}$. Hence

$$\mathscr{A}\phi_m^{(0)} = D^{(m)}(\mathscr{A})\phi_m^{(0)} = \chi^{(m)}(\mathscr{A})\phi_m^{(0)} , \tag{4:9.2}$$

where Γ_m is the 1-dimensional representation of G_0 belonging to $E_m^{(0)}$. If H possesses the entire symmetry of H_0 we have

$$\mathscr{A}\phi_n = D^{(n)}(\mathscr{A})\phi_n = \chi^{(n)}(\mathscr{A})\phi_n\,, \tag{4:9.3}$$

so by multiplying (4:9.1) by $\mathscr{A}$ we obtain

$$\chi^{(n)}(\mathscr{A})\phi_n = \mathop{\mathbf{S}}_m a_{nm}\chi^{(m)}(\mathscr{A})\phi_m^{(0)}\,,$$

and multiplying by the complex conjugate $\chi^{(k)*}(\mathscr{A})$ of any primitive character of G, summing over $\mathscr{A}$, and using the orthogonality relations for characters we obtain

$$\phi_n = \mathop{\mathbf{S}}_m a_{nm}\,\delta(\Gamma_n, \Gamma_m)\phi_m^{(0)}\,. \tag{4:9.4}$$

The delta function in the above equation is zero if $\Gamma_n \neq \Gamma_m$ and one otherwise. Consequently, if H possesses the full symmetry of H_0 only eigenfunctions $\phi_m^{(0)}$ of H_0 which generate the representation Γ_n of G_0 enter the expansion (4:9.1) of ϕ_n; that is, those eigenfunctions entering the expansion must transform in the same way as the eigenfunctions being expanded. If H possesses less symmetry than H_0, then, because the representations generated by the eigenfunctions are all 1-dimensional, the preceding discussion holds if the smaller symmetry group G of H is substituted for G_0. In particular (4:9.4) still holds except that the Γ's are now 1-dimensional representations of G instead of G_0.

Now let us develop the analogous theory for the case in which both H_0 and H are allowed to have degenerate energy levels. First let us rewrite (4:9.1) in the form

$$\phi_{nj} = \mathop{\mathbf{S}}_{m,i} a_{nj}^{mi}\phi_{mi}^{(0)}\,, \tag{4:9.5}$$

where $\phi_{mi}^{(0)}$ is the ith linearly independent eigenfunction of H_0 belonging to the eigenvalue $E_m^{(0)}$ and ϕ_{nj} is the jth eigenfunction of H belonging to E_n. Again we first consider the case in which H possesses all the symmetry of H_0, and multiply (4:9.5) by the symmetry operator $\mathscr{A}$. This yields

$$\mathop{\mathbf{S}}_l D_{lj}^{(n)}(\mathscr{A})\phi_{nl} = \mathop{\mathbf{S}}_{m,i} a_{nj}^{mi}\mathop{\mathbf{S}}_k D_{ki}^{(m)}(\mathscr{A})\phi_{mk}^{(0)}\,,$$

where Γ_m and Γ_n are the representations of G_0 belonging to $E_m^{(0)}$ and E_n, respectively, and are assumed irreducible (no accidental degeneracy). We also assume that the eigenfunctions have been chosen so that the representations belonging to any two energy levels are either identical or inequivalent. By multiplying by $[D^{(p)-1}(\mathscr{A})]_{st}$, summing over $\mathscr{A}$, and using the orthogonality relations for matrix elements we obtain

$$\phi_{nj} = \mathop{\mathbf{S}}_m a_{nk}^{mk}\,\delta(\Gamma_n, \Gamma_m)\phi_{mj}^{(0)}\,. \tag{4:9.6}$$

This equation again says that only eigenfunctions of H_0 transforming according to the same representation as ϕ_{nj} enter in the expansion of ϕ_{nj}. However, it also says that only eigenfunctions of H_0 belonging to the same row of the representation as ϕ_{nj} enter, and that the same coefficients are used for the expansion of each row. Equation (4:9.6) can therefore be simplified slightly to the form

$$\phi_{nj} = \mathop{\mathbf{S}}_{m} b_n^m \, \delta(\Gamma_n, \Gamma_m) \phi_{mj}^{(0)} . \tag{4:9.7}$$

Finally let us consider the degenerate case in which H has less symmetry than H_0; i.e. G is a subgroup of G_0. In this case even though the eigenfunctions of H_0 belonging to a single energy level generate an irreducible representation of G_0 they will not in general generate an irreducible representation of the subgroup G. However, by forming suitable linear combinations of these eigenfunctions of H_0 we can if necessary find a new set of eigenfunctions of H_0 such that they generate a representation of G_0 which subduces a completely reduced representation of G. This can be done by using one of the previously described (see Chapter III) methods of reducing representations. Let us assume that the eigenfunctions of H_0 are so chosen. Let us designate the eigenfunction of H_0 belonging to $E_m^{(0)}$ and transforming according to the ith row of the irreducible representation $\Gamma_{n'}$ of G by $\phi_{mn'i}^{(0)}$. Then, let us rewrite the expansions (4:9.1) and (4:9.5) in the form

$$\phi_{nj} = \mathop{\mathbf{S}}_{m,n',i} a_{nj}^{mn'i} \phi_{mn'i}^{(0)} . \tag{4:9.8}$$

Again going through the standard procedure of multiplying by a G, multiplying by $[D^{(p)-1}(\mathscr{A})]_{st}$, summing over all $\mathscr{A}$ in G, and applying the orthogonality relations for matrix elements, we find

$$\phi_{nj} = \mathop{\mathbf{S}}_{m,n'} a_{nk}^{mn'k} \delta(\Gamma_n, \Gamma_{n'}) \phi_{mn'j}^{(0)} , \tag{4:9.9}$$

where Γ_n and $\Gamma_{n'}$ are both irreducible representations of the symmetry group G of H. Again this can be simplified slightly to the form

$$\phi_{nj} = \mathop{\mathbf{S}}_{m,n'} b_n^{mn'} \delta(\Gamma_n, \Gamma_{n'}) \phi_{mn'j}^{(0)} . \tag{4:9.10}$$

Again, only functions transforming according to the same row of the same irreducible representations of G, as ϕ_{nj}, enter the expansion, and again the expansion of every eigenfunction belonging to a single energy level of H has the same coefficients. In this case, however, the sum extends not only over energy levels of H_0 but also over the irreducible components of the representations of G subduced by the irreducible representations of G_0 belonging to these energy levels.

It should be observed that the preceding theory holds for systems of particles with spin as well as for spinless systems. This will also be true of the perturbation theory which will follow.

Let us begin with nondegenerate perturbation theory; i.e., let us consider a system of particles with a Hamiltonian operator H_0 whose wave equation can be solved exactly in terms of known functions and whose eigenvalues are all nondegenerate. We then consider the eigenvalues and eigenfunctions of a "slightly" altered system whose Hamiltonian is in consequence "slightly" different from H_0. More precisely, let

$$H_0 \phi_m^{(0)} = E_m^{(0)} \phi_m^{(0)}, \tag{4:9.11}$$

where every $E_m^{(0)}$ is nondegenerate. Also let

$$H = H_0 + \lambda H_1 + \lambda^2 H_2 + \dots = \sum_{k=0}^{\infty} \lambda^k H_k, \tag{4:9.12}$$

where $\sum_{k=1}^{\infty} \lambda^k H_k$ is called the perturbation and operates on the same functions as H_0 (and perhaps others), and λ is a "small" parameter so that $\sum_{k=1}^{\infty} \lambda^k H_k$ is "small" in some sense compared to H_0. In particular, in the case of finitely separated eigenvalues, if $E_m^{(0)}$ and $E_{m+1}^{(0)}$ are two adjacent eigenvalues and E_m is the eigenvalue of H which reduces to $E_m^{(0)}$ when $\lambda = 0$, then one wants the shift $|E_m - E_m^{(0)}|$ to be small compared with the spacing $|E_m^{(0)} - E_{m+1}^{(0)}|$. If $\{\phi_n\}$ and $\{E_n\}$ are the eigenfunctions and eigenvalues of H we have

$$H\phi_n = E_n \phi_n, \tag{4:9.13}$$

again assuming no degeneracy of any E_n. We then assume a power series expansion of both ϕ_n and E_n in terms of λ

$$\phi_n = \sum_{k=0}^{\infty} \lambda^k \phi_n^{(k)} \tag{4:9.14a}$$

$$E_n = \sum_{k=0}^{\infty} \lambda^k E_n^{(k)}, \tag{4:9.14b}$$

where $\phi_n^{(0)}$ and $E_n^{(0)}$ in these expansions must be the unperturbed eigenfunction and eigenvalue defined in (4:9.11). Substituting expansions (4:9.14) in the wave equation (4:9.13) and equating coefficients of equal powers of λ we obtain

$$H_0 \phi_n^{(0)} = E_n^{(0)} \phi_n^{(0)} \tag{4:9.15a}$$

$$H_0 \phi_n^{(1)} + H_1 \phi_n^{(0)} = E_n^{(0)} \phi_n^{(1)} + E_n^{(1)} \phi_n^{(0)} \tag{4:9.15b}$$

$$H_0 \phi_n^{(2)} + H_1 \phi_n^{(1)} + H_2 \phi_n^{(0)} = E_n^{(0)} \phi_n^{(2)} + E_n^{(1)} \phi_n^{(1)} + E_n^{(2)} \phi_n^{(0)} \tag{4:9.15c}$$

$$\sum_{k=0}^{l} H_k \phi_n^{(l-k)} = \sum_{k=0}^{l} E_n^{(k)} \phi_n^{(l-k)}. \tag{4:9.15d}$$

If we then expand each $\phi_n^{(k)}$ in terms of unperturbed functions $\phi_m^{(0)}$,

$$\phi_n^{(k)} = \mathbf{S}_m\, a_{nm}^{(k)} \phi_m^{(0)} \tag{4:9.16}$$

und substitute in (4:9.15) we can solve for the unknown a's and E's by making ase of the orthonormality of the $\phi_m^{(0)}$'s and ϕ_n's. One obtains thus

$$a_{nm}^{(1)} = \frac{\langle m|H_1|n\rangle}{E_n^{(0)} - E_m^{(0)}} \qquad m \neq n \tag{4:9.17a}$$

$$a_{nn}^{(1)} = 0 \tag{4:9.17b}$$

$$E_n^{(1)} = \langle n|H_1|n\rangle \tag{4:9.17c}$$

$$a_{nm}^{(2)} = \frac{\langle m|H_2|n\rangle}{E_n^{(0)} - E_m^{(0)}} - \frac{\langle m|H_1|n\rangle\langle n|H_1|n\rangle}{(E_n^{(0)} - E_m^{(0)})^2} + \\ + \mathbf{S}'_{m'} \frac{\langle m|H_1 m'\rangle\langle m'|H_1|n\rangle}{(E_n^{(0)} - E_m^{(0)})(E_n^{(0)} - E_{m'}^{(0)})} \quad m \neq n \tag{4:9.17d}$$

$$a_{nn}^{(2)} = -\tfrac{1}{2}\,'\mathbf{S}_m \frac{|\langle m|H_1|n\rangle|^2}{(E_n^{(0)} - E_m^{(0)})^2} \tag{4:9.17e}$$

$$E_n^{(2)} = \langle n|H_2|n\rangle + \mathbf{S}'_m \frac{|\langle n|H_1|m\rangle|^2}{E_n^{(0)} - E_m^{(0)}}\,, \tag{4:9.17f}$$

where

$$\langle m|H_k|n\rangle = \int \phi_m^{(0)*} H_k \phi_n^{(0)} \tag{4:9.18a}$$

if H is spin independent, and

$$\langle m|H_k|n\rangle = \int \phi_m^{(0)\dagger} H_k \phi_n^{(0)} \tag{4:9.18b}$$

if H is spin dependent, and $\mathbf{S}'$ means that the term with the dummy index equal to n is omitted. Actually, the imaginary parts of $a_{nn}^{(1)}$ and $a_{nn}^{(2)}$ were arbitrarily chosen to be zero. The higher order approximations have not been written out because of complexity. Substituting (4:9.17) in (4:9.14) we find to second order in λ

$$\phi_n = \phi_n^{(0)} + \lambda \mathbf{S}'_m \frac{\langle m|H_1|n\rangle}{E_n^{(0)} - E_m^{(0)}} \phi_m^{(0)} + \lambda^2 \mathbf{S}'_m \left\{ \left[\frac{\langle m|H_2|n\rangle}{E_n^{(0)} - E_m^{(0)}} - \frac{\langle m|H_1|n\rangle\langle n|H_1|n\rangle}{(E_n^{(0)} - E_m^{(0)})^2} \right.\right. \\ \left.\left. + \mathbf{S}'_{m'} \frac{\langle m|H_1|m'\rangle\langle m'|H_1|n\rangle}{(E_n^{(0)} - E_m^{(0)})(E_n^{(0)} - E_{m'}^{(0)})} \right] \phi_m^{(0)} - \frac{1}{2} \frac{|\langle m|H_1|n\rangle|^2}{(E_n^{(0)} - E_m^{(0)})^2} \phi_n^{(0)} \right\} \tag{4:9.19a}$$

$$E_n = E_n^{(0)} + \lambda\langle n|H_1|n\rangle + \lambda^2 \left[\langle n|H_2|n\rangle + \mathbf{S}'_m \frac{|\langle n|H_1|m\rangle|^2}{E_n^{(0)} - E_m^{(0)}} \right]. \tag{4:9.19b}$$

We can now apply our earlier symmetry considerations of eigenfunctions expansions. If we suppose that infinite-order perturbation theory will yield ϕ_n exactly, then we know that only $\phi_m^{(0)}$'s transforming like ϕ_n under the symmetry group G of H can enter the perturbation expansion. Further, since we know that $\phi_n^{(0)}$ enters the expansion, we also know that ϕ_n and $\phi_n^{(0)}$ must transform in the same way under G; and from the first-order term of the expansion of ϕ_n, we know that every matrix element $\langle m|H_1|n\rangle$ involving $\phi_m^{(0)}$'s which transform differently from $\phi_n^{(0)}$ under G must be zero.

The last statement can also be proved easily in a direct manner for the case in which the symmetry coordinate transformation S is a linear inhomogeneous orthogonal transformation and the symmetry spin transformation T is unitary.

$$S\mathbf{r} = D\mathbf{r} + \mathbf{c} \tag{4:9.20a}$$

$$DD^t = I \tag{4:9.20b}$$

$$TT^\dagger = I. \tag{4:9.20c}$$

In this case one has

$$\langle m|H_1|n\rangle = \int \Phi_m^{(0)}(\mathbf{r})H_1(\mathbf{r}, -i\mathbf{h}\boldsymbol{\nabla}, \boldsymbol{\sigma})\Phi_n^{(0)}(\mathbf{r})d^{(3N)}r, \tag{4:9.21}$$

where N is the number of particles and $\mathbf{r}$ is an abbreviation for the set of all N coordinate vectors which can be considered as $3N$-dimensional vector, so that by transforming to the coordinates $S\mathbf{r}$ one has

$$\begin{aligned}
\langle m|H_1|n\rangle &= \int \Phi_m^{(0)\dagger}(S\mathbf{r})H_1(S\mathbf{r}, -ih\, D^{-1t}\boldsymbol{\nabla},\boldsymbol{\sigma})\Phi_n^{(0)}(S\mathbf{r})d^{(3N)}(Sr)\\
&= \int \Phi_m^{(0)\dagger}(S\mathbf{r})H_1(S\mathbf{r}, -ih\, D^{-1t}\boldsymbol{\nabla},\boldsymbol{\sigma})\Phi_n^{(0)}(S\mathbf{r})d^{(3N)}r\\
&= \int [T^{-1}\Phi_m^{(0)}(S\mathbf{r})]^\dagger H_1(S\mathbf{r}, -ih\, D^{-1t}\boldsymbol{\nabla}, T^{-1}\boldsymbol{\sigma}T)T^{-1}\Phi_n^{(0)}(S\mathbf{r})d^{(3N)}r\\
&= \int [T^{-1}\Phi_m^{(0)}(S\mathbf{r})]^\dagger H_1(\mathbf{r}, -ih\,\boldsymbol{\nabla},\boldsymbol{\sigma})T^{-1}\Phi_n^{(0)}(S\mathbf{r})d^{(3N)}r\\
&= \sum_{j=1}^{d_m}\sum_{k=1}^{d_n} D_{jm}^{(m)*}(S,T)D_{kn}^{(n)}(S,T)\int \Phi_j^{(0)\dagger}(\mathbf{r})H_1(\mathbf{r}, -ih\,\boldsymbol{\nabla},\boldsymbol{\sigma})\Phi_k^{(0)}(\mathbf{r})d^{(3N)}r\\
&= \sum_{j=1}^{d_m}\sum_{k=1}^{d_n} D_{jm}^{(m)*}(S,T)D_{kn}^{(n)}(S,T)\langle j|H_1|k\rangle
\end{aligned} \tag{4:9.22}$$

Summing (4:9.22) over all group elements (S, T) we obtain

$$\langle m|H_1|n\rangle = \sum_{j=1}^{dm}\sum_{k=1}^{dn}\langle j|H_1|k\rangle\left\{\frac{1}{g}\sum_{(ST)\epsilon G}[D^{(m)-1}(S,T)]_{mj}[D^{(n)}S,(T)]_{kn}\right\}. \tag{4:9.23}$$

Applying the orthogonality relations for matrix elements to the expression in braces we see that if $\Gamma_m \neq \Gamma_n$ then $\langle m|H_1|n\rangle = 0$. Thus we again obtain

$$[1 - \delta(\Gamma_m, \Gamma_n)]\langle m|H_1|n\rangle = 0, \tag{4:9.24}$$

which holds also for H_k and for H.

Now let us turn to degenerate perturbation theory. Again we expand H, ϕ, and E in power series in λ

$$H = H_0 + \lambda H_1 + \lambda^2 H_2 + \ldots = \sum_{k=0}^{\infty}\lambda^k H_k \tag{4:9.25a}$$

$$\phi_{nj} = \phi_{nj}^{(0)} + \lambda\phi_{nj}^{(1)} + \lambda^2\phi_{nj}^{(2)} + \ldots = \sum_{k=0}^{\infty} \lambda^k \phi_{nj}^{(k)} \tag{4:9.25b}$$

$$E_{nj} = E_n^{(0)} + \lambda E_{nj}^{(1)} + \lambda^2 E_{nj}^{(2)} + \ldots = E_n^{(0)} + \sum_{k=1}^{\infty} \lambda^k E_{nj}^{(k)}, \tag{4:9.25c}$$

where j labels the linearly independent degenerate eigenfunctions $\phi_{nj}^{(0)}$ belonging to $E_n^{(0)}$ as well as the eigenfunctions ϕ_{nj} into which they go under the perturbation. Again we see that $\lim_{\lambda \to 0} \phi_{nj} = \phi_{nj}^{(0)}$. However, since there is now a d-dimensional manifold of eigenfunctions of H_0 belonging to $E_n^{(0)}$ we must somehow select those which the eigenfunctions of H approach as $\lambda \to 0$. Suppose then that we are given a complete linearly independent set of eigenfunctions $\chi_{nj}^{(0)}$ of H_0 belonging to $E_n^{(0)}$, and that we want to find the correct $\phi_{nj}^{(0)}$'s which must of course be linear combinations of the χ's

$$\phi_{nj}^{(0)} = \sum_{l=1}^{d} c_{nj}^l \chi_{nl}^{(0)}. \tag{4:9.26}$$

The c's will be determined from the usual equations one obtains by substituting the expansions (4:9.25) in the wave equation

$$H\phi_{nj} = E_{nj}\phi_{nj} \ . \tag{4:9.27}$$

The resulting equations are

$$H_0\phi_{nj}^{(0)} = E_n^{(0)}\phi_{nj}^{(0)} \tag{4:9.28a}$$

$$H_0\phi_{nj}^{(1)} + H_1\phi_{nj}^{(0)} = E_n^{(0)}\phi_{nj}^{(1)} + E_{nj}^{(1)}\phi_{nj}^{(0)} \tag{4:9.28b}$$

$$H_0\phi_{nj}^{(0)} + H_1\phi_{nj}^{(1)} + H_2\phi_{nj}^{(0)} = E_n^{(0)}\phi_{nj}^{(2)} + E_{nj}^{(1)}\phi_{nj}^{(1)} + E_{nj}^{(2)}\phi_{nj}^{(0)} \tag{4:9.28c}$$

$$\sum_{k=0}^{l} H_k\phi_{nj}^{(l-k)} = \sum_{k=0}^{l} E_{nj}^{(k)}\phi_{nj}^{(l-k)} \tag{4:9.28d}$$

where $E_{nj}^{(0)} = E_n^{(0)}$.

The second equation (4:9.28b) can be rewritten

$$(H_1 - E_{nj}^{(1)})\phi_{nj}^{(0)} = (E_n^{(0)} - H_0)\phi_{nj}^{(1)} \tag{4:9.28b}$$

so that by multiplying by $\chi_{nk}^{(0)}$ we obtain

$$\langle\chi_{nk}^{(0)}|H_1 - E_{nj}^{(1)}|\phi_{nj}^{(0)}\rangle = \langle\chi_{nk}^{(0)}|E_n^{(0)} - H_0|\phi_{nj}^{(1)}\rangle. \tag{4:9.29}$$

Since $\chi_{nk}^{(0)}$ is by definition an eigenfunction of H_0 belonging to $E_n^{(0)}$ we see that the right side of (4:9.29) is zero, so that

$$\langle\chi_{nk}^{(0)}|H_1 - E_{nj}^{(1)}|\phi_{nj}^{(0)}\rangle = 0. \tag{4:9.30}$$

This equation will now determine the c's in the expansion of the correct zero-order eigenfunctions $\phi_{nj}^{(0)}$ in terms of the given eigenfunctions $\chi_n^{(0)}$, because if we substitute the expansion (4:9.26) in the above equation (4:9.30) we obtain

$$\sum_{l=1}^{d} \langle \chi_{nk}^{(0)} | H_1 - E_{nj}^{(1)} | \chi_{nl}^{(0)} \rangle c_{nj} = 0. \tag{4:9.31}$$

This is a set of d linear homogeneous equations for the c's, so the determinant of the coefficients must be zero in order for a nontrivial solution to exist. Thus we must have

$$\det(\langle \chi_{nk}^{(0)} | H_1 - E_{nj}^{(1)} | \chi_{nl}^{(0)} \rangle) = 0 \tag{4:9.32}$$

where the rows are labelled by k and the columns by l. This equation is a dth degree equation in the only unknown $E_{nj}^{(1)}$. Consequently, we get d values of $E_{nj}^{(1)}$ by solving this secular equation. These are of course the d different first-order energy perturbations $E_{nl}^{(1)}, \ldots, E_{nd}^{(1)}$. We can then substitute each of these values of $E_{nj}^{(1)}$ in the equation (4:9.31) for $c_{nj}^{(1)}, \ldots, c_{nj}^{(d)}$ and obtain one set of c's for each $E_{nj}^{(1)}$. We thus obtain the d correct zero-order eigenfunctions $\phi_{nj}^{(0)}$ from the d given zero-order eigenfunctions $\chi_n^{(0)}$.

If the secular equation has no multiple roots, then every ϕ_{nj} into which the eigenfunctions of H_0 belonging to $E_n^{(0)}$ go will belong to a different eigenvalue of H and will therefore be orthogonal. Since the correct $\phi_{nj}^{(0)}$'s are obtained from the ϕ_{nj}'s by letting $\lambda \to 0$, they will also be orthogonal. In case the secular equation has multiple roots, some degeneracy will remain and the correct zero-order wave function will not be forced to be orthogonal. But even in this case they can be chosen orthogonal; consequently we shall assume that all correct zero-order wave functions $\phi_{nj}^{(0)}$ are orthonormal.

$$\langle \phi_{mi}^{(0)} | \phi_{nj}^{(0)} \rangle = \delta_{mk} \delta_{ij}. \tag{4:9.33}$$

Let us now consider the matrix elements of H_1 with respect to $\phi_{nj}^{(0)}$'s. We have

$$\begin{aligned} \langle \phi_{nk}^{(0)} | H_1 | \phi_{nl}^{(0)} \rangle &= \sum_{i,j} c_{nk}^{i*} c_{nl}^{j} \langle \chi_{ni}^{(0)} | H_1 | \chi_{nj}^{(0)} \rangle \\ &= \sum_{i,j} c_{nk}^{i*} c_{nl}^{j} E_{nl}^{(1)} \langle \chi_{ni}^{(0)} | \chi_{nj}^{(0)} \rangle \\ &= E_{nl}^{(1)} \sum_{i,j} \langle c_{nk}^{i} \chi_{ni}^{(0)} | c_{nl}^{j} \chi_{nj}^{(0)} \rangle \\ &= E_{nl}^{(1)} \langle \phi_{nk}^{(0)} | \phi_{nl}^{(0)} \rangle \\ &= E_{nl}^{(1)} \delta_{kl} \end{aligned} \tag{4:9.34}$$

so we see that the correct zero-order eigenfunctions make the secular equation diagonal.

$$\langle \phi_{nk}^{(0)} | H_1 - E_{nj}^{(1)} | \phi_{nl}^{(0)} \rangle = (E_{nl}^{(1)} - E_{nj}^{(1)}) \delta_{kl}. \tag{4:9.35}$$

Conversely, suppose that the χ's we are given are orthonormal and diagonalize the secular matrix

$$\langle \chi_{nk}^{(0)} | H_1 | \chi_{nl}^{(0)} \rangle = h_k \delta_{kl} \tag{4:9.36a}$$

$$\langle \chi_{nk}^{(0)} | \chi_{nl}^{(0)} \rangle = \delta_{kl}. \tag{4:9.36b}$$

Then the secular equation is

$$\prod_{k=1}^{d} (h_k - E_{nj}^{(1)}) = 0, \tag{4:9.37}$$

so that $E_{nk}^{(1)} = h_k$. The equation (4:9.30) for $\phi_{nj}^{(0)}$ is then satisfied by $\chi_{nj}^{(0)}$ because

$$\begin{aligned}\langle \chi_{nk}^{(0)} | H_1 - E_{nj}^{(1)} | \chi_{nj}^{(0)} \rangle &= h_k \delta_{kj} - E_{nj}^{(1)} \delta_{kj} = (h_j - E_{nj}^{(1)}) \delta_{kj} \\ &= (E_{nj}^{(1)} - E_{nj}^{(1)}) \delta_{kj} = 0. \end{aligned} \tag{4:9.38}$$

Hence we conclude that eigenfunctions of H_0 belonging to $E_n^{(0)}$ which diagonalize the secular matrix are correct zero-order eigenfunctions.

Hence, the problem of finding correct zero-order eigenfunctions is just the problem of finding orthonormal linear combinations of the χ's which will diagonalize the secular matrix. We see also that

$$E_{nj}^{(1)} = \langle \phi_{nj}^{(0)} | H_1 | \phi_{nj}^{(0)} \rangle = \langle nj | H_1 | nj \rangle \tag{4:9.39}$$

if the ϕ's are correct zero-order eigenfunctions.

If we again assume an eigenfunction expansion

$$\phi_{nj}^{(1)} = \mathbf{S}_{m,i} \, a_{nj}^{(1)mi} \phi_{mi}^{(0)}, \tag{4:9.40}$$

we find by substituting this expansion in (4:9.28b) that

$$a_{nj}^{(1)mi} = \frac{\langle mi | H_1 | nj \rangle}{E_n^{(0)} - E_n^{(0)}} \qquad m \neq n \tag{4:9.41a}$$

$$a_{nj}^{(1)ni} = 0. \tag{4:9.41b}$$

So to the first order in λ we have

$$\phi_{nj} = \phi_{nj}^{(0)} + \lambda \, \mathbf{S}'_{m,i} \frac{\langle mi | H_1 | nj \rangle}{E_n^{(0)} - E_m^{(0)}} \phi_{mi}^{(0)} \tag{4:9.42a}$$

$$E_{nj} = E_n^{(0)} + \lambda \langle \phi_{nj}^{(0)} | H_1 | \phi_{nj}^{(0)} \rangle, \tag{4:9.42b}$$

where the $\phi_{nj}^{(0)}$'s are assumed to be correct zero-order eigenfunctions, and the prime on $\mathbf{S}'$ means that terms with $m = n$ are to be omitted.

If the degenerate energy levels of H_0 are completely split into non-degenerate levels in first-order perturbation theory, then the "correct" zero-order wave functions $\phi_{nj}^{(0)}$ determined by diagonalizing the secular matrix $\langle \chi_{nk}^{(0)} | H_1 - E_{nj}^{(1)} | \chi_{nl}^{(0)} \rangle$ really are correct. If, however, degeneracy remains in first order, then more splitting may occur in second- or higher-order perturbation theory so that more secular equations would have to be solved and the correct zero-order wave functions redetermined. In other words, the arbitrariness in the choice of correct zero-order $\phi_{nj}^{(0)}$'s which resulted from degeneracy in first-order theory might be removed by second-order theory. Because of the complexity of higher-order degenerate perturbation theory, we shall omit any consideration of it here.

Let us now return to symmetry considerations. Again, we know from previous considerations that only unperturbed eigenfunctions $\phi_{mj}^{(0)}$ which transform according to the same row of the same irreducible representation of the symmetry group G of H as ϕ_{nj} can enter the perturbation expansion of ϕ_{nj}. And since $\phi_{nj}^{(0)}$ enters the expansion we know that all eigenvectors entering the expansion must transform like $\phi_{nj}^{(0)}$. From the perturbation expansion (4:9.41a) we see that the matrix element $\langle mi|H_1|nj\rangle$, $(m \neq n)$, must be zero unless $\phi_{mi}^{(0)}$ and $\phi_{nj}^{(0)}$ transform according to the same row of the same irreducible representation of G. In equation form

$$[1 - \delta_{ij}\delta(\Gamma_m, \Gamma_n)]\langle mi|H_1|nj\rangle = 0 \quad (m \neq n). \tag{4:9.43}$$

This result can of course be obtained directly via a derivation analogous to that of (4:9.24), although one then obtains the stronger result

$$[1 - \delta_{ij}\delta(\Gamma_m, \Gamma_n)]\langle mi|H_k|nj\rangle = 0, \tag{4:9.44}$$

which holds for any m and n.

This result (4:9.43) enables us partially to solve the problem of correct zero-order wave functions on the basis of symmetry alone. Suppose the orthonormal zero-order wave functions $\{\chi_{nl}^{(0)}\}$ belonging to $E_n^{(0)}$ generate the irreducible representation $\Gamma_n^{(0)}$ of G_0. For the case where H has the full symmetry of H_0, it follows from (4:9.44) that

$$\langle ni|H_1|nj\rangle = h_i\delta_{ij}, \tag{4:9.45}$$

so that the secular matrix is diagonalized by the χ's, and they must therefore be correct zero-order wave functions. Since any set of zero-order wave functions is correct, it follows that in this case the perturbation causes no splitting in first order. If, however, the symmetry of H is less than that of H_0, so that G is a subgroup of G_0, then the perturbation will usually cause splitting because $\Gamma_n^{(0)}$ is no longer an irreducible representation of G and (4:9.44) therefore no longer holds.

However, in this case $(G \subset G_0)$ let us introduce new zero-order wave functions $\{\xi_{ni}^{(0)}\}$ which are linear combinations of the χ's and which completely reduce the representation of G subduced by $\Gamma_n^{(0)}$. The ξ's can of course be found by the method of idempotents. Let us add another index n' to the ξ's to denote which irreducible representation $\Gamma_{n'}$ of G they generate, so that

$$\mathscr{S}T\xi_{nn'i}^{(0)} = \sum_{j=1}^{d_{n'}} D_{ji}^{(n')}(S, T)\xi_{nn'j}^{(0)}. \tag{4:9.46}$$

From (4:9.43) we see that $\langle \xi_{nn'i}^{(0)}|H_1|\xi_{nn''j}^{(0)}\rangle$ is zero unless $\Gamma_{n'} = \Gamma_{n''}$ and $i = j$. Thus in particular there are no matrix elements between ξ's belonging to different irreducible representations of G. Hence, the ξ's partially diagonalize the secular matrix; or more precisely they reduce it. After finding the ξ's we are left with the problem of finding linear combinations of ξ's belonging to a particular irreducible representation $\Gamma_{n'}$ of G which will diagonalize the block of the secular matrix corresponding to $\Gamma_{n'}$. If, however, a $\Gamma_{n'}$ occurs only once in $\Gamma_n^{(0)}$ then its $\xi^{(0)}$'s are correct zero-order eigenfunctions. Thus one is left with the problem of finding correct linear combinations of $\xi^{(0)}$'s for irreducible representations $\Gamma_{n'}$ which occur more than once in $\Gamma_n^{(0)}$, and this can not be done by group theory alone.

The present problem is analogous to the problem of normal coordinates and normal vibrations treated in Section 1 of this Chapter, so we will simply repeat some results here. The number of energy levels into which a single level $E^{(0)}$ of H_0 is split by a perturbation is equal to the number of irreducible components of the representation of G subduced by $\Gamma_n^{(0)}$ The degeneracy of each new level is equal to the dimension of the irreducible representation of G belonging to it. These results can be seen intuitively from the fact that an irreducible representation of G belongs to each energy level of H, and that when $\lambda = 0$ the irreducible representations of G belonging to energy levels of H which coalesce for $\lambda = 0$ must add up to the irreducible representation of G_0 belonging to that level of H_0.

Finally, let us consider a set of $\xi_{nn'i}^{(0)}$'s belonging to a given energy level $E_n^{(0)}$ and a given irreducible representation $\Gamma_{n'}$ of G which occurs several times, say c. Then the correct zero-order wave functions $\phi_{nn'i}^{(0)}$ can be chosen to be of the form (where the c components $\Gamma_{n'}$ are distinguished by $n'_1, n'_2, \ldots, n'_c$)

$$\phi_{nn'i}^{(0)} = \gamma_1 \xi_{nn'_1 i}^{(0)} + \gamma_2 \xi_{nn'_2 i}^{(0)} + \ldots + \gamma_c \xi_{nn'_c i}^{(0)}, \tag{4:9.47}$$

which says that only ξ's transforming according to the same row as $\phi^{0)}$ need be used and that the same expansion coefficients can be used for all $\phi^{(0)}$'s which transform together.

To prove this consider the perturbed eigenfunctions belonging to one of the c_p energy levels into which $E_n^{(0)}$ splits. These eigenfunctions can be so chosen that they generate exactly the same representation $\Gamma_{n'}$ of G as one set of ξ's. Hence, the correct $\phi_{nn'i}^{(0)}$'s can be chosen so they do also. Since the $\phi_{nn'i}^{(0)}$'s can be expanded as linear combinations of $\xi_{nn'j}^{(0)}$'s in which the coefficient of any ξ is $\langle \xi | \phi_{nn'i}^{(0)} \rangle$, and since by a slight generalization of (4:9.44) this is zero, unless $\xi_{nn'i}^{(0)}$ and $\phi_{nn'i}^{(0)}$ transform according to the same row of $\Gamma_{n'}$, we see that only $\xi_{nn'i}^{(0)}$s enter the expansion of $\phi_{nn'i}^{(0)}$ The fact that the same coefficients γ can be used for every ϕ is a consequence of the orthogonality relations for matrix elements. Suppose that

$$\phi_{nk'i}^{(0)} = \sum_{q=1}^{c} \gamma_q^{(i)} \xi_{nn'_q i}^{(0)} \tag{4:9.48}$$

and that $\mathcal{O}$ is a symmetry operator so that

$$\mathcal{O}\,\phi^{(0)}_{nn'i} = \sum_{j=1}^{d_{n'}} D^{(n')}_{ji}(\mathcal{O})\,\phi^{(0)}_{nn'j}$$

$$= \sum_{q=1}^{c} \gamma^{(i)}_q \sum_{j=1}^{d_{n'}} D^{(n')}_{ji}\,(\mathcal{O})\xi^{(0)}_{nn'_q j} \tag{4:9.49}$$

By multiplying by $D^{-1}_{ik}(\mathcal{O})$, summing over $\mathcal{O}$, and using the orthogonality relations for matrix elements, we obtain

$$\phi^{(0)}_{nn'k} = \sum_{q=1}^{c} \gamma^{(i)}_q \xi_{nn'_q k}, \tag{4:9.50}$$

which is the desired result. It should be noted that c sets of γ's will be needed corresponding to the c sets of $\phi^{(0)}$'s, each of which generate $\Gamma_{n'}$.

10. Lattice Harmonics

In quantum mechanical problems involving crystals it frequently happens that one wants to solve a one-electron Schrödinger wave equation in which that potential has the symmetry of the crystal. This problem is then frequently considered as a perturbation-theoretic problem (or eigenfunction expansion problem) in which the unperturbed potential is spherically symmetric and the unperturbed eigenfunctions are eigenfunctions of the associated unperturbed spherically symmetric Hamiltonian. As is easily seen by separation of variables in spherical coordinates, the unperturbed eigenfunctions must be of the form

$$\phi^{(0)}_{nlm} = f_{nl}(r)\,Y_{lm}(\theta, \phi), \tag{4:10.1}$$

where

$$n = 1, 2, 3, \ldots, \infty$$

$$l = 0, 1, 2, \ldots, n$$

$$m = -l, -l+1, \ldots, l,$$

and the Y_{lm}'s are the spherically harmonics which are written out explicitly in Section 6 of this Chapter. The f_{nl}'s, however, must be determined separately for each problem (or potential). We know from the preceding Section that only unperturbed eigenfunctions (or linear combinations of degenerate ones) with the same symmetry as the perturbed eigenfunction can enter the eigenfunction expansion. Hence, in all such problems one starts by finding linear combinations of degenerate eigenfunctions of the form (4:10.1) having the desired symmetry.

It can be shown that it is only necessary to consider the transformations of the unperturbed wave functions (4:10.1) under the point group of the crystal and under its subgroups (which are also point groups). Since $f_{nl}(r)$ is invariant under orthogonal transformations and is the same for all degenerate eigenfunctions belonging to the energy level E_{nl}, we see that it is only necessary to consider the transformation of the spherical harmonics $Y_{l,m}$. In brief then we need to find linear combinations of the spherical harmonics Y_{lm} which will generate irreducible representations of the point groups of interest. Since all Y's and all point groups are already known it should be possible to construct tables of such linear combinations for each point group (11, 120, 178), and this has been done. These linear combinations of spherical harmonics are called lattice harmonics.

Let us now restate the problem in a slightly different way which will make clear how the problem can always be solved (with sufficient labor). We know from Section 6 that the set of $2l + 1$ spherical harmonics $Y_{l,m}(m = -l,..., l)$ generates the $(2l + 1)$-dimensional irreducible representation Γ of the 3-dimensional rotation group (also of the 3-dimensional orthogonal group). Γ in turn subduces a representation $\Gamma_l^{(s)}$ of the point group of interest, and the problem is to reduce the representation $\Gamma_l^{(s)}$ into irreducible representations of the point group by finding new basis functions which are linear combinations of the old Y's. Since the transformation of the Y's under all orthogonal coordinate transformations is given in Section 6 of this Chapter, we can write out $\Gamma_l^{(s)}$ explicitly and employ one of the idempotent methods of Chapter III to reduce it. The new basis functions so obtained are the lattice harmonics, and we see that lattice harmonics generate irreducible representations of point groups just as spherical harmonics do for the rotation and orthogonal groups. It should incidentally be noted that in general more than one choice of basis functions is possible so the lattice harmonics are not uniquely defined functions.

Although the method of finding lattice harmonics which was just described will always work it is extremely laborious, and various special techniques have been devised.

Example. Let us now work out in detail some lattice harmonics for a simple case. Let us choose the point group D_4 and the 3-dimensional representation $\Gamma_1^{(s)}$ which is generated by Y_{11}, Y_{10}, Y_{1-1}. From Section 4 we see that D_4 is generated by the two matrices

$$A = R_x\left(\frac{\pi}{2}\right) = \begin{pmatrix} 1 & 0 & 0 \\ 0 & 0 & -1 \\ 0 & 1 & 0 \end{pmatrix}, B = R_z(\pi) = \begin{pmatrix} -1 & 0 & 0 \\ 0 & -1 & 0 \\ 0 & 0 & 1 \end{pmatrix}. \qquad (4:10.2)$$

If we choose the x-axis to be the polar axis then we see that

$$
\begin{aligned}
A[\theta, \phi] &= \left[\theta, \phi + \frac{\pi}{2}\right] \\
A^{-1}[\theta, \phi] &= \left[\theta, \phi - \frac{\pi}{2}\right] \\
B[\theta, \phi] &= [\pi - \theta, \pi - \phi] \\
B^{-1}[\theta, \phi] &= [\pi - \theta, \pi - \phi]
\end{aligned}
\tag{4:10.3}
$$

so

$$\mathscr{A} Y_{l,m}(\theta, \phi) = Y_{l,m}(A^{-1}[\theta, \phi]) = Y_{l,m}\left(\theta, \phi - \frac{\pi}{2}\right) = (-i)^m Y_{l,m}(\theta, \phi) \tag{4:10.4a}$$

$$\mathscr{B} Y_{l,m}(\theta, \phi) = Y_{l,m}(B^{-1}[\theta, \phi]) = Y_{l,m}(\pi - \theta, \pi - \phi) = (-1)^l Y_{l,-m}(\theta, \phi). \tag{4:10.4b}$$

From equations (4:10.4) we see that Y_{10} generates a 1-dimensional representation of D_4 because

$$\mathscr{A} Y_{10} = Y_{10} \tag{4:10.5a}$$

$$\mathscr{B} Y_{10} = - Y_{10} \ . \tag{4:10.5b}$$

Hence Y_{10} is itself a lattice harmonic. From the table on page 145 in Section 4 of this Chapter we see that $\Gamma_1^{(s)} \cdot\!\equiv\!\cdot \Delta_2 \oplus \Delta_5$. Hence Y_{10} must generate the 1-dimensional representation Δ_2 of D_4, and the remaining two Y's must generate the 2-dimensional irreducible representation Δ_5 of D_4. Thus the other two Y's, Y_{11} and Y_{1-1}, are also lattice harmonics for D_4.

11. Molecular Orbitals

The quantum mechanical problem of finding wave functions for systems composed of three or more particles is very difficult, and in consequence many approximation methods have been developed. The LCAO (linear combinations of atomic orbitals) molecular orbital method which will be discussed here is a method for obtaining approximate one-electron wave functions. The method is also known as the Hund-Mulliken method, and the extension of the theory to electrons in crystals is known as the tight-binding method.

Suppose we consider a molecule formed from n atoms and containing N electrons. We shall neglect the motion of the atomic nuclei (Born-Oppenheimer approximation) and consider only the electronic motion. Also, we shall assume that each electron of each atom in the unbound state can be assigned an approximate time-independent wave function; thus let the kth electron on atom j possess the wave function $\phi_{jk}(\boldsymbol{\rho})$, where $\boldsymbol{\rho}$ is the vector from the nucleus of atom j to the kth electron of atom j. It will be noted that spin has been neglected. We now want to construct N one-electron functions which will describe, at least roughly, the states of the N electrons in the molecule. The LCAO molecular orbital method assumes that these N molecular wave functions $\psi_a(\mathbf{r})$ have the form

$$\psi_a(\mathbf{r}) = \sum_{j=1}^{n} \sum_{k=1}^{N_j} a_{a,jk} \phi_{jk}(\mathbf{r} - \mathbf{r}_j) \tag{4:11.1}$$

where N_j is the number of electrons on atom j, the $a_{a,jk}$'s are constants and $\mathbf{r}_j$ is the position vector of the nucleus of atom j.

Since the atomic orbitals $\phi_{jk}(\boldsymbol{\rho})$ are assumed known, and the $\mathbf{r}_j$'s can be experimentally determined, we need only find the N^2 coefficient $a_{a,jk}$ to have the N molecular wave functions $\psi_a(\mathbf{r})$ completely determined. To find the coefficients without symmetry considerations, one needs a one-electron Hamiltonian H which will describe the motion of an electron in the molecule. Let us now consider the real functional

$$I[f] = \langle f|H - \lambda I|f\rangle, \tag{4:11.2}$$

where $f(\mathbf{r})$ is any function of $\mathbf{r}$ for which $\langle f|f\rangle$ is finite, and λ is a real parameter. We shall now require the coefficients $a_{a,jk}$ to be so chosen that

$$I[\psi_a] = \langle \psi_a|H - \lambda|\psi_a\rangle \tag{4:11.3}$$

shall be a minimum. This will also determine a value of λ for each ψ which will be the energy belonging to ψ. This requirement is analogous to the well-known variational principle of quantum mechanics which states that if H is a Hamiltonian, E an eigenvalue, and ψ a corresponding eigenvector, then

$$\langle \psi|H - E|\psi\rangle \tag{4:11.4}$$

is a minimum. In the molecular orbital problem, however, we restrict our choice of functions to those of the form (4:11.1).

If we write out $I[\psi_a]$ in more detail we obtain

$$I[\psi_a] = \sum_{\substack{j,k \\ j',k'}} a^*_{a,jk}\, a_{a,j'k'} \langle \phi_{jk}(\mathbf{r} - \mathbf{r}_j)|H - \lambda|\phi_{j'k'}(\mathbf{r} - \mathbf{r}_{j'})\rangle \tag{4:11.5}$$

from which follows

$$\frac{\partial I[\psi_a]}{\partial a^*_{a,jk}} = \sum_{j',k'} a_{a,j'k'} \langle \phi_{jk}(\mathbf{r} - \mathbf{r}_j)|H - \lambda|\phi_{j'k'}(\mathbf{r} - \mathbf{r}_{j'})\rangle. \tag{4:11.6}$$

If we now require these derivatives to be zero so as to minimize $I[\psi_a]$ we obtain

$$\sum_{j',k'} (H_{jk,j'k'} - \lambda S_{jk,j'k'}) a_{a,j'k'} = 0, \tag{4:11.7}$$

where

$$H_{jk,j'k'} = \langle \phi_{jk}(\mathbf{r} - \mathbf{r}_j)|H|\phi_{j'k'}(\mathbf{r} - \mathbf{r}_{j'})\rangle \tag{4:11.7a}$$

$$S_{jk\,j'k'} = \langle \phi_{jk}(\mathbf{r} - \mathbf{r}_j)|\phi_{j'k'}(\mathbf{r} - \mathbf{r}_{j'})\rangle. \tag{4:11.7b}$$

In order for the N linear, homogeneous equations (4:11.7) for the a's to have a solution, the determinant of the coefficients must be zero

$$|H_{jk,j'k'} - \lambda S_{jk,j'k'}| = 0. \tag{4:11.8}$$

This secular equation is an Nth degree equation for λ, and the N roots are the energies of the N molecular orbitals. Each molecular orbital is obtained by substituting a root $\lambda_a = E_a$ of (4:11.8) in (4:11.7) and solving (4:11.7) for the corresponding N coefficients $a_{a,j'k'}$.

The ground state of the molecule is then obtained by filling the lowest energy molecular orbitals (M.O.) with two electrons apiece (spin up and spin down). The Pauli exclusion principle of course prohibits more than one electron per state, and hence two per M.O. The total electronic wave function of the molecule can then be taken to be the product of filled M.O.'s times spin function or it can be taken to be the Slater determinant of the filled M.O.'s times their spin functions.

It might be mentioned at this point that this entire procedure can be carried through for any assumed values of the $\mathbf{r}_j$'s. Consequently, we can compute the molecular electronic energy as a function of the $\mathbf{r}_j$'s

$$E = E(\mathbf{r}_1, \mathbf{r}_2, \ldots, \mathbf{r}_n), \tag{4:11.9}$$

and determine the $\mathbf{r}_j$'s theoretically by requiring $E(\mathbf{r}_1, \ldots, \mathbf{r}_n)$ to be a minimum.

One final point which should be mentioned here is that one does not usually consider all of the electrons belonging to an atom in connection with the M.O. method, but only the outer valence electrons, which actually take part in chemical binding.

Now let us consider the use of molecular symmetry in this problem (73, 117, 120, 129). By a symmetry transformation of a molecule let us mean a 3-dimensional orthogonal alibi transformation such that the transformed molecule is physically indistinguishable from the untransformed molecule. A symmetry transformation therefore interchanges identical atoms, and the set of all symmetry transformations is a group. If D is a symmetry transformation, such that

$$D\mathbf{r}_j = \mathbf{r}_{j'} . \tag{4:11.10}$$

we must have

$$\phi_{j'k}(D[\mathbf{r} - \mathbf{r}_j]) = \phi_{jk}(\mathbf{r} - \mathbf{r}_j), \tag{4:11.11}$$

where atoms j and j' are identical except for position and orientation, in order for atom j to be transformed into atom j'. If now we define the matrix $\bar{D}$ associated with D by means of the equation

$$\phi_{jk}(D^{-1}[\mathbf{r} - \mathbf{r}_j]) = \sum_{j'',k''} \bar{D}_{j''k'',jk} \phi_{j''k''}(\mathbf{r} - \mathbf{r}_j), \tag{4:11.12}$$

we see that the set of matrices $\bar{\Gamma} = \{\bar{D}\}$ is a representation of the symmetry group, and from (4:11.11) that

$$\bar{D}_{j''k'',jk} = \delta_{j''j'}\,\delta_{k''k} \tag{4:11.13}$$

(unless there is a change of phase of a wave function). Hence we can conclude that the N atomic orbitals generate an N-dimensional permutation representation of the molecular point group if there are no phase changes.

Since the molecular orbitals are linear combinations of the atomic orbitals they must generate a representation of the point group which is equivalent to $\bar{\Gamma}$. According to the discussion of Section 8 of this Chapter, the degenerate M.O.'s belonging to a single energy level should generate an irreducible representation of the point group if there is no accidental degeneracy. Hence, the M.O.'s should generate a completely reduced representation of the point group.

The first step in finding the M.O.'s is therefore to find a transformation S which will completely reduce the representation $\bar{\Gamma}$ generated by the atomic orbitals; i.e., one is to find an N-dimensional matrix S such that $\{S^{-1}\bar{D}S\}$ is completely reduced. The new basis is

$$\chi_{jk}(\mathbf{r}) = \sum_{j'k'} S_{j'k',jk}\,\phi_{j'k'}(\mathbf{r} - \mathbf{r}_{j'}). \tag{4:11.14}$$

This can of course be done by one of the idempotent methods of Chapter III. The new basis functions χ are uniquely determined by the requirement that they generate a completely reduced representation except for the possibility of linear transformations of basis functions belonging to the same irreducible representation (not necessarily the same component of $\bar{\Gamma}$). The preceding assertion follows easily by considering two possible sets of χ's and applying the corollary to Schur's lemma (see Section 2 of this Chapter). The M.O.'s belonging to a particular irreducible representation must therefore be linear combinations of the χ's belonging to it and vice versa. If a particular irreducible representation occurs only once as a component of $\bar{\Gamma}$, then every χ belonging to that component must be a linear combination of M.O.'s of the same energy and must therefore be an M.O. itself. Hence, if no irreducible representation occurs more than once as a component of $\bar{\Gamma}$, every χ must be a molecular orbital and the M.O.'s can be found by purely group-theoretic means. If however, some irreducible representations do occur more than once, then the M.O.'s can not be determined by group theory alone and the secular equation must be used.

Example. Hydrogen Molecule H_2.

The two atomic orbitals are the hydrogen 1s-state wave function

$$\phi_1(\boldsymbol{\rho}) = \phi_2(\boldsymbol{\rho}) = \frac{e^{-\rho/a}}{a\sqrt{\pi a}} \tag{4:11.15}$$

where

$$a = \frac{\hbar^2}{me^2} = 0{\cdot}529\text{Å}. \tag{4:11.15a}$$

The symmetry group is of infinite order and contains the following symmetry transformations:

(a) all rotations about the line L joining the two hydrogen atoms
(b) all reflections through planes containing L
(c) the reflection through the plane P which is perpendicular to L and midway between the two atoms
(d) all rotations through the angle π whose axes are lines in P which intersect L.

The first two sets of transformations do not interchange the two atoms, and the second two sets do.

Since $N = 2$ the representation $\bar{\Gamma}$ generated by the two atomic orbitals $\phi_1(\mathbf{r} - \mathbf{r}_1)$ and $\phi_2(\mathbf{r} - \mathbf{r}_2)$ will be 2-dimensional. From (4:11.13) and (4:11.10) it is easily seen that all transformations of types (a) and (b) are represented by the identity matrix, and those of type (c) and (d) are represented by the matrix

$$\bar{D} = \begin{pmatrix} 0 & 1 \\ 1 & 0 \end{pmatrix}. \tag{4:11.16}$$

The representation $\bar{\Gamma}$ is reduced by the matrix

$$S = \frac{1}{\sqrt{2}}\begin{pmatrix} 1 & -1 \\ 1 & 1 \end{pmatrix} \tag{4:11.17}$$

because

$$S^{-1}\bar{D}S = \begin{pmatrix} -1 & 0 \\ 0 & 1 \end{pmatrix}. \tag{4:11.18}$$

Since each irreducible representation occurs only once in $\bar{\Gamma}$, we have

$$\begin{pmatrix} \psi_1(\mathbf{r}) \\ \psi_2(\mathbf{r}) \end{pmatrix} = S^t \begin{pmatrix} \phi_1(\mathbf{r} - \mathbf{r}_1) \\ \phi_2(\mathbf{r} - \mathbf{r}_2) \end{pmatrix} = \frac{1}{\sqrt{2}}\begin{pmatrix} 1 & 1 \\ -1 & 1 \end{pmatrix}\begin{pmatrix} \phi_1(\mathbf{r} - \mathbf{r}_1) \\ \phi_2(\mathbf{r} - \mathbf{r}_2) \end{pmatrix}$$

$$\begin{pmatrix} \frac{1}{\sqrt{2}}[\phi_1(\mathbf{r} - \mathbf{r}_1) + \phi_2(\mathbf{r} - \mathbf{r}_2)] \\ \frac{1}{\sqrt{2}}[-\phi_1(\mathbf{r} - \mathbf{r}_1) + \phi_2(\mathbf{r} - \mathbf{r}_2)] \end{pmatrix}. \tag{4:11.19}$$

The two M.O.'s are therefore just the sum and the difference of the two atomic orbitals. These two M.O.'s are not degenerate since they generate different irreducible representations, and the ground state of H_2 is the state in which the lower energy M.O. contains two electrons. Consideration of the secular equation shows that $\psi_1(\mathbf{r})$ has the lower energy.

Example. Benzene C_6H_6.
Benzene is usually pictured by the following Kekule structural formula:

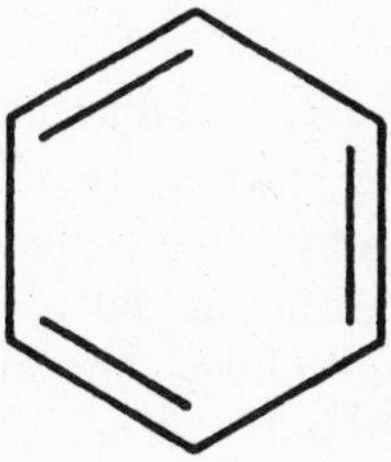

In M.O. theory each carbon atom is assumed to have three valence electrons (σ-electrons) whose wave functions lie on and near the plane of the benzene molecule, and form three lobes at 120° angles to each other like a cloverleaf. The σ-electrons are fairly well immobilized by their bonding. The fourth valence electron belonging to each carbon atom (π-electron) is assumed to be in a M.O. shared by all six carbon atoms. The π-electrons then are mobile and are distributed around the benzene ring. The atomic orbitals from which the π-electron M.O.'s are formed are dumbbell shaped, and are oriented perpendicular to the plane of the benzene ring.

Here we shall be interested in the π-electrons, and we shall treat them as independent of the σ-electrons (Debye-Hückel approximation). Also we ignore inner shell electrons. For a π-electron atomic orbital one can take

$$\phi(\mathbf{r}) = 1{\cdot}71\, r \cos\theta\, e^{-1.56r}, \tag{4:11.20}$$

and in the benzene molecule the polar axis is to be taken perpendicular to the plane of the molecule. A typical M.O. is then of the form

$$\psi(\mathbf{r}) = \sum_{j=1}^{6} a_j \phi(\mathbf{r} - \mathbf{r}_j), \tag{4:11.21}$$

where the a's are still to be determined.

Let L be a straight line perpendicular to the plane of the molecule and passing through the center of the molecule. Then by inspection we see that rotations about L through 60°, 120°, 180°, 240°, 300° are symmetry transformations. Also, there are six planes containing L which are planes of symmetry. Finally, the plane of the molecule is a plane of symmetry. Thus we see that the symmetry group of benzene is the group D_{6h} of order 24.

To find the M.O.'s we must now find the representation $\bar{\Gamma}$ of D_{6h} generated by the six atomic orbitals and reduce it. Let us for convenience introduce the function space operator $\mathscr{D}$ which is associated with a symmetry transformation D by the operation

$$\mathscr{D}\phi_j(\mathbf{r}) = \phi_j(D^{-1}\mathbf{r}) = \sum_{j'=1}^{6} \bar{D}_{j'j}\phi_{j'}(\mathbf{r}) \tag{4:11.22}$$

so that if $D\mathbf{r}_j = \mathbf{r}_{j'}$ then $\mathscr{D}\phi_j = \phi_{j'}$. Also let us number the carbon atoms in clockwise order around the ring starting from the left. Then the point group D_{6h} is generated by the following three elements:

(a) R = clockwise rotation through 60°

(b) V = reflection through plane containing L and passing through carbon atoms one and four

(c) H = reflection through plane of atom.

We then find by inspection the following operational table

	ϕ_1	ϕ_2	ϕ_3	ϕ_4	ϕ_5	ϕ_6
$\mathscr{R}$	ϕ_2	ϕ_3	ϕ_4	ϕ_5	ϕ_6	ϕ_1
$\mathscr{V}$	ϕ_1	ϕ_6	ϕ_5	ϕ_4	ϕ_3	ϕ_2
$\mathscr{H}$	$-\phi_1$	$-\phi_2$	$-\phi_3$	$-\phi_4$	$-\phi_5$	$-\phi_6$

The representation matrices are, therefore

$$\bar{R} = \begin{pmatrix} 0 & 0 & 0 & 0 & 0 & 1 \\ 1 & 0 & 0 & 0 & 0 & 0 \\ 0 & 1 & 0 & 0 & 0 & 0 \\ 0 & 0 & 1 & 0 & 0 & 0 \\ 0 & 0 & 0 & 1 & 0 & 0 \\ 0 & 0 & 0 & 0 & 1 & 0 \end{pmatrix} \quad \bar{V} = \begin{pmatrix} 1 & 0 & 0 & 0 & 0 & 0 \\ 0 & 0 & 0 & 0 & 0 & 1 \\ 0 & 0 & 0 & 0 & 1 & 0 \\ 0 & 0 & 0 & 1 & 0 & 0 \\ 0 & 0 & 1 & 0 & 0 & 0 \\ 0 & 1 & 0 & 0 & 0 & 0 \end{pmatrix}, \tag{4:11.22}$$

and $\bar{H} = -I$. Clearly a matrix S which will reduce the matrix group $\bar{D}_6$ of order twelve which is generated by $\bar{R}$ and $\bar{V}$ will also reduce the group $\bar{D}_{6h}$ of order 24 generated by $\bar{R}$, $\bar{V}$, and $\bar{H}$. By generating the rest of the representation $\bar{D}_6$ of D_6 and evaluating traces one finds that

$$\bar{D}_6 = \Gamma_1 \oplus \Gamma_3 \oplus \Gamma_5 \oplus \Gamma_6 \tag{4:11.23}$$

(see the character table of D_6 on page 145, Chapter IV). Thus the six M.O.'s belong to two nondegenerate energy levels (Γ_1 and Γ_3) and two doubly degenerate levels.

Since no irreducible representation of D_6 occurs more than once in $\bar{D}_6$ we can determine the M.O.'s completely by group theory. The first idempotent method yields the following reduction matrix:

$$S = \begin{pmatrix} \frac{1}{\sqrt{6}} & \frac{1}{\sqrt{6}} & \frac{2}{\sqrt{12}} & \frac{-1}{\sqrt{12}} & \frac{2}{\sqrt{12}} & \frac{1}{\sqrt{12}} \\ \frac{1}{\sqrt{6}} & \frac{-1}{\sqrt{6}} & \frac{-1}{\sqrt{12}} & \frac{2}{\sqrt{12}} & \frac{1}{\sqrt{12}} & \frac{2}{\sqrt{12}} \\ \frac{1}{\sqrt{6}} & \frac{1}{\sqrt{6}} & \frac{-1}{\sqrt{12}} & \frac{-1}{\sqrt{12}} & \frac{-1}{\sqrt{12}} & \frac{1}{\sqrt{12}} \\ \frac{1}{\sqrt{6}} & \frac{-1}{\sqrt{6}} & \frac{2}{\sqrt{12}} & \frac{-1}{\sqrt{12}} & \frac{-2}{\sqrt{12}} & \frac{-1}{\sqrt{12}} \\ \frac{1}{\sqrt{6}} & \frac{1}{\sqrt{6}} & \frac{-1}{\sqrt{12}} & \frac{2}{\sqrt{12}} & \frac{-1}{\sqrt{12}} & \frac{-2}{\sqrt{12}} \\ \frac{1}{\sqrt{6}} & \frac{-1}{\sqrt{6}} & \frac{-1}{\sqrt{12}} & \frac{-1}{\sqrt{12}} & \frac{1}{\sqrt{12}} & \frac{-1}{\sqrt{12}} \end{pmatrix} \qquad (4{:}11.24)$$

which is not orthogonal but does make $S^{-1}\bar{D}S$ a completely reduced representation. The column matrix ψ of M.O.'s is given in terms of the column matrix ϕ of atomic orbitals by $\psi = S^t\phi$, so we have

$$\begin{aligned} \psi_1 &= \frac{1}{\sqrt{6}} (\phi_1 + \phi_2 + \phi_3 + \phi_4 + \phi_5 + \phi_6) \quad \Gamma_1 \\ \psi_2 &= \frac{1}{\sqrt{6}} (\phi_1 - \phi_2 + \phi_3 - \phi_4 + \phi_5 - \phi_6) \quad \Gamma_3 \\ \psi_3 &= \frac{1}{\sqrt{12}} (2\phi_1 - \phi_2 - \phi_3 + 2\phi_4 - \phi_5 - \phi_6) \; \Gamma_5 \qquad (4{:}11.25) \\ \psi_4 &= \frac{-1}{\sqrt{12}} (\phi_1 - 2\phi_2 + \phi_3 + \phi_4 - 2\phi_5 + \phi_6) \; \Gamma_5 \\ \psi_5 &= \frac{1}{\sqrt{12}} (2\phi_1 + \phi_2 - \phi_3 - 2\phi_4 - \phi_5 + \phi_6) \; \Gamma_6 \\ \psi_6 &= \frac{1}{\sqrt{12}} (\phi_1 + 2\phi_2 + \phi_3 - \phi_4 - 2\phi_5 - \phi_6) \; \Gamma_6, \end{aligned}$$

where ϕ_j means $\phi(\mathbf{r} - \mathbf{r}_j)$, and the Γ following each M.O. indicates the representation of D_6 to which it belongs. Since S was not chosen orthogonal, the M.O.'s belonging to the same representation are also not orthogonal. Consideration of the secular equation shows that the energies belonging to the four irreducible representations occurring in $\bar{D}_6$ increase in the order Γ_1, Γ_6, Γ_5, Γ_3. Therefore, the levels corresponding to Γ_1 and Γ_6 contain two and four π-electrons, respectively, in the ground state of benzene, and the other levels are empty.

12. Crystallographic Lattices

In Section 4 of this Chapter we defined a 3-dimensional lattice to be the set of all integral linear combinations of some basic set of three linearly independent 3-dimensional vectors (the vectors being real column matrices). The vectors of a lattice therefore form a group if the group operation is taken to be vector addition. The holohedry of a lattice T was defined to be the group of all orthogonal matrices which leave T invariant. Since all lattices are isomorphic another kind of classification is adopted. They are customarily divided into Bravais classes (62, 156). Two lattices (with a lattice point at the origin) are said to belong to the same Bravais class if there exists a homogeneous linear transformation which will transform one lattice into the other, and will transform the holohedry of the one lattice into the holohedry of the other. More precisely, if $T_1 = \{v_1\}$ and $T_2 = \{v_2\}$ are two lattices with elements $\{v_1\}$ and $\{v_2\}$, and if $G_1 = \{R_1\}$ and $G_2 = \{R_2\}$ are their holohedry, then T_1 and T_2 belong to the same Bravais class if and only if there exists a matrix S such that

(a) $T_2 = ST_1$
i.e., every vector Sv_1 is a vector of T_2, and conversely every vector of T_2 is of this form,

(b) $G_2 = SG_1S^{-1}$.

In brief then, there must be a coordinate system in which the second lattice and its holohedry are identical in form with the first lattice and its holohedry. Since any lattice can be transformed into any other, it is the second condition that is restrictive.

It can be shown that all 3-dimensional lattices fall into 14 Bravais classes. In the following we shall give a table of the 14 Bravais classes of lattices, and shall present forms into which all lattices can be transformed when their holohedry are in the form specified by the generators of the table on page 140 of Section 4. The tables do not give all possible lattices which are invariant under the indicated holohedry. If a holohedry is invariant under an equivalence transformation then the transformed lattice must belong to the same Bravais class and be invariant under the same holohedry as the untransformed lattice. However, the holohedry may contain subgroups which are not invariant under such a transformation because the transformation need not commute with each element of the holohedry (it may produce an automorphism of the holohedry). Hence, some of the lattices in the following table will be given in two forms which are related by a transformation leaving the holohedry, but not all its subgroups, invariant. It should be emphasized that two such forms are equivalent in the sense that they belong to the same Bravais class. Further, every lattice belonging to a Bravais class can be transformed into any of the equivalent forms.

Let us denote the three basis vectors (or fundamental translations) of a lattice by $\mathbf{v}_1$, $\mathbf{v}_2$, and $\mathbf{v}_3$, and the components of $\mathbf{v}_i$ by v_{i1}, v_{i2}, v_{i3}. The basis vectors can then be represented by the square matrix

$$\begin{pmatrix} v_{11} & v_{21} & v_{31} \\ v_{12} & v_{22} & v_{32} \\ v_{13} & v_{23} & v_{33} \end{pmatrix},$$

and this is the way they will be presented in the following table.

Lattice	*Basis Vectors*	*Holohedry*	*Centering*
T_{Tr}	$\begin{pmatrix} v_{11} & v_{21} & v_{31} \\ v_{12} & v_{22} & v_{32} \\ v_{13} & v_{23} & v_{33} \end{pmatrix}$	S_2	Simple
T_M	$\begin{pmatrix} v_{11} & 0 & 0 \\ 0 & v_{22} & v_{32} \\ 0 & 0 & v_{33} \end{pmatrix}$	C_{2h}	Simple
T'_M	$\begin{pmatrix} v_{11} & -v_{11} & 0 \\ v_{12} & v_{12} & v_{32} \\ 0 & 0 & v_{33} \end{pmatrix}$	C_{2h}	Side
T_R	$\begin{pmatrix} v_{11} & 0 & 0 \\ 0 & v_{22} & 0 \\ 0 & 0 & v_{33} \end{pmatrix}$	D_{2h}	Simple
T'_R	$\begin{pmatrix} v_{11} & 0 & 0 \\ 0 & v_{22} & -v_{22} \\ 0 & v_{23} & v_{23} \end{pmatrix}$	D_{2h}	Face
T''_R	$\begin{pmatrix} v_{11} & -v_{11} & 0 \\ v_{12} & v_{12} & v_{12} \\ 0 & 0 & v_{33} \end{pmatrix}$	D_{2h}	Side
T'''_R	$\begin{pmatrix} v_{11} & 0 & 0 \\ v_{12} & 2v_{12} & 0 \\ v_{13} & 0 & 2v_{13} \end{pmatrix}$	D_{2h}	Body
T_{Tg}	$\begin{pmatrix} v_{11} & 0 & 0 \\ 0 & -\frac{3\sqrt{3}}{2}v_{13} & \frac{3\sqrt{3}}{2}v_{13} \\ 0 & \frac{3}{2}v_{13} & \frac{3}{2}v_{13} \end{pmatrix}$	D_{3v}	Simple
T_T	(1) $\begin{pmatrix} v_{11} & 0 & 0 \\ 0 & v_{22} & 0 \\ 0 & 0 & v_{22} \end{pmatrix}$	D_{4h}	Simple

	(2) $\begin{pmatrix} v_{11} & 0 & 0 \\ 0 & v_{22} & -v_{22} \\ 0 & v_{22} & v_{22} \end{pmatrix}$		
T'_T	(1) $\begin{pmatrix} v_{11} & 0 & 0 \\ v_{12} & v_{12} & v_{12} \\ 0 & -v_{12} & v_{12} \end{pmatrix}$	D_{4h}	Body
	(2) $\begin{pmatrix} v_{11} & 0 & 0 \\ v_{12} & 2v_{12} & 0 \\ v_{12} & 0 & 2v_{12} \end{pmatrix}$		
T_H	(1) $\begin{pmatrix} v_{11} & 0 & 0 \\ 0 & \frac{1}{2}v_{21} & -\frac{1}{2}v_{22} \\ 0 & \frac{\sqrt{3}}{2}v_{22} & \frac{\sqrt{3}}{2}v_{22} \end{pmatrix}$	D_{6h}	Simple
	(2) $\begin{pmatrix} v_{11} & 0 & 0 \\ 0 & -\frac{\sqrt{3}}{2}v_{12} & \frac{\sqrt{3}}{2}v_{12} \\ 0 & \frac{1}{2}v_{12} & \frac{1}{2}v_{12} \end{pmatrix}$		
T_c	$\begin{pmatrix} v_{11} & 0 & 0 \\ 0 & v_{11} & 0 \\ 0 & 0 & v_{11} \end{pmatrix}$	O_h	Simple
T'_c	$\begin{pmatrix} v_{11} & -v_{11} & 0 \\ v_{11} & v_{11} & v_{11} \\ 0 & 0 & v_{11} \end{pmatrix}$	O_h	Face
T''_c	$\begin{pmatrix} v_{11} & 0 & 0 \\ v_{11} & 2v_{11} & 0 \\ v_{11} & 0 & 2v_{11} \end{pmatrix}$	O_h	Body

The subscripts on the T's denote the crystal systems to which the corresponding lattices belong. The crystal systems are arranged in the same order as in Section 4 of this Chapter.

Let us discuss the centering column of the preceding table. If T is any 3-dimensional lattice with basis vectors $\mathbf{v}_1, \mathbf{v}_2, \mathbf{v}_3$, then we can define another lattice with the basis vectors $\frac{1}{2}(\mathbf{v}_1 + \mathbf{v}_2), \frac{1}{2}(\mathbf{v}_2 + \mathbf{v}_3), \frac{1}{2}(\mathbf{v}_3 + \mathbf{v}_1)$ which is called the face-centered lattice associated with the original lattice. Similarly we can define associated side-centered and body-centered lattices by means of the basis vectors

$$\tfrac{1}{2}(\mathbf{v}_1 + \mathbf{v}_2), \tfrac{1}{2}(\mathbf{v}_1 - \mathbf{v}_2), \mathbf{v}_3$$

and

$$\tfrac{1}{2}(\mathbf{v}_1 + \mathbf{v}_2 - \mathbf{v}_3), \tfrac{1}{2}(\mathbf{v}_1 - \mathbf{v}_2 + \mathbf{v}_3), \tfrac{1}{2}(-\mathbf{v}_1 + \mathbf{v}_2 + \mathbf{v}_3),$$

respectively. In the preceding table a face-centered lattice is face-centered relative to some simple lattice of the same crystal system. The same is true of the side-centered and body-centered lattices.

The reason for the centering nomenclature is that a face-centered lattice, for example, has lattice points in the centers of the faces of the unit cells of the associated simple lattice. To make apparent the symmetry of a centered lattice, a so-called structure cell is frequently drawn instead of the Bravais unit cell. The cell for the hexagonal lattice is not even a parallelopiped.

Since a lattice is an abelian group all its irreducible representations are 1-dimensional (even though a lattice is of infinite order). A representation will be said to be bounded if the set of absolute values of all matrices' elements of the representation has a finite upper bound. All bounded irreducible representations of a lattice $T = \{v\}$ can easily be seen to be of the form

$$\Gamma_{\mathbf{k}}: \quad \mathbf{v} \to e^{i\mathbf{k}\cdot\mathbf{v}} \tag{4:12.1}$$

where $\mathbf{k}$ is a real vector.

One other concept of interest is the reciprocal lattice. If T is a lattice with basis vectors $\mathbf{v}_1$, $\mathbf{v}_2$, and $\mathbf{v}_3$, then the reciprocal lattice is generated by the vectors

$$\mathbf{K}_1 = \frac{\mathbf{v}_2 \times \mathbf{v}_3}{\mathbf{v}_1 \cdot \mathbf{v}_2 \times \mathbf{v}_3}, \qquad \mathbf{K}_2 = \frac{\mathbf{v}_3 \times \mathbf{v}_1}{\mathbf{v}_1 \cdot \mathbf{v}_2 \times \mathbf{v}_3}, \qquad \mathbf{K}_3 = \frac{\mathbf{v}_1 \times \mathbf{v}_2}{\mathbf{v}_1 \cdot \mathbf{v}_2 \times \mathbf{v}_3}. \tag{4:12.2}$$

Some direct consequences of this definition are

$$(1)\ \mathbf{K}_1 \cdot \mathbf{K}_2 \times \mathbf{K}_3 = \frac{1}{\mathbf{v}_1 \cdot \mathbf{v}_2 \times \mathbf{v}_3} \tag{4:12.3}$$

$$(2)\ \mathbf{K}_i \cdot \mathbf{v}_j = \delta_{ij}. \tag{4:12.4}$$

Thus the volume of the unit cell of the reciprocal lattice is the reciprocal of the volume of the unit cell of the direct lattice.

Also, the reciprocal lattice has the same point group as the direct lattice so that the two belong to the same crystal system.

If $\mathbf{K}$ is a vector of the reciprocal lattice, then

$$\Gamma_{\mathbf{k}+2\pi\mathbf{K}} = \Gamma_{\mathbf{k}} \tag{4:12.5}$$

because in $\Gamma_{\mathbf{k}+2\pi\mathbf{K}}$ we have $\mathbf{v} \to e^{i(\mathbf{k}+2\pi\mathbf{K})\cdot\mathbf{v}} = e^{2\pi i\mathbf{K}\cdot\mathbf{v}}e^{i\mathbf{k}\cdot\mathbf{v}}$ and, as is easily seen from (4:12.4), $\mathbf{K}\cdot\mathbf{v}$ is an integer, so that $e^{2\pi i\mathbf{K}\cdot\mathbf{v}} = 1$. Two $\mathbf{k}$-vectors differing by 2π times any vector of the reciprocal lattice are said therefore to be equivalent.

If $\mathbf{K}$ is a vector of the reciprocal lattice then the equation

$$\mathbf{k}\cdot\mathbf{K} = \pi K^2 \qquad (\mathbf{K} \neq \mathbf{0}) \tag{4:12.6}$$

defines a plane in $\mathbf{k}$-space. As $\mathbf{K}$ varies over the reciprocal lattice we get an infinite set of such planes. The set of all such planes defines a region around the origin of **k**-space such that any point of the region can be joined to the origin by a straight line which does not intersect any of the above-described planes. This region is called the first Brillouin zone of the lattice. It has the property that every **k** is equivalent to some **k** in the first Brillouin zone or on its boundary, and that no distinct two **k**'s inside (not on the boundary) of the first Brillouin zone are equivalent. The first Brillouin zone also has the property of being invariant under the point group. The smallest vector of a set of all equivalent **k**-vectors is called the reduced **k**-vector, so the first Brillouin zone is composed of all reduced **k**-vectors. Obviously we can get all irreducible representations of a lattice by using only reduced **k**'s in $\Gamma_{\mathbf{k}}$. The volume of the first Brillouin zone is

$$(2\pi)^3\mathbf{K}_1\cdot\mathbf{K}_2\times\mathbf{K}_3=\frac{(2\pi)^3}{\mathbf{v}_1\cdot\mathbf{v}_2\times\mathbf{v}_3}. \tag{4:12.7}$$

13. Crystallographic Space Groups

So far we have discussed rotational symmetry of crystals (point groups) and translational symmetry (lattices). There are, however, other kinds of symmetry which are combinations of the preceding two types of symmetry.

These other symmetry transformations are linear inhomogeneous transformations

$$\mathbf{r}'=D\mathbf{r}+\mathbf{v}, \tag{4:13.1}$$

where D is a real nonsingular 3-dimensional matrix and $\mathbf{v}$ is any real 3-dimensional vector. For brevity we denote such an inhomogeneous transformation by $(D|\mathbf{v})$.

If $\mathbf{r}'=(D_1|\mathbf{v}_1)\mathbf{r}$, and $\mathbf{r}''=(D_2|\mathbf{v}_2)\mathbf{r}'$, then $\mathbf{r}''=(D_3|\mathbf{v}_3)\mathbf{r}$, where

$$(D_3|\mathbf{v}_3)\equiv(D_2|\mathbf{v}_2)(D_1|\mathbf{v}_1)=(D_2D_1|D_2\mathbf{v}_1+\mathbf{v}_2). \tag{4:13.2}$$

This is the multiplication law for inhomogeneous transformations. The inverse of such a transformation is found from (4:13.2) to be

$$(D|\mathbf{v})^{-1}=(D^{-1}|-D^{-1}\mathbf{v}), \tag{4:13.3}$$

and the conjugate of an element is found to be

$$(D|\mathbf{v})^{-1}(D_0|\mathbf{v}_0)(D|\mathbf{v})=(D^{-1}D_0D|D^{-1}D_0\mathbf{v}+D^{-1}\mathbf{v}_0-D^{-1}\mathbf{v}). \tag{4:13.4}$$

The set of all real nonsingular inhomogeneous transformations $(D|\mathbf{v})$ is a group which is called the real general inhomogeneous linear group GIL $(3, R)$, or the real affine group.

Definition. A crystallographic space group is a discrete subgroup of GIL $(3, R)$ such that

(1) the set of transformations $\mathbf{v}$ occurring in elements of G contains a smallest nonzero translation,
(2) this same set of translations contains three linearly independent translations.

By discrete is meant countable.

Let us now give a brief survey of the main features of space groups other than their representations (**17, 31, 32, 33, 48, 58, 139, 141, 156**). The representations will be discussed in Chapter VI.

If one classifies space groups according to isomorphism one finds that all space groups fall into 219 isomorphism classes. This, however, is not the usual way of classifying space groups. Normally one puts two space groups in the same class if and only if they are conjugate subgroups of GIL $(3, R)$; that is, if and only if there exists an element $(D|\mathbf{v})$ of GIL $(3, R)$ such that $(D|\mathbf{v})^{-1}G_1(D|\mathbf{v}) = G_2$. In other words two space groups are the same if and only if there is a new coordinate system in which G_1 attains the form that G_2 had in the original coordinate system. One finds with this method of classification 230 classes of space groups. In fact, this method of classification simply splits up each of 11 isomorphism classes into two classes. The resulting 11 pairs of classes are in Schoenflies notation: (C_3^2, C_3^2); (C_4^2, C_4^4); (C_6^2, C_6^3); (C_6^4, C_6^5); (D_3^3, D_3^5); (D_3^4, D_3^6); (D_4^3, D_4^7); (D_4^4, D_4^8); (D_6^2, D_6^3); (D_6^5, D_6^6); $(0^6, 0^7)$. Normally one simply says that these are the 11 pairs of isomorphic space groups.

This method of classification of space groups together with the transformation equation (4:13.4) makes clear the incentive for using the Bravais classification of lattices.

If the vectors $\{\mathbf{v}\}$ form a lattice then the elements $\{(I|\mathbf{v})\}$ form a space group (which we shall call a lattice). Since

$$(D|\mathbf{v}^{-1})(I|\mathbf{v}_0)(D|\mathbf{v}) = (I|D^{-1}\mathbf{v}_0), \tag{4:13.5}$$

and since $(I|D^{-1}\mathbf{v})_0$ is also a lattice we see that the conjugate of a lattice is a lattice. Since also any two lattices T and T' are related by a transformation $T' = DT$, we see that all lattices are mutually conjugate. Therefore we can conclude that one class of space groups consists of all lattices. This is the class of space groups which is denoted in Schoenflies notation by C_1^1.

Let us now (as is customary) refer to a class of space groups as a space group, so that in this terminology there are 230 different space groups. It can be shown that every element of a space group can simultaneously be put in the form

$$(D|\mathbf{u}(D) + \mathbf{v}) \tag{4:13.6}$$

where D is an orthogonal matrix, the set of all D's is a crystallographic point group, $\mathbf{u}(D)$ is a vector function of D such that $\mathbf{u}(I) = \mathbf{0}$, the set of all $\mathbf{v}$'s for a fixed D is a crystallographic lattice, every D possesses the same set of

$\mathbf{v}$'s, and the lattice of $\mathbf{v}$'s is left invariant by the point group of D's. The set of D's is called the point group P belonging to the space group G, and the set of $\mathbf{v}$'s is called the lattice T belonging to G. Also, the $\mathbf{u}$'s satisfy the relation

$$\mathbf{u}(D_1 D_2) = D_1 \mathbf{u}(D_2) + \mathbf{u}(D_1). \tag{4:13.7}$$

If D has order δ it follows directly from the fact that $\mathbf{u}(I) = \mathbf{0}$ that

$$(D|\mathbf{u}(D) + \mathbf{v})^{\delta} = (I|\mathbf{v}'), \tag{4:13.8}$$

where $\mathbf{v}'$ is a vector of the lattice T of G.

The set of elements $\{(I|\mathbf{v})\}$ is the lattice T of G, and as is readily seen from (4:13.4)

$$(D|\mathbf{u} + \mathbf{v})^{-1}(I|\mathbf{v}_0)(D|\mathbf{u} + \mathbf{v}) = (I|D^{-1}\mathbf{v}_0) = (I|\mathbf{v}_0'), \tag{4:13.9}$$

where $\mathbf{v}_0'$ is also in T. Hence, $T = \{(I|\mathbf{v})\}$ is a normal subgroup of G. It is in fact a maximal, normal, abelian subgroup. The quotient group G/T can then be shown to be isomorphic to the point group P

$$G/T = P. \tag{4:13.10}$$

Since T is abelian it is also solvable, and since the order of P must be less than 60 it also is solvable. From the fact that T and G/T are solvable it follows that G also must be solvable. Hence, every space group is solvable. In Schoenflies notation the letter and subscript denote the point group belonging to a space group. The superscript distinguishes different space groups having the same point group.

If $\mathbf{u}(D) = \mathbf{0}$ for all D of a space group, then the space group is simply the semidirect product of T and P; i.e.,

$$G = T \boxed{S} P. \tag{4:13.11}$$

This is easily seen from the fact that P is a group of automorphisms of T and from (4:13.2). By using different forms of a lattice (see Section 12 of this Chapter) with the same point group one can construct more than one semidirect product space group from the same point group and lattice. The number of semidirect product (or symmorphic) space groups is exactly 73, and they are (again in Schoenflies notation): C_1^1, C_i^1, C_S^1, C_S^3, C_2^1, C_2^3, C_{2h}^1, C_{2h}^3, D_2^1, D_2^6, D_2^7, D_2^8, C_{2V}^1, C_{2V}^{11}, C_{2V}^{14}, C_{2V}^{18}, C_{2V}^{20}, D_{2h}^1, D_{2h}^{10}, D_{2h}^{23}, D_{2h}^{25}, C_4^1, C_4^5, S_4^1, S_4^2, D_4^1, D_4^9, C_{4h}^1, C_{4h}^5, C_{4V}^1, C_{4V}^9, D_{2d}^1, D_{2d}^5, D_{2d}^9, D_{2d}^{11}, D_{4h}^1, D_{4h}^{17}, T^1, T^2, T^3, 0^1, 0^3, 0^5, T_h^1, T_h^3, T_h^5, T_d^1, T_d^2, T_d^3, 0_h^1, 0_h^5, 0_h^9, C_3^1, C_3^4, D_3^1, D_3^2, D_3^7, C_{3V}^1, C_{3V}^2, C_{3V}^5, C_{3i}^1, C_{3i}^2, D_{3d}^1, D_{3d}^3, D_{3d}^5, C_{3h}^1, D_{3h}^1, D_{3h}^1, C_6^1, D_6^1, C_{6h}^1, C_{6V}^1, C_{6h}^1. It is also true that every other space group is isomorphic to a subgroup of one of the above 73 semidirect product space groups. These other 157 space groups contain elements which are referred to as glide planes and screw axes, which have $\mathbf{u}(D) \neq O$.

Let us define the space group of a crystal to be the set of all alibi transformations $(D|\mathbf{v})$ which transform the crystal into itself. Every such space group must then be one of the above-mentioned 230. The point group of the crystal is the group of all distinct D's, and the lattice the set of translations $\{(I|\mathbf{v})\}$. Crystals whose space groups are of semidirect product type are the "simple" crystals mentioned in Section 4. The point group of this type of crystal leaves not only the lattice invariant but also the crystal.

The space groups are usually separated into crystal systems as are the point groups and lattices. In most cases the point group and the lattice of a space group belong to the same crystal system, and the space group is naturally assigned to that system. There are some exceptions however in which the point group belongs to the trigonal system and the lattice to the hexagonal system. Consequently the trigonal and hexagonal systems are frequently merged in space group classifications. A complete list of space groups and their generators can be found in Seitz (156). Following is the simple example of the simple, square, 2-dimensional lattice. The generators are

$$A = (D_1|\mathbf{0}) \quad B = (D_2|\mathbf{0}) \quad C = (I|\mathbf{v}_1) \quad D = (I|\mathbf{v}_2) \tag{4:13.12}$$

where

$$D_1 = \begin{pmatrix} 0 & 1 \\ -1 & 0 \end{pmatrix} \quad D_2 = \begin{pmatrix} 1 & 0 \\ 0 & -1 \end{pmatrix} \quad \mathbf{v}_1 = \begin{pmatrix} a \\ 0 \end{pmatrix} \quad \mathbf{v}_2 = \begin{pmatrix} 0 \\ a \end{pmatrix}. \tag{4:13.13}$$

The defining relations are

$$A^4 = I \quad B^2 = I \quad ABA = B \quad ACA^{-1} = D \quad ADA^{-1} = C^{-1}$$
$$BCB^{-1} = C \quad BDB^{-1} = D^{-1} \quad CD = DC \tag{4:13.14}$$

Now let us tabulate the numbers of groups in different systems.

System	*Holohedry*	*No. of Point Groups*	*No. of Lattices*	*No. of Space Groups*	*No. of Semidirect Product Space Groups*
Triclinic	S_2	2	1	2	2
Monoclinic	C_{2h}	3	2	13	6
Rhombic	D_{2h}	3	4	59	13
Tetragonal	D_{4h}	7	2	68	16
Cubic	O_h	5	3	36	15
Trigonal	D_{3V}	5	1	52	21
Hexagonal	D_{6h}	7	1	52	21

A summary of the number of groups of dimensions one, two, and three is given in the next table.

Dimension	No. of Non-isomorphic Point Groups	No. of Point Groups	No. of Lattices	No. of Non-isomorphic Space Groups	No. of Space Groups
1	2	2	1	2	2
2	9	10	5	17	17
3	18	32	14	219	230

According to Buerger (28) all nonisomorphic space groups are distinguishable by diffraction data.

Two miscellaneous topics remain to be mentioned. First, a real, faithful reduced 4-dimensional representation can easily be written. If $(D|\mathbf{v})$ is an element of a space group, then

$$(D|\mathbf{v}) \to \begin{pmatrix} D_{11} & D_{12} & D_{13} & v_1 \\ D_{21} & D_{22} & D_{23} & v_2 \\ D_{31} & D_{32} & D_{33} & v_3 \\ 0 & 0 & 0 & 1 \end{pmatrix} \tag{4:13.15}$$

is such a representation. The irreducible representations will be discussed in Chapter VI. Second, double space groups are of some interest (46) and will simply be defined here. Let $G = \{(D|\mathbf{v})\}$ be a space group, and let $D \to \pm\, U(D)$ be the 2-dimensional, 2-valued representation of the point group P of G (so $\{U\}$ is the double point group ${}^{(d)}P$). Then the double space group ${}^{(d)}G$ is the set of elements $(\pm U(D)|\mathbf{v})$ with multiplication defined by

$$(U(D_1)|\mathbf{v}_1)(U(D_2)|\mathbf{v}_2) = (U(D_1)U(D_2)|D_1\mathbf{v}_2 + \mathbf{v}_1). \tag{4:13.16}$$

14. Wave Functions in Crystals

In this Section we shall consider solutions of the time-independent Schrödinger wave equation which describes electrons in a crystal. We shall assume that a valence electron of an atom of the crystal moves in an electric field which is caused first by the ionized atoms and second by the other valence electrons (conduction electrons we shall subsequently call them). If we assume the crystal to be perfect, and neglect displacements of ions from their equilibrium positions due to thermal vibration, then the electric field due to the ions will have the symmetry of the space group of the crystal. Thus the Hamiltonian is of the form

$$H = -\frac{\hbar^2}{2m}\sum_{j=1}^{N}\nabla_j^2 + V_I(\mathbf{r}_1,\ldots,\mathbf{r}_N) + e^2\sum_{j<j'}\frac{1}{|\mathbf{r}_j - \mathbf{r}_{j'}|}, \tag{4:14.1}$$

where N is the number of electrons, $V_I(\mathbf{r}_1,\ldots,\mathbf{r}_N)$ is the potential due to the crystal ions and has the symmetry of the crystal space group, the last term is the potential due to the electron-electron interactions, and spin has of course been neglected. Since the first and last terms are invariant under all inhomogeneous orthogonal transformations, they must also be invariant under the space group of the crystal. Hence, the Hamiltonian H is invariant under the transformations of the crystal space group.

From the preceding considerations we can conclude that a complete linearly independent set of eigenfunctions of H belonging to a single energy level will generate an irreducible representation of the crystal space group (if there is no accidental degeneracy). Let us call such a representation Γ_E, and the representation of the lattice $T = \{(I|\mathbf{v})\}$ subduced by Γ_E, $\Gamma_E^{(s)}$. Since T is abelian we can choose a set of eigenfunctions such that $\Gamma_E^{(s)}$ is completely reduced into 1-dimensional representations of T. If

$$\{\phi_1(\mathbf{r}_1,\ldots,\mathbf{r}_N),\ldots,\phi_a(\mathbf{r}_1,\ldots,\mathbf{r}_N)\}$$

is such a set of eigenfunctions belonging to E, then from the preceding sentence it follows that for each ϕ there is a real vector $\mathbf{k}$ (which we attach as a subscript) such that

$$\begin{aligned}\phi_\mathbf{k}((I|\mathbf{v})^{-1}\mathbf{r}_1,\ldots,(I|\mathbf{v})^{-1}\mathbf{r}_N) &= \phi_\mathbf{k}(\mathbf{r}_1-\mathbf{v},\ldots,\mathbf{r}_N-\mathbf{v})\\ &= e^{-i\mathbf{k}\cdot\mathbf{v}}\phi_\mathbf{k}(\mathbf{r}_1,\ldots,\mathbf{r}_N). \qquad (4{:}14.2)\end{aligned}$$

This just means that $\phi_\mathbf{k}$ generates the 1-dimensional representation $\Delta_\mathbf{k}$ of T. The unbounded representations are not considered because the wave function must be bounded and could not be if it generated an unbounded representation.

Thus we can choose a complete set of wave functions such that a lattice translation of the arguments produces the same effect as multiplying by a constant $e^{-i\mathbf{k}\cdot\mathbf{v}}$. Now let us define

$$u_\mathbf{k}(\mathbf{r}_1,\ldots,\mathbf{r}_N) = e^{-i\mathbf{k}\cdot\mathbf{R}}\phi_\mathbf{k}(\mathbf{r}_1,\ldots,\mathbf{r}_N) \qquad (4{:}14.3)$$

where

$$\mathbf{R} = \frac{1}{N}\sum_{j=1}^{N}\mathbf{r}_j \qquad (4{:}14.4)$$

is the center of mass position vector. Then

$$\begin{aligned}u_\mathbf{k}(\mathbf{r}_1-\mathbf{v},\ldots,\mathbf{r}_N-\mathbf{v}) &= e^{-i\mathbf{k}\cdot(\mathbf{R}-\mathbf{v})}\phi_k(\mathbf{r}_1-\mathbf{v},\ldots,\mathbf{r}_N-\mathbf{v})\\ &= e^{-i\mathbf{k}\cdot(\mathbf{R}-\mathbf{v})}e^{-i\mathbf{k}\cdot\mathbf{v}}\phi_\mathbf{k}(\mathbf{r}_1,\ldots,\mathbf{r}_N) \qquad (4{:}14.5)\\ &= e^{-i\mathbf{k}\cdot\mathbf{R}}\phi_\mathbf{k}(\mathbf{r}_1,\ldots,\mathbf{r}_N)\\ &= u_\mathbf{k}(\mathbf{r}_1,\ldots,\mathbf{r}_N).\end{aligned}$$

Hence, we conclude that the function $u_\mathbf{k}$ defined in (4:14.3) has the periodicity of the lattice, and that every wave function $\phi_\mathbf{k}$ can be written in the form

$$\phi_{\mathbf{k}}(\mathbf{r}_1,\ldots,\mathbf{r}_N) = e^{i\mathbf{k}\cdot\mathbf{R}}\, u_{\mathbf{k}}(\mathbf{r}_1,\ldots,\mathbf{r}_N), \tag{4:14.6}$$

where $u_{\mathbf{k}}$ has the periodicity of the lattice. According to (4:12.5) any $\mathbf{k}$ from the infinite set of equivalent $\mathbf{k}$'s will work equally well in (4:14.6).

Frequently the electron-electron interaction term of the N-electron Hamiltonian (4:14.1) is replaced by a sum of approximate 1-electron potentials which are supposed to represent some kind of average effect due to the other electrons. Since the ionic potential V_I is also a sum of 1-electron ionic potentials, it follows that H is a sum of 1-electron Hamiltonians. Furthermore, each 1-electron Hamiltonian must possess the symmetry of the space group if the approximation is to be a reasonable one. We can now separate the N-electron wave equation into N 1-electron wave equations. Hence, replacing the electron-electron potential of the N-electron problem by a sum of 1-electron potentials allows us to reduce the N-electron problem to a 1-electron problem with the same symmetry. Therefore, we can assert that it is possible to choose a complete set of 1-electron wave functions of the form

$$\phi_{\mathbf{k}}(\mathbf{r}) = e^{i\mathbf{k}\cdot\mathbf{r}} u_{\mathbf{k}}(\mathbf{r}), \tag{4:14.7}$$

where $\mathbf{k}$ is real, and $u_{\mathbf{k}}(\mathbf{r})$ has the periodicity of the lattice.

$$u_{\mathbf{k}}(\mathbf{r} - \mathbf{v}) = u_{\mathbf{k}}(\mathbf{r}) \tag{4:14.8}$$

if $\mathbf{v}$ is a lattice vector. Wave functions of this form are called Bloch functions. If $\phi_{\mathbf{k}}(\mathbf{r})$ satisfies the equation

$$\left[-\frac{\hbar^2}{2m}\nabla^2 + V(\mathbf{r})\right]\phi_{\mathbf{k}}(\mathbf{r}) = E\phi_{\mathbf{k}}(\mathbf{r}), \tag{4:14.8a}$$

then $u_{\mathbf{k}}(\mathbf{r})$ satisfies the equation

$$\left[-\frac{\hbar^2}{2m}(\nabla^2 + 2i\mathbf{k}\cdot\boldsymbol{\nabla} - k^2) + V(\mathbf{r})\right]u_{\mathbf{k}}(\mathbf{r}) = Eu_{\mathbf{k}}(\mathbf{r}). \tag{4:14.8b}$$

According to (4:14.8b) the energy is a function of the Bloch wave number $\mathbf{k}$, $E = E(\mathbf{k})$, although it may be a many-valued function. If we plot E against $\mathbf{k}$ using always the reduced vector, then we obtain several energy surfaces, which are defined for all values of $\mathbf{k}$ in the first Brillouin zone. This scheme of considering $E(\mathbf{k})$ is called the reduced zone scheme. On the other hand, one can uniquely define higher order Brillouin zones which all have the same volume (19) and are all equivalent. Then one can associate the energy surface with lowest $E(\mathbf{0})$ with the first zone, that with next lowest $E(\mathbf{0})$ with the second zone, etc. This unreduced zone scheme is the usual alternative method of considering $E(\mathbf{k})$. More precisely, the nth Brillouin zone is the set of all points in $\mathbf{k}$-space which can be joined to the origin by a straight line which intersects exactly $(n - 1)$ planes of the type described by (4:12.6). The nth energy surface of the reduced zone scheme (the lowest surface being first, etc.) is then moved out to the nth Brillouin zone in such a way that each energy value is moved to an equivalent point. In the unreduced zone scheme the jump discontinuities of $E(\mathbf{k})$ can occur only at Brillouin zone boundaries.

Even after approximately reducing the N-electron problem to a 1-electron problem one is left with the difficult job of solving the 1-electron problem. We shall now consider two approximate methods of doing this, the tight-binding method and the Wigner-Seitz method.

Let us first consider the tight-binding method, which is just an extension of the method of molecular orbitals discussed in Section (11) of this Chapter. For simplicity let us consider a simple monatomic crystal in which every atom is on a lattice point so there is one atom per unit cell. Also let us suppose that each atom contributes one conduction electron. The crystal wave function is assumed to be of the form

$$\phi_{\mathbf{k}}(\mathbf{r}) = \sum_j a(\mathbf{r}_j)\phi(\mathbf{r} - \mathbf{r}_j), \tag{4:14.9}$$

where $\mathbf{r}_j$ is the position vector of the jth atom and ϕ is the atomic orbital wave function which describes the state that the conduction electron contributed by an atom would be in if the atom were out of the crystal. In order to have $\phi_{\mathbf{k}}(\mathbf{r} - \mathbf{v}) = e^{-i\mathbf{k}\cdot\mathbf{v}}\phi_{\mathbf{k}}(\mathbf{r})$, we must have

$$\sum_j a(\mathbf{r}_j)\phi(\mathbf{r} - \mathbf{r}_j - \mathbf{v}) = e^{-i\mathbf{k}\cdot\mathbf{v}} \sum_j a(\mathbf{r}_j)\phi(\mathbf{r} - \mathbf{r}_j). \tag{4:14.10}$$

By manipulating summation indices we obtain

$$\sum_j [a(\mathbf{r}_j - \mathbf{v}) - e^{-i\mathbf{k}\cdot\mathbf{v}}a(\mathbf{r}_j)]\phi(\mathbf{r} - \mathbf{r}_j) = 0. \tag{4:14.11}$$

If we neglect the overlap between atomic orbitals belonging to different atoms, i.e., if we assume

$$\langle \phi(\mathbf{r} - \mathbf{r}_i) | \phi(\mathbf{r} - \mathbf{r}_j) \rangle = \delta_{ij}, \tag{4:14.12}$$

then, by multiplying (4:14.11) by $\phi^*(\mathbf{r} - \mathbf{r}_i)$ and integrating, we obtain

$$a(\mathbf{r}_j - \mathbf{v}) = e^{-i\mathbf{k}\cdot\mathbf{v}}a(\mathbf{r}_j). \tag{4:14.13}$$

Putting $\mathbf{r}_j = \mathbf{0}$ we find

$$a(\mathbf{v}) = e^{i\mathbf{k}\cdot\mathbf{v}}a(\mathbf{0}),$$

and since every $\mathbf{v}$ is an $\mathbf{r}_j$ and vice versa we find

$$a(\mathbf{r}_j) = a(\mathbf{0})e^{i\mathbf{k}\cdot\mathbf{r}_j}. \tag{4:14.14}$$

Hence we obtain finally

$$\phi_{\mathbf{k}}(\mathbf{r}) = \text{const.} \times \sum_j e^{i\mathbf{k}\cdot\mathbf{r}_j}\phi(\mathbf{r} - \mathbf{r}_j). \tag{4:14.15}$$

If $\phi_{\mathbf{k}}$ is to be normalized, $\langle \phi_{\mathbf{k}} | \phi_{\mathbf{k}} \rangle = 1$, then the constant must be chosen equal to $N^{-1/2}$.

Before turning to the Wigner-Seitz method let us consider some further symmetry properties of Bloch wave functions (21, 84, 143). Let us suppose $\phi_{\mathbf{k}}(\mathbf{r})$ has the Bloch wave number $\mathbf{k}$, and let us find the wave number of the function

$$\psi(\mathbf{r}) \equiv \phi_{\mathbf{k}}((D|\mathbf{v})^{-1}\mathbf{r}),$$

where $(D|\mathbf{v})$ is an element of the space group. First we have

$$\psi(\mathbf{r}) = \phi_{\mathbf{k}}((D^{-1}|-D^{-1}\mathbf{v})\mathbf{r}) = \phi_{\mathbf{k}}(D^{-1}\mathbf{r} - D^{-1}\mathbf{v}) \tag{4:14.16}$$

so that

$$\psi(\mathbf{r} - \mathbf{v}_0) = \phi_{\mathbf{k}}(D^{-1}\mathbf{r} - D^{-1}\mathbf{v} - D^{-1}\mathbf{v}_0). \tag{4:14.17}$$

If $\mathbf{v}_0$ is a lattice vector then so is $D^{-1}\mathbf{v}_0$ and we find with the aid of (4:14.2) that

$$\begin{aligned} \psi(\mathbf{r} - \mathbf{v}_0) &= e^{-i\mathbf{k}\cdot D^{-1}\mathbf{v}_0}\, \phi_{\mathbf{k}}(D^{-1}\mathbf{r} - D^{-1}\mathbf{v}) \\ &= e^{-i\mathbf{k}\cdot D^{-1}\mathbf{v}_0}\, \psi(\mathbf{r}). \end{aligned} \tag{4:14.18}$$

Since D is an element of a point group we can assume it to be orthogonal so that $D^{-1} = D^t$ and $\mathbf{k}\cdot D^{-1}\mathbf{v}_0 = \mathbf{k}\cdot D^t\mathbf{v}_0 = (D\mathbf{k})\cdot\mathbf{v}_0$. Using this result we can put (4:14.18) in the form

$$\psi(\mathbf{r} - \mathbf{v}_0) = e^{-i(D\mathbf{k})\cdot\mathbf{v}_0}\, \psi(\mathbf{r}) \tag{4:14.19}$$

or

$$\psi(\mathbf{r} - \mathbf{v}_0) = e^{-i\mathbf{k}'\cdot\mathbf{v}_0}\, \psi(\mathbf{r}), \tag{4:14.20}$$

where

$$\mathbf{k}' = D\mathbf{k}. \tag{4:14.20a}$$

In summary we can say that if $\phi_{\mathbf{k}}(\mathbf{r})$ generates the 1-dimensional representation $\Delta_{\mathbf{k}}$ of the lattice T, then $\psi(\mathbf{r}) \equiv \phi_{\mathbf{k}}((D|\mathbf{v})^{-1}\mathbf{r})$, where $(D|\mathbf{v})$ is an element of the space group, generates the 1-dimensional representation $\Delta_{\mathbf{k}'}$ of T, where $\mathbf{k}' = D\mathbf{k}$.

If $\mathbf{k}'$ is equivalent to $\mathbf{k}$, that is, $\mathbf{k}' - \mathbf{k} = 2\pi\mathbf{K}$, then $\Delta_{\mathbf{k}'} = \Delta_{\mathbf{k}}$. We see, therefore, that the only space group elements which transform a Bloch function with wave number $\mathbf{k}$ into another Bloch function with wave number $\mathbf{k}$ are those elements $(D|\mathbf{v})$ such that

$$D\mathbf{k} = \mathbf{k} + 2\pi\mathbf{K}, \tag{4:14.21}$$

where $\mathbf{K}$ is a vector of the reciprocal lattice. That is, the elements are those such that D transforms the wave number vector into an equivalent wave number vector. The group $G_{\mathbf{k}}$ of all space group elements $(D|\mathbf{v})$ such that D satisfies (4:14.21) will be called the space group of $\mathbf{k}$, and the group $P_{\mathbf{k}}$ of all point group elements D satisfying (4:14.21) will be called the point group of $\mathbf{k}$.

Let us consider a complete set of linearly independent Bloch energy eigenfunctions belonging to the energy E and the wave number $\mathbf{k}$. From our previous considerations we see that this set will generate a representation of $G_{\mathbf{k}}$. The reason is that if $\phi_{\mathbf{k}}(\mathbf{r})$ belongs to the set, and $(D|\mathbf{v})$ to $G_{\mathbf{k}}$, then by (4:14.20) and the fact that the Hamiltonian H is invariant under G it follows that $\phi_{\mathbf{k}}((D|\mathbf{v})^{-1}\mathbf{r})$ also belongs to the set. For the same reason such a set also generates a representation of $P_{\mathbf{k}}$, which is of course of the same dimension as the representation of $G_{\mathbf{k}}$.

Let these two representations be denoted by $\Gamma_{\mathbf{k},E}(G_{\mathbf{k}})$ and $\Gamma_{\mathbf{k},E}(P_{\mathbf{k}})$. Since

$$\begin{aligned}\phi_{\mathbf{k}}((D|\mathbf{v})^{-1}\mathbf{r}) &= \phi_{\mathbf{k}}((D^{-1}|-D^{-1}\mathbf{v})\mathbf{r}) \\ &= \phi_{\mathbf{k}}(D^{-1}\mathbf{r} - D^{-1}\mathbf{v}) \\ &= e^{-i\mathbf{k}\cdot D^{-1}\mathbf{v}}\,\phi_{\mathbf{k}}(D^{-1}\mathbf{r}) \\ &= e^{-i\mathbf{k}\cdot\mathbf{v}}\,\phi_{\mathbf{k}}(D^{-1}\mathbf{r}),\end{aligned} \tag{4:14.22}$$

we see that if in $\Gamma_{\mathbf{k}}(P_{\mathbf{k}})$

$$D \to \bar{D} \tag{4:14.23a}$$

then in $\Gamma_{\mathbf{k}}(G_{\mathbf{k}})$

$$(D|\mathbf{v}) \to e^{-i\mathbf{k}\cdot\mathbf{v}}\,\bar{D}, \tag{4:14.23b}$$

and vice versa. Hence. $\Gamma_{\mathbf{k},E}(P_{\mathbf{k}})$ is irreducible if and only if $\Gamma_{\mathbf{k},E}(G_{\mathbf{k}})$ is. It is generally assumed that these representations are irreducible, and the contrary cases are of course subsumed under the convenient catchall title of accidental degeneracy.

An important property of the representation $\Gamma_{\mathbf{k},E}(G_{\mathbf{k}})$ is that it subduces a multiple of $\Delta(\mathbf{k})$ on T. This is obvious from the fact that every Bloch eigenfunction which generates $\Gamma_{\mathbf{k},E}(G_{\mathbf{k}})$ has the wave vector $\mathbf{k}$. An irreducible representation of $G_{\mathbf{k}}$ having the property that it subduces a multiple of $\Delta(\mathbf{k})$ on T will subsequently (Chapter VI) be referred to as allowable.

We are now prepared to discuss the Wigner-Seitz method of obtaining approximate Bloch energy eigenfunctions. The first step is to partition the crystal into polyhedral regions containing one atom apiece. The Wigner-Seitz polyhedron surrounding an atom is constructed by first constructing straight lines joining the atom with each of its nearest neighbors and then constructing the planes which perpendicularly bisect these lines. These planes will enclose a polyhedral region and form the boundary of the Wigner-Seitz polyhedron of the atom.

The second step is to assume that the potential in each polyhedron is spherically symmetric. In particular, the ion potential is a possible potential. Because of the spherical symmetry of the potential, a complete orthonormal set of solutions of the time-independent Schrödinger wave equation

$$\left[-\frac{\hbar^2}{2m}\nabla^2 + V(r)\right]\phi(\mathbf{r}) = E\phi(\mathbf{r}) \tag{4:14.24}$$

for fixed E can be written in spherical coordinates in the form

$$\phi_{l,m}(\mathbf{r}, E) = Y_{l,m}(\theta, \phi)\frac{f_l(r, E)}{r}, \tag{4:14.25}$$

where $f(r, E)$ is a solution of the radial equation

$$-\left[\frac{\hbar^2}{2m}\frac{d^2}{dr^2} + V(r) + \frac{\hbar^2}{2m}\frac{(l+1)}{r^2}\right]f = Ef, \tag{4:14.26}$$

and $l = 0, 1, 2, \ldots, \infty$ (m in (4:14.26) being mass). If $[r^2V(r)]_{r=0}$ is finite, then the radial equation (4:14.26) has two linearly independent solutions which have the form $r^{l+1}F_1(r)$ and $[r^{-l}F_2(r) + Cr^{l+1}F_1(r)\ln r]$, where $F_1(r)$ and $F_2(r)$ are analytic at $r = 0$§, and C is a constant. Since $\phi_{l,m}(\mathbf{r}, E)$ is infinite at $r = 0$ when $f_l(r, E)$ has the second form, we shall be interested only in the first form of $f_l(r, E)$. Thus we have the result that

$$f_l(r, E) = r^{l+1}F_l(r, E), \tag{4:14.27}$$

where $F_l(r, E)$ is analytic at $r = 0$.

Now we can get down to the problem of finding the Bloch wave function. Suppose $\phi_{\mathbf{k}}(\mathbf{r}, E)$ is a Bloch energy eigenfunction belonging to energy E and Bloch wave number $\mathbf{k}$. In the Wigner-Seitz polyhedron centered at the origin $\phi_{\mathbf{k}}(\mathbf{r}, E)$ must satisfy the wave equation (4:14.24). Hence, since $\phi_{\mathbf{k}}(\mathbf{r}, E)$ must also be regular at the origin we can expand it in a series of regular eigenfunctions of the form (4:14.25)

$$\phi_{\mathbf{k}}(\mathbf{r}) = \sum_{l=0}^{\infty}\sum_{m=-l}^{l} A_{lm}Y_{l,m}(\theta, \phi)\frac{f_l(r, E)}{r} \tag{4:14.28}$$

where $f_l(r, E)$ has the form (4:14.27). It should be noted that the only boundary condition imposed on $f_l(r, E)$ is that it be regular at $r = 0$. For this reason we can obtain energy eigenfunctions over a continuous range of E instead of over a discrete range as in bound state atomic problems.

As yet we have not determined the expansion coefficients A_{lm}, nor have we specified any relation between the energy E and the wave number $\mathbf{k}$. The coefficients and the energy-wave number relation are determined by requiring the Bloch wave function $\phi_{\mathbf{k}}(\mathbf{r}, E)$ to satisfy some boundary and periodicity conditions. The conditions are that $\phi_{\mathbf{k}}(\mathbf{r}, E)$ and its normal derivative be continuous on the boundary of the Wigner-Seitz polyhedron, and that

$$\phi_{\mathbf{k}}(\mathbf{r} + \mathbf{v}, E) = e^{i\mathbf{k}\cdot\mathbf{v}}\phi_{\mathbf{k}}(\mathbf{r}, E).$$

The last condition is really a boundary condition also. Furthermore, it

§ See Coddington, E. A., and Levinson, N., "Theory of Ordinary Differential Equations," p. 122, McGraw-Hill, New York, 1955.

allows one to determine $\phi_{\mathbf{k}}(\mathbf{r})$ in all other cells. Finally, the possible values of E are restricted by the condition that $\mathbf{k}$ always be real.

As yet we have said nothing about group theory in connection with the Wigner-Seitz method (12, 89, 178, 209). The point at which group theory is useful is in the practical determination of the expansion coefficients. In practice one can not determine an infinite number of expansion coefficients by numerically satisfying an infinite number of boundary conditions. What one does then is to use only the lowest few l values in the expansion (4:14.28) and accordingly fit only a few boundary conditions. However, one can obtain a much better wave function without satisfying any more boundary conditions by making use of the known symmetry properties of $\phi_{\mathbf{k}}(\mathbf{r}, E)$.

In particular we know that a complete linearly independent set of $\phi_{\mathbf{k}}(\mathbf{r}, E)$'s must generate an irreducible representation of the point group $P_{\mathbf{k}}$ of $\mathbf{k}$. We note that $P_{\mathbf{k}}$ is one of the 32 crystallographic point groups because it is a subgroup of the point group of the crystal. Therefore, we can expand the $\phi_{\mathbf{k}}(\mathbf{r}, E)$'s in terms of lattice harmonics (see Section 10 of this Chapter). More specifically, let $\phi_{\mathbf{k}}^{1}(\mathbf{r}, E), \ldots, \phi_{\mathbf{k}}^{d}(\mathbf{r}, E)$ generate an irreducible representation of $P_{\mathbf{k}}$, and let $X_{l1}(\theta, \phi), \ldots, X_{ld}(\theta, \phi)$ be the lattice harmonics of degree l which generate the same irreducible representation of $P_{\mathbf{k}}$ (if there is more than one such set of lattice harmonics of degree l another index is required). Then we can rewrite the expansion (4:14.28) in the form

$$\phi_{\mathbf{k}}^{s}(\mathbf{r}, E) = \sum_{l=0}^{\infty} B_{ls} X_{ls}(\theta, \phi) \frac{f_l(r, E)}{r}. \tag{4:14.29}$$

The lattice harmonics X_{ls} of low degree have been tabulated. By using this expansion in which the symmetry of $\phi_{\mathbf{k}}(\mathbf{r}, E)$ has been incorporated we can get a greater accuracy from the same number of terms of the expansion.

The reader may have observed that nothing has been said about which irreducible representation of $P_{\mathbf{k}}$ the functions $\phi_{\mathbf{k}}^{s}(\mathbf{r}, E)$ generate. A discussion of this point will be postponed until Chapter VI, Section 6.

Example. Free Electron (Empty Lattice)

A trivial example is provided by the case $V(r) = 0$, which is the case of no lattice at all. In this case P is the 3-dimensional orthogonal group, and $P_{\mathbf{k}}$ is the 2-dimensional orthogonal group with axis $\mathbf{k}$. The Bloch function is of course $\phi_{\mathbf{k}}(\mathbf{r}, E) = e^{i\mathbf{k}\cdot\mathbf{r}}$, and $E = \hbar^2 k^2/2m$. Since there is never any degeneracy in both E and $\mathbf{k}$, $d = 1$. Also since $\phi_{\mathbf{k}}(\mathbf{r}, E) = e^{i\mathbf{k}\cdot\mathbf{r}}$ is invariant under $O(2)$, $X_l(\theta, \phi)$ must generate the scalar representation of $P_{\mathbf{k}} = O(2)$. If we choose $\mathbf{k}$ as the polar axis we see that $X_l(\theta, \phi) = Y_{l0}(\theta, \phi)$. Furthermore, the radial equation for $f_l(r, E)$ can be solved exactly to yield

$$f_l(r, E) = r^{1/2} J_{l+1/2}\left(\frac{1}{\hbar}\sqrt{2mE}\, r\right), \tag{4:14.30}$$

where

$$J_{l+1/2}(z) = \sqrt{\frac{2}{\pi}} z^{l+1/2} \left(-\frac{1}{z}\frac{d}{dz} \right)^l \frac{\sin z}{z} \tag{4:14.31}$$

is the Bessel function of the first kind of order $l + \frac{1}{2}$. Consequently, we find

$$e^{i\mathbf{k}\cdot\mathbf{r}} = \frac{1}{\sqrt{r}} \sum_{l=0}^{\infty} B_l Y_{l0}(\theta, \phi) J_{l+1/2}\left(\frac{1}{\hbar}\sqrt{2mE}\, r \right). \tag{4:14.32}$$

By putting $\sqrt{2mE}/\hbar = k$ and evaluating B_l by means of the standard techniques of orthogonal functions we arrive at Bauer's expansion

$$e^{i\mathbf{k}\cdot\mathbf{r}} = \sqrt{\pi/2kr} \sum_{l=0}^{\infty} (2l + 1) i^l P_l(\cos\theta) J_{l+1/2}(kr). \tag{4:14.33}$$

BIBLIOGRAPHY

Auld, B. A. (1952). Applications of Group Theory in the Study of Symmetrical Waveguide Junctions. Stanford Univ. Microwave Lab. Rep. 157. Palo Alto, California.

Barriol, J. (1947). "Application of the Theory of Groups to the Study of Molecular and Crystalline Vibrations." Masson, Paris.

Bhagavantam, S., and Venkatarayudu, T. (1951). "Theory of Groups and Its Application to Physical Problems." Andhra Univ. Press, Waltair, India.

Bitter, F. (1937). "Introduction to Ferromagnetism." McGraw-Hill, New York.

Bouman, J. (1951). "X-ray Crystallography." North Holland Publ., Amsterdam.

Bragg, W., and Bragg, W. L. (1929). "Stereoscopic Photographs of Crystal Models." Adam Hilger, London.

Bravais, A. (1850). On the Systems Formed by Points Regularly Distributed on a Plane or in Space (Eng. transl., 1949). Crystallographic Soc. of Am., Houston, Texas.

Brester, C. J. (1923). Crystal Symmetry and Residual Radiation. Ph.D. Dissertation.

Bruhns, W., and Ramdohr, P. (1926). "Crystallography." Walter de Gruyter, Berlin.

Buerger, M. J. (1942). "X-ray Crystallography." Wiley, New York.

Buerger, M. J. (1956). "Elementary Crystallography." Wiley, New York.

Bunn, C. W. (1946). "Chemical Crystallography." Oxford Univ. Press, London and New York.

Burckhardt, J. J. (1947). "The Motion Groups of Crystallography." Birkhäuser, Basel.

Carter, J. L. (1953). A Study of the Symmetry Properties of Wave Functions in Crystals with Application to Graphite. Ph.D. Dissertation. Cornell Univ., Ithaca, New York.

Corson, E. M. (1951). "Perturbation Methods in the Quantum Mechanics of n-Electron Systems." Hafner, New York.

Coxeter, H. S. M. (1948). "Regular Polytopes." Methuen, London.

Davey, W. P. (1934). "Study of Crystal Structure and its Applications." McGraw-Hill, New York.

Delauney, B., Paduroff, N., and Alexandroff, A. (1934). "Mathematical Foundations of Crystal Structure Analysis and the Determination of Elementary Parallelopipeds with the Help of Roentgen Rays." State Technical-Theoretical Press, Leningrad.

Donnay, J. D. H., and Nowacki, N. (1954). "Crystal Data." Geological Soc. of Am., New York.

Edmonds, A. R. (1954). "Angular Momentum in Quantum Mechanics." Princeton Univ. Press, Princeton, New Jersey.

Ewald, P. P., et al. (1931-1943). "Structure Reports." Akademische Verlagsgesellschaft M.B.H., Leipzig.

Eyring, H., Walter, J., and Kimball, G. E. (1944). "Quantum Chemistry." Wiley, New York.

Fischer, E. (1956). "Introduction to Geometrical Crystallography." Akademie-Verlag, Berlin.

Geilen, V. (1916). Reflection and Rotation Groups Graphically Treated with Special Emphasis on Crystallographic Groups. Ph.D. Dissertation.

Gelfand, I. M., and Shapiro, Z. Y. (1956). Representations of the Group of Rotations of Three-dimensional Space and Their Applications. *Am. Math. Soc. Transl.* **2**, 207.

Günzburg, A. M. (1936). "Symmetry in the Plane." State Scientific-Technical Press of the Ukraine, Kharkov.

Hamermesh, M. Group Theory and its Application to Physical Problems (Notes). Argonne Natl. Lab., Lemont, Illinois.

Henry, N. F. M., and Lonsdale, K. V. (1952). "International Tables for X-Ray Crystallography." Kynoch Press, Birmingham, England.

Henry, N. F. M., Lipson, H. S., and Wooster, W. A. (1951). "The Interpretation of X-Ray Diffraction Photographs." Van Nostrand, Princeton, New Jersey.

Hermann, C. (1935). "International Tables for the Determination of Crystal Structures." Gebr. Borntraeger, Berlin.

Herring, C. (1937). On Energy Coincidences in the Theory of Brillouin Zones. Ph.D. Dissertation. Princeton Univ., Princeton, New Jersey.

Hessel, J. F. C. (1830). Crystal. "Gehler's Physikalisches Wörterbuch," Vol. 5, p. 1023. E. B. Schwickert, Leipzig.

Higman, B. (1955). Applied Group-Theoretic and Matrix Methods." Oxford Univ. Press, London and New York.

Hilton, H. (1903). "Mathematical Crystallography and the Theory of Groups of Movements." Oxford Univ. Press, London and New York.

Hund, F. (1933). General Quantum Mechanics of Atomic and Molecular Structures." "Handuch der Physik," Vol. 24, Series 1, p. 561. J. Springer, Berlin.

Hund, F. (1956). Quantum Mechanics of the Atom. "Encyclopedia of Physics," Vol. 36, Series 2. Springer-Verlag, Berlin.

Inui, T., and Yanagawa, S. (1950). "The Application of Group Representations to Atoms and Molecules" (in Japanese). Japan.

Jaeger, F. M. (1917). "Lectures on the Principle of Symmetry and its Application in all Natural Sciences." Elsevier, Amsterdam.

Jagodzinski, H. (1955). Crystallography. "Encyclopedia of Physics," Vol. 7, Series 1, p. 1. Springer-Verlag, Berlin.

James, R. W. (1950). "X-ray Crystallography." Methuen, London.

Koster, G. F. (1956). Notes on Group Theory. Mass. Inst. of Technol. Solid-State and Molecular Theory Group Technical Rep. No. 8, Cambridge, Mass.

Kotani, M., et al. (1955). "Table of Molecular Integrals." Maruzen, Tokyo.

Landau, L., and Lifschitz, E. (1948). "Quantum Mechanics." Ogiz, Moscow.

Liebisch, T. et al. (1905). Crystallography. "Encycl. der Math. Wiss." Vol. 5, p. 391. B. G. Teubner, Leipzig.

Lipson, H., and Cochran, W. (1953). "The Determination of Crystal Structures." G. Bell and Sons, London.

Lonsdale, K. Y. (1936). "Simplified Structure Factor and Electron Density Formulae for the 230 Space Groups of Mathematical Crystallography." G. Bell & Sons, London.

Ludwig, G. (1954). "The Foundations of Quantum Mechanics." Springer-Verlag, Berlin.

Madelung, E. (1949). "Mathematical Aids for Physicists." Springer, Berlin.

Margenau, H., and Murphy, G. M. (1943). "The Mathematics of Physics and Chemistry." Van Nostrand, New York.

Mathieu, J. P. (1945). "Vibration Spectra and Symmetry." Hermann, Paris.

Murnaghan, F. D. (1938). "The Theory of Group Representations." Johns Hopkins Press, Baltimore, Maryland.

Nicolle, J. "Symmetry and Its Applications." Albin Michel, Paris.

Niggli, P. (1919). "Geometrical Crystallography of a Discontinuum." Gebr. Borntraeger, Leipzig.

Niggli, P. (1924). "Textbook of Mineralogy." Gebr. Borntraeger, Berlin.

Niggli, P. (1928). Fundamental Crystallographic and Structure—Theoretic Concepts. "Handbuch der Experimentalphysik." Vol. 7. Akademische Verlagsgesellschaft M.B.H., Leipzig.

Niggli, P. (1945). "Foundations of Stereochemistry." Birkhäuser, Basel.

Nowacki, W. (1935). Homogeneous Space Partition and Crystal Structure. Ph.D. Dissertation.

Nowacki, W. (1952). "Fourier Synthesis of Crystals." Birkhäuser, Basel.

Phillips, F. C. (1946). "An Introduction to Crystallography." Longmans, Green, London.

Reeks, M. (1908). "Hints for Crystal Drawing." Longmans, Green, London.

Rutgers, A. J. (1948). "Physical Chemistry." Intersience, New York.

Schiebold, E. (1929). "A New Derivation and Nomenclature of the 230 Crystallographic Space Groups." S. Hirzel, Leipzig.

Schoenflies, A. (1891). "Crystal Systems and Crystal Structure."

Schoenflies, A. (1923). "Theory of Crystal Structure." Gebr. Borntraeger, Berlin.

Schouten, J. A. (1951). "Tensor Analysis for Physicists." Oxford Univ. Press, London and New York.

Silberman-Roman, E. (1936). "On the Moebius Strips for Crystalline Symmetries." Les Presses Univ. de France, Paris.

Simon, A. L. (1957). Numerical Table of the Clebsch Gordan Coefficients. Rept. No. ORNL-1718, Oak Ridge Natl. Lab., Oak Ridge, Tennessee.

Simon, A. L., Vander Sluis, J. H., and Biedenharn, L. C. (1954). Tables of the Racah Coefficients. Rept. No. ORNL-1679, Oak Ridge Nat. Lab., Oak Ridge, Tennessee.

Slater, J. C. (1953). Electronic Structure of Solids. Mass. Inst. of Technol. Solid-State and Molecular Theory Group Technical Report No. 4, Cambridge, Mass.

Speiser, A. (1956). "Theory of Groups of Finite Order," 4th ed. Birkhäuser, Basel.

Terpstra, P. (1955). "Introduction to the Space Groups." J. B. Wolters, Groningen.

van der Waerden, B. L. (1932). "The Group Theoretic Method in Quantum Mechanics." Springer, Berlin.

van der Waerden, B. L. (1935). "Groups of Linear Transformations." J. Springer, Berlin.

Venkatarayudu, T. (1954). Applications of Group Theory to Physical Problems (Notes). New York Univ., New York.

von der Lage, F. C. G. (1943). A Method for Obtaining the Energy Levels and Wave Functions of Crystalline Solids and the Application of the Method to Sodium. Ph.D. Dissertation. Cornell Univ., Ithaca, New York.

von Laue, M., and von Mises, R. E. (1926.) "Stereoscopic Drawings of Crystal Structures." J. Springer, Berlin.

Weyl, H. (1931). "The Theory of Groups and Quantum Mechanics." Methuen, London.

Weyl, H. (1946). Theory of Groups (Notes). Princeton Univ., Princeton, New Jersey.

Weyl, H. (1952). "Symmetry." Princeton Univ. Press, Princeton, New Jersey.

Wigner, E. P. (1931). "Group Theory and its Application to the Quantum Mechanics of Atomic Spectra." Friedr. Vieweg & Sohn Akt.-Ges., Braunschweig.

Wigner, E. P. (1932). Lectures on the Properties of the Solid State (Notes). Princeton Univ., Princeton, New Jersey.

Wigner, E. P. (1945). Properties of Solids (Notes). Princeton Univ., Princeton, New Jersey.

Wigner, E. P. (1951). On the Matrices Which Reduce the Kronecker Products of S.R. Groups (Notes). Princeton Univ., Princeton, New Jersey.

Wilson, A. J. C. (1951-1957). "Structure Reports." A. Oosthoek, Utrecht.

Wilson, E. B., Decius, J. C., and Cross, P. C. (1955). "Molecular Vibrations." McGraw-Hill, New York.

Winkler, H. G. F. (1950). "Structure and Properties of Crystals." Springer-Verlag, Berlin.

Wolf, K. L., and Wolff, R. (1956). "Symmetry." Böhlau, Köln, Germany.

Wooster, W. A. (1938). "Crystal Physics." Cambridge Univ. Press, London and New York.

Wyckoff, R. W. G. (1930). "The Analytical Expression of the Results of the Theory of Space Groups." Carnegie Inst. of Washington, Washington, D.C.

Wyckoff, R. W. G. (1948). "Crystal Structures." Interscience, New York.

Zachariasen, W. H. (1945). "Theory of X-Ray Diffraction in Crystals." Wiley, New York.

Chapter V

SUBGROUPS AND REPRESENTATIONS

So far we have restricted our considerations of the relations between the representations of a group and its subgroups to the definition of a subduced representation of a subgroup. In this chapter we shall discuss a number of such relations.

1. Subduced Representations

To begin with let us state Frobenius' two fundamental equations on subduced representations.

Theorem. Let G be a group; $\{\Gamma_i\}$ the set of all irreducible representations of G; H a subgroup of G; $\{\Delta_j\}$ the set of all irreducible representations of H; $\Gamma_i^{(s)}$ the representation of H subduced by Γ_i; $\chi^{(i)}$ the character of Γ_i; $\chi^{(i)(s)}$ the character of $\Gamma_i^{(s)}$; $\phi^{(j)}$ the character of Δ_j; r the number of classes of G; and s the number of classes of H. Then there exist rs nonnegative integers k_{ij} such that

$$\Gamma_i^{(s)} \cdot\equiv\cdot \sum_{j=1}^{s} k_{ij} \Delta_j \qquad (i = 1,\ldots,r)$$

$$\chi^{(i)(s)} = \sum_{j=1}^{s} k_{ij} \phi^{(j)} \qquad (i = 1,\ldots,r).$$

This first Frobenius theorem is simply a formal statement of the fact that a subduced representation of a subgroup can be decomposed into irreducible representations of the subgroup.

Corollary. $k_{ij} = \frac{1}{h} \sum_{l=1}^{s} s_l \chi_l^{(i)(s)} \phi_l^{(j)*}$

where h is the order of H, and s_l is the order of the lth class of H.

Example. $G = Q \qquad H = C_4$

Q has the character table

	C_1	C_2	C_3	C_4	C_5
	1	1	2	2	2
Γ_1	1	1	1	1	1
Γ_2	1	1	1	−1	−1
Γ_3	1	1	−1	1	−1
Γ_4	1	1	−1	−1	1
Γ_5	2	−2	0	0	0

For H we can take the subgroup consisting of the classes C_1, C_2, and C_3 of Q so that H is the cyclic group of order four. The character table of $H = C_4$ is

	C_1	C_2	C_3	C_4
	1	1	1	1
Δ_1	1	1	1	1
Δ_2	1	1	-1	-1
Δ_3	1	-1	i	$-i$
Δ_4	1	-1	$-i$	i

and the table of characters of H subduced by the primitive characters of G is

	C_1	C_2	C_3	C_4
	1	1	1	1
$\Gamma_1^{(s)}$	1	1	1	1
$\Gamma_2^{(s)}$	1	1	1	1
$\Gamma_3^{(s)}$	1	1	-1	-1
$\Gamma_4^{(s)}$	1	1	-1	-1
$\Gamma_5^{(s)}$	2	-2	0	0

Hence we have $\Gamma_1^{(s)} = \Delta_1$, $\Gamma_2^{(s)} = \Delta_1$, $\Gamma_3^{(s)} = \Delta_2$, $\Gamma_4^{(s)} = \Delta_2$, and $\Gamma_5^{(s)} = \Delta_3 \oplus \Delta_4$. From these equations we find

$$||k_{ij}|| = \begin{pmatrix} 1 & 0 & 0 & 0 \\ 1 & 0 & 0 & 0 \\ 0 & 1 & 0 & 0 \\ 0 & 1 & 0 & 0 \\ 0 & 0 & 1 & 1 \end{pmatrix}.$$

The second Frobenius theorem is somewhat more complicated.

Theorem. Using the notation of the preceding theorem and letting C be a class of G, r_l be the order of C_l, $M_l = C_l \cap H$, $\{c_{l'(l)}\}$ be the set of all classes of H contained in M_l, and s_l' the order of c_l' we have

$$\sum_{i=1}^{r} k_{ij} \chi_l^{(i)} = \frac{g}{hr_l} \sum_{l'(l)} s_{l'} \phi_{l'(l)}^{(j)}$$

Example. $G = Q \qquad H = C_4$

Let us take $l = 3$ and $j = 2$. Then

$$\sum_{i=1}^{5} k_{i2} \chi_3^{(i)} = k_{32} \chi_3^{(3)} + k_{42} \chi_3^{(4)} = 1 \times (-1) + 1 \times (-1) = -2.$$

The set M_3 consists of the two classes C_3 and C_4 of $H = C_4$ which have order one. Hence

$$\sum_{l'(l)} s_{l'} \phi_{l'(l)}^{(j)} = \phi_3^{(2)} + \phi_4^{(2)} = (-1) + (-1) = -2.$$

Also $g = 8$, $h = 4$, and $r_3 = 2$ so that $g/hr_3 = 8/(4 \times 2) = 1$. Thus we see that in this case the second Frobenius equation is satisfied.

The remaining theorems on subduced representations which will assume the subgroup to be normal are due to Clifford.

Theorem. Every irreducible representation of a normal subgroup H of G occurs as a component of at least one of the r representations of H subduced by the r irreducible representations of G.

The example used for the first Frobenius theorem illustrates this. This result can be reformulated to say that no column of the matrix $||k_{ij}||$ can be zero if H is a normal subgroup.

Definition. Two representations $\Delta_1 = \{D^{(1)}(B)\}$ and $\Delta_2 = \{D^{(2)}(B)\}$ (where $D^{(i)}(B)$ is the matrix of Δ_i belonging to the group element B) of a normal subgroup H of a group G are *conjugate* to each other relative to G if there exists an element A of G such that $D^{(2)}(B) = D^{(1)}(A^{-1}BA)$ for all B in H (or if the representation $\{D^{(1)}(A^{-1}BA)\}$ is equivalent to Δ_2).

Example. $G = Q \quad H = C_4$

The representations Δ_3 and Δ_4 of $H = C_4$ are conjugate to each other relative to $G = Q$ because the classes C_3 and C_4 of H consist of the elements i and $-i$ respectively of Q, and $j^{-1}ij = -i$ so that

$$D^{(3)}(j^{-1}ij) = D^{(3)}(-i) = D^{(4)}(i)$$

Theorem. Using the preceding notation and letting H be a normal subgroup of G we have the following results.

(1) If Γ is irreducible then $\Gamma^{(s)}$ is either irreducible or is completely reducible into irreducible representations of H of the same dimension.
(2) If Δ is one irreducible component of $\Gamma^{(s)}$, then all the other irreducible components of $\Gamma^{(s)}$ are conjugates of Δ.
(3) Every conjugate of Δ must occur as a component.
(4) Each conjugate of Δ occurs equally often as a component of $\Gamma^{(s)}$.

This is illustrated by the preceding examples. This result can be stated more compactly by introducing the concept of orbits.

Definition. An *orbit* of a normal subgroup H of G is a maximal set of inequivalent irreducible representations of H which are mutually conjugate relative to G.

Example. $G = Q \quad H = C_4$

H has three orbits which are

$$\mathcal{O}_1 = \Delta_1, \qquad \mathcal{O}_2 = \Delta_2, \qquad \mathcal{O}_3 = \{\Delta_3, \Delta_4\}.$$

We can now restate the preceding theorem.

Theorem. Every representation of a normal subgroup H of G subduced by an irreducible representation of G is a multiple of the direct sum of all irreducible representations in some fixed orbit of H.

Definition. If $\Gamma^{(s)}$ is a multiple of the direct sum of all irreducible representations of the orbit $\mathcal{O}$ of the normal subgroup H of G, then $\mathcal{O}$ is called the orbit of the irreducible representation Γ of G.

Example. $G = Q \qquad H = C_4$

$$\mathcal{O}(\Gamma_1) = \mathcal{O}_1 \qquad \mathcal{O}(\Gamma_2) = \mathcal{O}_1 \qquad \mathcal{O}(\Gamma_3) = \mathcal{O}_2$$
$$\mathcal{O}(\Gamma_4) = \mathcal{O}_2 \qquad \mathcal{O}(\Gamma_5) = \mathcal{O}_3.$$

Corollary. If the orbit of Γ consists of the single irreducible representation Δ, then Δ is equivalent to all its conjugates with respect to G.

Since every irreducible representation of a normal subgroup occurs as a component of the representation of H subduced by some irreducible representation of G we see also that every orbit of H is the orbit of some irreducible representation of G.

Definition. (1) The number of inequivalent irreducible representations in an orbit is the *order* of the orbit.

(2) The number of times each irreducible representation of an orbit $\mathcal{O}(\Gamma)$ of an irreducible representation Γ occurs in the subduced representation $\Gamma^{(s)}$ of the normal subgroup H of G is called the *multiplicity* of $\mathcal{O}(\Gamma)$ relative to Γ.

Theorem. Let H be a normal subgroup of G; G/H a cyclic group; Γ an irreducible representation of G; $\Gamma^{(s)}$ the representation of H subduced by Γ; $\mathcal{O}(\Gamma)$ the orbit of Γ relative to H; $o(\Gamma)$ the order of $\mathcal{O}(\Gamma)$; and $m(\mathcal{O}(\Gamma))$ the multiplicity of $\mathcal{O}(\Gamma)$ relative to Γ. Then

(1) $o(\Gamma)$ is a divisor of g/h

(2) $m(\Gamma) = 1$.

Again this is illustrated by the preceding examples.

Definition. Two representations Γ_1 and Γ_2 of a group G are said to be *associate* relative to a subgroup H if $\Gamma_1^{(s)}$ and $\Gamma_2^{(s)}$ contain an irreducible representation of H in common.

Example. Γ_1 and Γ_2 of Q are associate relative to $H = C_4$ because $\Gamma_1^{(s)} = \Gamma_2^{(s)} = \Delta_1$.

We see that two irreducible representations of a group are associate relative to a normal subgroup if and only if they have the same orbit.

Theorem. If H is a normal subgroup of G; G/H a cyclic group; Γ an irreducible representation of G; $\mathcal{O}(\Gamma)$ the orbit of Γ relative to H; and $o(\Gamma)$ the order of $\mathcal{O}(\Gamma)$, then the number of irreducible associates of Γ relative to H is $\dfrac{g}{ho(\Gamma)} - 1$.

Example. $G = Q \quad H = C_4 \quad g = 8 \quad h = 4$

Since $o(\Gamma_1) = o(\Gamma_2) = o(\Gamma_3) = o(\Gamma_4) = 1$ and $o(\Gamma_5) = 2$ we see that $\dfrac{g}{ho(\Gamma_1)} = \dfrac{g}{ho(\Gamma_2)} = \dfrac{g}{ho(\Gamma_3)} = \dfrac{g}{ho(\Gamma_4)} = 2$ and $\dfrac{g}{ho(\Gamma_5)} = 1$.

Hence each of the first four irreducible representations of Q has one associate relative to C_4, whereas Γ_5 has no associates. This agrees with the fact that Γ_1 and Γ_2 are associates, and Γ_3 and Γ_4 are associates.

Theorem. Let H be a normal subgroup of G; Γ an irreducible representation of G; $\mathcal{O}(\Gamma)$ the orbit of Γ relative to H; $m = m(\mathcal{O}(\Gamma))$ the multiplicity of $\mathcal{O}(\Gamma)$ relative to Γ; $\Delta_1, \ldots, \Delta_{o(\Gamma)}$ the inequivalent, conjugate, irreducible representations of H belonging to $\mathcal{O}(\Gamma)$; and V_j the carrier space of $m\Delta_j$. Then $V_1, \ldots, V_{o(\Gamma)}$ is a system of imprimitivity of Γ.

Example. $G = Q \quad H = C_4 \quad \Gamma = \Gamma_5$

Since $\Gamma_5 = \Delta_3 \oplus \Delta_4$ we see that the spaces $V_1 = \left\{\begin{pmatrix} x \\ 0 \end{pmatrix}\right\}$ and $V_2 = \left\{\begin{pmatrix} 0 \\ y \end{pmatrix}\right\}$ should and do form a system of imprimitivity of Γ_5. This is the example that was given in Chapter I.

Corollary. Γ is imprimitive if and only if $o(\Gamma) \neq 1$.

Theorem. Let $V_1, \ldots, V_{o(\Gamma)}$ be the system of imprimitivity of Γ described in the preceding theorem, let G_j be the largest subgroup of G such that the representation $\Gamma_j^{(s)}$ of G_j subduced by Γ leaves V_j invariant, let γ_j be the component of $\Gamma_j^{(s)}$ whose carrier space is V_j, and let $\gamma_j^{(s)}$ be the representation of H subduced by γ_j. Then

(1) γ_j is an irreducible representation of G_j

(2) $\gamma^{(s)} = m(\mathcal{O}(\gamma))\Delta_j$.

A similar result is the following.

Theorem. Let G be a group; H a normal subgroup; Δ an irreducible representation of H; A an arbitrary element of G; B an arbitrary element of H; $\Delta(A)$ the irreducible representation of H conjugate to Δ defined by $B \to D^{(\Delta)}(ABA^{-1})$; and G' the set of all elements A' of G such that $\Delta(A') \equiv \Delta$. Then G' contains H and there exists an irreducible representation Γ' of G' such that $\Gamma'^{(s)} = m\Delta$, where m is a positive integer. Further, G' is the largest subgroup of G which has such an irreducible representation.

2. Induced Representations

If we are given a subgroup H of a group G together with a representation Δ of H, then we can construct from Δ a representation Γ of G. It is not necessary for H to be normal or for Δ to be irreducible and of course Γ need not be irreducible. The resulting representation Γ of G is said to be induced by the representation Δ of the subgroup H. Let us now describe this procedure in detail.

Theorem. Let $G = \{A\}$ be a group; $H = \{B\}$ a subgroup of G; $\{A_i\}$ $(i = 1,\ldots,g/h)$ a set of elements of G such that $A_1 H, A_2 H,\ldots, A_{g/h} H$ are all distinct left cosets of H; $\sigma_{ij}(A, B)$ $(i, j = 1,\ldots,g/h)$ a function defined by

$$\begin{aligned}\sigma_{ij}(A, B) &= 1 \quad \text{if } A_i B A_j^{-1} = A \\ &= 0 \quad \text{otherwise;}\end{aligned}$$

$\sigma(A, B) = ||\sigma_{ij}(A, B)||$; Δ a representation of H defined by $B \rightarrow D^{(\Delta)}(B)$; and $D^{(\Gamma)}(A) = \sum_{B \epsilon H} \sigma(A, B) \otimes D^{(\Delta)}(B)$, where $\sum$ denotes an ordinary matrix sum. Then $A \rightarrow D^{(\Gamma)}(A)$ is a representation Γ of G which we shall call the representation of G *induced* by the representation Δ of the subgroup H. We shall use the notation $\Gamma = \Delta^{(\mathscr{I})}$.

Example. $G = C_2$ $H = I$ $\Delta = 1$ (the trivial representation). Then if A is the generator of C_2 we have $g/h = 2$ $\quad A_1 = I \quad A_2 = A$

$$\sigma(I, I) = \begin{pmatrix} 1 & 0 \\ 0 & 1 \end{pmatrix} \qquad \sigma(A, I) = \begin{pmatrix} 0 & 1 \\ 1 & 0 \end{pmatrix}$$

$$D^{(\Gamma)}(I) = \sigma(I, I) = \begin{pmatrix} 1 & 0 \\ 0 & 1 \end{pmatrix} \qquad D^{(\Gamma)}(A) = \sigma(A, I) = \begin{pmatrix} 0 & 1 \\ 1 & 0 \end{pmatrix}.$$

The character of $\Gamma \equiv \Delta^{(\mathscr{I})}$ is $(2, 0)$ so we see that if Γ_1 and Γ_2 are the two irreducible representations of C_2 we have $\Gamma \equiv \Delta^{(\mathscr{I})} = \Gamma_1 \oplus \Gamma_2$. Hence, $\Gamma = \Delta^{(\mathscr{I})}$ is in this case the regular representation.

Since the σ-matrices of the preceding theorem have dimension g/h we see:

Corollary. If $d(\Delta)$ is the dimension of Δ then the dimension $d(\Delta^{(\mathscr{I})})$ of the induced representation is

$$d(\Delta^{(\mathscr{I})}) = \frac{g}{h}\, d(\Delta).$$

This result incidentally shows us that the dimension of Δ is a divisor of the dimension of $\Delta^{(\mathscr{I})}$ (because h is a divisor of g). Also, if Δ is irreducible then $d(\Delta^{(\mathscr{I})})$ is a divisor of g.

More thorough considerations yield the following result:

Corollary. If C_j is the jth class of G; r_j its order; $M_j = C_j \cap H$, $\{c_{j'(j)}\}$ the set of all classes of H contained in M_j; $s_{j'}$ the order of $c_{j'(j)}$; $\phi^{(\Delta)}$ the character of Δ; and $\chi^{(\Delta \mathscr{I})}$ the character of $\Delta^{(\mathscr{I})}$; then

$$\chi_j^{(\Delta \mathscr{I})} = \frac{g}{hr_j} \sum_{j'(j)} s_{j'} \phi_{j'(j)}^{(\Delta)}\,.$$

This equation provides a simple direct method of evaluating the character of an induced representation. Another simple form for the character of $\Delta^{(\mathscr{I})}$ can also be given.

Corollary. Let $\psi^{(\Delta)}(A) = \phi^{(\Delta)}(A)$ if $A \in H$
$= 0$ if $A \notin H$.

Then

$$\chi^{(\Delta\mathscr{I})}(A) = \frac{1}{h} \sum_{A' \in G} \psi^{(\Delta)}(A'^{-1}AA').$$

Another obvious consequence of the method of construction of $\Delta^{(\mathscr{I})}$ is that if Δ is real so is $\Delta^{(\mathscr{I})}$.

Now let us state criteria due to Shoda and Mackey for the irreducibility and for the equivalence of induced representations in terms of the subgroups and their representations.

Theorem. Let G be a group; H a subgroup of G; Δ a representation of H; X an element of $G - H$; $H_X = (X^{-1}HX) \cap H$; Y an arbitrary element of H_X; $\Delta^{(s)}$ the representation of H_X defined by $Y \to D^{(\Delta)}(Y)$; and $\Delta^{(s)}(X)$ the representation of H_X conjugate to $\Delta^{(s)}$ defined by $Y \to D^{(\Delta)}(XYX^{-1})$. Then the representation $\Delta^{(\mathscr{I})}$ of G induced by Δ is irreducible if and only if for every X in $G - H$ the representations $\Delta^{(s)}$ and $\Delta^{(s)}(X)$ have no irreducible component in common.

Theorem. Let G be a group; H_1 and H_2 two subgroups of G; Δ_1 and Δ_2 representations of H_1 and H_2 respectively; A an element of G; $H_A = (A^{-1}H_1A) \cap H_2$; Y an arbitrary element of H_A; $\Delta_2^{(s)}$ the representation of H_A defined by $Y \to D^{(\Delta_2)}(Y)$; and $\Delta_1^{(s)}(A)$ the representation of H_A defined by $Y \to D^{(\Delta_1)}(AYA^{-1})$. Then the representations $\Delta_1^{(\mathscr{I})}$ and $\Delta_2^{(\mathscr{I})}$ of G induced by Δ_1 and Δ_2 are inequivalent if and only if for every A in G the representations $\Delta_2^{(s)}$ and $\Delta_1^{(s)}(A)$ have no irreducible component in common.

Definition. The representation of a group G induced by the trivial 1-dimensional representation of a subgroup H is called the *principal* induced representation of G relative to H.

Thus the example given earlier was a principal induced representation.

Theorem. (1) The character of a principal induced representation is

$$\chi_j = \frac{g}{hr_j} \sum_{j'(j)} s_{j'(j)} = \frac{gm_j}{hr_j}$$

where $m.$ is the order of $M_j = C_j \cap H$.

(2) Every principal induced representation contains the trivial representation exactly once.

(3) Every principal induced representation is a component (not necessarily irreducible) of the regular representation.

(4) A principal induced representation is faithful if and only if neither H nor any of its subgroups is normal in G.

(5) The principal representation induced by the trivial representation of the identity element is the regular representation.

(6) Let $\{S_1,\ldots,S_{g/h}\}$ be the g/h distinct left cosets of H,

$$\{S_{i_1},S_{i_2},\ldots,S_{i_{g/h}}\} = \{AS_1, AS_2,\ldots, AS_{g/h}\},$$

$$D_{jk}(A) = \delta_{j,i_k}, D(A) = ||D_{jk}(A)||.$$

Then the set of matrices $\{D(A)\}$ is the principal induced representation relative to H.

(7) The principal induced representation relative to the commutator subgroup contains each 1-dimensional representation exactly once.

Let us call a representation of a group induced by a linear (i.e. 1-dimensional) representation of a subgroup a *Brauer* representation. Then it can be shown that every character of a group can be expressed as a linear integral combination of Brauer characters.

3. Induced and Subduced Representations

The most important theorem connecting induced and subduced representations is the famous Frobenius reciprocity theorem which we now state.

Theorem. The representation of G induced by the jth irreducible representation of H contains the ith irreducible representation of G exactly as often as the representation of H subduced by the ith irreducible representation of G contains the jth irreducible representation of H.

Example. $G = Q \quad H = C_4 \quad \Gamma = \Gamma_5 \quad \Delta = \Delta_4$

Then $\Gamma_5^{(s)} = \Delta_3 \oplus \Delta_4$ and $\Delta_4^{(\mathscr{I})} = \Gamma_5$. Hence, we see that $\Delta_4^{(\mathscr{I})}$ contains Γ_5 exactly as often as $\Gamma_5^{(s)}$ contains Δ_4; namely once.

Another useful result is due to Ito.

Theorem. $(\Delta \otimes \Gamma^{(s)})^{(\mathscr{I})} = \Delta^{(\mathscr{I})} \otimes \Gamma.$

This has the following immediate consequence.

Corollary. $(\Gamma^{(s)})^{(\mathscr{I})} = \Delta_1{}^{(\mathscr{I})} \otimes \Gamma,$

where Δ_1 is the trivial representation and $\Delta_1^{(\mathscr{I})}$ is the principal induced representation.

Example. $G = Q \quad H = C_4 \quad \Gamma = \Gamma_5 \quad \Delta = \Delta_4$

Ito's result predicts that

$$[\Delta_4 \otimes (\Delta_3 \oplus \Delta_4)]^{(\mathscr{I})} = \Gamma_5 \otimes \Gamma_5.$$

Since $\Delta_1^{(\mathscr{I})} = \Gamma_1 \oplus \Gamma_2$, the corollary predicts that

$$(\Gamma_5^{(s)})^{(\mathscr{I})} \cdot\!\equiv\!\cdot (\Gamma_1 \oplus \Gamma_2) \otimes \Gamma_5 \cdot\!\equiv\!\cdot 2\Gamma_5.$$

The next result is really the third part of the theorem on subduced representations and the subgroup G_j.

Theorem. Let G be a group; Γ an irreducible representation of G; H a normal subgroup of G; $\Delta_1, \ldots, \Delta_o$ the conjugate, inequivalent, irreducible representations of H composing $\mathcal{O}(\Gamma)$; V_j the carrier space of $m(\mathcal{O}(\Gamma))\Delta_j$; G_j the largest subgroup of G such that the representation $\Gamma_j^{(s)}$ subduced by Γ leaves V_j invariant; and γ_j the component of $\Gamma_j^{(s)}$ whose carrier space is V_j. Then $\Gamma = \gamma_j^{(\mathscr{I})}$.

Again we have a similar result.

Theorem. Let G be a group; H a normal subgroup; Δ an irreducible representation of H; A an element of G; $\Delta(A)$ the irreducible representation of H which is conjugate to Δ and is defined by $B \to D^{(\Delta)}(ABA^{-1})$; G' the subgroup of all elements A of G such that $\Delta(A) \cdot\!\equiv\!\cdot \Delta$; and $\gamma(\Delta)$ an irreducible representation of G' such that $\gamma^{(s)}(\Delta) = m\Delta$. Then the representation $\gamma^{(\mathscr{I})}(\Delta)$ of G is irreducible.

Finally:

Theorem. Let G be a group; H a normal subgroup; Δ an irreducible representation of H; $\mathcal{O}(\Delta)$ the orbit of H containing Δ; $o(\Delta)$ the order of $\mathcal{O}(\Delta)$; and $\Delta^{(\mathscr{I})}$ the representation of G induced by Δ. Then $\Delta^{(\mathscr{I})}$ is irreducible if and only if $o(\Delta) = g/h$.

Example. $G = T \quad H = D_2$

Since $T = D_2 \circledS C_3$ (see Chapter II, page 29, on semidirect products), D_2 must be a normal subgroup of T. It can easily be shown that D_2 has only two orbits relative to T, namely, $\mathcal{O}_1 = \{\Delta_1\}$, $\mathcal{O}_2 = \{\Delta_2, \Delta_3, \Delta_4\}$, where Δ_1 is the trivial representation of D_2. Since $g/h = 12/4 = 3$ and $o(\Delta_2) = 3$, we see that Δ_2 must induce the irreducible 3-dimensional representation of T.

4. Projective Representations

A very brief presentation of the salient features of projective representation will be given here.

Definition. A *projective* (or ray, or collineatory) representation of a group $G = \{A\}$ is a set $\Gamma = \{D(A)\}$ of square, nonsingular, d-dimensional matrices $D(A)$ together with a correspondence $A \to D(A)$ such that

$$AB = C \text{ implies } D(A)D(B) = \lambda(A, B)D(C),$$

where A, B, and C are elements of G, and $\lambda(A, B)$ is a single-valued function on $G \times G$ to the complex numbers which does not assume the value zero.

Let us call the ordinary representations, which we have considered exclusively until this section, *vector* representations. From the preceding definition we see that the essential difference between vector and projective representations is the admission of the function $\lambda(A, B)$ in a projective representation. The function $\lambda(A, B)$ belonging to a particular projective representation Γ is called the *factor system* of the representation.

Example. $G = D_2$

I	A	B	C
A	I	C	B
B	C	I	A
C	B	A	I

Since D_2 is abelian its irreducible vector representations are all 1-dimensional. However, the following projective representation

$$I \to \begin{pmatrix} 1 & 0 \\ 0 & 1 \end{pmatrix} \quad A \to \begin{pmatrix} 0 & 1 \\ 1 & 0 \end{pmatrix} = \sigma_x \quad B \to \begin{pmatrix} 0 & -i \\ i & 0 \end{pmatrix} = \sigma_y \quad C \to \begin{pmatrix} 1 & 0 \\ 0 & -1 \end{pmatrix} = \sigma_z$$

is 2-dimensional but nevertheless irreducible (the set of matrices being irreducible). The entries in the following table are the values of the factor system $\lambda(A_1, A_2)$.

	I	A	B	C
I	1	1	1	1
A	1	1	i	$-i$
B	1	$-i$	1	i
C	1	i	$-i$	1

Theorem. A function $\lambda(A, B)$ on $G \times G$ is a factor system of some projective representation of G if and only if

$$\lambda(A, B)\lambda(AB, C) = \lambda(B, C)\lambda(A, BC)$$

for all A, B, C in G.

Theorem. Every reducible projective representation is completely reducible.

As with vector representations we will want to consider certain superficially different projective representations as the same.

Definition. Two projective representations $\Gamma_1 = \{D^{(1)}(A)\}$ and $\Gamma_2 = \{D^{(2)}(A)\}$ of a group $G = \{A\}$ are *projective-equivalent* (or *p*-equivalent) if there exists a function $\mu(A)$ on G to the complex numbers and a square nonsingular matrix S such that $D^{(-)}(A) = \mu(A) S D^{(1)}(A) S^{-1}$ for every A in G.

Theorem. Every projective representation is *p*-equivalent to a unitary projective representation.

Let us call two factor systems of a group *p-equivalent* if they belong to two *p*-equivalent projective representations for which the transformation matrix $S = I$, so $D^{(2)}(A) = \mu(A) D^{(1)}(A)$. Thus if two factor systems are

p-equivalent the function $\mu(A)$ on G relates them according to the equation

$$\lambda_2(A, B) = \frac{\mu(A)\,\mu(B)}{\mu(AB)}\,\lambda_1(A, B).$$

In a set of p-equivalent factor systems there is always one whose values are all gth roots of unity.

If the factor systems of a group are classified according to p-equivalence it can be shown that there is only a finite number of such classes. Further, any two of these classes can be multiplied to give a third class by simply multiplying one factor system from the first with one from the second and defining the third class to be the class containing the product of the two factor systems. It can then be shown that with this kind of multiplication the classes of factor systems form a finite abelian group. This group is called the *multiplicator* of the original group.

Theorem. If G has order g and its multiplicator M has order m, then the dimension of every irreducible projective representation of G is a divisor of mg. Also, the number of irreducible p-inequivalent project representations is $\leqslant mg$.

Example. $G = D_2 \quad M = C_2 \quad m = 2$
There are only two p-inequivalent irreducible projective representations of D_2. One was given in a preceding example, and the other is the trivial vector representation.

Definition. Let G be a group, and G' another group which contains a subgroup H' in its center such that $G'/H' = G$. Then G' is called a *covering group* of G extended by the abelian group H'.

We shall now see how to obtain irreducible projective representations of a group from the irreducible vector representations of a covering group.

Theorem. Let $G = \{A\}$ be a group; $G' = \{A'\}$ a covering group of G extended by the abelian group H'; Γ' an irreducible vector representation of G'; $\{S'\}$ the distinct cosets of H'; $\{A'(S')\}$ any subset of G' consisting of one element $A'(S')$ from each coset S' of H'; and $S' \leftrightarrow A$ the isomorphism between G'/H' and G. Then $A \to D^{(\Gamma')}(A')$ is an irreducible projective representation of G.

Example. $G = D_2 \quad G' = Q \quad H' = C_2 \quad \Gamma' = \Gamma_5$
Since $H' = C_2 = \{I, A_1\}$, the cosets of H' are $S_1' = H' = \{I, A_1\}$, $S_2' = \{A_2, A_3\}$, $S_3' = \{A_4, A_5\}$, and $S_4' = \{A_6, A_7\}$. An isomorphism is $S_1' \leftrightarrow I \;\; S_2' \leftrightarrow C \;\; S_3' \leftrightarrow B \;\; S_4' \leftrightarrow A$. If we choose the set $\{A'(S')\}$ to be $A'(S_1') = I \;\; A'(S_2') = A_2 \;\; A'(S_3') = A_4 \;\; A'(S_4') = A_6$, we obtain the projective representation

$$I \to \begin{pmatrix} 1 & 0 \\ 0 & 1 \end{pmatrix} \quad A \to \begin{pmatrix} 0 & -i \\ -i & 0 \end{pmatrix} \quad B \to \begin{pmatrix} 0 & 1 \\ -1 & 0 \end{pmatrix} \quad C \to \begin{pmatrix} -i & 0 \\ 0 & i \end{pmatrix}$$

which is p-equivalent to the projective representation of D_2 given earlier.

It can be shown that every group has a covering group from which every irreducible projective representation can be obtained in the above manner. Such a covering group of minimal order is called a *representation group* of the original group, and can be shown to have order mg. Further, a general method of constructing representation groups is known. In the case of $G = D_2$ a representation group is the quaternion group.

Finally, it is worth observing that the spin representations of the 3-dimensional rotation group can be considered as projective representations. The set of all faithful irreducible vector representations and all irreducible spin representations of $R(3)$ is the set of all irreducible, p-inequivalent projective representations of $R(3)$. The 2-dimensional, unitary, unimodular group is of course a representation group of $R(3)$.

5. Little Groups

This section will be to a large extent nothing but a reformulation of the preceding sections in the language of little groups. The theory will, however, be more specifically directed toward the needs of the next chapter. In brief, this section will show how the irreducible representations of a group G can be derived from the irreducible representations of any normal subgroup H together with the irreducible representations of G/H and its subgroups. First let us define the term little group.

Definition. Let G be a group; H a normal subgroup of G; A an element of G; B an arbitrary element of H; Δ an irreducible representation of H; $\Delta(A)$ the irreducible representation of H which is conjugate to Δ and defined by $B \to D^{(\Delta)}(ABA^{-1})$; and $L^{(II)}$ the subgroup of all elements A of G such that $\Delta(A) \cdot\equiv\cdot \Delta$. Then $L^{(II)}$ is a *little group* of the *second kind* relative to G, H, and Δ. The quotient group $L^{(I)} = L^{(II)}/H$ is the corresponding *little group* of the *first kind* relative to G, H, and Δ.

Example. $G = 0 \quad H = D_2$

Consider the octahedral group (see the multiplication table in Chapter II). The subgroup $D_2 = \{I, A_6, A_{17}, A_{19}\}$ is normal. If we take Δ to be the representation $I \to 1 \; A_6 \to 1 \; A_{17} \to -1 \; A_{19} \to -1$, we find

$$L^{(II)} = \{I, A_1, A_6, A_7, A_{16}, A_{17}, A_{18}, A_{19}\},$$

which is isomorphic to D_4. The little group of first kind $L^{(I)} = L^{(II)}/H$ is of course isomorphic to C_2.

We can now draw two immediate conclusions about the little group. First, $L^{(II)} \supseteq H$, and second $L^{(I)}$ is isomorphic to a subgroup of G/H.

If Δ is a representation of a subgroup H of G, and if K is a subgroup of G containing H, let us say that Δ can be *extended* to K if K possesses a representation Δ' such that $\Delta'^{(s)} = \Delta$. Two less obvious conclusions about little groups are that $L^{(II)}$ is the largest subgroup of G to which Δ can be extended as a projective representation, and that there is essentially only one such extension (i.e., all such extensions are p-equivalent).

Definition. Let G be a group, H a normal subgroup, Δ an irreducible representation of H, $L^{(II)}(\Delta)$ the little group of the second kind, and γ an irreducible representation of $L^{(II)}(\Delta)$. Then γ will be said to be an *allowable* (or small) representation of $L^{(II)}(\Delta)$ relative to H and Δ if γ subduces a multiple of Δ on H; $\gamma^{(s)} \cdot\!\equiv\!\cdot m\Delta$.

The key theorem which will be stated now is simply a restatement of two earlier theorems.

Theorem. Let G be a group; H a normal subgroup; $\mathcal{O}$ an orbit of H; Δ any irreducible representation of H belonging to $\mathcal{O}$; $L^{(II)}$ the little group of the second kind relative to G, H, and Δ; and γ an irreducible representation of $L^{(II)}$ such that the representation $\gamma^{(s)}$ of H subduced by γ is a multiple of Δ: $\gamma^{(s)} = m\Delta$ (i.e. γ is an allowable representation). Then

(1) The representation $\gamma^{(\mathcal{I})}$ of G induced by γ is irreducible and has orbit $\mathcal{O}$.
(2) Every irreducible representation of G with orbit $\mathcal{O}$ is induced by one such γ.
(3) If only one little group per orbit is used to induce the irreducible representations of G then each irreducible representation of G is found once and only once.

Example. $G = O \quad H = D_2 = \{I, A_6, A_{17}, A_{19}\}$

Again choosing Δ to be $I \to 1 \; A_6 \to 1 \; A_{17} \to -1 \; A_{19} \to -1$ so

$$L^{(II)} = \{I, A_1, A_6, A_7, A_{16}, A_{17}, A_{18}, A_{19}\},$$

we can choose γ to be $I \to 1, A_1 \to 1, A_6 \to 1, A_7 \to 1, A_{16} \to -1, A_{17} \to -1, A_{18} \to -1, A_{19} \to -1$. Then $\gamma^{(s)} = \Delta$ and $\gamma^{(\mathcal{I})} = \Gamma_5$ (see the character table of O in Chapter III).

Example. $G = 0 \quad H = D_2 = \{I, A_6, A_{17}, A_{19}\}$

Let us consider this problem more thoroughly than we did in the preceding example. The normal subgroup $H = D_2$ has only two orbits: $\mathcal{O}_1 = \Delta_1$ and $\mathcal{O}_2 = \{\Delta_2, \Delta_3, \Delta_4\}$, where the character table is:

	I	A_6	A_{17}	A_{19}
Δ_1	1	1	1	1
Δ_2	1	1	−1	−1
Δ_3	1	−1	1	−1
Δ_4	1	−1	−1	1

D_2

The little groups of the second kind belonging to the four irreducible representations are:

$$L^{(II)}(\Delta_1) = G = 0$$
$$L^{(II)}(\Delta_2) = D_4 = \{I, A_1, A_6, A_7, A_{16}, A_{17}, A_{18}, A_{19}\}$$
$$L^{(II)}(\Delta_3) = D_4 = \{I, A_3, A_5, A_6, A_{17}, A_{19}, A_{21}, A_{23}\}$$
$$L^{(II)}(\Delta_4) = D_4 = \{I, A_6, A_8, A_{10}, A_{13}, A_{15}, A_{17}, A_{19}\}.$$

Let us consider now only the last three little groups. From the character table of D_4,

	C_1	C_2	C_3	C_4	C_5	
	1	1	2	2	2	
Γ_1	1	1	1	1	1	
Γ_2	1	1	1	-1	-1	
Γ_3	1	1	-1	1	-1	D_4
Γ_4	1	1	-1	-1	1	
Γ_5	2	-2	0	0	0	

one easily sees that each little group $L^{(II)}(\Delta_i)$ possesses exactly two irreducible representations which subduce a multiple of Δ_i. Both of these are of course 1-dimensional and real. All of them will induce real 3-dimensional irreducible representations of the orthogonal group. The two allowable γ-representations of $L^{(II)}(\Delta_2)$ are:

	I	A_6	A_1, A_7	A_{16}, A_{18}	A_{17}, A_{19}
γ_1	1	1	1	-1	-1
γ_2	1	1	-1	1	-1

These induce the irreducible representations Γ_5 and Γ_4 of O, which are the only 3-dimensional irreducible representations of O. The little groups belonging to the conjugate representations Δ_3 and Δ_4 are not needed because their allowable γ-representations will subduce the same irreducible representations of O as those of Δ_2. Returning to $L^{(II)}(\Delta_1) = G$ we see from the character table of O that each of the three remaining irreducible representations of O subduces a multiple of Δ_1 and is therefore an allowable γ-representation. However, we want to construct the irreducible representations of G.

From the preceding theorem we see that if we can construct the irreducible, allowable (or *small*) γ-representations of the little groups of H then we can construct all of the irreducible representations of G.

Theorem. Let $\Delta_{ext.}$ be an extension (possibly projective) of Δ to $L^{(II)}(\Delta)$, and let Ω be any irreducible projective representation of $L^{(II)}(\Delta)$ which subduces a multiple of the trivial representation on H, and whose factor system is the reciprocal of that of $\Delta_{ext.}$. Then the representation $\gamma = \Delta_{ext.} \otimes \Omega$

is an irreducible vector representation of $L^{(II)}(\Delta)$ which subduces on H a multiple of Δ (i.e., $\Delta_{ext.} \otimes \Omega$ is an allowable γ-representation).

Conversely

Theorem. Every irreducible representation γ of $L^{(II)}(\Delta)$ which subduces a multiple of Δ on H can be expressed in the form $\gamma = \Delta_{ext.} \otimes \Omega$, where $\Delta_{ext.}$ is a projective extension of Δ, and where Ω is the unique, irreducible projective representation of $L^{(II)}(\Delta)$ which subduces a multiple of the trivial representation on H, and whose factor system is the reciprocal of that of $\Delta_{ext.}$.

This still leaves us with the problem of finding irreducible projective representations Ω of $L^{(II)}$ in finding γ's.

Theorem. It is always possible to choose $\Delta_{ext.}$ so that the kernel K of Ω contains H. Since $L^{(I)}(\Delta) = \dfrac{L^{(II)}(\Delta)}{H}$ is then homomorphic to $\dfrac{L^{(II)}(\Delta)}{K}$, it follows that Ω, which is isomorphic to $\dfrac{L^{(II)}(\Delta)}{K}$, is a representation of $L^{(I)}(\Delta)$.

Thus we have now reduced the problem of finding allowable γ-representations of little groups of the second kind to the problems

(1) of finding irreducible representations of H

(2) of extending these irreducible representations of H to their little groups of the second kind

(3) of finding irreducible, projective representations of the little groups of the first kind.

Example. $G = O \quad H = D_2 \quad \Delta = \Delta_1 \quad L^{(II)}(\Delta) = G = O$

Let us now consider the remaining three irreducible representations of O which were not determined in the preceding examples from $L^{(II)}(\Delta_2)$. From the dimension formula $g = \sum_{i=1}^{r} d_i^2$ we know that the remaining three irreducible representations must have dimension 1, 1, and 2. These representations must be of the forms $\Delta_{ext.} \otimes \Omega$. In the case of the two 1-dimensional representations Ω must be 1-dimensional and therefore the trivial representation. Hence, the two 1-dimensional representations must be extensions of the trivial representations of $H = D_2$ to $G = O$. Since $H = D_2$ is in the kernels K_i $(i = 1,2)$ of these representations, and since $G \to G/H \to G/K_i$, it follows that these two 1-dimensional representations must also be 1-dimensional representations of G/H. Let us therefore briefly consider $G/H = O/D_2 = D_3$. The cosets of $H = D_2$ are

$$S_1 = H = D_2 = \{I, A_6, A_{17}, A_{19}\}$$
$$S_2 = \{A_1, A_7, A_{16}, A_{18}\}$$
$$S_3 = \{A_2, A_4, A_{20}, A_{22}\}$$
$$S_4 = \{A_3, A_5, A_{21}, A_{23}\}$$
$$S_5 = \{A_8, A_{10}, A_{13}, A_{15}\}$$
$$S_6 = \{A_9, A_{11}, A_{12}, A_{14}\}.$$

The three classes of D_3 are $C_1 = \{S_1\}$, $C_2 = \{S_3, S_6\}$, and $C_3 = \{S_2, S_4, S_5\}$. The character table is

	C_1	C_2	C_3
Γ_1	1	1	1
Γ_2	1	1	--1
Γ_3	2	−1	0

The two 1-dimensional representations of O are therefore the trivial one and Γ_2:

$$C_1 + C_2 = S_1 + S_3 + S_6 = \{I, A_2, A_4, A_6, A_9, A_{11}, A_{12}, A_{14}, A_{17}, A_{19}, A_{20}, A_{22}\} \to 1$$
$$C_3 = S_2 + S_4 + S_5 = \{I, A_1, A_3, A_5, A_7, A_8, A_9, A_{13}, A_{15}, A_{16}, A_{18}, A_{21}, A_{23}\} \to -1.$$

Similarly, the 2-dimensional representation of O can be found from the 2-dimensional representation of D_3.

The little group method which we shall use in the next chapter is a variation of the preceding which does not use projective representations. This variation is based on the following two theorems.

Theorem. Let G be a group; H a normal subgroup; Δ an irreducible representation of H; $L^{(II)}(\Delta)$ the corresponding little group; and K the kernel of Δ. Then K is a normal subgroup of $L^{(II)}(\Delta)$.

Example. $G = O \quad H = D_2 \quad \Delta = \Delta_2$
The kernel of Δ_2 is $K = \{I, A_6\}$ and the little group is

$$L^{(II)}(\Delta_2) = \{I, A_1, A_6, A_7, A_{16}, A_{17}, A_{18}, A_{19}\}.$$

Since A_6 commutes with all elements of $L^{(II)}(\Delta_2)$, K is certainly a normal subgroup of $L^{(II)}(\Delta_2)$.

If we are given a group G, a quotient group G/H, and a representation Γ of G/H, then Γ establishes a representation of G through the sequence of homomorphisms $G \to G/H \to \Gamma$. Let us say that Γ *engenders* a representation of G.

Theorem. Let G be a group; H a normal subgroup; Δ an irreducible representation of H; $L^{(II)}(\Delta)$ the corresponding little group; and K the kernel of Δ. Then every irreducible representation γ of $L^{(II)}(\Delta)$, which subduces a multiple of Δ on H, $\gamma^{(s)} = m\Delta$ (i.e., every allowable γ), is engendered by some irreducible representation of the quotient group $L^{(II)}/K$.

This is exactly what was used in determining the three irreducible representations of O in the preceding example. In that case Δ was the trivial representation Δ_1 of $H = D_2$, $L^{(II)}(\Delta_1)$ was $G = O$, and K was $H = D_2$. Each of the three irreducible representations of $L^{(II)}/K = G/H = O/D_2 = D_3$ then engendered an irreducible representation of $L^{(II)}(\Delta_1) = G = O$.

We might note that $L^{(I)} = L^{(II)}/H$ is a homomorph of $L^{(II)}/K$ so that every irreducible representation of $L^{(I)}$ engenders an irreducible representation of $L^{(II)}/K$.

Let us now briefly summarize the little group technique of finding irreducible representations of a group which we have just discussed. Let G be a group and H a normal subgroup of G. The technique goes as follows.

(1) Find all irreducible representations of H.

(2) Group the irreducible representations of H into orbits $\mathcal{O}_i$ (relative to G).

(3) Select arbitrarily one irreducible representation Δ_i from each orbit $\mathcal{O}_i$.

(4) Find the little group of the second kind $L_i^{(II)}$ belonging to each of the irreducible representations Δ_i of (3).

(5) Find the kernel K_i of each of the irreducible representations Δ_i of (3).

(6) Find the quotient groups $L_i^{(II)}/K_i$.

(7) Determine all irreducible representations $\Delta_j^{(i)}$ of the quotient groups $L^{(II)}/K_i$.

(8) From the irreducible representations $\Delta_j^{(i)}$ of $L_i^{(II)}/K_i$ select those which engender irreducible representations of $L_i^{(II)}$ which in turn subduce on H a multiple of Δ_i. Designate these irreducible representations of $L_i^{(II)}/K_i$ by $\Delta_j^{(i)(a)}$ (a for allowable), and designate the irreducible representation of $L_i^{(II)}$ engendered by $\Delta_j^{(i)(a)}$ by the same symbol.

(9) Compute $[\Delta_j^{(i)(a)}]^{(\mathscr{I})}$. Every irreducible representation of G is found exactly once in this way.

Finally, let us briefly mention two miscellaneous points.

First, the extended representation $\Delta_{ext.}$ of $L^{(II)}(\Delta)$ can be chosen to be a vector representation if either g/h is a prime or G possesses a subgroup K isomorphic to G/H such that $H \cap K = I$ and $HK = G$. The latter condition holds when G is a semidirect product: $G = H \circledS K$.

Second, let us consider the case in which G is solvable. Let $G, H_1, H_2, \ldots, I$ be the composition series. If we choose $H = H_1$ we have g/h_1 equal to a prime so that $L^{(II)}$ must be either H_1 or G. Hence, the irreducible representations of G are either induced by irreducible representations of H_1 or engendered by irreducible representations of G/H_1. Since G/H_1 is a cyclic group its representations are known. The irreducible representations of H_1 on the other hand are either induced by irreducible representations of H_2 or engendered by irreducible representations of H_1/H_2 which is again cyclic. In this way one can reduce the problem of finding the irreducible representations of a solvable group to the problems of finding the irreducible representations of cyclic groups and of finding the composition series of the group.

CHAPTER VI

SPACE GROUP REPRESENTATIONS AND ENERGY BANDS

In this chapter the theory of little groups (Chapter V, Section 5) will be applied to the determination of the bounded, irreducible, finite-dimensional representations of crystallographic space groups (21, 40, 84, 143, 157, 175, 199, 200). Also, the relations between the irreducible representation and the electronic energy bands (see Chapter IV, Section 14) will be discussed.

1. Representation Theory

In this section we shall essentially just restate little group theory in the language of space groups. Although most of the preceding representation theory of this book was stated for finite groups we shall callously apply some of it to space groups.

The group G to be considered now is a space group, and the normal subgroup H of G is the subgroup of translations $T = \{(I, v)\}$. The bounded irreducible representations of T are (as discussed in Chapter IV, Section 12) labelled by a real vector $\mathbf{k}$ and are given by

$$\Delta(\mathbf{k}): (I|\mathbf{v}) \rightarrow e^{i\mathbf{k}\cdot\mathbf{v}}, \tag{6:1.1}$$

where $\mathbf{k}$ lies in the first Brillouin zone of $\mathbf{k}$-space. In little group theory the prescription for deriving the irreducible representations of the space group G is as follows:

(1) find a little group of the second kind belonging to one $\Delta(\mathbf{k})$ of each orbit $\mathcal{O}$,
(2) find the kernel of each such $\Delta(\mathbf{k})$,
(3) find the quotient group of the little group of the second kind divided by the kernel for each such $\Delta(\mathbf{k})$,
(4) find the irreducible representations of this quotient group for each such $\Delta(\mathbf{k})$,
(5) find the irreducible representations of the little group engendered by those of the quotient group for each such $\Delta(\mathbf{k})$,
(6) eliminate those engendered irreducible representations of the little group which do not subduce a multiple of $\Delta(\mathbf{k})$ on T,
(7) with the remaining allowable (or small) irreducible engendered representations of the little groups induce the irreducible representations of the space group.

The prescription will be reformulated later in space group language.

Orbits. To carry out the preceding prescription let us first find the orbit containing $\Delta(\mathbf{k})$; i.e., the set of all irreducible representations of T which are conjugate to $\Delta(\mathbf{k})$ relative to G. From the equation

$$(D|\mathbf{v}_0)^{-1}(I|\mathbf{v})(D|\mathbf{v}_0) = (I|D^{-1}\mathbf{v}) \tag{6:1.2}$$

we see that the conjugate representation

$$(D|\mathbf{v}_0)^{-1}(I|\mathbf{v})(D|\mathbf{v}_0) \to e^{i\mathbf{k}\cdot\mathbf{v}}$$

can also be written

$$(I|D^{-1}\mathbf{v}) \to e^{i\mathbf{k}\cdot\mathbf{v}},$$

or replacing $D^{-1}\mathbf{v}$ by $\mathbf{v}'$ and dropping the prime

$$(I|\mathbf{v}) \to e^{i\mathbf{k}\cdot(D\mathbf{v})}. \tag{6:1.3}$$

Letting D operate on $\mathbf{k}$ and remembering that D is orthogonal we obtain finally for the conjugate representation

$$(I|\mathbf{v}) \to e^{i(D\mathbf{k})\cdot\mathbf{v}}. \tag{6:1.4}$$

Thus the conjugates of $\Delta(\mathbf{k})$ are the representations $\Delta(D\mathbf{k})$. The set of all distinct inequivalent vectors $D\mathbf{k}$ for fixed $\mathbf{k}$ is called the *star* of $\mathbf{k}$. The orbit of $\Delta(\mathbf{k})$ is thus the set of all $\Delta(\mathbf{k}')$'s for which $\mathbf{k}'$ is in the star of $\mathbf{k}$.

Little Groups. Next let us find the little group of the second kind belonging to $\Delta(\mathbf{k})$. This is the subgroup of all elements of G which leave $\Delta(\mathbf{k})$ invariant under conjugation. From (6:1.4) we see that it is the set of all elements $(D|v)$ such that

$$D\mathbf{k} = \mathbf{k} + 2\pi\mathbf{K} \tag{6:1.5}$$

where $\mathbf{K}$ is a vector of the reciprocal lattice. The little group of the second kind belonging to $\Delta(\mathbf{k})$ is thus the space group $G_{\mathbf{k}}$ of $\mathbf{k}$.

Kernels. The kernel of $\Delta(\mathbf{k})$ is the set of all translations $(I|\mathbf{v})$ which are mapped onto one by $\Delta(\mathbf{k})$. From (6:1.1) we see that this is the set of all translations $(I|\mathbf{v})$ such that

$$\mathbf{k}\cdot\mathbf{v} = 2n\pi, \tag{6:1.6}$$

where n is an integer. Let us designate this subgroup of T by $T_{\mathbf{k}}$.

Quotient Groups. We now see that the desired quotient groups $Q_{\mathbf{k}}$ are

$$Q_{\mathbf{k}} = G_{\mathbf{k}}/T_{\mathbf{k}}. \tag{6:1.7}$$

Let us restate the recipe in space group language. First we find the groups $P_{\mathbf{k}}$, $G_{\mathbf{k}}$, $T_{\mathbf{k}}$, and $Q_{\mathbf{k}}$ for one $\mathbf{k}$ of each star belonging to the first Brillouin zone. Next we find the irreducible representations of $Q_{\mathbf{k}}$, and the representations $\Gamma_{\mathbf{k}}$ of $G_{\mathbf{k}}$ which they engender. We then select those engendered representations $\Gamma_{\mathbf{k}}$ of $G_{\mathbf{k}}$ which subduce multiples of $\Delta(\mathbf{k})$ on T. Finally we induce irreducible representations of G with these selected irreducible representations of $G_{\mathbf{k}}$.

Let us at this point observe some miscellaneous points. First, we observe from the fact that T is a maximal normal abelian subgroup of G together with Ito's theorem that the dimension of every irreducible representation of G is a divisor of the order of the point group $P = G/T$ of G. Although this is an illegitimate application of Ito's theorem (because G is an infinite group) the result can be justified directly. Next, let us call $\mathbf{k}$ a *general* vector if it is not invariant under any D's other than the identity. The star of a general vector then contains p vectors if p is the order of the point group P. Also, the space group of a general vector is T. From the last theorem of Chapter V, Section 3, we see that the representation $\Delta^{(\mathscr{G})}(\mathbf{k})$ of G induced by $\Delta(\mathbf{k})$ is irreducible if and only if $\mathbf{k}$ is a general vector. A vector $\mathbf{k}$ which is not general is called a *point of symmetry*. A line consisting entirely of points of symmetry is called a line of symmetry, and similarly for a plane. Next let us note that the space group of $\mathbf{k} = \mathbf{0}$ is the space group G, the kernel is T, and the quotient group is the point group $P = G/T$. Hence, as one might expect, some irreducible representations of G are engendered by irreducible representations of P. We note incidentally that all of these subduce a multiple of the trivial representation $\Delta(\mathbf{0})$ on T. Next we note in passing that the little group method automatically associates certain irreducible representations of G with each real vector $\mathbf{k}$. Finally we note that the point group of $\mathbf{k}$ is the little group of the first kind of $\Delta(\mathbf{k})$: $P_{\mathbf{k}} = G_{\mathbf{k}}/T$.

2. Example—Two-Dimensional Square Lattice

As a simple but illustrative example let us consider a monatomic 2-dimensional plane crystal whose atoms lie on a square grid.

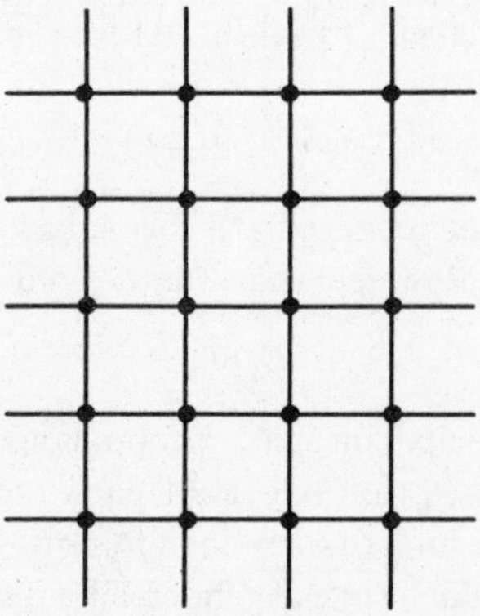

The point group is D_4, and the space group (see Chapter IV, Section 13) is generated by the four elements

$$A = (D_1|\mathbf{0}) \qquad B = (D_2|\mathbf{0}) \qquad C = (I|\mathbf{v}_1) \qquad D = (I|\mathbf{v}_2), \tag{6:2.1}$$

where

$$D_1 = \begin{pmatrix} 0 & 1 \\ -1 & 0 \end{pmatrix} \quad D_2 = \begin{pmatrix} 1 & 0 \\ 0 & -1 \end{pmatrix} \quad \mathbf{v}_1 = \begin{pmatrix} a \\ 0 \end{pmatrix} \quad \mathbf{v}_2 = \begin{pmatrix} 0 \\ a \end{pmatrix}, \tag{6:2.2}$$

and where

$$A^4 = B^2 = I \qquad ABA = B \qquad ACA^{-1} = D \qquad ADA^{-1} = C^{-1}$$
$$BCB^{-1} = C \qquad BDB^{-1} = D^{-1} \qquad CD = DC. \tag{6:2.3}$$

The reciprocal lattice is generated by the two basis vectors

$$\mathbf{K}_1 = \begin{pmatrix} a^{-1} \\ 0 \end{pmatrix} \quad \mathbf{K}_2 = \begin{pmatrix} 0 \\ a^{-1} \end{pmatrix}. \tag{6:2.4}$$

The first Brillouin zone (see Chapter IV, Section 12) is a square with side $2\pi/a$ which is centered at the origin.

Since we need consider only points in **k**-space which are inequivalent and which do not belong to the same star, we need to consider only a part of the first Brillouin zone. Since the point group D_4 contains 90° rotations as well as reflections about vertical, horizontal, and 45° lines, we see that a general vector will have the following type of star:

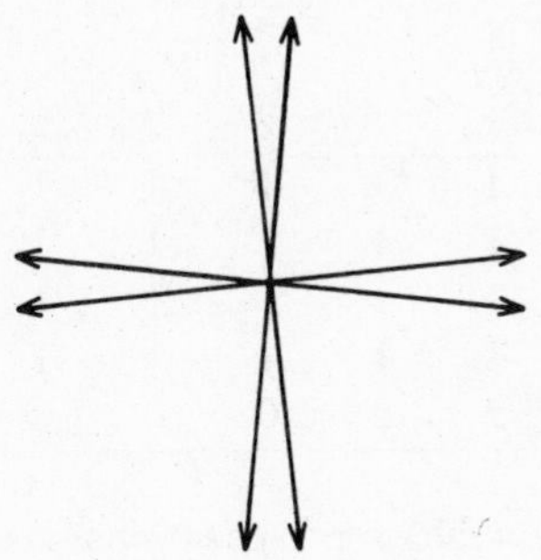

Thus only one-eighth of the first Brillouin zone is required:

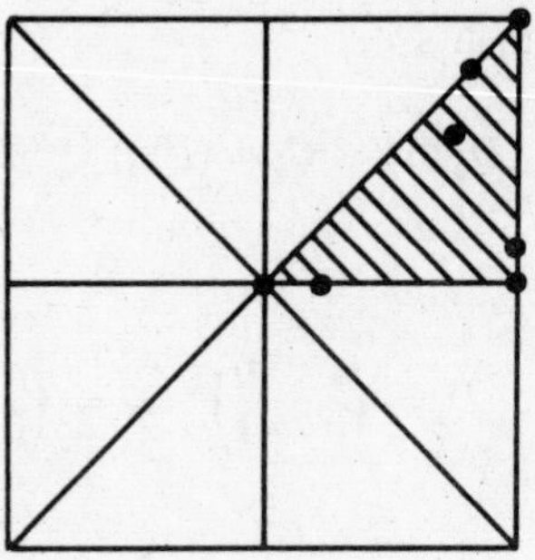

In the above figure the first Brillouin zone together with its lines of symmetry is indicated. Also, a suitable one-eighth section is indicated by shading, and the seven symmetry types of **k**-vectors are marked by heavy dots.

Let us consider these seven symmetry types of **k**-vectors one by one and determine $P_{\mathbf{k}}$, $G_{\mathbf{k}}$, $T_{\mathbf{k}}$, $Q_{\mathbf{k}}$, and the irreducible representations of G belonging to each.

$$\boxed{\mathbf{k} = \mathbf{0}}$$

The point group $P_{\mathbf{0}}$ of the origin is D_4, the space group $G_{\mathbf{0}}$ of the origin is the full space group G, and the translation group $T_{\mathbf{0}}$ of the origin is the full translation group. Hence, the quotient group

$$Q_{\mathbf{0}} = G_{\mathbf{0}}/T_{\mathbf{0}} = G/T = P = D_4$$

is the point group D_4. The classes of D_4 are $C_1 = \{I\}$, $C_2 = \{D_1{}^2 = -I\}$, $C_3 = \{D_1, -D_1\}$, $C_4 = \{D_2, -D_2\}$, $C_5 = \{D_1\,D_2, -D_1\,D_2\}$; and the character table is

	C_1	C_2	C_3	C_4	C_5	
	1	1	2	2	2	
Γ_1	1	1	1	1	1	
Γ_2	1	1	1	-1	-1	
Γ_3	1	1	-1	1	-1	D_4
Γ_4	1	1	-1	-1	1	
Γ_5	2	-2	0	0	0	

Each of these five irreducible representations of $Q_{\mathbf{0}} = D_4$ engenders an irreducible representation of G which subduces a multiple of the trivial representation $\Delta(\mathbf{0})$ on T. Hence, $\mathbf{k} = \mathbf{0}$ contributes five irreducible representations of G. The engendered representations of G have of course the same dimensions and the same representing matrices as the irreducible representations of D_4.

$$\boxed{\mathbf{k} = \begin{pmatrix} \pi a^{-1} \\ \pi a^{-1} \end{pmatrix}}$$

This point of symmetry is the upper right corner of the first Brillouin zone. Although this point is not invariant under all elements of D_4, its point group is nevertheless D_4 because those elements of D_4 which do not leave the point invariant transform it into an equivalent point. Hence, $P_{\mathbf{k}} = D_4$ and $G_{\mathbf{k}} = G$. The group $T_{\mathbf{k}}$ is the set of all vectors $\mathbf{v}$ of T such that $\mathbf{k}\cdot\mathbf{v} = 2n\pi$. Since $\mathbf{v} = \begin{pmatrix} m_1 a \\ m_2 a \end{pmatrix}$, the condition on $\mathbf{v}$ becomes $m_1 + m_2 = 2n$. Thus $T_{\mathbf{k}}$ is the set of all lattice vectors $\begin{pmatrix} m_1 a \\ m_2 a \end{pmatrix}$ for which $m_1 + m_2$ is even. Before considering representations we must find the quotient group $Q_{\mathbf{k}} = G_{\mathbf{k}}/T_{\mathbf{k}} = G/T_{\mathbf{k}}$. The translations of T can be divided into two types, the "even" ones $\mathbf{v}_e = \begin{pmatrix} m_1 a \\ m_2 a \end{pmatrix}$ for which $m_1 + m_2$ is even, and the "odd" ones $\mathbf{v}_o$ for which $m_1 + m_2$ is odd. If $(D|\mathbf{v})$ is an element of G and $(I|\mathbf{v}_e)$ is an element of $T_{\mathbf{k}}$, then

$$(D|\mathbf{v})(I|\mathbf{v}_e) = (D|\mathbf{v} + D\mathbf{v}_e) = (D|\mathbf{v} + \mathbf{v}_e'),$$

where $\mathbf{v}_e' = D\mathbf{v}_e$. Since $\mathbf{v} + \mathbf{v}_e'$ is in $T_{\mathbf{k}}$ if and only if $\mathbf{v}$ is in $T_{\mathbf{k}}$, we see that the cosets of $T_{\mathbf{k}}$ are the sixteen sets of elements $(D|\mathbf{v}_e)$ and $(D|\mathbf{v}_o)$, where D is fixed in each coset, but $\mathbf{v}_e$ (or $\mathbf{v}_o$) varies over all even (or odd) lattice vectors. If we designate the sixteen cosets by their typical elements, we find the following multiplication law for the cosets

$$\begin{aligned}(D_i|\mathbf{v}_e)(D_j|\mathbf{v}_e) &= (D_i D_j|\mathbf{v}_e)\\ (D_i|\mathbf{v}_o)(D_j|\mathbf{v}_o) &= (D_i D_j|\mathbf{v}_e)\\ (D_i|\mathbf{v}_e)(D_j|\mathbf{v}_o) &= (D_i D_j|\mathbf{v}_o)\\ (D_i|\mathbf{v}_o)(D_j|\mathbf{v}_e) &= (D_i D_j|\mathbf{v}_o).\end{aligned} \tag{6:2.5}$$

The quotient group $Q_{\mathbf{k}}$ of cosets of $T_{\mathbf{k}}$ is therefore isomorphic to $D_4 \times C_2$ through the isomorphism

$$(D|\mathbf{v}_e) \leftrightarrow (D, I) \qquad (D|\mathbf{v}_o) \leftrightarrow (D, A), \tag{6:2.6}$$

where A is the generator of C_2. The lattice T, which consists of the two cosets $(I|\mathbf{v})$ and $(I|\mathbf{v}_o)$, is mapped by (6:2.6) onto the elements (I, I) and (I, A) of $D_4 \times C_2$.

Now let us consider the irreducible representations of $Q_{\mathbf{k}} = D_4 \times C_2$. The character table is as follows:

	C_1	C_2	C_3	C_4	C_5	C_1'	C_2'	C_3'	C_4'	C_5'
	1	1	2	2	2	1	1	2	2	2
Γ_1	1	1	1	1	1	1	1	1	1	1
Γ_2	1	1	1	−1	−1	1	1	1	−1	−1
Γ_3	1	1	−1	1	−1	1	1	−1	1	−1
Γ_4	1	1	−1	−1	1	1	1	−1	−1	1
Γ_5	2	−2	0	0	0	2	−2	0	0	0
Γ_6	1	1	1	1	1	−1	−1	−1	−1	−1
Γ_7	1	1	1	−1	−1	−1	−1	−1	1	1
Γ_8	1	1	−1	1	−1	−1	−1	1	−1	1
Γ_9	1	1	−1	−1	1	−1	−1	1	1	−1
Γ_{10}	2	−2	0	0	0	−2	2	0	0	0

$D_4 \times C_2$

The lattice T is mapped onto the two classes C_1 and C_1'. We must now determine which of these irreducible representations of $Q_\mathbf{k} = D_4 \times C_2$ are allowable, i.e., which ones engender a representation of $G_\mathbf{k} = G$ which in turn subduces a multiple of $\Delta(\mathbf{k})$ on T. Since $\mathbf{k} = \begin{pmatrix} \pi a^{-1} \\ \pi a^{-1} \end{pmatrix}$ one easily finds that $\Delta(\mathbf{k})$ is given by $(I|\mathbf{v}_e) \to 1$, $(I|\mathbf{v}_0) \to -1$, or $C_1 \to 1$, $C_1' \to -1$. Hence, only the last five irreducible representations of $Q_\mathbf{k} = D_4 \times C_2$ are allowable. They engender five more irreducible representations of G whose dimensions are of course 1, 1, 1, 1, and 2.

The first five irreducible representations of $Q_\mathbf{k} = D_4 \times C_2$ also engender irreducible representations of G, but these are the irreducible representations of G belonging to the origin $\mathbf{k} = \mathbf{0}$.

$$\boxed{\mathbf{k} = \begin{pmatrix} \pi a^{-1} \\ 0 \end{pmatrix}}$$

This point of symmetry is on the center of the right edge of the first Brillouin zone. Its point group is $P_\mathbf{k} = \{I, D_1{}^2 = -I, D_2, -D_2\}$, which is isomorphic to the dihedral group D_2. The group $T_\mathbf{k}$ consists of the translations $\begin{pmatrix} m_1 a \\ m_2 a \end{pmatrix}$ in which m_1 is even. If we call such translations even, $\mathbf{v}_e$, and the rest odd, $\mathbf{v}_o$, we find that $Q_\mathbf{k} = G_\mathbf{k}/T_\mathbf{k}$ is of order eight and is isomorphic to $D_2 \times C_2$ through the isomorphism

$$\begin{aligned} \{(D|\mathbf{v}_e)\} &\leftrightarrow (D, I) \qquad \text{all } \mathbf{v}_e \\ \{(D|\mathbf{v}_o)\} &\leftrightarrow (D, A) \qquad \text{all } \mathbf{v}_o. \end{aligned} \tag{6:2.7}$$

In (6:2.7) every matrix D is an element of $P_\mathbf{k} = D_2$, and A is the generator of C_2. The lattice T consists of the elements $\{(I|\mathbf{v}_e)\}$ and $\{(I|\mathbf{v}_o)\}$ which are mapped on the elements (I, I) and (I, A) of $Q_\mathbf{k} = D_2 \times C_2$.

The character table of $Q_\mathbf{k} = D_2 \times C_2$ is

	C_1	C_2	C_3	C_4	C_1'	C_2'	C_3'	C_4'	
	1	1	1	1	1	1	1	1	
Γ_1	1	1	1	1	1	1	1	1	
Γ_2	1	1	−1	−1	1	1	−1	−1	
Γ_3	1	−1	1	−1	1	−1	1	−1	
Γ_4	1	−1	−1	1	1	−1	−1	1	$D_2 \times C_2$
Γ_5	1	1	1	1	−1	−1	−1	−1	
Γ_6	1	1	−1	−1	−1	−1	1	1	
Γ_7	1	−1	1	−1	−1	1	−1	1	
Γ_8	1	−1	−1	1	−1	1	1	−1	

The class C_1 is the element (I, I) and the class C_1' is the element (I, A). Hence, these two classes are the two images of the lattice T in the homomorphism of $G_{\mathbf{k}}$ onto $Q_{\mathbf{k}}$. The irreducible representation $\Delta(\mathbf{k})$ of T is given by

$$\mathbf{v} = \begin{pmatrix} m_1 a \\ m_2 a \end{pmatrix} \rightarrow (-1)^{m_1} \tag{6:2.8}$$

or

$$\mathbf{v}_e \rightarrow 1 \qquad \mathbf{v}_o \rightarrow -1. \tag{6:2.8a}$$

Hence we see from the character table of $Q_{\mathbf{k}} = D_2 \times C_2$ that only the last four irreducible representations engender allowable representations of $G_{\mathbf{k}}$ because only they subduce $\Delta(\mathbf{k})$ on T. The irreducible representations of G induced by the four allowable engendered representations of $G_{\mathbf{k}}$ have dimension 2 because $G_{\mathbf{k}}$ has two cosets in G. Hence, we see that $\mathbf{k} = \begin{pmatrix} \pi a^{-1} \\ 0 \end{pmatrix}$ contributes four 2-dimensional irreducible representations of G. The representation matrices and the characters, however, we shall not derive.

$$\boxed{\mathbf{k} = \begin{pmatrix} k_x \\ 0 \end{pmatrix}} \qquad 0 < k_x < \pi a^{-1}$$

This set of points is the line of symmetry which lies on the k_x-axis. Let us consider an arbitrary point $\mathbf{k}$ on this line of symmetry and derive the irreducible representations of the space group contributed by it. The point group $P_{\mathbf{k}}$ of such a point $\mathbf{k}$ is $P_{\mathbf{k}} = C_2 = \{I, D_2\}$.

The translation group $T_{\mathbf{k}}$ of $\mathbf{k}$ is infinite, so instead of discussing its properties in detail we shall show that the quotient group $Q_{\mathbf{k}} = G_{\mathbf{k}}/T_{\mathbf{k}}$ is abelian. The irreducible representation $\Delta(\mathbf{k})$ of T is given by

$$\mathbf{v} = \begin{pmatrix} m_1 a \\ m_2 a \end{pmatrix} \rightarrow e^{i m_1 a k_x}, \tag{6:2.9}$$

so the kernel $T_{\mathbf{k}}$ is the set of all translations $\mathbf{v}$ such that

$$m_1 a k_x = 2n\pi. \tag{6:2.10}$$

The integers m_1 which satisfy this equation will depend on the value of k_x chosen, but in any case they will form an additive group. Let us therefore take $T_{\mathbf{k}}$ to be of the form

$$T_{\mathbf{k}} = \left\{\begin{pmatrix} m_1 a \\ m_2 a \end{pmatrix}\right\}, \tag{6:2.11}$$

where the set of integers $\{m_1\}$ is some subgroup of the additive group of all integers. The cosets of $T_{\mathbf{k}}$ are

$$S = T_{\mathbf{k}} = \left\{\begin{pmatrix} m_1 a \\ m_2 a \end{pmatrix}\right\} = \left\{\left(I\middle|\begin{pmatrix} m_1 a \\ m_2 a \end{pmatrix}\right)\right\} \tag{6:2.12}$$

$$S_m = \left(I\middle|\begin{pmatrix} ma \\ 0 \end{pmatrix}\right) S = \left\{\begin{pmatrix} (m+m_1)a \\ m_2 a \end{pmatrix}\right\} = \left\{\left(I\middle|\begin{pmatrix} (m+m_1)a \\ m_2 a \end{pmatrix}\right)\right\} \quad m \notin \{m_1\}$$

$$S_m(D_2) = \left(D_2\middle|\begin{pmatrix} ma \\ 0 \end{pmatrix}\right) S = \left\{\left(D_2\middle|\begin{pmatrix} (m_1+m_2)^a \\ m_2 a \end{pmatrix}\right)\right\} \qquad m = 0 \text{ or } m \notin \left\{m_1\right\}.$$

The multiplication table for the group $Q_{\mathbf{k}}$ of cosets of $T_{\mathbf{k}}$ relative to $G_{\mathbf{k}}$ is

$$\begin{aligned} &S^2 = S \qquad SS_m = S_m \qquad SS_m(D_2) = S_m(D_2) \\ &S_m S_n = S_{m+n} \qquad S_m S_n(D_2) = S_{m+n}(D_2) = S_n(D_2) S_m \\ &S_m(D_2) S_n(D_2) = S_{m+n}, \end{aligned} \tag{6:2.13}$$

so we see that $Q_{\mathbf{k}}$ is indeed Abelian.

Since $Q_{\mathbf{k}}$ is Abelian its irreducible representations are all 1-dimensional, and therefore the allowable engendered representations of $G_{\mathbf{k}}$ must be 1-dimensional. Since they must also subduce $\Delta(\mathbf{k})$ on T it follows that the allowable irreducible representations of $G_{\mathbf{k}}$ are extensions of $\Delta(\mathbf{k})$.

Let us now determine the allowable irreducible representations of $G_{\mathbf{k}}$. We know that

$$(I|\mathbf{v}) \to e^{i\mathbf{k}\cdot\mathbf{v}}, \tag{6:2.14}$$

so we need only find the numbers representing the elements $(D_2|\mathbf{v})$. Let us write the representation in the form

$$(D_2|\mathbf{v}) \to e^{i\alpha(D_2,\mathbf{v})} \tag{6:2.15}$$

where $\alpha(D_2, \mathbf{v})$ is a real scalar function on $G_{\mathbf{k}}$. Since

$$(D_2|\mathbf{v}_1 + \mathbf{v}_2) = (I|\mathbf{v}_1)(D_2|\mathbf{v}_2), \tag{6:2.16}$$

we see from (6:2.15) and (6:2.14) that

$$e^{i\alpha({}_2D,\mathbf{v}_1+\mathbf{v}_2)} = e^{i\mathbf{k}\cdot\mathbf{v}} \, e^{i\alpha(D_2,\mathbf{v}_2)} \tag{6:2.17}$$

or

$$\alpha(D_2, \mathbf{v}_1 + \mathbf{v}_2) = \mathbf{k}\cdot\mathbf{v}_1 + \alpha(D_2, \mathbf{v}_2) + 2N\pi. \tag{6:2.18}$$

Putting $\mathbf{v}_2 = \mathbf{0}$ we find

$$\alpha(D_2, \mathbf{v}_1) = \mathbf{k}\cdot\mathbf{v}_1 + \alpha(D_2, \mathbf{0}) + 2N\pi \tag{6:2.19}$$

and putting $\beta(D_2) = \alpha(D_2, 0)$ we find

$$(D_2|\mathbf{v}) \to e^{i\beta(D_2)} \, e^{i\mathbf{k}\cdot\mathbf{v}} \tag{6:2.20}$$

From

$$(D_2|\mathbf{0})^2 = (I|\mathbf{0}) \to 1 \tag{6:2.21}$$

together with (6:2.20), we find

$$e^{2i\beta(D_2)} = 1 \tag{6:2.22}$$

or

$$e^{i\beta(D_2)} = \pm 1. \tag{6:2.23}$$

Hence, there are just two allowable irreducible representations of $G_{\mathbf{k}}$, and these are

$$(1) \begin{cases} (I|\mathbf{v}) \to e^{i\mathbf{k}\cdot\mathbf{v}} \\ (D_2|\mathbf{v}) \to e^{i\mathbf{k}\cdot\mathbf{v}} \end{cases} \tag{6:2.24}$$

$$(2) \begin{cases} (I|\mathbf{v}) \to e^{i\mathbf{k}\cdot\mathbf{v}} \\ (D_2|\mathbf{v}) \to -e^{i\mathbf{k}\cdot\mathbf{v}} \end{cases} \tag{6:2.25}$$

Since $G_{\mathbf{k}}$ has four left cosets in G we see that each of the two allowable irreducible representations of $G_{\mathbf{k}}$ induces a 4-dimensional irreducible representation of G. Thus each point on this line of symmetry contributes two 4-dimensional irreducible representations of G.

$$\boxed{\mathbf{k} = \begin{pmatrix} k_x \\ k_x \end{pmatrix}} \qquad 0 < k_x < \pi a^{-1}$$

This line of symmetry is the upper right 45° diagonal of the first Brillouin zone. The point group $P_{\mathbf{k}}$ of an arbitrary point $\mathbf{k}$ on the line is

$$P_{\mathbf{k}} = C_2 = \{I, D_2 D_1\}.$$

The quotient group $Q_{\mathbf{k}} = G_{\mathbf{k}}/T_{\mathbf{k}}$ is again abelian, and the space group $G_{\mathbf{k}}$ of $\mathbf{k}$ again has two allowable irreducible representations. In fact, essentially the same analysis as was used to obtain (6:2.24) and (6:2.25) holds. The two allowable irreducible representations of $G_{\mathbf{k}}$ are

$$(1) \begin{cases} (I|\mathbf{v}) \to e^{i\mathbf{k}\cdot\mathbf{v}} \\ (D_2 D_1|\mathbf{v}) \to e^{i\mathbf{k}\cdot\mathbf{v}} \end{cases} \tag{6:2.26}$$

$$(2) \begin{cases} (I|\mathbf{v}) \to e^{i\mathbf{k}\cdot\mathbf{v}} \\ (D_2 D_1|\mathbf{v}) \to -e^{i\mathbf{k}\cdot\mathbf{v}} \end{cases} \tag{6:2.27}$$

We see that every point on this line of symmetry contributes two 4-dimensional irreducible representations of G.

$$\boxed{\mathbf{k} = \begin{pmatrix} \pi a^{-1} \\ k_y \end{pmatrix}} \qquad 0 < k_y < \pi a^{-1}$$

This line of symmetry is the upper right vertical boundary of the first Brillouin zone. The point group $P_{\mathbf{k}}$ of an arbitrary point on the line is $P_{\mathbf{k}} = C_2 = \{I, D_1^2 D_2\} = \{I, -D_2\}$. The quotient group $Q_{\mathbf{k}}$ is again abelian, and $G_{\mathbf{k}}$ again has two allowable irreducible representations. These are

$$(1) \begin{cases} (I|\mathbf{v}) \to e^{i\mathbf{k}\cdot\mathbf{v}} \\ (-D_2|\mathbf{v}_1) \to e^{i\mathbf{k}\cdot\mathbf{v}} \end{cases} \tag{6:2.28}$$

$$(2) \begin{cases} (I|\mathbf{v}) \to e^{i\mathbf{k}\cdot\mathbf{v}} \\ (-D_2|\mathbf{v}) \to -e^{i\mathbf{k}\cdot\mathbf{v}} \end{cases} \tag{6:2.29}$$

Again each point on this line of symmetry contributes two 4-dimensional irreducible representations of G.

$$\boxed{\mathbf{k} = \begin{pmatrix} k_x \\ k_y \end{pmatrix}} \qquad 0 < k_x < \pi a^{-1} \qquad 0 < k_y < \pi a^{-1}$$
$$k_y < k_x$$

Every such point is a general vector in the upper right eighth of the first Brillouin zone. Since $\mathbf{k}$ is a general vector, $P_\mathbf{k} = C_1 = \{I\}$. The space group $G_\mathbf{k}$ of $\mathbf{k}$ is $G_\mathbf{k} = T$, and the kernel $T_\mathbf{k}$ is $T_\mathbf{k} = C_1 = \{I\}$. The quotient group $Q_\mathbf{k} = G_\mathbf{k}/T_\mathbf{k} = T/C_1 = T$, and the only allowable irreducible representation of $Q_\mathbf{k} = G_\mathbf{k} = T$ is $\Delta(\mathbf{k})$. Since the number of cosets of $G_\mathbf{k} = T$ in G is equal to the order eight of the point group $P = G/T = D_4$ we see that $\Delta(\mathbf{k})$ induces an 8-dimensional irreducible representation of G. Hence, each general vector contributes one 8-dimensional irreducible representation of G.

Let us summarize some of these results in a table.

$\mathbf{k}$	$P_\mathbf{k}$	*No. Irred. Reps. G*	*Dim. Irred. Reps. G*
$\begin{pmatrix} 0 \\ 0 \end{pmatrix}$	D_4	5	1, 1, 1, 1, 2
$\begin{pmatrix} \pi a^{-1} \\ \pi a^{-1} \end{pmatrix}$	D_4	5	1, 1, 1, 1, 2
$\begin{pmatrix} \pi a^{-1} \\ 0 \end{pmatrix}$	D_2	4	2, 2, 2, 2
$\begin{pmatrix} k_x \\ 0 \end{pmatrix}$	C_2	2	4, 4
$\begin{pmatrix} k_x \\ k_x \end{pmatrix}$	C_2	2	4, 4
$\begin{pmatrix} \pi a^{-1} \\ k_y \end{pmatrix}$	C_2	2	4, 4
$\begin{pmatrix} k_x \\ k_y \end{pmatrix}$	C_1	1	8

3. Reality of Representations

Herring (82) has developed a simple method for determining the reality class to which an irreducible representation of a symmorphic (i.e., semidirect product) space group belongs. This method is based on the usual method which involves computing $\sum_{A\epsilon G}\chi(A^2)$, but is useful because only a finite number of terms in the sum need to be evaluated.

The method is as follows. Let $P = \{D\}$ be the point group of order p belonging to the symmorphic space group G, Γ a bounded irreducible representation of G, and $G_{\mathbf{k}}$ the little group of the second kind whose allowable irreducible representation $\Gamma_{\mathbf{k}}$ induces Γ. Further, let $P_{\mathbf{k}}^{(-)}$ be the subset of P whose elements transform $\mathbf{k}$ into a wave vector equivalent to $-\mathbf{k}$: $D\mathbf{k} = -\mathbf{k} + 2\pi K$. Then if $\sigma(\mathbf{k})$ is the order of the star of $\mathbf{k}$ we have

$$\sum_{D\epsilon P_{\mathbf{k}}^{(-)}} \chi^{(\Gamma_{\mathbf{k}})}[(D|\mathbf{0})^2] = \frac{p}{\sigma(\mathbf{k})} \quad \text{if } \Gamma \text{ is of first kind}$$

$$= -\frac{p}{\sigma(\mathbf{k})} \quad \text{if } \Gamma \text{ is of second kind} \tag{6:3.1}$$

$$= 0 \quad \text{if } \Gamma \text{ is of third kind.}$$

Since this result can be derived by fairly elementary methods let us derive it. As a preliminary, let us evaluate a sum. Let us consider a finite lattice with $(2N + 1)^3$ points in it and evaluate the sum

$$S \equiv \frac{1}{(2N+1)^3}\sum_{\mathbf{v}} e^{i\eta\cdot\mathbf{v}}, \tag{6:3.2}$$

where the sum is over all lattice vectors and $\boldsymbol{\eta}$ is a vector having the property

$$\boldsymbol{\eta}\cdot\mathbf{v} = \frac{n}{N}\pi, \ (\text{all } \mathbf{v}) \tag{6:3.2a}$$

where n is an integer. To be more explicit it will be assumed that every lattice vector has the form

$$\mathbf{v} = l_1\mathbf{v}_1 + l_2\mathbf{v}_2 + l_3\mathbf{v}_3, \tag{6:3.3}$$

where $\mathbf{v}_1$, $\mathbf{v}_2$, $\mathbf{v}_3$ are basis vectors and l_1, l_2, l_3 are integers which assume all values between and including $-N$ and N. The sum then becomes

$$S = \frac{1}{(2N+1)^3}\sum_{l_1=-N}^{N} e^{i(\eta\cdot v_1)l_1} \sum_{l_2=-N}^{N} e^{i(\eta\cdot\mathbf{v}_2)l_2} \sum_{l_3=-N}^{N} e^{i(\eta\cdot\mathbf{v}_3)l_3} \tag{6:3.4}$$

Each of these sums is a geometric progression which can easily be evaluated to yield

$$S = \frac{1}{(2N+1)^3}\,\frac{\sin[(N+\frac{1}{2})(\boldsymbol{\eta}\cdot\mathbf{v}_1)]}{\sin(\frac{1}{2}\boldsymbol{\eta}\cdot\mathbf{v}_1)}\,\frac{\sin[(N+\frac{1}{2})(\boldsymbol{\eta}\cdot\mathbf{v}_2)]}{\sin(\frac{1}{2}\boldsymbol{\eta}\cdot\mathbf{v}_2)}\,\frac{\sin[(N+\frac{1}{2})(\boldsymbol{\eta}\cdot\mathbf{v}_3)]}{\sin(\frac{1}{2}\boldsymbol{\eta},\mathbf{v}_3)} \tag{6:3.5}$$

if each $\boldsymbol{\eta}\cdot\mathbf{v}_j$ is not a multiple of 2π. Since $\boldsymbol{\eta}\cdot\mathbf{v}_j = \frac{n_j}{N}\pi$ we find in this case

$$S = \frac{(-1)^{n_1+n_2+n_3}}{(2N+1)^3} \tag{6:3.6}$$

which approaches zero as $N \to \infty$. If for some $\mathbf{v}_j$, say $\mathbf{v}_1$, $\boldsymbol{\eta}\cdot\mathbf{v}_1 = 2m_1\pi$ then

$$\sum_{l_1=-N}^{N} e^{i(\eta\cdot\mathbf{v}_1)l_1} = 2N + 1 \tag{6:3.7}$$

and S is still zero unless $\boldsymbol{\eta}\cdot\mathbf{v}_j = 2m_j\pi$ for all basis vectors. In that case $S = 1$ so we have

$$S \equiv \frac{1}{(2N+1)^3}\sum_{\mathbf{v}} e^{i\eta\cdot\mathbf{v}} = 1 \text{ if } \boldsymbol{\eta}\cdot\mathbf{v}_j = 2m_j\pi \tag{6:3.8}$$
$$= 0 \text{ otherwise.}$$

But in the first case

$$\boldsymbol{\eta} = 2m_1\pi\mathbf{K}_1 + 2m_2\pi\mathbf{K}_2 + 2m_3\pi\mathbf{K}_3, \tag{6:3.9}$$

where $\mathbf{K}_j$ is the jth basis vector of the reciprocal lattice. Hence, in this case $\boldsymbol{\eta}$ is 2π times a vector of the reciprocal lattice. Thus we can rewrite our result in the final form

$$S \equiv \frac{1}{(2N+1)^3}\sum_{\mathbf{v}} e^{i\eta\cdot\mathbf{v}} = \delta_{\eta,2\pi\mathbf{K}}. \tag{6:3.10}$$

Now we can proceed with the derivation. If f is any function on the symmorphic space group we can write

$$\sum_{A\epsilon G} f(A) = \sum_{D\epsilon P}\sum_{\mathbf{v}\epsilon T} f[(D|\mathbf{v})] \tag{6:3.11}$$

so that in particular

$$\sum_{A\epsilon G} \chi(A^2) = \sum_{D\epsilon P}\sum_{\mathbf{v}\epsilon T} \chi[(D|\mathbf{v})^2]. \tag{6:3.12}$$

We want to reduce such a sum to a finite, easily evaluated sum.

Let Γ be the irreducible representation of G under consideration, and

$$(D|\mathbf{v}) \to M[(D|\mathbf{v})], \tag{6:3.13}$$

where $M[(D|\mathbf{v})]$ is the representing matrix of $(D|\mathbf{v})$, which is chosen such that $M[(I|\mathbf{v})]$ is diagonal for every $\mathbf{v}$. Further, let $\{\mathbf{v}_{\mathbf{k},\mu}\}$ be a complete orthonormal set of eigenvectors of the matrices $M[(I|\mathbf{v})]$ such that

$$M[(I|\mathbf{v})]\mathbf{v}_{\mathbf{k},\mu} = e^{i\mathbf{k}\cdot\mathbf{v}}\mathbf{v}_{\mathbf{k},\mu}. \tag{6:3.14}$$

The $\mathbf{k}$'s are the $\mathbf{k}$'s appearing in the star of Γ, and the number of times each occurs is $p/\sigma(\mathbf{k})$. Using the identity

$$(D|\mathbf{v})^2 = (D|\mathbf{0})^2(I|D^{-1}\mathbf{u} + \mathbf{u}), \tag{6:3.15}$$

where

$$\mathbf{u} = D^{-1}\mathbf{v}, \tag{6:3.16}$$

we have

$$\begin{aligned}\chi^{(\Gamma)}[(D|\mathbf{v})^2] &= \mathrm{tr}\{M^2[D|\mathbf{v})]\}\\ &= \mathrm{tr}\{M^2[(D|\mathbf{0})]M[(I|D^{-1}\mathbf{u}+\mathbf{u})]\}\\ &= \sum_{\mathbf{k},\mu} \mathbf{v}^{\dagger}_{\mathbf{k},\mu} M^2[(D|\mathbf{0})]M[(I|D^{-1}\mathbf{u}+\mathbf{u})]\mathbf{v}_{\mathbf{k},\mu} \qquad (6{:}3.17)\\ &= \sum_{\mathbf{k},\mu} e^{i\mathbf{k}\cdot(D^{-1}\mathbf{u}+\mathbf{u})}\mathbf{v}^{\dagger}_{\mathbf{k},\mu} M^2[(D|\mathbf{0})]\mathbf{v}_{\mathbf{k},\mu}\\ &= \sum_{\mathbf{k},\mu} e^{i(D\mathbf{k}+\mathbf{k})\cdot\mathbf{v}}\mathbf{v}^{\dagger}_{\mathbf{k},\mu} M^2[(D|\mathbf{0})]\mathbf{v}_{\mathbf{k},\mu}.\end{aligned}$$

We still want to sum (6:3.17) over all space group elements in order to apply the usual reality criterion.

Since the usual reality criterion for irreducible representations does not apply to an infinite discrete group, we shall replace the space group G by a finite group G_N which will approach G as $N \to \infty$.

Let us define the finite group G_N. We can obtain this group from G by identifying all elements of G which differ only by $2N$ times a translation of T. This process is the same as choosing the lattice of G_N to be finite with the vectors

$$\mathbf{v} = l_1\mathbf{v}_1 + l_2\mathbf{v}_2 + l_3\mathbf{v}_3 \qquad (6{:}3.18)$$

$$-N \leqslant l_j \leqslant N, \qquad \mathbf{v}_1, \mathbf{v}_2, \mathbf{v}_3 \text{ basis vectors of } T$$

and identifying opposite edges of the lattices. In short, we apply Born-von Karman boundary conditions to obtain a finite space group G_N. The order g_N of G_N is $(2N+1)^3p$. The $\mathbf{k}$-values which give representations are now restricted because

$$\mathbf{v} \to e^{i\mathbf{k}\cdot\mathbf{v}}$$

requires

$$2N\mathbf{v} \to e^{2iN\mathbf{k}\cdot\mathbf{v}},$$

whereas

$$2N\mathbf{v} = \mathbf{0},$$

so that

$$e^{2iN\mathbf{k}\cdot\mathbf{v}} = 1 \qquad (6{:}3.19)$$

or

$$\mathbf{k}\cdot\mathbf{v} = \frac{n}{N}\pi. \qquad (6{:}3.20)$$

The desired sum now becomes with the aid of (6:3.17)

$$\frac{1}{g_N}\sum_{A\in G_N}\chi^{(\Gamma)}(A^2)$$

$$= \frac{1}{p}\sum_{D}\sum_{\mathbf{k},\mu}\mathbf{v}^{\dagger}_{\mathbf{k},\mu}M^2[(D|\mathbf{0})]\mathbf{v}_{\mathbf{k},\mu}\frac{1}{(2N+1)^3}\sum_{\mathbf{v}} e^{i(D\mathbf{k}+\mathbf{k})\cdot\mathbf{v}} \qquad (6{:}3.21)$$

By (6:3.10) this is

$$\frac{1}{g_N} \sum_{A \epsilon G_N} \chi^{(\Gamma)}(A^2) = \frac{1}{p} \sum_{D} \sum_{\mathbf{k},\mu} \mathbf{v}_{\mathbf{k},\mu}^\dagger M^2(D|\mathbf{0}) \mathbf{v}_{\mathbf{k},\mu} \delta_{D\mathbf{k}+\mathbf{k},2\pi\mathbf{K}} \cdot \qquad (6:3.22)$$

We now have reduced the original infinite sum to a finite sum, but we can simplify it still further. Let us consider a fixed $\mathbf{k}$ in the sum (6:3.22). Then we sum over all D's in P such that

$$D\mathbf{k} = -\mathbf{k} + 2\pi\mathbf{K}. \qquad (6:3.23)$$

Thus

$$\frac{1}{g} \sum_{A} \chi^{(\Gamma)}(A^2) = \frac{1}{p} \sum_{\mathbf{k}} \sum_{\mu} \sum_{D}{}' \mathbf{v}_{\mathbf{k},\mu}^\dagger M^2[(D|\mathbf{0})] \mathbf{v}_{\mathbf{k},\mu}, \qquad (6:3.24)$$

where $\sum_{D}{}'$ means the sum over D's satisfying (6:3.23). From (6:3.23) we see that

$$D^2\mathbf{k} = \mathbf{k} + 2\pi\mathbf{K}'', \qquad (6:3.25)$$

so that D^2 is an element of $G_{\mathbf{k}}$. Further

$$\sum_{\mu} \mathbf{v}_{\mathbf{k},\mu}^\dagger M^2[(D|\mathbf{0})] \mathbf{v}_{\mathbf{k},\mu} = \chi^{(\Gamma_{\mathbf{k}})}(D^2), \qquad (6:3.26)$$

so we have

$$\frac{1}{g} \sum_{A} \chi^{(\Gamma)}(A^2) = \frac{1}{p} \sum_{\mathbf{k}} \sum_{D}{}' \chi^{(\Gamma_{\mathbf{k}})}(D^2). \qquad (6:3.27)$$

Now let $\mathbf{k}' = D_0 \mathbf{k}$ be another wave vector in the star of $\mathbf{k}$. Then if D satisfies (6:3.23) we see that $D' \equiv D_0 D D_0^{-1}$ (also an element of the point group P) satisfies

$$D'\mathbf{k}' = -\mathbf{k}' + 2\pi\mathbf{K}'. \qquad (6:3.28)$$

The converse is of course true also. We also have

$$\begin{aligned} \chi^{(\Gamma_{\mathbf{k}'})}(D'^2) &= \sum_{\mu} \mathbf{v}_{\mathbf{k}',\mu}^\dagger M^2[(D'|\mathbf{0})] \mathbf{v}_{\mathbf{k},\mu} \\ &= \sum_{\mu} \mathbf{v}_{\mathbf{k}',\mu}^\dagger M[(D_0|\mathbf{0})] M^2[(D|\mathbf{0})] M^{-1}[(D_0|\mathbf{0})] \mathbf{v}_{\mathbf{k},\mu} \\ &= \sum_{\mu} (M_0^{-1} \mathbf{v}_{\mathbf{k}',\mu})^\dagger M^2[(D|\mathbf{0})] M_0^{-1} \mathbf{v}_{\mathbf{k},\mu} \end{aligned} \qquad (6:3.29)$$

where $M_0 = M[(D_0|\mathbf{0})]$. But

$$M_0^{-1} \mathbf{v}_{\mathbf{k}',\mu} = \mathbf{v}_{\mathbf{k},\mu} \qquad (6:3.30)$$

because

$$(I|\mathbf{v})(D_0^{-1}|\mathbf{0}) = (D_0^{-1}|\mathbf{0})(I|D_0 \mathbf{v}) \qquad (6:3.31)$$

so that

$$\begin{aligned} M[(I|\mathbf{v})] M_0^{-1} \mathbf{v}_{\mathbf{k}',\mu} &= M_0^{-1} M[(I|D_0 \mathbf{v})] \mathbf{v}_{\mathbf{k}',\mu} \\ &= M_0^{-1} e^{i\mathbf{k}' \cdot D_0 \mathbf{v}} \mathbf{v}_{\mathbf{k}',\mu} \\ &= e^{i\mathbf{k} \cdot \mathbf{v}} M_0^{-1} \mathbf{v}_{\mathbf{k}',\mu} \end{aligned} \qquad (6:3.32)$$

Combining (6:3.30) with (6:3.29) we obtain the result

$$\chi^{(\Gamma_{\mathbf{k}'})}(D'^2) = \chi^{(\Gamma_{\mathbf{k}})}(D^2). \tag{6:3.33}$$

This allows us to dispose of the sum over **k** in (6:3.27) and obtain

$$\frac{1}{g}\sum_A \chi^{(\Gamma)}(A^2) = \frac{\sigma(\mathbf{k})}{p}\sum \chi^{(\Gamma_{\mathbf{k}})}(D^2). \tag{6:3.34}$$

This is the desired simplified form of the sum. In accordance with the usual criterion, the sum in (6:3.34) is 1, -1, or 0 according as Γ is of first, second, or third kind. This completes the derivation of the reality criterion (6:3.1).

Let us consider now the reality class of an irreducible representation with a general star. This can be done easily without resort to equation (6:3.1). If Γ is the irreducible representation, then the representation $\Gamma^{(s)}$ of T subduced by Γ must be real if Γ is real. But $\Gamma^{(s)}$ is a multiple of the direct sum of all $\Delta(\mathbf{k})$'s for which **k** is in the star of Γ; i.e.,

$$\Gamma^{(s)} = m\sum_{\mathbf{k}} \Delta(\mathbf{k}), \tag{6:3.35}$$

where the direct sum is over all **k**'s in the star of Γ. Since the representations $\Delta(\mathbf{k})$ are 1-dimensional they must either be of first or third kind, and if $\Gamma^{(s)}$ is to be of the first kind every $\Delta(\mathbf{k})$ of the third kind must occur in the sum in (6:3.35) together with its complex conjugate $\Delta^*(\mathbf{k}) = \Delta(-\mathbf{k})$. It is easily seen that all $\Delta(\mathbf{k})$'s belonging to the same star also belong to the same reality class. Hence, we can conclude the following. If Γ is real then either

(1) $\Delta(\mathbf{k})$ is real (**k** in the star of Γ)

or

(2) the star of **k** is centrosymmetric.

Let us now apply our criterion (6:3.1) to the irreducible representations of the space group of the square lattice discussed in Section 2.

Example. Two-dimensional Square Lattice

$$\boxed{\mathbf{k} = \begin{pmatrix} 0 \\ 0 \end{pmatrix}}$$

The five irreducible representations belonging to this **k** are all engendered by representations of D_4, and these are all real. Hence the five irreducible representations of G belonging to the origin are all real.

$$\boxed{\mathbf{k} = \begin{pmatrix} \pi a^{-1} \\ \pi a^{-1} \end{pmatrix}}$$

These five irreducible representations of G are all engendered by real irreducible representations of $D_4 \times C_2$. Hence, these irreducible representations of G are also real.

$$\boxed{\mathbf{k} = \begin{pmatrix} \pi a^{-1} \\ 0 \end{pmatrix}}$$

$P_{\mathbf{k}}^{(-)} = P_{\mathbf{k}} = \{I, -I, D_2, -D_2\}$. We want to evaluate

$$\chi(I^2) + \chi[(-I)^2] + \chi(D_2^2) + \chi[(-D_2)^2] = 4\chi(I)$$

for each of the four allowable irreducible representations of $G_{\mathbf{k}}$. Since each of these four representations is 1-dimensional, the sum is equal to 4 for all of them. Hence all four irreducible representations of G belonging to this $\mathbf{k}$ are real.

$$\boxed{\mathbf{k} = \begin{pmatrix} k_x \\ 0 \end{pmatrix}}$$

$P_{\mathbf{k}}^{(-)} = \{-I, -D_2\}$ and $\chi[(-I)^2] + \chi[(-D_2)^2] = 2\chi(I)$. Since $\chi(I)$ is positive these two irreducible representations of G must be real.

$$\boxed{\mathbf{k} = \begin{pmatrix} k_x \\ k_x \end{pmatrix}}$$

$P_{\mathbf{k}}^{(-)} = \{-I, -D_2 D_1\}$ so $\chi[(-I)^2] + \chi[(-D_2 D_1)^2] = 2\chi(I)$ and again the irreducible representations of G are real.

$$\boxed{\mathbf{k} = \begin{pmatrix} \pi a^{-1} \\ k_y \end{pmatrix}}$$

$P_{\mathbf{k}}^{(-)} = \{-I, D_2\}$ so $\chi[(-I)^2] + \chi(D_2^2) = 2\chi(I)$ and again the irreducible representations of G are real.

$$\boxed{\mathbf{k} = \begin{pmatrix} k_x \\ k_y \end{pmatrix}}$$

$P_{\mathbf{k}}^{(-)} = \{-I\}$ so $\chi[(-I)^2] = \chi(I)$ and the representations are again real.

Thus we find that all irreducible representations of the space group of the square lattice are of first kind.

For examples of unreal representations the reader is referred to the article by Herring (82).

4. Analysis

In this section a number of useful results on continuity properties will be stated without proof (see reference 21).

(a) The general $\mathbf{k}$ vectors form an open set in $\mathbf{k}$-space. That is, about any general point a sphere can be constructed which contains only general points.

(b) $E(\mathbf{k})$ is a continuous (possibly multiple-valued) function of $\mathbf{k}$ at every general $\mathbf{k}$. The same is true of a Bloch eigenvector $\phi_{\mathbf{k}}(\mathbf{r})$ considered as a function of $\mathbf{k}$.

(c) $\Gamma_{\mathbf{k}}$ is a continuous function of $\mathbf{k}$ at every general $\mathbf{k}$. By this is meant that each matrix element of an allowable $\Gamma_{\mathbf{k}}$ can be considered as a continuous function of $\mathbf{k}$ for a general $\mathbf{k}$. Since $\Gamma_{\mathbf{k}} = \Delta(\mathbf{k})$ for a general $\mathbf{k}$, the statement is obvious for this case.

(d) On a line or plane of given symmetry $\Gamma_{\mathbf{k}}$ is a continuous (possibly multiple-valued) function of $\mathbf{k}$.

(e) If a line $L = \{k\}$ of given symmetry terminates in a point $\mathbf{k}_0$ of higher symmetry (so $P_{\mathbf{k}}$ is a subgroup of $P_{\mathbf{k}_0}$, then every allowable irreducible representation $\Gamma_{\mathbf{k}_0}$ of $G_{\mathbf{k}_0}$ must subduce a representation of $G_{\mathbf{k}}$ which is decomposable into a direct sum of allowable irreducible limit representations of $G_{\mathbf{k}}$. By a limit representation of $G_{\mathbf{k}}$ is meant $\lim_{\mathbf{k}\to\mathbf{k}_0} \Delta_{\mathbf{k}}$, where $\Delta_{\mathbf{k}}$ is a representation of $G_{\mathbf{k}}$. An irreducible limit representation also must be engendered by an irreducible representation of the quotient group $G_{\mathbf{k}}/T_{\mathbf{k}_0}$. The analogous result holds for planes of symmetry terminating in lines or planes of symmetry.

(f) An irreducible representation $\Gamma_{\mathbf{k}_0}$ at a symmetry point and a limit representation $\Delta_{\mathbf{k}_0}$ on a symmetry line which are related as above are said to be compatible. That is if $\mathbf{k}_0$ terminates the line $\{k\}$ and if $\Delta_{\mathbf{k}_0}$ is a component of $\Gamma_{\mathbf{k}_0}^{(s)}$, then $\Delta_{\mathbf{k}_0}$ and $\Gamma_{\mathbf{k}_0}$ are compatible. A table of $\Delta_{\mathbf{k}_0}$'s into which $\Gamma_{\mathbf{k}_0}^{(s)}$ decomposes is called a compatibility table.

(*g*) Consider the Bloch energy eigenvectors of a wave equation for a crystal which generate a representation $\Gamma_{\mathbf{k}}$ occurring as a limit representation in a decomposition described in (*e*). The limits of these eigenvectors are eigenvectors belonging to $\mathbf{k}_0$, and the limit of their energy is $E(\mathbf{k}_0)$.

(h) Brillouin zones as defined previously can be further divided into what will be referred to here as proper Brillouin zones in the following way. A proper Brillouin zone is a maximal connected set of general $\mathbf{k}$-vectors together with its boundary points. That is, one starts at a general $\mathbf{k}$-vector and forms a set out of all $\mathbf{k}$-vectors which can be reached by a continuous curve which does not include any point of higher symmetry. To this set is then added the boundary points of higher symmetry. The triangular section of the first Brillouin zone of the square lattice which was considered in Section 2 provides an example.

(i) An energy function $E(\mathbf{k})$ can have discontinuities not only at Brillouin zone boundaries but also at proper Brillouin zone boundaries. The discontinuity at a proper B-Z boundary is due to a touching or coalescence or sticking of several energy surfaces there. The number of sticking energy surfaces is equal to the number of limit representations into which the irreducible representation belonging to the given $\mathbf{k}$ and E decomposes when the limit is taken from a general vector direction.

(j) A proper functional Brillouin zone is a set of functions obtained in the following manner. Choose a Bloch eigenvector $\phi_{\mathbf{k}}(\mathbf{r})$ belonging to a general vector $\mathbf{k}$ of a proper B-Z. The proper functional B-Z is the set of Bloch eigenvectors generated continuously from the original one by letting $\mathbf{k}$ vary over the proper B-Z. At each point $\mathbf{k}_0$ of the boundary, the Bloch eigenvector generated in the above manner will be a member of a set of Bloch eigenvectors which generate an allowable irreducible representation of $G_{\mathbf{k}_0}$ which is compatible with $\Delta_{\mathbf{k}_0}$. In brief, all allowable irreducible representations of $G_{\mathbf{k}}$'s generated in this way must be compatible. Thus the group theoretic properties of a proper functional B-Z can be specified by specifying a set of compatible irreducible representations of $G_{\mathbf{k}}$'s for every symmetry type of $\mathbf{k}$ in the proper B-Z. Since only one allowable irreducible representation of $G_{\mathbf{k}}$ exists for a general $\mathbf{k}$ it is not necessary to specify the representations belonging to general points.

5. Compatibility

The compatibility tables for the symmetry points of $\mathbf{k}$-space for the 2-dimensional square lattice of Section 2 will be given here as an example. The allowable irreducible representations of $G_{\mathbf{k}}$ will be denoted by Γ's and the allowable irreducible limit representations belonging to a line terminating in $\mathbf{k}$ will be denoted by Δ's. The numbering of the representations will be the same as in the character tables of Section 2. The symmetry point will be denoted by $\mathbf{k}_0$, and the line by L. The numbers in the tables are the coefficients $c_q^{(p)}$ in the decompositions

$$\Gamma_q^{(s)} = \sum_p c_q^{(p)} \Delta_p. \qquad (6:5.1)$$

The s superscripts are omitted.

$$\mathbf{k}_0 = \mathbf{0}$$

$$L = \left\{\begin{pmatrix} k_x \\ 0 \end{pmatrix}\right\}$$

	Δ_1	Δ_2
Γ_1	1	0
Γ_2	0	1
Γ_3	1	0
Γ_4	0	1
Γ_5	1	1

$$\mathbf{k}_0 = \mathbf{0}$$

$$L = \left\{\begin{pmatrix} k_x \\ k_x \end{pmatrix}\right\}$$

	Δ_1	Δ_2
Γ_1	1	0
Γ_2	0	1
Γ_3	0	1
Γ_4	1	0
Γ_5	1	1

$$\mathbf{k}_0 = \begin{pmatrix} \pi a^{-1} \\ \pi a^{-1} \end{pmatrix}$$

$$L = \left\{\begin{pmatrix} k_x \\ k_x \end{pmatrix}\right\}$$

	Δ_1	Δ_2
Γ_6	1	0
Γ_7	0	1
Γ_8	0	1
Γ_9	1	0
Γ_{10}	1	1

$$\mathbf{k}_0 = \begin{pmatrix} \pi a^{-1} \\ \pi a^{-1} \end{pmatrix}$$

$$L = \left\{\begin{pmatrix} \pi a^{-1} \\ k_y \end{pmatrix}\right\}$$

	Δ_1	Δ_2
Γ_6	1	0
Γ_7	0	1
Γ_8	1	0
Γ_9	0	1
Γ_{10}	1	1

$$\mathbf{k}_0 = \begin{pmatrix} \pi a^{-1} \\ 0 \end{pmatrix}$$

$$L = \left\{\begin{pmatrix} \pi a^{-1} \\ k_y \end{pmatrix}\right\}$$

	Δ_1	Δ_2
Γ_5	1	0
Γ_6	0	1
Γ_7	0	1
Γ_8	1	0

$$\mathbf{k}_0 = \begin{pmatrix} \pi a^{-1} \\ 0 \end{pmatrix}$$

$$L = \left\{\begin{pmatrix} k_x \\ 0 \end{pmatrix}\right\}$$

	Δ_1	Δ_2
Γ_5	1	0
Γ_6	0	1
Γ_7	1	0
Γ_8	0	1

Since there are three symmetry points and three symmetry lines we need six compatible representations to specify the symmetry of a proper functional Brillouin zone. Following is a table of all twenty-four symmetry types of functional Brillouin zones for the 2-dimensional square lattice.

0	$\begin{pmatrix} k_x \\ k_x \end{pmatrix}$	$\begin{pmatrix} \pi a^{-1} \\ \pi a_{-1} \end{pmatrix}$	$\begin{pmatrix} \pi a^{-1} \\ k_y \end{pmatrix}$	$\begin{pmatrix} \pi a^{-1} \\ 0 \end{pmatrix}$	$\begin{pmatrix} k_x \\ 0 \end{pmatrix}$
Γ_1	Δ_1	Γ_6	Δ_1	Γ_5	Δ_1
Γ_1	Δ_1	Γ_9	Δ_2	Γ_6	Δ_1
Γ_1	Δ_1	Γ_{10}	Δ_1	Γ_5	Δ_1
Γ_1	Δ_1	Γ_{10}	Δ_2	Γ_6	Δ_1
Γ_2	Δ_2	Γ_7	Δ_2	Γ_6	Δ_2
Γ_2	Δ_2	Γ_8	Δ_1	Γ_8	Δ_2
Γ_2	Δ_2	Γ_{16}	Δ_2	Γ_6	Δ_2
Γ_2	Δ_2	Γ_{10}	Δ_1	Γ_8	Δ_2
Γ_3	Δ_2	Γ_8	Δ_1	Γ_5	Δ_1
Γ_3	Δ_2	Γ_7	Δ_2	Γ_7	Δ_1
Γ_3	Δ_2	Γ_{10}	Δ_1	Γ_5	Δ_1
Γ_3	Δ_2	Γ_{10}	Δ_2	Γ_7	Δ_1
Γ_4	Δ_1	Γ_9	Δ_2	Γ_6	Δ_2
Γ_4	Δ_1	Γ_6	Δ_1	Γ_8	Δ_2
Γ_4	Δ_1	Γ_{10}	Δ_2	Γ_6	Δ_2
Γ_4	Δ_1	Γ_{10}	Δ_1	Γ_8	Δ_2
Γ_5	Δ_1	Γ_6	Δ_1	Γ_5	Δ_1
Γ_5	Δ_1	Γ_7	Δ_2	Γ_7	Δ_1
Γ_5	Δ_2	Γ_7	Δ_2	Γ_6	Δ_2
Γ_5	Δ_2	Γ_8	Δ_1	Γ_8	Δ_2
Γ_5	Δ_1	Γ_{10}	Δ_1	Γ_5	Δ_1
Γ_5	Δ_1	Γ_{10}	Δ_2	Γ_7	Δ_1
Γ_5	Δ_2	Γ_{10}	Δ_2	Γ_6	Δ_2
Γ_5	Δ_2	Γ_{10}	Δ_1	Γ_8	Δ_2

6. Physics

The general considerations of Chapter IV with regard to Schrödinger equations with symmetry groups also apply when the symmetry group is a crystallographic space group. Again, of course, these considerations apply only in the absence of accidental degeneracy. For example, the dimensions of the irreducible representations of the space group encompass all possible degeneracies of the energy levels. The dimensions of the irreducible representations of the $G_{\mathbf{k}}$'s give the various possibilities for the number of linearly independent wave functions belonging to a given E and $\mathbf{k}$. Where this number is greater than one, the number of $E(\mathbf{k})$ *vs* $\mathbf{k}$ surface which touch (or stick) is $d_{\mathbf{k}}$.

One important result which we can now prove is that $E(\mathbf{k})$ has the symmetry of the point group P of the crystal under consideration. From the method of construction of the irreducible representations of space groups as well as from the theorems of Chapter V, Section 1, it can be seen that the irreducible representation belonging to a given energy level E is generated by Bloch eigenvectors belonging to all wave numbers of a particular star. Thus, every $\mathbf{k}$ belonging to the star has a wave function with the energy E. But the star has the symmetry of P, and therefore the energy must also have this symmetry.

The energy function $E(\mathbf{k})$ must also be centrosymmetric. This follows from the fact that if $\phi_{\mathbf{k}}(\mathbf{r})$ is a Bloch energy eigenvector belonging to energy E so is $\phi_{\mathbf{k}}{}^*(\mathbf{r}) = e^{i\mathbf{k}\cdot\mathbf{r}}u^*(\mathbf{r})$ so that $\phi_{\mathbf{k}}{}^*(\mathbf{r})$ generates the representation $\Delta(-\mathbf{k})$ of T and therefore really has wave vector $-\mathbf{k}$.

Now let us again relate the reality of the representation to the degeneracy of the energy level. Let the one-electron Hamiltonian of the crystal be real (as well as hermitian) and let M be a manifold of Bloch energy eigenvectors belonging to the energy E and generating the irreducible representation Γ of the space group G. Then

(*a*) M^* belongs to the same energy as M.

(b) M^* is linearly independent of M if Γ is of second or third kind. In this case there is additional degeneracy caused by time-reversal symmetry; i.e., by the reality of the Hamiltonian.

Finally we can make some remarks on the choice of an irreducible representation $\Gamma_{\mathbf{k},E}(P_{\mathbf{k}})$ of $P_{\mathbf{k}}$ in the Wigner-Seitz method of constructing crystal wave functions (see Chapter IV, Section 14). The corresponding irreducible representation $\Gamma_{\mathbf{k},E}(G_{\mathbf{k}})$ of $G_{\mathbf{k}}$ must of course be allowable. To decide which allowable representation to use one must have some other information. For example, if one wants the Bloch energy eigenvectors belonging to a given $\mathbf{k}$ and having the lowest energy for that $\mathbf{k}$, then one can make some kind of approximate computation to determine which $\Gamma_{\mathbf{k},E}(P_{\mathbf{k}})$ they generate.

Chapter VII

SYMMETRIC GROUPS

In this chapter a condensed review of the main properties of the symmetric groups will be given. The symmetric groups are amenable to treatment by the general methods of group theory discussed in Chapters II and III, and the results given here are specializations of the general theory to the case of symmetric groups.

Definition. A permutation on n ordered symbols is a recordering of the symbols (or a one-to-one transformation of the set of symbols into itself).

Let us consider n ordered symbols and number them from 1 to n in order. The permutation which changes these symbols into the order $i_1, i_2, \ldots, i_n$ can then be denoted by

$$\Big\uparrow\begin{pmatrix} i_1 & i_2 & i_3 & \ldots & i_n \\ 1 & 2 & 3 & \ldots & n \end{pmatrix}.$$

The identity permutation is

$$\Big\uparrow\begin{pmatrix} 1 & 2 & 3 & \ldots & n \\ 1 & 2 & 3 & \ldots & n \end{pmatrix}$$

which leaves the order unchanged. The inverse of a permutation is the permutation which restores the original order to the permutated set. That is

$$\Big\uparrow\begin{pmatrix} i_1 & i_2 & \ldots & i_n \\ 1 & 2 & \ldots & n \end{pmatrix}^{-1} = \begin{pmatrix} 1 & 2 & \ldots & n \\ i_1 & i_2 & \ldots & i_n \end{pmatrix}.$$

The product of two permutations is defined in the following way. Let P_1 and P_2 be two permutations on n symbols. If P_2 takes k into $j(k)$ and P_1 takes $j(k)$ into $i(j(k))$ then $P_1 P_2$ is defined as the permutation which takes k into $i(j(k))$.

Example.

$$\Big\uparrow\begin{pmatrix} 4 & 1 & 2 & 3 \\ 1 & 2 & 3 & 4 \end{pmatrix} \Big\uparrow\begin{pmatrix} 2 & 4 & 1 & 3 \\ 1 & 2 & 3 & 4 \end{pmatrix} = \Big\uparrow\begin{pmatrix} 1 & 3 & 4 & 2 \\ 1 & 2 & 3 & 4 \end{pmatrix}$$

With this definition of multiplication the permutations on n symbols form a group.

Definition. The symmetric group of degree n, $\mathscr{S}(n)$, is the group of all permutations on n symbols.

Thus, corresponding to each positive integer n there is a symmetric group $\mathscr{S}(n)$. The terms "symmetric group" and "symmetry group" should not be confused. The symmetry group of a physical system may or may not be a symmetric group.

Now let us list without derivation the properties of the symmetric groups.

1. Abstract Properties of $\mathscr{S}(n)$

(1) Order of $\mathscr{S}(n) = n!$

(2) $n! \cong \sqrt{2\pi n}\, n^n e^{-n}$ for large n. This is Stirling's asymptotic approximation.

(3) A *partition* of a positive integer n is a set of positive integers whose sum is n. If in a partition of n, the integer 1 occurs a_1 times, the integer 2 occurs a_2 times, etc., so $n = \sum_{j=1}^{n} j a_j$, then the partition can be written $\{1^{a_1} 2^{a_2} 3^{a_3} \ldots n^{a_n}\}$. The integers with zero exponent are omitted.

(4) The number of classes $r(n)$ of the symmetric group $\mathscr{S}(n)$ is equal to the number of partitions of n.

(5) $r(n)$ is the coefficient of x^n in the formal power series expansion of $E(x) \equiv \prod_{j=1}^{\infty} (1 - x^j)^{-1}$, where $E(x)$ is the Euler generating function.

(6) Following is a table of $r(n)$ *vs.* n:

n	$r(n)$	n	$r(n)$
1	1	16	231
2	2	17	297
3	3	18	395
4	5	19	490
5	7	20	627
6	11	30	5,604
7	15	40	37,388
8	22	50	204,266
9	30	60	966,467
10	42	70	4,087,968
11	56	80	15,796,476
12	77	90	56,634,173
13	101	100	190,569,292
14	135	200	3,972,999,029,388
15	176		

(7) $r(n) \cong \dfrac{1}{4n\sqrt{3}} e^{\pi\sqrt{2n/3}}$ for large n. This is the Hardy-Ramanujan asymptotic approximation.

(8) Corresponding to every partition $\{1^{a_1} 2^{a_2} 3^{a_3} \ldots\}$ of n there is a class of $\mathscr{S}(n)$ of order

$$r_{\{a\}}(n) = \frac{n!}{a_1! a_2! \ldots a_n! 2^{a_2} 3^{a_3} \ldots n^{a_n}}.$$

(9) Every class of $\mathscr{S}(n)$ is ambivalent.

(10) Every symmetric group $\mathscr{S}(n)$ is isomorphic to a crystallographic point group of an $(n-1)$-dimensional lattice.

(11) Every finite group is isomorphic to a subgroup of some symmetric group.

(12) $\mathscr{S}(n)$ is complete except for $n = 6$.

(13) $\mathscr{S}(n)$ is insolvable for $n > 4$.

(14) Rank of $\mathscr{S}(n) = 2$ for all $n > 2$.

(15) A *cycle* (or cyclic permutation) is a permutation which puts symbol j in position $j + 1$; e.g.

$$\uparrow\begin{pmatrix} i_2 & i_3 & i_4 & \cdots & i_r & i_1 \\ i_1 & i_2 & i_3 & \cdots & i_{r-1} & i_r \end{pmatrix}$$

A cycle need not cyclically permute all symbols, but only a subset. The preceding cycle can also be written $(i_1, i_2, i_3, \ldots, i_{r-1}, i_r)$.

(16) A *transposition* is a permutation interchanging two symbols.

(17) Every permutation can be expressed as a product of transpositions (and in fact, of transpositions of adjacent symbols). No permutation can be factored into transposition in two ways such that one factorization contains an even number of transpositions and the other an odd number.

(18) A permutation is called *even* if its transposition factorizations contain an even number of transpositions and *odd* otherwise.

(19) The even permutations of $\mathscr{S}(n)$ form a normal subgroup $\mathscr{A}(n)$ of order $n!/2$. This subgroup is called the alternating group.

(20) $\mathscr{A}(n)$ is the commutator subgroup of $\mathscr{S}(n)$.

(21) $\mathscr{A}(n)$ is simple for $n > 4$.

(22) The signature $\sigma(P)$ is a function on $\mathscr{S}(n)$ which is 1 if P is even and -1 if P is odd.

(23) Two cycles are *disjoint* if they do not contain any symbol in common.

(24) Every permutation can be expressed uniquely as a product of disjoint cycles.

(25) The order of a permutation is the least common multiple of the orders of the cycles in its disjoint cycle factorization.

(26) Let P be a permutation of $\mathscr{S}(n)$ and $\alpha_j(P)$ the number of cycles of order j in the disjoint cycle factorization of P. The set of numbers $(\alpha_1(P), \alpha_2(P), \ldots, \alpha_n(P))$ is called the *cycle structure* of P.

(27) Two permutations of $\mathscr{S}(n)$ are in the same class if and only if they have the same cycle structure. Thus each cycle structure specifies a class.

(28) If $(\alpha_1(P), \alpha_2(P), \ldots, \alpha_n(P))$ is a cycle structure of a permutation of $\mathscr{S}(n)$ then $\sum_{j=1}^{n} j\alpha_j(P) = n$. Hence, $\{1^{\alpha_1}2^{\alpha_2}\ldots n^{\alpha_n}\}$ is a partition of n, and each partition of n specifies a class of $\mathscr{S}(n)$.

(29) A class of $\mathscr{S}(n)$ is called *even* or *odd* according as $\alpha_2 + \alpha_4 + \alpha_6 + \dots$ is even or odd.

(30) An even class contains only even permutations.

(31) A *binary partition* of n is a partition expressing n as the sum of at most two positive integers. A *d-ary* partition of n is a partition expressing n as the sum of at most d positive integers.

(32) The number of binary partitions of n is

$$[\tfrac{1}{2}n] + 1,$$

where

$$[\tfrac{1}{2}n] = \tfrac{1}{2}n \text{ if } n \text{ is even}$$
$$= \tfrac{1}{2}(n-1) \text{ if } n \text{ is odd.}$$

(33) The number of square roots of the identity element of $\mathscr{S}(n)$ is given by

$$\zeta_n(I) = n! \sum_{i,j} \frac{2^{-j}}{i!j!},$$

where the sum is over-all nonnegative, integral i and j satisfying $i + 2j = n$.

(34) $$\zeta_n(I) = \zeta_{n-1}(I) + (n-1)\zeta_{n-2}(I).$$

(35) $$\frac{\zeta_n(I)}{\zeta_{n-1}(I)} \simeq \sqrt{n} \text{ for large } n.$$

(36) The number $N(n, r)$ of permutations of $\mathscr{S}(n)$ which leave exactly r symbols fixed (unpermuted) is given by

$$N(n, r) = \frac{n!}{r!} \sum_{k=0}^{n-r} \frac{(-1)^k}{k!}.$$

(37) $N(n, r)$ satisfies the two relations

$$\frac{1}{n!} \sum_{r=0}^{n} rN(n, r) = 1$$

$$\frac{1}{n!} \sum_{r=0}^{n} (r-1)^2 N(n, r) = 1.$$

(38) $$\sum_{j=0}^{n} \binom{n}{j} = 2^n.$$

(39) $$\sum_{k=0}^{[\frac{1}{2}n]} (n - 2k + 1)\left[\binom{n}{k} - \binom{n}{k-1}\right] = 2^n,$$

where

$$[\tfrac{1}{2}n] = \tfrac{1}{2}n \text{ if } n \text{ is even}$$
$$= \tfrac{1}{2}(n-1) \text{ if } n \text{ is odd.}$$

(2) Representations of $\mathscr{S}(n)$.

(1) $\mathscr{S}(n)$ has $r(n)$ irreducible inequivalent representations.

(2) Every representation of $\mathscr{S}(n)$ is integral.

(3) Since the index of $\mathscr{A}(n)$ in $\mathscr{S}(n)$ is two, there are two 1-dimensional representations of $\mathscr{S}(n) (n > 1)$.

(4) One of the two 1-dimensional representations is the trivial representa-

tion. The other is the *alternating* representation Γ_σ in which $P_{even} \to 1$ and $P_{odd} \to -1$. In brief, Γ_σ is defined by $P \to \sigma(P)$.

(5) If Γ is a representation of $\mathscr{S}(n)$, the *associated* representation $\bar{\Gamma}$ is defined by $\bar{\Gamma} = \Gamma \otimes \Gamma_\sigma$.

(6) Γ is irreducible if and only if $\bar{\Gamma}$ is irreducible.

(7) For $n > 4$ every irreducible representation of $\mathscr{S}(n)$ of dimension greater than one has dimension at least $n - 1$.

(8) For $n > 4$ but $\neq 6$ there are exactly two irreducible representations of $\mathscr{S}(n)$ of dimension $n - 1$, and these are associated.

(9) For $n > 4$ every irreducible representation of $\mathscr{S}(n)$ of dimension greater than one is faithful.

(10) Corresponding to every partition of n

$$n = \lambda_1 + \lambda_2 + \dots + \lambda_\rho$$
$$\lambda_1 \geqslant \lambda_2 \geqslant \lambda_3 \geqslant \dots \geqslant \lambda_\rho$$

there is an irreducible representation $\Gamma_{\{\lambda\}}$ of $\mathscr{S}(n)$.

(11) The dimension $d_{\{\lambda\}}$ of $\Gamma_{\{\lambda\}}$ is as follows. Let

$$l_i = \lambda_i + \rho - i \qquad i = 1, 2, \dots, \rho$$
$$\Delta(l_1, l_2, \dots) = \prod_{i<j} \prod (l_i - l_j) \text{ if } \rho \neq 1$$
$$= 1 \text{ if } \rho = 1.$$

Then

$$d_{\{\lambda\}} = \frac{n!\Delta(l_1, l_2, \dots).}{l_1!l_2!\dots l_\rho!}$$

The function $\Delta(l_1, l_2, \dots)$ can also be written as a Vandermonde determinant

$$\Delta(l_1, l_2, \dots) = -\begin{vmatrix} 1 & l_1 & l_1^2 & \dots & l_1^{\rho-1} \\ 1 & l_2 & l_2^2 & \dots & l_2^{\rho-1} \\ \cdot & \cdot & \cdot & & \cdot \\ \cdot & \cdot & \cdot & & \cdot \\ \cdot & \cdot & \cdot & & \cdot \\ 1 & l_\rho & l_\rho^2 & \dots & l_\rho^{\rho-1} \end{vmatrix}$$

(12) The character $\chi^{\{\lambda\}}$ of $\Gamma_{\{\lambda\}}$ is as follows. Let

$$\Delta(z_1, z_2, \dots, z_n) = -\begin{vmatrix} 1 & z_1 & z_1^2 & \dots & z_1^{n-1} \\ 1 & z_2 & z_2^2 & \dots & z_2^{n-1} \\ \cdot & \cdot & \cdot & & \cdot \\ \cdot & \cdot & \cdot & & \cdot \\ \cdot & \cdot & \cdot & & \cdot \\ 1 & z_n & z_n^2 & \dots & z_n^{n-1} \end{vmatrix}$$

$$= \prod_{i<j} \prod (z_i - z_j)$$

$\{a\} = \{1^{a_1}2^{a_2}3^{a_3}\ldots n^{a_n}\}$ be any other partition of n,
$C_{\{a\}}$ = the class of $\mathscr{S}(n)$ corresponding to the partition $\{a\}$ of n,
$\chi^{\{\lambda\}}_{\{a\}}$ = the value of $\chi^{\{\lambda\}}$ belonging to the class $C_{\{a\}}$,

$$f_{\{a\}}(z_1,\ldots,z_n) = (\sum_{i=1}^{n} z_i)^{a_1}(\sum_{i=1}^{n} z_i^2)^{a_2}\ldots(\sum_{i=1}^{n} z_i^n)^{a_n}$$

$$F_{\{a\}}(z_1, z_2,\ldots, z_n) = \Delta(z_1,\ldots, z_n)f_a(z_1,\ldots, z_n)$$

= The Frobenius generating function.

Then

$$F_{\{a\}}(z_1,\ldots, z_n) = \sum_{\{\lambda\}} \sum_{P\in\mathscr{S}(n)} \sigma(P)\chi^{\{\lambda\}}_{\{a\}}Pz_1^{\lambda_1+n-1}z_2^{\lambda_2+n-2}\ldots z_n^{\lambda_n}$$

where the P in the summand operates on the subscripts of the z's, and the first sum is over all partitions $\{\lambda\}$ of n.

Example. Character Table of $\mathscr{S}(4) = 0$

Class	1^4	2^2	1^22	4	13
Order	1	3	6	6	8
4	1	1	1	1	1
1^4	1	1	−1	−1	1
2^2	2	2	0	0	−1
1^22	3	−1	−1	−1	0
13	3	−1	1	1	0

Comparing this with the character table for O in Chapter III (p. 81) we see that

$$\begin{aligned} C_1 &= 1^4 & \Gamma_1 &= 4 \\ C_2 &= 2^2 & \Gamma_2 &= 1^4 \\ C_3 &= 1^22 & \Gamma_3 &= 2^2 \\ C_4 &= 4 & \Gamma_4 &= 1^22 \\ C_5 &= 13 & \Gamma_5 &= 13 \end{aligned}$$

The classes and representations are denoted simply by the corresponding partitions.

(13) The trivial representations of $\mathscr{S}(n)$ always belongs to the partition n and the alternating representation always belongs to the partition 1^n.

(14) Consider the binary partition $n = (n - k) + k$ of n, and let Γ_k be the corresponding irreducible representation of $\mathscr{S}(n)$. For convenience we can assume $n - k \geqslant k$, or $k \leqslant \frac{1}{2}n$.

(a) $$\dim \Gamma_k = \binom{n}{k} - \binom{n}{k-1}$$

(b) Let $n = \lambda_1 + \lambda_2 + \ldots + \lambda_\rho$ be any partition of n, let $\chi^k_{\{\lambda\}}$ be the value of χ^k belonging to the class corresponding to the partition $\{\lambda\}$, and let $G_{\{\lambda\}}(z) \equiv (1-z) \prod_{j=1}^{\rho} (1 + z^{\lambda_j})$ Then

$$G_{\{\lambda\}}(z) = \sum_{k=0}^{n} \chi^{k}_{\{\lambda\}} z^k.$$

(c) $\bar{\Gamma}_k$ belongs to the partition $\{1^{n-2k}2^k\}$ of n.

(d) $\bar{\chi}^k$ is given by the equation

$$(1 - z)G_{\{\lambda\}}(z) = (-1)^{n-\rho} \sum_{k=0}^{n} \bar{\chi}^{k}_{\{\lambda\}} z^k.$$

(15) The cycle structure of a transposition is

$$a_1 = n - 2 \qquad a_2 = 1.$$

Hence the transpositions of $\mathscr{S}(n)$ belong to the class corresponding to the partition $\{1^{n-2}2\}$ of n. The character of this class in the irreducible representation Γ_k corresponding to the binary partition $n = (n - k) + k$ $(k \leqslant \frac{1}{2}n)$ is

$$\chi^{k}_{\{1^{n-2}2\}} = \binom{n-2}{k} + \binom{n-2}{k-2} - \binom{n-2}{k-1} - \binom{n-2}{k-3}$$

The value of the character of the associated representation belonging to this class is

$$\bar{\chi}^{k}_{\{1^{n-2}2\}} = - \chi^{k}_{\{1^{n-2}2\}}$$

(16) Let $n = \lambda_1 + \lambda_2 + \dots + \lambda_\rho$ with $\lambda_1 \geqslant \lambda_2 \geqslant \lambda_3 \geqslant \dots \geqslant \lambda_\rho > 0$ be a partition of n. The *graph* (or Young diagram) corresponding to this partition is the set of ρ rows of blocks with λ_j blocks in the jth row and the integers $1 + \sum_{i=1}^{j-1} \lambda_i$, $2 + \sum_{i=1}^{j-1} \lambda_i, \dots, \lambda_j + \sum_{i=1}^{j-1} \lambda_i$ appearing in order in these blocks.

That is, the graph is

1	2	$\dots$	λ_1	λ_1 columns
$1 + \lambda_1$	$2 + \lambda_1$	$\dots$	$\lambda_1 + \lambda_2$	λ_2 columns
$1 + \lambda_1 + \lambda_2$		$\dots$	$\lambda_1 + \lambda_2 + \lambda_3$	λ_3 columns

ρ rows

(17) Now let us define the Young symmetrizer $Y_{\{\lambda\}}$ corresponding to the partition $\{\lambda\}$ of n.

(a) Let P_r be an element of $\mathscr{S}(n)$ which does not permute numbers of the graph of $\{\lambda\}$ belonging to different rows.

(b) Let H_r be the subgroup of $\mathscr{S}(n)$ consisting of all P_r's. H_r has order

$$\prod_{i=1}^{\rho} \lambda_i! \,.$$

(c) Let $S_r = \sum_{P_r \epsilon H_r} P_r$. The permutations P_r are considered to be operators in order to give the sum a meaning. They might for example operate on tensor indices, but we shall not consider that further here.

(d) Let P_c be any element of $\mathscr{S}(n)$ which does not permute numbers in the graph of $\{\lambda\}$ belonging to different columns.

(e) Let H_c be the subgroup of $\mathscr{S}(n)$ consisting of all P_c's.

(f) Let $A_c = \sum_{P_c \epsilon H_c} \sigma(P_c) P_c$.

The Young symmetrizer $Y_{\{\lambda\}}$ is the operator defined by

$$Y_{\{\lambda\}} = A_c S_r.$$

Example. $n = 3$

$$Y_{\{3\}} = I + \Big\uparrow\begin{pmatrix}2 & 1\\ 1 & 2\end{pmatrix} + \Big\uparrow\begin{pmatrix}3 & 1\\ 1 & 3\end{pmatrix} + \Big\uparrow\begin{pmatrix}3 & 2\\ 2 & 3\end{pmatrix} + \Big\uparrow\begin{pmatrix}2 & 3 & 1\\ 1 & 2 & 3\end{pmatrix} + \Big\uparrow\begin{pmatrix}3 & 1 & 2\\ 1 & 2 & 3\end{pmatrix}$$

$$Y_{\{1,2\}} = I + \Big\uparrow\begin{pmatrix}2 & 1\\ 1 & 2\end{pmatrix} - \Big\uparrow\begin{pmatrix}3 & 1\\ 1 & 3\end{pmatrix} - \Big\uparrow\begin{pmatrix}2 & 3 & 1\\ 1 & 2 & 3\end{pmatrix}$$

$$Y_{\{1^3\}} = I - \Big\uparrow\begin{pmatrix}2 & 1\\ 1 & 2\end{pmatrix} - \Big\uparrow\begin{pmatrix}3 & 1\\ 1 & 3\end{pmatrix} - \Big\uparrow\begin{pmatrix}3 & 2\\ 2 & 3\end{pmatrix} + \Big\uparrow\begin{pmatrix}2 & 3 & 1\\ 1 & 2 & 3\end{pmatrix} + \Big\uparrow\begin{pmatrix}3 & 1 & 2\\ 1 & 2 & 3\end{pmatrix}.$$

(18)
$$Y_{\{n\}} = \sum_{P \epsilon \mathscr{S}(n)} P$$
$$Y_{\{1^n\}} = \sum_{P \epsilon \mathscr{S}(n)} \sigma(PP).$$

(19)
$$Y^2 = \frac{n!}{d_{\{\lambda\}}} Y.$$

(20) If $\{\lambda\}$ and $\{\lambda'\}$ are two partitions of n

$$n = \lambda_1 + \lambda_2 + \ldots$$
$$n = \lambda_1' + \lambda_2' + \ldots$$

such that $\lambda_i \geqslant \lambda_{i+1}, \lambda_i' \geqslant \lambda_{i+1}'$, then by definition $\{\lambda\} > \{\lambda'\}$ if the first non vanishing difference $\lambda_i - \lambda_i'$ is positive.

(21) Some properties of the Young symmetrizer are as follows.

(a) No permutation occurs in any Y more than once.

(b) Let $Z = \sum_{P \epsilon \mathscr{S}(n)} z(P) P$, where $z(P)$ is a function on $\mathscr{S}(n)$. Then $P_c Z P_r = Z$ for all P_c and P_r belonging to a given partition $\{\lambda\}$ if and only if $Z = c Y_{\{\lambda\}}$, where c is a constant.

(c) If again $Z = \sum_{P \epsilon \mathscr{S}(n)} z(P) P$, then

$$YZY = \text{const.} \times Y$$
$$YZY' = 0 \text{ if } \{\lambda'\} > \{\lambda\}$$
$$YZS_r' = 0 \text{ if } \{\lambda'\} > \{\lambda\}$$

(22) The character of $\Gamma_{\{\lambda\}}$ can be obtained from $Y_{\{\lambda\}}$ as follows. If

$$Y_{\{\lambda\}} = \sum_{P \epsilon \mathscr{S}(n)} y_{\{\lambda\}}(P) P,$$

then

$$\chi^{\{\lambda\}}_{(P)} = \frac{d_{\{\lambda\}}}{n!} \sum_{P' \epsilon \mathscr{S}(n)} y_{\{\lambda\}}(P'^{-1}PP').$$

(23) Consider the irreducible representation $\Gamma_{\{\lambda\}}$ of $\mathscr{S}(n)$, where $\{\lambda\}$ is the partition

$$n = \lambda_1 + \lambda_2 + \dots \qquad \lambda_i \geqslant \lambda_{i+1}$$

of n. Let $\mathscr{S}(n-1)$ be the subgroup of $\mathscr{S}(n)$ consisting of those permutations of $\mathscr{S}(n)$ which leave the nth symbol fixed, and let $\Gamma^{(s)}_{\{\lambda\}}$ be the representation of $\mathscr{S}(n-1)$ subduced by $\Gamma_{\{\lambda\}}$. Then

$$\Gamma^{(s)}_{\{\lambda\}} = \Gamma_{\{\lambda_1-1,\lambda_2,\lambda_3,\dots\}} \oplus \Gamma_{\{\lambda_1,\lambda_2-1,\lambda_3,\dots\}} \oplus \dots$$

where any irreducible representation of $\mathscr{S}(n-1)$ whose partition exceeds the preceding is to be omitted. This formula is the branching law for $\mathscr{S}(n)$.

(24) Let $\mathscr{S}(m)$ be the symmetric group of permutations on a set of m symbols, $\mathscr{S}(n)$ the symmetric group of permutations on another set of n symbols, and $\mathscr{S}(m+n)$ the symmetric group of permutations on all $m+n$ symbols. Then $\mathscr{S}(m)\mathscr{S}(n)$ is a subgroup of $\mathscr{S}(m+n)$ which is naturally isomorphic to $\mathscr{S}(m) \times \mathscr{S}(n)$. If $\Gamma_{\{\kappa\}}$ and $\Gamma_{\{\lambda\}}$ are irreducible representations of $\mathscr{S}(m)$ and $\mathscr{S}(n)$ respectively, then $\Gamma_{\{\kappa\}} \times \Gamma_{\{\lambda\}}$ is an irreducible representation of $\mathscr{S}(m)\mathscr{S}(n)$. The problem of completely reducing the induced representation $(\Gamma_{\{\kappa\}} \times \Gamma_{\{\lambda\}})^{(\mathscr{I})}$ of $\mathscr{S}(m+n)$ is an important one which has been attacked by many people. Any particular induced representation can in principle be reduced by the standard method if the character table of $\mathscr{S}(m+n)$ is known. The object of the many investigations mentioned before is to develop a general technique which will depend only on knowing the partitions $\{\kappa\}$ and $\{\lambda\}$ of m and n. These investigations have met with some success but will not be discussed here. Any such problem can in principle be handled by the standard methods already developed.

3. Miscellany and the Full Linear Groups

(1) With the aid of Young symmetrizers the concepts of symmetric and anti-symmetric tensors can now be generalized. To do this let us allow the permutation operators and Young symmetrizers to operate on tensor indices. First we note that if $T_{i_1,\dots i_n}$, is any nth rank tensor then $Y_{\{n\}}T_{i_1,\dots,i_n}$ is symmetric and $Y_{\{1^n\}}T_{i_1,\dots,i_n}$ is antisymmetric. The obvious generalization is to consider the tensors $Y_{\{\lambda\}}T_{i_1,\dots,i_n}$ for all partitions $\{\lambda\}$ of n. The tensor $Y_{\{\lambda\}}T_{i_1,\dots,i_n}$ might be called $\{\lambda\}$-symmetric.

(2) The number $\delta_{\{\lambda\}}$ of independent components of $Y_{\{\lambda\}}T_{i_1,\dots,i_n}$ for a symmetryless d-dimensional tensor $T_{i_1,\dots,i_n}$ is given as follows.

Let $n = \lambda_1 + \lambda_2 + \dots, \lambda_1 \geqslant \lambda_2 \geqslant \dots \geqslant \lambda_\rho > 0, \rho \leqslant d$,

$$m_j = \lambda_j + d - j (j = 1,\dots,d), \text{ and } \Delta(m_1, m_2,\dots) = \prod_{i<j} \prod (m_i - m_j).$$

Then

$$\delta_{\{\lambda\}} = \frac{\Delta(m_1, m_2, \ldots)}{\prod_{j=1}^{d-1} (d-j)!}.$$

(3) Let $T_{i_1,\ldots,i_n}$ be a d-dimensional tensor and $\{\lambda\}$ be a partition $n = \lambda_1 + \lambda_2 + \ldots + \lambda_\rho$ $(\lambda_1 \geqslant \lambda_2 \geqslant \ldots \geqslant \lambda_\rho > 0)$ of n such that $\rho > d$. Then

$$Y_{\{\lambda\}} T_{i_1,\ldots,i_n} = 0.$$

(4) The concepts of symmetrized and antisymmetrized powers of matrices can similarly be generalized to $\{\lambda\}$-symmetrized powers. Let T_i be a vector in the carrier space of the matrix D and $T_{i_1,\ldots,i_n}$ an nth rank tensor in the carrier space of the nth Kronecker power of D. Then the independent components of $Y_{\{\lambda\}} T_{i_1,\ldots,i_n}$ form a tensor in the carrier space of the nth $\{\lambda\}$-symmetrized Kronecker power $D_{n,\{\lambda\}}$ of D.

(5) The dimension of $D_{n,\{\lambda\}}$ is $\delta_{\{\lambda\}}$ (see (2)).

(6) The trace of $D_{n,\{\lambda\}}$ is given by the formula

$$\operatorname{tr}(D_{n,\{\lambda\}}) = \frac{1}{n!} \sum_{\{a\}} r_{\{a\}} \chi^{\{\lambda\}}_{\{a\}} T_{\{a\}},$$

where the sum is over all classes $\{a\} = \{1^{a_1} 2^{a_2} \ldots n^{a_n}\}$ of $\mathscr{S}(n)$ $T_{\{a\}} = T_1^{a_1} T_2^{a_2} \ldots T_n^{a_n}$, $T_j = \operatorname{tr}(D^j)$, and $r_{\{a\}}$ is the order of the class $\{a\}$ of $\mathscr{S}(n)$

(7) If Γ is a representation of a group then a $\{\lambda\}$-symmetrized nth Kronecker power $\Gamma_{n,\{\lambda\}}$ of Γ can be defined by replacing each matrix D of Γ by $D_{n,\{\lambda\}}$.

(8) If $\delta_{\{\lambda\}}$ is defined as in (2) then

$$\sum_{\{\lambda\}} \delta^2_{\{\lambda\}} = \binom{d^2 + n - 1}{n},$$

where the sum is over all d-ary partitions $\{\lambda\}$ of n.

(9) If $\delta_{\{\lambda\}}$ is defined as in (2) and $d_{\{\lambda\}}$ as in (11) Section 2, then

$$\sum_{\{\lambda\}} d_{\{\lambda\}} \delta_{\{\lambda\}} = d^n,$$

where the sum is again over all d-ary partitions $\{\lambda\}$ of n.

Example. $d = n = 3$

$d_{\{1^3\}} = 1 \qquad \delta_{\{1^3\}} = 1$

$d_{\{1,2\}} = 2 \qquad \delta_{\{1,2\}} = 8$

$d_{\{3\}} = 1 \qquad \delta_{\{3\}} = 10$

$\operatorname{tr}(D_{\{1^3\}}) = \frac{1}{6}(T_1{}^3 - 3T_1 T_2 + 2T_3)$ (antisymmetric cube)

$\operatorname{tr}(D_{\{1,2\}}) = \frac{1}{3}(T_1{}^3 - T_3)$

$\operatorname{tr}(D_{\{3\}}) = \frac{1}{6}(T_1{}^3 + 3T_1 T_2 + 2T_3)$ (symmetric cube)

$d^2_{\{1^3\}} + d^2_{\{1,2\}} + d^2_{\{3\}} = 6$

$$\delta^2_{\{1^3\}} + \delta^2_{\{1,2\}} + \delta^2_{\{3\}} = 165 = \binom{11}{3}$$
$$d_{\{1^3\}}\delta_{\{1^3\}} + d_{\{1,2\}}\delta_{\{1,2\}} + d_{\{3\}}\delta_{\{3\}} = 27 = 3^3.$$

(10) The concepts of determinant and permanant can now be generalized to the concept of *immanant*. Let $D = ||d_{ij}||$ be a d-dimensional matrix and $\{\lambda\}$ a partition of d. Then the immanant $|D|^{\{\lambda\}}$ is defined by the equation

$$|D|^{\{\lambda\}} \equiv \sum_{P\epsilon\mathscr{S}(d)} \chi^{\{\lambda\}}(P) P d_{11} d_{22} \ldots d_{dd},$$

where the sum is over all permutations P in $\mathscr{S}(d)$, and the permutation P in the summand operates on the set of second subscripts of the d's.

(11) $|D|^{\{1^d\}} = \det(D)$
$|D|^{\{d\}} = \operatorname{perm}(D)$.

(12) If D is any d-dimensional matrix and P is a d-dimensional permutation matrix then

$$|P^{-1}DP|^{\{\lambda\}} = |D|^{\{\lambda\}}.$$

(13) The trace of $D_{n,\{\lambda\}}$ can be expressed as an immanant in the following way. Let

$$T(n) = \begin{pmatrix} T_1 & 1 & 0 & 0 & \ldots & 0 \\ T_2 & T_1 & 2 & 0 & \ldots & 0 \\ \cdot & \cdot & & & & \\ \cdot & \cdot & & & & \\ \cdot & \cdot & & & & \\ T_n & T_{n-1} & \cdot & \cdot & \ldots & T_1 \end{pmatrix},$$

where $T_j = \operatorname{tr}(D^j)$. Then

$$\operatorname{tr}(D_{n,\{\lambda\}}) = \frac{1}{n!}|T(n)|^{\{\lambda\}},$$

where $\{\lambda\}$ is a partition of n.

(14) Another useful expression for $\operatorname{tr}(D_{n,\{\lambda\}})$ can be given as follows. Let the numbers λ_j of the partition $\{\lambda\}$ be ordered so that $j < j'$ implies $\lambda_j \geqslant \lambda_{j'}$. Then let $l_j = \lambda_j + n - j (j = 1, \ldots, n)$, and let the value of $p_k (k \geqslant 0)$ for the matrix D be determined by

$$|I - zD|^{-1} = \sum_{k=0}^{\infty} p_k z^k.$$

Also let $p_k = 0$ for $k < 0$. Then

$$\operatorname{tr}(D_{n,\{\lambda\}}) = \begin{vmatrix} pl_1 - (n-1) & pl_1 - (n-2) & \ldots & pl_1 \\ pl_2 - (n-1) & pl_2 - (n-2) & \ldots & \cdot \\ \cdot & \cdot & & \cdot \\ \cdot & \cdot & & \cdot \\ \cdot & \cdot & & \cdot \\ pl_n - (n-1) & pl_n - (n-2) & \ldots & pl_n \end{vmatrix}$$

(15) If D is a 2-dimensional matrix and $\chi = \text{tr}\,(D)$, $\delta = \det\,(D)$, then $p_0 = 1$, $p_1 = \chi$, $p_2 = \chi^2 - \delta$, $p_3 = \chi(\chi^2 - 2\delta)$, and $p_4 = \chi^4 - 3\chi^2\delta + \delta^2$.

(16) Now the Schur functions or *S-functions* can be defined. First let us note that it is not necessary to know the matrix D to find the $\text{tr}\,(D_{n,\{\lambda\}})$; it is sufficient to know the eigenvalues of D. Hence we can consider $\text{tr}\,(D_{n,\{\lambda\}})$ as a function of the eigenvalues of D. If the eigenvalues of D are $x_1,\ldots,x_d$ then the various S-functions of weight n of the arguments $x_1,\ldots,x_d$ are simply the functions $\text{tr}\,(D_{n,\{\lambda\}})$ for the various partitions $\{\lambda\}$ of n. In brief

$$S_{n,\{\lambda\}}\,(x_1,\ldots,x_d) \equiv \text{tr}\,(D_{n,\{\lambda\}})$$

where D has the eigenvalues $x_1,\ldots,x_d$.

(17) Many properties of S-functions have been discovered, but they will not be given here.

(18) Because the multiplicative group of all nonsingular d-dimensional matrices $GL(d,C)$ is closely related to $\mathscr{S}(d)$, some relevant results on $GL(d,C)$ will be stated now.

(a) Let us denote $GL(d,C)$ by Γ. Then $\Gamma_{n,\{\lambda\}}$ is an irreducible representation of $GL(d,C)$ of dimension $\delta_{\{\lambda\}}$.

(b) The d^n-dimensional nth Kronecker power Γ_n of $GL(d,C)$ can be completely reduced into the irreducible representations $\Gamma_{n,\{\lambda\}}$ of $GL(d,C)$.

(c) The number of times $\Gamma_{n,\{\lambda\}}$ occurs as a component of Γ_n is $d_{\{n\}}$.

(d) The nth Kronecker power $GL_n(2,C)$ of $GL(2,C)$ has the decomposition

$$GL_n(2,C) \cdot\!\equiv\!\cdot \sum_{s=\frac{1}{2}n-[\frac{1}{2}n]}^{\frac{1}{2}n} c_n^s \Gamma_{n,s}$$

$$\text{where } c_n^s = \binom{n}{\frac{1}{2}n - s} - \binom{n}{\frac{1}{2}n - s - 1}$$

$\Gamma_{n,s} =$ the $\{\lambda\}$ — symmetrized power of $GL(2,C)$, where $\{\lambda\}$ is the binary partition $n = (\frac{1}{2}n + s) + (\frac{1}{2}n - s)$ of n.

$\dim \Gamma_{n,s} = 2s + 1.$

(e) If $s \geqslant r$ then, see (d),

$$\Gamma_{m,r} \otimes \Gamma_{n,s} \cdot\!\equiv\!\cdot \sum_{j=0}^{2r} \Gamma_{m+n,r+s-j}.$$

This is a generalized Clebsch-Gordan expansion.

(f) The character $\chi^{n,\{\lambda\}}$ of $\Gamma_{n,\{\lambda\}}$ is the S-function $S_{n,\{\lambda\}}(x_1,\ldots,x_d)$, where $x_1,\ldots,x_d$ are the eigenvalues of the matrix D of $GL(d,C)$ for which the character $\chi^{n,\{\lambda\}}$ is being evaluated.

(19) The space of nth rank tensors of $GL(d,C)$ can be considered as a carrier space of $GL(d,C) \times \mathscr{S}(n)$ in the following way. Let $v_1,\ldots,v_n$ be

n d-dimensional vectors; $T = v_1 \otimes v_2 \otimes \dots \otimes v_n$ an nth rank tensor; D a matrix of $GL(d,C)$; and P a permutation of $\mathcal{S}(n)$. Then by definition

$$(D,P)T \equiv P[(Dv_1) \otimes (Dv_2) \otimes \dots \otimes (Dv_n)],$$

where the P on the right side operates on the subscripts of the v's. In general then

$$[(D,P)T]_{i_1\dots i_n} = P \sum_{j_1,\dots,j_n} D_{i_1j_1} D_{i_2j_2} \dots D_{i_nj_n} T_{j_1\dots j_n},$$

where P operates on the subscripts of the i-indices of the D's.

(20) Consider those invariant subspaces of the space of nth rank tensors of $GL(d,C)$ which generate the irreducible representation $\Gamma_{n,\{\lambda\}}$ of $GL(d,C)$ The subspace of all these subspaces generates the irreducible representation $\Gamma_{n,\{\lambda\}} \times \Gamma_{\{\lambda\}}$ of $GL(d,C) \times \mathcal{S}(n)$ If, then, Γ is the representation of $GL(d,C) \times \mathcal{S}(n)$ generated by the space of nth rank tensors of $GL(d,C)$ as described in (19), we have

$$\Gamma \cdot\equiv\cdot \sum_{\{\lambda\}} \Gamma_{n,\{\lambda\}} \times \Gamma_{\{\lambda\}}$$

where the sum is over all d-ary partitions $\{\lambda\}$ of n.

(21) An n-dimensional representation of $\mathcal{S}(n)$ will now be constructed. Let P be a permutation of $\mathcal{S}(n)$, and $\mathbf{v}_1,\dots,\mathbf{v}_n$ a set of basis vectors of an n-dimensional vector space. The matrix $D(P)$ is defined as follows. Let P operate on the subscripts of the basis vectors so that $P\mathbf{v}_i = \mathbf{v}_{i'(i)}$. Then $D_{j,i} \equiv \delta_{j,i'(i)}$. The representation is $P \to D(P)$. (It will be noted that it was not necessary for the $\mathbf{v}$'s to be vectors.)

(22) Let χ be the character of the n-dimensional representation of $\mathcal{S}(n)$ described in (21). If P is a permutation of $\mathcal{S}(n)$ leaving exactly r basis vectors fixed, then $\chi(P) = r$.

(23) From (37) of Section 1 we see that the preceding n-dimensional representation of $\mathcal{S}(n)$ is reducible into the trivial representation and into an irreducible $(n-1)$-dimensional representation which belongs to the binary partition $\{n-1, 1\}$.

(24) A 2^n-dimensional representation of $\mathcal{S}(n)$ will now be constructed. Consider the following set of 2^n monomials in the n variables $s_1, s_2, \dots, s_n$:

1

$s_1, s_2, \dots, s_n$

$s_1 s_2, s_1 s_3, \dots, s_1 s_n, s_2 s_3, \dots, s_2 s_n, \dots, s_{n-1} s_n$

.

.

.

$s_1 s_2 s_3 \dots s_n.$

The jth row (numbering from zero) contains $\binom{n}{j}$ monomials of degree j. If P is a permutation of $\mathcal{S}(n)$, and if P operates on the subscripts of the

s's in a monomial, then P times any monomial is another monomial in the same row. Hence each row generates a representation of $\mathscr{S}(n)$. Let the representation generated by the jth row be denoted by $\Gamma\left[\binom{n}{j}\right]$ so that $\dim \Gamma\left[\binom{n}{j}\right] = \binom{n}{j}$. Then $\Gamma\left[\binom{n}{1}\right]$ is the n-dimensional representation of $\mathscr{S}(n)$ described in (21). Let us denote the 2^n:dimensional representation of $\mathscr{S}(n)$ generated by all 2^n monomials by $\Gamma(2^n)$. Then $\Gamma(2^n) \cdot\!\equiv\!\cdot \sum_{j=0}^{n} \Gamma\left[\binom{n}{j}\right]$.

(25)
$$\Gamma\left[\binom{n}{j}\right] \cdot\!\equiv\!\cdot \Gamma\left[\binom{n}{j-1}\right] + \Gamma_j \qquad j \leqslant \tfrac{1}{2}n,$$

where Γ_j is the irreducible representation of $\mathscr{S}(n)$ associated with the binary. partition $\{n - j, j\}$. Also

$$\Gamma\left[\binom{n}{n-j}\right] \cdot\!\equiv\!\cdot \Gamma\left[\binom{n}{j}\right] \qquad j \leqslant \tfrac{1}{2}n.$$

(26) If P has the cycle structure $(\alpha_1(P), \alpha_2(P), \ldots, \alpha_n(P))$, and if $\chi^{(2^n)}$ is the character of $\Gamma(2^n)$, then

$$\chi^{(2^n)}(P) = 2^{\alpha_1+\alpha_2+\ldots+\alpha_n}.$$

(27)
$$\Gamma(2^n) \cdot\!\equiv\!\cdot \sum_{j-0}^{[\frac{1}{2}n]} c_{nj}\Gamma_j$$

where

$$c_{nj} = n - 2j + 1$$

Thus $\Gamma(2^n)$ is completely reducible into irreducible representations associated with binary partitions.

(28) The total number of irreducible components of $\Gamma(2^n)$ is

$$\sum_{j=0}^{[\frac{1}{2}n]} c_{nj} = \frac{(n+2)^2}{4} \quad \text{if } n \text{ is even}$$

$$= \frac{(n+1)(n+3)}{4} \quad \text{if } n \text{ is odd.}$$

4. Construction of Irreducible Representations of the Symmetric Groups

In this section a recipe for constructing one particular form of the irreducible representations of $\mathscr{S}(n)$ will be given.* This particular form is called the orthogonal seminormal representation, and its construction is based on the use of graphs

* For a complete derivation see Thrall, R. M., Young's semi-normal representation of the symmetric group, *Duke Math. J.* 8, 611 (1941).

In this section we shall generalize slightly the term "graph." If $\{\lambda\}$ is a partition of n

$$n = \lambda_1 + \lambda_2 + \dots + \lambda_\rho \qquad \lambda_1 \geqslant \lambda_2 \geqslant \dots \geqslant \lambda_\rho > 0,$$

then a graph will again consist of an array of n squares with λ_1 squares in the first row, λ_2 in the second, etc. However, we will no longer require the numbers 1 to n to be filled in in order (from left to right and top to bottom). We will now permit any filling-in of the numbers 1 to n such that

(1) in any row the numbers increase from left to right

(2) in any column the numbers increase from top to bottom.

Corresponding to every partition $\{\lambda\}$ of n there will now be several graphs. The number of graphs belonging to a given partition $\{\lambda\}$ is in fact $d_{\{\lambda\}}$.

Let us now introduce some convenient symbolism. Let $\mathcal{G}(ij)$ denote the jth graph belonging to the ith partition of n. These $d_{\{\lambda\}}$ graphs will be numbered from 1 to $d_{\{\lambda\}}$ as follows, $\mathcal{G}(ij)$ will precede $\mathcal{G}(ik)$ if the squares containing $n, n-1, \dots, n-l+1$ lie in the same row in each graph, but the square in $\mathcal{G}(ij)$ containing $n-l$ lies in a lower row than the square in $\mathcal{G}(ik)$ containing $n-l$. Also, let t_r be a transposition of the $(r-1)$-th and rth symbols; and $D^{(i)}_{jk}(t_r)$ the element of $D^{(i)}(t_r)$ in the jth row and kth column (i here denotes the irreducible representation belonging to the ith partition of n).

The recipe is that $D^{(i)}_{jk}(t_r)$ is zero except in the following cases.

(1) $D^{(i)}_{jj}(t_r) = 1$ if $r-1$ and r are in the same row of $\mathcal{G}(ij)$
$= -1$ if $r-1$ and r are in the same column of $\mathcal{G}(ij)$.

(2) Suppose $\mathcal{G}(ij)$ has $r-1$ in position (α, β) and r in position (γ, δ), where $\alpha \neq \gamma, \beta \neq \delta$ and the coordinates are the numbers of the row and column. Also, suppose $\mathcal{G}(ij)$ and $\mathcal{G}(ik)$ differ only by the interchange of $r-1$ and r. Then

$$\begin{pmatrix} D^{(i)}_{jj}(t_r) & D^{(i)}_{jk}(t_r) \\ D^{(i)}_{kj}(t_r) & D^{(i)}_{kk}(t_r) \end{pmatrix} = \begin{pmatrix} -\rho & \sqrt{1-\rho^2} \\ \sqrt{1-\rho^2} & \rho \end{pmatrix}$$

where

$$\rho = -\frac{1}{\alpha - \beta - \gamma + \delta}.$$

We now know how to construct the matrices representing transpositions of adjacent elements. Since every permutation of $\mathcal{S}(n)$ can be expressed as a product of such transpositions, the entire representation can be constructed.

The irreducible representations constructed according to the above recipe are orthogonal.

BIBLIOGRAPHY

Boerner, H. (1955). "Representations of Groups." Springer-Verlag, Berlin.

Dehn, E. (1930). "Algebraic Equations." Columbia Univ. Press, New York.

Garnir, H. (1950). Theory of Linear Representations of Symmetric Groups. Ph.D. Dissertation. Univ. of Liege, Liege, Belgium.

Littlewood, D. E. (1950). "The Theory of Group Characters." Oxford Univ. Press, London and New York.

Manning, Wm. A. (1921). "Primitive Groups". Stanford University Press, Palo Alto.

Molenaar, P. G. (1930). Finite Substitution Groups. Ph.D. Dissertation.

Murnaghan, F. D. (1938). "The Theory of Group Representations." Johns Hopkins Press, Baltimore, Maryland.

Netto, E. (1892). "The Theory of Substitutions." George Wahr, Ann Arbor, Mich.

Piccard, S. (1946). "On the Bases of the Symmetric Group." Librairie Vuibert, Paris.

Rutherford, D. E. (1948). "Substitutional Analysis." Edinburgh Univ. Press. Edinburgh, Scotland.

Schur, J. (1936). "The Algebraic Foundations of the Representation Theory of Groups." Gebr. Frey & Kratz, Zürich.

Chapter VIII

APPLICATIONS

In this chapter some applications of the symmetric groups to the theory of atomic, molecular, and nuclear structures will be discussed. The physical reason for the importance of the symmetric groups is the Pauli exclusion principle, which states that the wave function of an N-electron system must be totally antisymmetric. Thus if $\psi(\mathbf{r}_1, s_1; \mathbf{r}_2, s_2; ... \mathbf{r}_N, s_N; t)$ is the wave function of an N-electron system, where $\mathbf{r}_j$ is the coordinate vector of the jth electron, and s_j is the spin coordinate of the jth electron $(s_j = \pm 1)$, and if P is any permutation of the symmetric group $\mathscr{S}(N)$ of degree N, then

$$P\psi(\mathbf{r}_1, s_1; \mathbf{r}_2, s_2; ... \mathbf{r}_N, s_N; t) = \sigma(P)\psi(\mathbf{r}_1, s_1; \mathbf{r}_2, s_2; ...; \mathbf{r}_N, s_N; t)$$

where P operates on the set of $\mathbf{r}, s$ subscripts, and $\sigma(P)$ is the signature of P. By saying P operates on the set of $\mathbf{r}, s$ subscripts we mean that P permutes the arguments of ψ in $\mathbf{r}, s$ pairs, or more briefly P permutes the electrons.

The Pauli exclusion principle also applies to neutrons and protons. It is convenient to lump both neutrons and protons under the single term nucleon. With each nucleon one then associates a third variable t (not time) which is $+1/2$ if the nucleon is a proton and $-1/2$ if the nucleon is a neutron. The value of t is called the isotopic spin of the nucleon. For an N-nucleon system the Pauli exclusion principle reads

$$P\psi(\mathbf{r}_1, s_1, t_1; ...; \mathbf{r}_N, s_N, t_N; t) = \sigma(P)\psi(\mathbf{r}_1, s_1, t_1; ...; \mathbf{r}_N, s_N, t_N; t),$$

where P now interchanges one triplet of arguments with another.

In passing we might note that the Pauli exclusion principle applies to all elementary particles with half-odd-integer spin. Particles obeying the Pauli exclusion principle are collectively termed fermions. All others are bosons.

1. Permutation Degeneracy and the Pauli Exclusion Principle

Let us consider an N-electron system and denote the space-spin coordinates of the jth electron simply by j so that a time-independent wave function is denoted by $\phi(1, 2, ..., N)$. Let us consider an energy eigenvector $\phi(1, 2, ..., N)$ belonging to the energy level E so that

$$H\phi(1, 2, ..., N) = E\phi(1, 2, ..., N). \tag{8:1.1}$$

Since electrons are indistinguishable from one another the Hamiltonian must be invariant under electron interchange. Hence, if P is any permutation of $\mathscr{S}(N)$, then

$$H[P\phi(1, 2, ..., N)] = E[P\phi(1, 2, ..., N)]. \tag{8:1.2}$$

Thus we see that if $\phi(1, 2, \ldots, N)$ is an energy eigenfunction belonging to energy E so is $P\phi(1, 2, \ldots, N)$.

Let us now consider an energy level E whose only degeneracy is permutation degeneracy. By this we mean that there is some energy eigenfunction $\phi(1, 2, \ldots, N)$ belonging to E such that the set of energy eigenfunctions $\{P\phi(1, 2, \ldots, N)\}$, for all P in $\mathscr{S}(N)$, is a complete set of energy eigenfunctions for the level E.

So far we have completely ignored the Pauli principle. Let us now determine the number of linearly independent energy eigenfunctions which belong to an energy level E with no degeneracy other than permutation degeneracy and which satisfy the Pauli principle.

To do this let us first consider the representation Γ of $\mathscr{S}(N)$ generated by the complete set of $N!$ degenerate energy eigenfunctions $\{P\phi(1, 2, \ldots, N)\}$, for all $P \epsilon \mathscr{S}(N)$. If $\phi(1, 2, \ldots, N)$ possesses any permutational symmetry it is to be ignored in generating Γ. The character of P_0 in this $N!$-dimensional representation Γ is easily seen to be equal to the number of functions $P\phi(1, 2, \ldots, N)$ left invariant by P_0. This number is zero unless $P_0 = I$ in which case it is $N!$ Hence the character of Γ is $\chi = (N!, 0, 0, \ldots, 0)$, and we see that Γ is the regular representation of $\mathscr{S}(N)$.

Now suppose $\phi_\sigma(1, 2, \ldots, N)$ is an energy eigenfunction belonging to E and satisfying the Pauli principle. Then $\phi_\sigma(1, 2, \ldots, N)$ must be a linear combination of the $N!$ eigenvectors $\{P\phi(1, 2, \ldots, N)\}$, and it must satisfy the equation

$$P\phi_\sigma(1, 2, \ldots, N) = \sigma(P)\phi_\sigma(1, 2, \ldots, N), \tag{8:1.3}$$

which says that $\phi_\sigma(1, 2, \ldots, N)$ generates the alternating representation Γ_σ of $\mathscr{S}(N)$.

Let us now perform a nonsingular linear transformation on the $N!$ functions $\{P\phi(1, 2, \ldots, N)\}$ in the following way. First let us choose a complete linearly independent subset of $\{P\phi(1, 2, \ldots, N)\}$ and perform a nonsingular linear transformation on this subset such that the transformed subset contains all linearly independent antisymmetric eigenfunctions $\phi_\sigma(1, 2, \ldots, N)$. The remaining dependent eigenfunctions are to be transformed into themselves. The number of times the alternating representation occurs as a component of the representation generated by the transformed functions is seen to be greater than or equal to the number of linearly independent antisymmetric energy eigenfunctions $\phi_\sigma(1, 2, \ldots, N)$. But the transformed functions still generate the regular representation which we know contains the alternating representation Γ_σ exactly once. Hence we can conclude that there is at most one energy eigenfunction belonging to E and satisfying the Pauli exclusion principle.

If a basis of the eigenmanifold is known, the antisymmetric eigenfunction $\phi_\sigma(1, 2, \ldots, N)$ can be constructed with the aid of the Young symmetrizer (really antisymmetrizer) $Y_{\{1^N\}} = \sum_{P' \epsilon \mathscr{S}(N)} \sigma(P')P'$. This Young operator has the property

$$PY_{\{1^N\}} = P \sum_{P'} \sigma(P')P' = \sum_{P'} \sigma(P')PP' = \sigma(P) \sum_{P'} \sigma(P)\sigma(P')PP'$$
$$= \sigma(P) \sum_{P'} \sigma(PP')PP' = \sigma(P) \sum_{P'} \sigma(P')P' = \sigma(P)Y_{\{1^N\}}.$$

Therefore if $\phi(1, 2,..., N)$ is any wave function, then the function $Y_{\{1^N\}}\,\phi(1, 2,..., N)$, where $Y_{\{1^N\}}$ operates on the arguments $1, 2,..., N$, is antisymmetric.

$$PY_{\{1^N\}}\phi(1, 2,..., N) = \sigma(P)Y_{\{1^N\}}\phi(1, 2,..., N).$$

The product $Y_{\{1^N\}}\,\phi$ may of course be zero.

2. Atomic Structure

The structure of an atom is quite independent of any calculational methods used by physicists to investigate it, but the picture a physicist forms of an atom may depend very strongly on the calculational method he uses. The two main perturbation approximations used in atomic theory are the *LS* coupling scheme and the *jj* coupling scheme.

In both the *LS* and the *jj* coupling schemes there are three stages of approximation. In the first stage of both, the electrons are assumed to move independently of each other in a central field (such as a Hartree field). In the second stage of the *LS* coupling scheme, the electron-electron Coulomb interaction is added to the Hamiltonian, and in the third stage the spin-orbit interaction is added to the Hamiltonian. By spin-orbit interaction we mean the energy due to the interaction of the intrinsic magnetic moment of the electron with its magnetic field due to its orbital motion. In the second stage of the *jj* coupling scheme the spin-orbit interaction is added to the Hamiltonian, and in the third stage the electron-electron coulomb interaction is added to the Hamiltonian. In brief then, when the *LS* coupling scheme is used, the electron-electron interaction is assumed to be large compared to the spin-orbit interaction, and when the *jj* coupling scheme is used the reverse is assumed to be true. In both cases the central field is assumed to be of primary importance.

Here we shall investigate the *LS* coupling scheme according to the following procedure. First we shall find the function space in which the energy eigenvectors must lie. Second we shall find the symmetry group of the Hamiltonian. Third we shall find the irreducible representation of the symmetry group which the energy eigenvectors can generate. Actually this order will not be adhered to strictly.

A. The Central Field Approximation

$$H_0 = -\frac{\hbar^2}{2m}\sum_{j=1}^{N}\nabla_j^2 - e\sum_{j=1}^{N}V(|\mathbf{r}_j|) \tag{8:2.1}$$

The N orbital electrons are assumed to move in a common central potential $V(|\mathbf{r}|)$ which may be taken to be the Coulomb field of the nucleus or may be taken to be a Hartree field. Although the Hamiltonian contains no spin terms, the wave function nonetheless must contain spin coordinates. An energy eigenvector is therefore a function of the following independent variables $\phi = \phi(\mathbf{r}_1, s_1; \mathbf{r}_2, s_2; \ldots; \mathbf{r}_N, s_N)$.

Let us now determine the symmetry group of the Hamiltonian. First we observe that a rotation of any one of the coordinate vectors will leave H_0 invariant. Hence, if all the coordinate vectors are simultaneously rotated by different rotations, the Hamiltonian will be left invariant. In fact, the coordinate vectors can be simultaneously transformed by different orthogonal transformations and the Hamiltonian will still be left invariant.

Next we see that any permutation of the coordinate vectors will leave H_0 invariant.

Now we come to the symmetry of H_0 with respect to spin transformations. Lince H_0 contains no spin terms it is invariant with respect to any kind of spin transformation. Thus, for example, H_0 is invariant under the irreducible group of linear transformations $GL(2^N, C)$ in the 2^N-dimensional spin space.

Let us now return to the spatial symmetry of H_0. We see that H_0 is invariant under the group of all transformations consisting of any product of coordinate rotation operators (or orthogonal transformations) and coordinate permutation operators. If we call this group $G_0(S)$ then the total symmetry group G_0 of H_0 is

$$G_0 = G_0(S) \times GL(2^N, C). \tag{8:2.2}$$

Unfortunately the irreducible representations of $G_0(S)$ are not known. Consequently we cannot perform a straightforward group-theoretic analysis of this problem.

If we ignore the permutational symmetry we get a subgroup of $G_0(S)$ which is tractable. This subgroup is $O_1(3) \times O_2(3) \times \ldots \times O_N(3)$, where $O_j(3)$ is the group of orthogonal transformations of $\mathbf{r}_j$. This subgroup of $G_0(S)$ yields the following subgroup of G_0 as a total symmetry subgroup

$$G_{00} = O_1(3) \times O_2(3) \times \ldots \times O_N(3) \times GL(2^N, C). \tag{8:2.3}$$

A typical irreducible representation of G_{00} is

$$\Gamma_{00} = \Gamma_{l_1} \times \Gamma_{l_2} \times \ldots \times \Gamma_{l_N} \times GL(2^N, C), \tag{8:2.4}$$

where Γ_l is a $(2l + 1)$-dimensional representation of $O(3)$. The dimension d_{00} of Γ_{00} is therefore

$$d_{00} = (2l_1 + 1)(2l_2 + 1)\ldots(2l_N + 1)2^N. \tag{8:2.5}$$

If there were no permutational degeneracy then these dimensions d_{00} would also be the possible degeneracies of the energy levels of H_0.

Let us now briefly consider this problem from the more conventional point of view. First, we observe that the Hamiltonian H_0 (8:2.1) can be written as a sum of 1-electron central field Hamiltonians. We can therefore express each wave function of a complete set as a product of 1-electron central field wave functions. By separation of variables we know that a 1-electron central field wave function can be written in spherical coordinates in the form

$$\phi_{n,l,m}(\mathbf{r}) = f_{nl}(|\mathbf{r}|) Y_{lm}(\theta, \phi) \tag{8:2.6}$$

where $f_{nl}(r)$ satisfies the radial wave equation

$$\left[-\frac{\hbar^2}{2m} \frac{1}{r^2} \frac{d}{dr} r^2 \frac{d}{dr} + V(|\mathbf{r}|) + \frac{\hbar^2}{2m} \frac{l(l+1)}{r^2} - E \right] f_{n,l}(r) = 0. \tag{8:2.7}$$

The 1-electron energy depends on the principal quantum number n and on the angular momentum (or azimuthal) quantum number l, but not on the magnetic quantum number m. These quantum numbers have the following ranges of values

$$\begin{aligned} n &= 1, 2, 3, 4, \ldots, \infty \\ l &= 0, 1, 2, \ldots, n-1 \\ m &= -l, -l+1, \ldots, l. \end{aligned} \tag{8:2.8}$$

A complete set of N-electron central field wave functions can now be written in the form

$$\begin{aligned} \phi(\mathbf{r}_1, s_1; \mathbf{r}_2, s_2; \ldots; \mathbf{r}_N, s_N) = \phi_{n_1, l_1, m_1}(\mathbf{r}_1) \phi_{n_2, l_2, m_2}(\mathbf{r}_2) \ldots \\ \phi_{n_N l_N m_N}(\mathbf{r}_N) f_k(s_1, s_2; \ldots; s_N) \end{aligned} \tag{8:2.9}$$

where the spin functions $f_k(s_1, s_2, \ldots, s_N)$ are to be taken to be any complete set of 2^N functions. An N-electron energy level is specified by the set of n, l-values $(n_1, l_1; n_2, l_2; \ldots; n_N, l_N)$, which is also called a configuration. The degeneracy of such a level is easily seen to be $(2l_1 + 1)(2l_2 + 1) \ldots (2l_N + 1)2^N$ if interchange of electrons is not considered to lead to different states.

So far the Pauli exclusion principle has been assiduously ignored. We can, however, very easily find the number of linearly independent antisymmetric N-electron states belonging to a given configuration by elementary considerations. Suppose the number of electrons having the quantum numbers n, l is $\mathcal{N}(n, l)$. The number of 1-electron states having the quantum numbers n, l is $2(2l + 1)$, and the number of ways of putting $\mathcal{N}(n, l)$ electrons in them (without regard to order) without putting two electrons in any 1-electron state is

$$\binom{2(2l+1)}{\mathcal{N}(n, l)}.$$

Hence, the number $\mathcal{N}$ of N-electron states belonging to a given configuration is

$$\mathcal{N} = \prod_{n=1}^{\infty} \prod_{l=0}^{n-1} \binom{2(2l+1)}{\mathcal{N}(n,l)}. \tag{8:2.10}$$

B. LS Coupling

1. Electron-Electron Approximation

$$H_{e\text{-}e} = H_0 + \frac{e^2}{2} \sum_{i=j} \frac{1}{|\mathbf{r}_i - \mathbf{r}_j|} \tag{8:2.11}$$

Because of the added electron-electron Coulomb interaction term this Hamiltonian has less symmetry than H_0. The added term, in fact, is not invariant under a transformation which rotates $\mathbf{r}_i$ and $\mathbf{r}_j$ differently. Hence, for the symmetry group of $H_{e\text{-}e}$ we can take the group

$$G_{e\text{-}e} = [O_1(3) \otimes O_2(3) \otimes \ldots \otimes O_N(3)] \times \mathscr{S}_S(N) \times GL(2^N, C) \tag{8:2.12}$$

where by $O_i \otimes O_j$ we mean that $\mathbf{r}_i$ and $\mathbf{r}_j$ are transformed by the same orthogonal transformation, and by $\mathscr{S}_S(N)$ we mean the group of permutations of coordinate vectors. The group $O_1(3) \otimes O_2(3) \otimes \ldots \otimes O_N(3)$ is of course isomorphic to the single orthogonal group $O(3)$. The symmetry group $G_{e\text{-}e}$ is therefore isomorphic to the group $O(3) \times \mathscr{S}(N) \times GL(2_N, C)$.

A typical irreducible representation of $G_{e\text{-}e}$ is

$$\Gamma_{e\text{-}e} = \Gamma_L \times \Gamma_{\{\lambda\}} \times GL(2^N, C), \tag{8:2.13}$$

where $\{\lambda\}$ is a partition of N, and Γ_L is an irreducible $(2L + 1)$-dimensional representation of $O(3)$. The parity of Γ_L will not be important here and is therefore left unspecified. The dimension of $\Gamma_{e\text{-}e}$ is

$$d_{e\text{-}e} = (2L + 1) \times d_{\{\lambda\}} \times 2^N. \tag{8:2.14}$$

We see from (8:2.13) that energy levels depend on L but not on spin.

Let us now impose the Pauli principle. This means that we want to consider only wave functions which generate the alternating representation of the group $\mathscr{S}_S(N) \otimes \mathscr{S}_\Sigma(N)$, where S means spatial permutations and $\sum$ means spin permutation.

The Pauli principle, as we shall now see, has an unexpected consequence. It forces us to consider a smaller symmetry group. This follows from the fact that a function which is antisymmetric to begin with will not be antisymmetric after a spin transformation of the form $D_1 \times D_2 \times \ldots \times D_N$, where each matrix D is 2-dimensional and different from the other D's. Consequently, let us consider the following smaller symmetry group

$$G_{e\text{-}e}^{(P} = [O_1(3) \otimes \ldots \otimes O_N(3)] \times [GL_1(2,C) \otimes \ldots \otimes GL_N(2,C)] \times [\mathscr{S}_S(N) \otimes \mathscr{S}_\Sigma(N)], \tag{8:2.15}$$

which is isomorphic to $O(3) \times GL(2, C) \times \mathscr{S}(N)$. A typical irreducible representation of $G_{e-e}^{(P)}$ which subduces the alternating representation of $\mathscr{S}_S(N) \otimes \mathscr{S}_\Sigma(N)$ is

$$\Gamma^{(P)}_{e\text{-}e} = \Gamma_L \times \Gamma_S \times \Gamma_\sigma, \tag{8:2.16}$$

where Γ_L is an irreducible $(2L + 1)$-dimensional irreducible representation of $O(3)$, and Γ_S is the $(2S + 1)$-dimensional irreducible representation of $GL(2, C)$ generated by the independent components of the 2-dimensional tensor $Y_{\{\frac{1}{2}n+S,\frac{1}{2}n-S\}}\, T_{i_1\ldots i_N}$. This type of irreducible representation of $GL(2, C)$ is typical because the Nth inner Kronecker power of $GL(2, C)$ is being reduced to get (8:2.16) (see (8:2.26)). The dimension of $\Gamma^{(P)}_{e\text{-}e}$ is

$$d^{(P)}_{e\text{-}e} = (2L + 1)(2S + 1). \tag{8:2.17}$$

A set of $(2L + 1)(2S + 1)$ linearly independent, antisymmetric, degenerate, N-electron, atomic wave functions generating such an irreducible representation of $G^{(P)}_{e\text{-}e}$ is called a term and is specified by the symbol ${}^{2S+1}L$. Terms arising from the same configuration and having the same value of L must, according to (8:2.13), have the same energy.

A detailed consideration of the 3-dimensional rotation group shows that L is the total orbital angular momentum quantum number of each such wave function, and that S is the total spin angular momentum quantum number of each such wave function.

Let us look at this stage of approximation from a perturbation-theoretic point of view. We can consider the exact energy eigenfunctions of $H_{e\text{-}e}$ (8:2.11) to be obtained from some exact energy eigenfunctions of H_0 (8:2.1) by a small perturbation which does not change the symmetry. In other words the correct zero-order eigenfunctions generate an irreducible representation of $G_{e\text{-}e}$ (or of $G^{(P)}_{e\text{-}e}$ if the Pauli principle is to be used).

2. Spin-Orbit Approximation

$$H_{s\text{-}o} = H_{e\text{-}e} + \frac{\hbar}{4m^2c^2} \sum_{j=1}^{N} \frac{1}{r_j} \frac{dV(r_j)}{dr_j}\, \mathbf{L}_j \cdot \boldsymbol{\sigma}_j \tag{8:2.18}$$

where

$$\mathbf{L}_j = -i\hbar \mathbf{r}_j \times \boldsymbol{\nabla}_j, \tag{8:2.19}$$

$\boldsymbol{\sigma}_j$ is the Pauli spin vector operator for the jth electron, and $V(r)$ is the Hartree central field.

The symmetry group of $H_{s\text{-}o}$ is still smaller than that of $H_{e\text{-}e}$ and is easily seen to be

$$G^{(P)}_{s\text{-}o} = \{[R_1(3) \otimes U_1(2)] \otimes [R_2(3) \otimes U_2(2)] \otimes \ldots \otimes [R_N(3) \otimes U_N(2)]\}\ [\mathscr{S}_S(N) \otimes \mathscr{S}_\Sigma(N)] \tag{8:2.20}$$

where $U(2)$ is the 2-dimensional unitary unimodular representation of $R(3)$ and where all coordinate vectors and spin vectors are subjected to the same rotation. This is necessary to preserve the invariance of the $\mathbf{L}\cdot\boldsymbol{\sigma}$ terms in $H_{s\text{-}o}$. The group $G^{(P)}_{s\text{-}o}$ is isomorphic to $R(3) \times \mathscr{S}(N)$.

The representation ($\Gamma_L \times \Gamma_S \times \Gamma^{(s)}_\sigma$ of $G_{s\text{-}o}$) subduced by the irreducible representation $\Gamma_L \times \Gamma_S \times \Gamma_\sigma$ of $G_{e\text{-}e}$ is reducible. The Clebsch-Gordan series gives us

$$(\Gamma_L \times \Gamma_S \times \Gamma_\sigma)_{(S)} = (\Gamma_L \otimes \Gamma_S) \times \Gamma_\sigma = \left(\sum_{J=|L-S|}^{|L+S|} \Gamma_J \right) \times \Gamma_\sigma \qquad (8:2.21)$$
$$= \sum_{J=|L-S|}^{|L+S|} \Gamma_J \times \Gamma_\sigma.$$

The irreducible representation $\Gamma_J \times \Gamma_\sigma$ of $G^{(P)}_{s\text{-}o}$ has dimension $2J + 1$. A set of $2J + 1$ linearly independent, antisymmetric, degenerate, N-electron, atomic-wave functions generating such a representation of $G^{(P)}_{s\text{-}o}$ is called a multiplet level and is specified by the symbol ${}^{2S+1}L_J$.

From the expansion (8:2.21) we see that spin-orbit coupling splits a term into $2S + 1$ multiplet levels if $S \geqslant L$ and into $2L + 1$ multiplet levels if $S \leqslant L$.

Consideration of the rotation group shows that J is the total angular momentum quantum number.

3. The Terms Arising from a Configuration

Let us consider the space S_c of N-electron atomic energy eigenfunctions belonging to the N-electron configuration $(n_1, l_1; n_2, l_2; \ldots; n_N, l_N)$. This function space will generate a representation Γ_c of the symmetry group G_0 of H_0, and therefore of the symmetry group $G^{(P)}_{e\text{-}e} = O(3) \times \mathcal{S}(N) \times GL(2,C)$ of $H_{e\text{-}e}$ which is a subgroup of G_0. In terms of operators, $G^{(P)}_{e\text{-}e}$ is

$$G^{(P)}_{e\text{-}e} = [O_1(3) \otimes \ldots \otimes O_N(3)] \times [GL_1(2,C) \otimes \ldots \otimes GL_N(2,C)] \times [\mathcal{S}_S(N) \otimes \mathcal{S}_\Sigma(N)]. \qquad (8:2.22)$$

A term is a basis of a subspace of S_c which generates an irreducible representation of $G^{(P)}_{e-e}$ of the form $\Gamma_L \times \Gamma_S \times \Gamma_\sigma$.

Therefore, to find the terms contained in S_c we want to decompose S_c into subspaces which are invariant under $G^{(P)}_{e-e}$; i.e., we want to reduce the representation $\Gamma^{(s)}_c$ of $G^{(P)}_{e-e}$ which is generated by S_c. The problem is thus to find $\Gamma^{(s)}_c$ and to reduce it.

Part of the finding and reducing of $\Gamma^{(s)}_c$ can be carried out in complete generality. Let $\sum$ be the 2^N-dimensional space of spin vectors and let S be the space of all spin-independent, N-electron atomic energy eigenfunctions belonging to the configuration $(n_1, l_1; n_2, l_2; \ldots; n_N, l_N)$. Then $S_c = S \times \sum$. Also, let us consider the groups

$$G_S = [O_1(3) \otimes \ldots \otimes O_N(3)] \times \mathcal{S}_S(N) \qquad (8:2.23)$$
$$G_\Sigma = [GL_1(2,C) \otimes \ldots \otimes GL_N(2,C)] \times \mathcal{S}_\Sigma(N) \qquad (8:2.24)$$
$$G_{S,\Sigma} = G_S \times G_\Sigma \qquad (8:2.25)$$

We see that $G^{(P)}_{e-e}$ is a subgroup of $G_{S,\Sigma}$ that S generates a representation of G_S, and that $\sum$ generates a representation of G_Σ.

We know from Chapter VII, Section 3, item (18) what the representation of G_Σ generated by $\sum$ is in terms of irreducible representations of $GL(2,C)$ and $\mathscr{S}(N)$. Let $N = (\frac{1}{2}N + S) + (\frac{1}{2}N - S)$ be a binary partition of N in which S is an integer or half-odd-integer, according as N is even or odd. Let $\Gamma_{\frac{1}{2}N-S}$ be the irreducible representation of $\mathscr{S}(N)$ of dimension

$$\binom{N}{\frac{1}{2}N - S} - \binom{N}{\frac{1}{2}N - S - 1}$$

belonging to this binary partition, and let Γ_S be the irreducible $(2S + 1)$-dimensional representation of $GL(2,C)$ generated by the independent components of the tensor $Y_{\{\frac{1}{2}N+S,\, \frac{1}{2}N-S\}}\, T_{i_1,\dots i_N}$. Then the representation of G_Σ generated by $\sum$ is

$$\sum_{S=\frac{1}{2}N-[\frac{1}{2}N]}^{\frac{1}{2}N} \Gamma_S \times \Gamma_{\frac{1}{2}N-S}. \tag{8:2.26}$$

The representation of G_S generated by S will be a direct sum of irreducible representations of the form $\Gamma_L \times \Gamma_{\{\lambda\}}$, where Γ_L is a $(2L + 1)$-dimensional, irreducible representation of $O(3)$, and $\Gamma_{\{\lambda\}}$ is the irreducible representation of $\mathscr{S}(N)$ belonging to the partition $\{\lambda\}$ of N. A typical irreducible component of the representation of $G_{S,\Sigma}$ generated by $S \times \Sigma$ will therefore be of the form

$$\Gamma_L \times \Gamma_{\{\lambda\}} \times \Gamma_S \times \Gamma_{\frac{1}{2}N-S} \tag{8:2.27}$$

This subduces the representation

$$\Gamma_L \times \Gamma_S \times [\Gamma_{\{\lambda\}} \otimes \Gamma_{\frac{1}{2}N-S}] \tag{8:2.28}$$

of $G_{e-e}^{(P)} = O(3) \times GL(2,C) \times \mathscr{S}(N)$. Since we are interested only in eigenfunctions which satisfy the Pauli principle, and which therefore generate the alternating representation Γ_σ of $\mathscr{S}(N)$, we are only interested in irreducible components of (8:2.21) of the form $\Gamma_L \times \Gamma_S \times \Gamma_\sigma$ (see (8:2.16)). The representation $\Gamma_{\{\lambda\}} \otimes \Gamma_{\frac{1}{2}N-S}$ of $\mathscr{S}(N)$ contains Γ_σ as a component exactly once if $\Gamma_{\{\lambda\}} \cdot\!\equiv\!\cdot \bar{\Gamma}_{\frac{1}{2}N-S}$, and not at all otherwise. Therefore, the subspace of $S \times \Sigma$ which generates the irreducible representation $\Gamma_L \times \Gamma_{\{\lambda\}} \times \Gamma_S \times \Gamma_{\frac{1}{2}N-S}$ of $G_{S,\Sigma}$ contains the single term ${}^{2S+1}L$ if $\Gamma_{\{\lambda\}} \cdot\!\equiv\!\cdot \bar{\Gamma}_{\frac{1}{2}N-S}$, and otherwise it contains no terms.

As a result of the preceding considerations we can now simplify the problem of finding the terms arising from a given configuration. We need only determine and decompose the representation of G_S generated by the space S of spatial energy eigenfunctions. Each irreducible component of the form $\Gamma_L \times \bar{\Gamma}_{\frac{1}{2}N-S}$ is generated by the term ${}^{2S+1}L$. The other irreducible components are not generated by terms. Γ_L is an irreducible $(2L + 1)$-dimensional representation of $O(3)$, and $\bar{\Gamma}_{\frac{1}{2}N-S}$ is the associate of the irreducible representation of $\mathscr{S}(N)$ belonging to the binary partition $N = (\frac{1}{2}N + S) + (\frac{1}{2}N - S)$ of N.

Let us consider now the case in which all N electrons have the same n, l-value. A set of basis functions of S can be written in the product form $\phi_{nlm_1}(\mathbf{r}_1)\phi_{nlm_2}(\mathbf{r}_2)\dots\phi_{nlm_N}(\mathbf{r}_N)$. The set of all such product functions transforms as an Nth rank tensor of the $(2l + 1)$-dimensional representation Γ_l of $O(3)$.

Let us consider the space of Nth rank tensors of $GL(2l + 1, C)$. From Chapter VII, Section 3, item (20) we know how this tensor space decomposes into subspaces which generate irreducible representations of $GL(2l+1, C) \times \mathscr{S}(N)$ This decomposition of the tensor space is accomplished by means of Young symmetrizers, and the same decomposition can be applied to the space S when all N electrons have the same n, l-value. The subspaces of S obtained in this way generate representations of $O(3) \times \mathscr{S}(N)$ of the form $\Gamma_{l,\{\lambda\}} \times \Gamma_{\{\lambda\}}$ where $\Gamma_{l,\{\lambda\}}$ is the $\{\lambda\}$-symmetrized power of Γ_l, and $\Gamma_{\{\lambda\}}$ is the irreducible representation of $\mathscr{S}(N)$ belonging to the partition $\{\lambda\}$ of N.

After the decomposition of S and the corresponding partial reduction of the representation of G_S generated by S are performed by means of Young symmetrizers, the representations $\Gamma_{l,\{\lambda\}} \times \Gamma_{\{\lambda\}}$ must still be reduced. Since $\Gamma_{\{\lambda\}}$ is irreducible, only $\Gamma_{l,\{\lambda\}}$ need be reduced. This can be done by computing the character of $\Gamma_{l,\{\lambda\}}$ from Chapter VII, Section 3, item (6) and using the integration-reduction formula of Chapter IV, Section 6, item (12).

Example. $(np)^2 \quad N = 2 \quad l_1 = l_2 = 1$

S is a second rank tensor space of Γ_1 and generates the representation $\Gamma_1 \otimes \Gamma_1$ of $O(3)$. Young symmetrizer reduction yields $\Gamma_1 \otimes \Gamma_1 \cdot\!\equiv\!\cdot \Gamma_{1(2)} \oplus \Gamma_{1[2]}$, where $\Gamma_{1(2)}$ is the symmetrized square of Γ_1 and $\Gamma_{1[2]}$ is the antisymmetrized square of Γ_1. The representation of $G_S = O(3) \times \mathscr{S}(2)$ is $[\Gamma_{1[2]} \times \Gamma_{\text{triv}}] \oplus [\Gamma_{1[2]} \times \Gamma_\sigma]$. The characters of $\Gamma_{1(2)}$ and $\Gamma_{1[2]}$ are $\chi_{1(2)}^{(\theta)} = 2 \cos \theta\, (1 + 2 \cos \theta)$ and $\chi_{1[2]}^{(\theta)} = 1 + 2 \cos \theta$. Thus we see that $\Gamma_{1(2)} = \Gamma_0 \oplus \Gamma_2$ and that $\Gamma_{1[2]} = \Gamma_1$ is irreducible. The representation of G_S generated by S is now found to be

$$[\Gamma_0 \times \Gamma_{\text{triv}}] \oplus [\Gamma_2 \times \Gamma_{\text{triv}}] \oplus [\Gamma_1 \times \Gamma_\sigma].$$

The trivial representation Γ_{triv} is the associate of the representation Γ_σ of $\mathscr{S}(2)$ belonging to the binary partition $2 = (2/2 + 0) + (2/2 - 0)$, so $\Gamma_{\text{triv}} = \bar{\Gamma}_{\frac{1}{2}N-0}$. Similarly $\Gamma_\sigma = \bar{\Gamma}_{\frac{1}{2}N-1}$. Hence, the terms corresponding to the above three irreducible representations of G_S are ${}^1S$, ${}^1D$, ${}^3P$. The letters used here follow the spectroscopic notation

L	0	1	2	3	4	5
L	S	P	D	F	G	H

Therefore we have the following scheme for the terms arising from the configuration $(np)^2$:

$$(np)^2 \to {}^1S + {}^1D + {}^3P.$$

The number of states is $\mathscr{N} = 15$. Similarly one finds

$$(np)^3 \to {}^4S + {}^2P + {}^2D \qquad \mathscr{N} = 20.$$

This method also shows that any closed shell configuration $(nl)^{2(2l+1)}$ must be a ${}^1S$ term. The representation of G_s generated by the space S is

$$\sum_{\{\lambda\}} [\Gamma_l]_{\{\lambda\}} \times \Gamma_{\{\lambda\}}$$

where the sum is over all $(2l + 1)$-ary partitions of $2(2l + 1)$. However, the only $(2l + 1)$-ary partition $\{\lambda\}$ such that $\bar{\Gamma}_{\{\lambda\}}$ belongs to a binary partition is $\{\lambda\} = \{2^{2l+1}\}$. For this partition $\delta_{\{\lambda\}} = 1$ so $[\Gamma_l]_{\{\lambda\}} = \Gamma_{\text{triv}}$ and $L = 0$. Furthermore, $\bar{\Gamma}_{\{\lambda\}} = \Gamma_{2l+1}$ so $S = 0$.

Let us now consider the case in which the electrons do not all have the same n, l-value and work out a particular case.

Example. $(n_1 p)(n_2 p) \quad n_1 \neq n_2 \quad N = 2 \quad l_1 = l_2 = 1$

The set of 18 product functions $\phi_{n_1,1,m_1}(\mathbf{r}_1)\phi_{n_2,1,m_2}(\mathbf{r}_2)$; $m_1, m_2 = -1, 0, 1$; $\phi_{n_1,1,m_1}(\mathbf{r}_2)\phi_{n_2,1,m_2}(\mathbf{r}_1)$; $m_1, m_2 = -1, 0, 1$ forms a basis of S. The basis functions can be written more briefly and conveniently in the form $\phi_{ij,\alpha}(\mathbf{r}_1, \mathbf{r}_2)$, where $i, j = -1, 0, 1$ and $\alpha = 1, 2$. The i and j indices are rotation indices and α is a permutation index. The representation of $G_S = O(3) \times \mathscr{S}(2)$ generated by the 18 basis functions $\phi_{ij,\alpha}(\mathbf{r}_1, \mathbf{r}_2)$ is

$$[\Gamma_1 \otimes \Gamma_1] \times \Gamma_{II},$$

where Γ_1 is a 3-dimensional irreducible representation of $O(3)$ and Γ_{II} is a 2-dimensional representation of $\mathscr{S}(2)$. A little consideration shows that

$$\Gamma_{II} = \Gamma_{\text{triv}} \oplus \Gamma_\sigma$$

so the representation of G_S generated by S is

$$[\Gamma_1 \otimes \Gamma_1] \times [\Gamma_{\text{triv}} \oplus \Gamma_\sigma].$$

Since

$$\Gamma_1 \otimes \Gamma_1 = \Gamma_0 \oplus \Gamma_1 \oplus \Gamma_2$$

we have for the representation of G_s

$$[\Gamma_0 \times \Gamma_{\text{triv}}] \oplus [\Gamma_1 \times \Gamma_{\text{triv}}] \oplus [\Gamma_2 \times \Gamma_{\text{triv}}] \oplus [\Gamma_0 \times \Gamma_\sigma] \oplus [\Gamma_1 \times \Gamma_\sigma] \oplus [\Gamma_2 \times \Gamma_\sigma].$$

We already know from the preceding example that Γ_{triv} corresponds to $S = 0$ and that Γ_σ corresponds to $S = 1$. Therefore, the terms corresponding to the above irreducible components are

$$(n_1 p)(n_2 p) \to {}^1S + {}^1P + {}^1D + {}^3S + {}^3P + {}^3D.$$

The ${}^1S$ and ${}^3S$ terms have the same energy, as do also the terms of pairs ${}^1P$, ${}^3P$ and ${}^1D$, ${}^3D$.

3. Multiplet Splitting in Crystalline Electric Fields

If an atom or ion in a given multiplet level state ${}^{2S+1}L_J$ is placed in a conservative external electric field then its energy will be altered because of the interaction between the orbital electrons and the electric field. We shall consider only the simple case in which the electric field in the neighborhood of the atom has the symmetry of some crystal point group and is so weak that its effect on the energy levels of the atom is small compared to the spin-orbit coupling of the atom. The electric field will thus give rise to an additional perturbation term in the Hamiltonian, and since the electric field is not spherically symmetric it will split the $(2J + 1)$ degenerate levels of the multiplet (14, 118, 120).

The Hamiltonian is now (see 8:2.18)

$$H = H_{S\text{-}O} - e \sum_{i=1}^{N} V_{\text{ext}}(\mathbf{r}_i), \tag{8:3.1}$$

where $V_{\text{ext}}(\mathbf{r})$ is the potential of the external field. The symmetry group $G^{(P)}$ of H is

$$G^{(P)} = \{[P_1(3) \otimes UP_1(2)] \otimes \ldots \otimes [P_N(3) \otimes UP_N(2)]\} \times \\ \times [\mathscr{S}_S(N) \otimes \mathscr{S}_\Sigma(N)] = P \times \mathscr{S}(N), \tag{8:3.2}$$

where P is the point group of the external field, and UP is the spin representation of P (or the double group of P).

To find how the multiplet ${}^{2S+1}L_J$ splits in such a field we need only reduce the representation $(\Gamma_J \times \Gamma_\sigma)^{(s)} = \Gamma_J^{(s)} \times \Gamma_\sigma$ of $G^{(P)} = P \times \mathscr{S}(N)$ which is subduced by the irreducible representation $\Gamma_J \times \Gamma_\sigma$ of $G^{(P)}_{S\text{-}O} = R(3) \times \mathscr{S}(N)$. To perform such a reduction we can utilize the tables of Chapter IV, Sections 4 and 7.

Example $P = D_4$

$J = 2 \qquad \Gamma_2^{(s)} \cdot\!\!\equiv\!\!\cdot\, \Delta_1 \oplus \Delta_3 \oplus \Delta_4 \oplus \Delta_5$

$J = 5/2 \qquad \Gamma_{5/2}^{(s)} \cdot\!\!\equiv\!\!\cdot\, \Delta_6 \oplus 2\Delta_7$

So we see that ${}^{2S+1}L_2$ splits into four levels in an electric field with symmetry D_4, and that ${}^{2S+1}L_{5/2}$ splits into three levels in such a field. The resulting levels can, of course, still be degenerate. Thus the level corresponding to Δ_6 is doubly degenerate.

It should be realized that the symmetry group of the electric field of a crystal at an atomic position need not be the full point group of the crystal. Graphite is one such crystal.

4. Molecular Structure

The method of analysis here (107, 108) will be analogous to that used in Section 2 for atomic structure. We shall, furthermore, consider only the electronic motion and ignore the nuclear motion (the Born-Oppenheimer approximation). Finally, we shall ignore spin-orbit effects throughout. In other words we shall assume that molecular binding energies are large compared to spin-orbit energies.

Let us now consider n free atoms, the jth of which contains N_j electrons, and is in a state of the term ${}^{2S+1}L_j$. Let us further suppose that these atoms can be made to combine with each other to form an n-atomic molecule. Let $\mathbf{R}_j$ be the position vector of the equilibrium position of the nucleus of the jth atom when the atoms are combined in the n-atomic molecule. Also, let H

be the Hamiltonian of the free (noninteracting, noncombining) jth atom when its nucleus is at $\mathbf{R}_j$.

The Hamiltonian of the n-atomic molecule is then

$$H = \sum_{j=1}^{n} H_j + H_I, \tag{8:4.1}$$

where H_I is an interaction term which takes account of the interactions between the electrons of one atom and the electrons and nuclei of the others. Thus

$$H_I = \frac{e^2}{2} \sum_{j' \neq j} \sum_{j} \sum_{i=1}^{N_j} \sum_{i'=1}^{N_{j'}} \frac{1}{|\mathbf{r}_i^{(j)} - \mathbf{r}_{i'}^{(j')}|} - e \sum_{j' \neq j} \sum_{j} \sum_{i=1}^{N_j} U_{j'}(|\mathbf{r}_i^{(j)} - \mathbf{R}_{j'}|), \tag{8:4.2}$$

where $\mathbf{r}_i^{(j)}$ is the position vector of the ith electron of the jth atom, and $U_j(r)$ is a central field associated with the jth atom. The Hamiltonian must of course be invariant under all electron interchanges.

We shall consider H_I as a perturbation term of H so that correct zero-order energy eigenfunctions can (except for antisymmetrization) be obtained by taking linear combinations of products of atomic energy eigenfunctions.

Because of the spatial distribution of the atoms the Hamiltonian H is not invariant under the full 3-dimensional rotation group. Instead it is invariant under the point group P of the molecule. Thus the symmetry group G of H is

$$G = P \times \mathscr{S}_S(N) \times GL(2^N, C), \tag{8:4.3}$$

where

$$N = \sum_{j=1}^{n} N_j \tag{8:4.3a}$$

is the total number of electrons.

Let Γ_p be an irreducible representation of P, so that a typical irreducible representation Γ of G is

$$\Gamma = \Gamma_p \times \Gamma_{N,\{\lambda\}} \times GL(2^N, C). \tag{8:4.4}$$

$GL(2^N, C)$ possesses irreducible representations other than itself, but we are interested only in representations generated by energy eigenfunctions, that is, in representations generated by 2^N-dimensional spin space. These are always $GL(2^N, C)$ itself.

So far, we have ignored the Pauli exclusion principle. To take it into account we want to consider the subgroup

$$\begin{aligned} G^{(P)} &= P \times [GL_1(2,C) \otimes \dots \otimes GL_N(2,C)] \otimes [\mathscr{S}_S(N) \otimes \mathscr{S}_\Sigma(N)] \\ &= P \times GL(2,C) \times \mathscr{S}(N) \end{aligned} \tag{8:4.5}$$

and admit only sets of energy eigenfunctions which generate irreducible representations of the form

$$\Gamma^{(P)} = \Gamma_p \times \Gamma_S \times \Gamma_\sigma ,$$

where Γ_σ is the 1-dimensional alternating representation of $\mathscr{S}(N)$. The representation Γ_S is a typical $(2S+1)$-dimensional irreducible representation of $GL(2, C)$ which appears in the reduction of the Nth Kronecker power of $GL(2, C)$ generated by 2^N-dimensional spin space.

Thus a molecular term is specified by p and S instead of by L and S as in the atomic case. If Γ_p is d_p-dimensional, the degeneracy of such a term is $(2S + 1)d_p$.

Let us now consider the molecular terms which can arise from a specified set of n atomic terms ${}^{2S_1+1}L_1, \ldots, {}^{2S_n+1}L_n$. Consider a term ${}^{2S+1}L$, and let $\{\psi^{(L,S)}_{m_L, m_S}\}$ $(-L \leqslant m_L \leqslant L; -S \leqslant m_S \leqslant S)$ be a set of $(2L + 1)(2S + 1)$ basis functions for the manifold of states belonging to the term ${}^{2S+1}L$. A typical zero-order molecular wave function will then be of the form

$$\psi_{m_{L1}, m_{L2}, \ldots, m_{Ln}; m_{S1}, m_{S2}, \ldots, m_{Sn}} = Y_{\{1^N\}} (\psi^{(1)}_{m_{L1}, m_{S1}} \psi^{(2)}_{m_{L2}, m_{S2}} \cdots \psi^{(n)}_{m_{Ln}, m_{Sn}}), \qquad (8{:}4.6)$$

where $\psi^{(j)}_{m_{Lj}, m_{Sj}}$ denotes the atomic wave function $\psi^{(Lj,Sj)}_{m_{Lj}, m_{Sj}}$ whose arguments are the space and spin coordinates of the electrons originally belonging to the jth atom. Further, the wave function $\psi^{(Lj,Sj)}_{m_{Lj}, m_{Sj}}$ is now centered at the position of the jth atom in the molecule. $Y_{\{1^N\}}$ is the Young antisymmetrizer which acts on the coordinates of the N electrons of the molecule. There are $\prod_{j=1}^{n} (2L_j + 1)(2S_j + 1)$ zero-order molecular wave functions of the form (8:4.6). It is easily seen that these functions generate a representation (call it Γ) of the group $G^{(P)}$. To find the molecular terms arising from the specified n atomic terms we need to determine Γ and then reduce it. Each irreducible component $\Gamma_p \times \Gamma_S \times \Gamma_\sigma$ occurring in the reduction of Γ is generated by a molecular term ${}^{2S+1}\Gamma_p$. The molecular ground state is usually a singlet $(S = 0)$ state.

Example. Methane CH_4

Let us assume that the C atom is in a ${}^3P$ state and that the four H atoms are all in ${}^2S$ states. The C atom is at the center of symmetry of the molecule, and the molecular point group is T_d. Let us denote the positions of the four H atoms by A, B, C, D; the spatial hydrogen ground state by $\phi(r)$; the two spin vectors $\begin{pmatrix}1\\0\end{pmatrix}$ and $\begin{pmatrix}0\\1\end{pmatrix}$ by χ_+ and χ_-; and the nine linearly independent C atom wave functions belonging to the ${}^3P$ term by $\psi_{1,1}, \psi_{1,0}, \psi_{1,-1}, \ldots, \psi_{-1,-1}$.

One zero-order molecular wave function is

$$\psi = Y\big(\phi_A(1)\chi_+(1)\phi_B(2)\chi_+(2)\phi_C(3)\chi_+(3)\phi_D(4)\chi_+(4)\psi_{11}\big),$$

where the letter subscripts indicate the centering of the wave functions. There are 144 such wave functions. Therefore Γ is 144-dimensional.

Since the C atom is at the center of symmetry its wave functions transform among each other under a rotation but do not mix with the hydrogen wave functions. Similarly the hydrogen wave functions do not mix with the carbon wave functions under a rotation transformation. To be more explicit, let R be the 120° rotation which effects the following permutation of hydrogen atoms:

$$RA = B \qquad RB = C \qquad RC = A \qquad RD = D.$$

Then

$$R\phi_A = \phi_B \qquad R\phi_B = \phi_C \qquad R\phi_C = \phi_A \qquad R\phi_D = \phi_D$$

but

$$R\psi_{1,1} = \sum_{i,j=-1}^{1} D_{,i,j1,1}(R)\psi_{i,j} \,.$$

As a result of this immiscibility of the wave functions under transformation the representation Γ is easily seen to be the direct product of the representation of $G^{(P)}$ generated by the hydrogenic component of the wave function and the representation of $G^{(P)}$ generated by the carbon components.

To be more precise consider the 16 wave functions of the form

$$\psi^{(H)}_{i_1 \ldots i_4} = Y\big(\phi_A(1)\chi_{i_1}(1)\phi_B(2)\chi_{i_2}(2)\phi_C(3)\chi_{i_3}(3)\phi_D(4)\chi_{i_4}(4)\big),$$

where each subscript i can assume the values ± 1. These 16 functions generate a representation Γ_H of $G^{(P)}$ Also, the nine carbon wave functions $\psi_{i,j}$ generate the representation§ $\Gamma_1^{(+)} \times \Gamma_{6,1} \times \Gamma_\sigma$ of $O(3) \times GL(2,C) \times \mathscr{S}(6)$ ($\Gamma_{6,1}$ being the 3-dimensional irreducible component of $[GL(2,C)]_6$ and $\Gamma^{(\oplus)}$, being the irreducible, 3-dimensional representation $\mathcal{O}(3)$ with positive parity). Consequently the carbon wave functions generate a representation Γ_C of $G^{(P)}$, which is (in accordance with customary notation)

$$\Gamma_C = T_1 \times \Gamma_{6,1} \times \Gamma_\sigma \,,$$

where T_1 is a 3-dimensional irreducible representation of T_d. The representation Γ is according to our previous conclusion given by

$$\Gamma = \Gamma_H \otimes \Gamma_C.$$

Therefore we need only determine Γ_H.

Let us first determine the effect of a general 2-dimensional matrix on the $\psi^{(H)}$'s. If

$$D = \begin{pmatrix} D_{11} & D_{12} \\ D_{21} & D_{22} \end{pmatrix}$$

then

$$D\chi_+ = D_{11}\chi_+ + D_{21}\chi_-$$
$$D\chi_- = D_{12}\chi_+ + D_{22}\chi_-.$$

Hence,

$$\begin{aligned} D\psi^{(H)}_{++++} &= Y\{\phi_A(1)[D_{11}\chi_+(1) + D_{21}\chi_-(1)]\phi_B(2)[D_{11}\chi_+(2) + D_{21}\chi_-(2)] \\ &\qquad \phi_C(3)[D_{11}\chi_+(3) + D_{21}\chi_-(3)]\phi_D(4)[D_{11}\chi_+(4) + D_{21}\chi_-(4)]\} \\ &= D_{11}^4\psi^{(H)}_{++++} + D_{11}^3 D_{21}(\psi^{(H)}_{+++-} + \psi^{(H)}_{++-+} + \psi^{(H)}_{+-++} + \psi^{(H)}_{-+++} \\ &\quad + D_{11}^2 D_{21}^2(\psi^{(H)}_{++--} + \psi^{(H)}_{+-+-} + \psi^{(H)}_{-++-} + \psi^{(H)}_{-+-+} + \psi^{(H)}_{--++} + \psi^{(H)}_{+--+}) \\ &\quad + D_{11} D_{21}^3(\psi^{(H)}_{+---} + \psi^{(H)}_{-+--} + \psi^{(H)}_{--+-} + \psi^{(H)}_{---+}) + D_{21}^4\psi^{(H)}_{----}. \end{aligned}$$

§ It should be remembered that carbon has six electrons.

Since all we need is the trace of the matrix representing D we need only calculate the diagonal terms. These are easily seen to be given by

$$D\psi^{(H)}_{i_1i_2i_3i_4} = D_{11}^{n+}D_{22}^{n-}\ \psi^{(H)}_{i_1i_2i_3i_4} + \ldots,$$

where n_+ is the number of i's equal to $+1$, and n_- is the number of i's equal to -1. The trace of the matrix representing D is easily found to be given by

$$\chi^{(H)}(D) = (D_{11} + D_{22})^4 = [\mathrm{tr}\,(D)]^4.$$

Now let us consider the representation of T_d generated by the hydrogenic wave functions. To do this we must consider the elements of the molecular point group T_d in more detail. Let C_3 be any 120° rotation of the group, C_2 any 180° rotation of T_d, σ_d any reflection in T_d, and S_4 any product of a rotation and a reflection which is not one of the preceding elements. The character table of T_d is as follows:

	I	$3C_2$	$6\sigma_d$	$6S_4$	$8C_3$
A_1	1	1	1	1	1
A_2	1	1	-1	-1	1
E	2	2	0	0	-1
T_1	3	-1	-1	1	0
T_2	3	-1	1	-1	0

Let R be the 120° rotation which effects the permutation

$$RA = B \qquad RB = C \qquad RC = A \qquad RD = D.$$

Then

$$\begin{aligned} R\Psi_{++++} &= RY\big(\phi_A(1)\chi_+(1)\phi_B(2)\chi_+(2)\phi_C(3)\chi_+(3)\phi_D(4)\chi_+(4)\big) \\ &= Y\big(\phi_B(1)\chi_+(1)\phi_C(2)\chi_+(2)\phi_A(3)\chi_+(3)\phi_D(4)\chi_+(4) \\ &= \psi_{++++}, \end{aligned}$$

$$\begin{aligned} R\psi_{+++-} &= \psi_{+++-} & R\psi_{-+-+} &= \psi_{--++} \\ R\psi_{++-+} &= \psi_{-+++} & R\psi_{--++} &= \psi_{+--+} \\ R\psi_{+-++} &= \psi_{++-+} & R\psi_{+---} &= \psi_{-+--} \\ R\psi_{-+++} &= \psi_{+-++} & R\psi_{-+--} &= \psi_{--+-} \\ R\psi_{++--} &= \psi_{-++-} & R\psi_{--+-} &= \psi_{+---} \\ R\psi_{+-+-} &= \psi_{++--} & R\psi_{---+} &= \psi_{---+} \\ R\psi_{-++-} &= \psi_{+-+-} & R\psi_{----} &= \psi_{----} \\ R\psi_{+--+} &= \psi_{-+-+} \end{aligned}$$

Hence $\chi^{(H)}(R) = 4$. Proceeding in this way we find

$$\chi^{(H)} = (16, 4, -8, -2, 4)$$

For the character of the product group $T_d \times GL(2, \mathrm{C})$ we have

	I	$3C_2$	$6\sigma_d$	$6S_4$	$8C_3$	D	(C_2, D)
$\chi^{(H)}$	16	4	-8	-2	4	$(D_{11} + D_{22})^4 = \chi^4$	$(\chi^2 - 2\delta)^2$

	(σ_d, D)	(S_4, D)	(C_3, D)
$\chi^{(H)}$	$-\chi^2(\chi^2 - 2\delta)$	$-\chi^4 + 4\chi^2\delta - 2\delta^2$	$\chi^2(\chi^2 - 3\delta)$

where $\chi = \mathrm{tr}\,(D)$ and $\delta = \det\,(D)$.

A straightforward calculation shows that

$$\Gamma_H = (A_2 \times \Gamma_{4,\{4,0\}}) \oplus (E \times \Gamma_{4,\{2,2\}}) \oplus (T_1 \times \Gamma_{4,\{3,1\}}),$$

where $\Gamma_{4,\{\lambda_1,\lambda_2\}}$ is the irreducible representation of $GL(2,C)$ generated by the independent components of the tensor $Y_{\{\lambda_1,\lambda_2\}} T_{i_1 i_2 i_3 i_4}$.

For the sake of completeness some properties of these representations will be listed here.

$$\begin{aligned}
&\dim(\Gamma_{4,\{4,0\}}) = 5\\
&\dim(\Gamma_{4,\{2,2\}}) = 1\\
&\dim(\Gamma_{4,\{3,1\}}) = 3\\
&\chi^{4,\{4,0\}}(D) = \chi^4 - 3\chi^2\delta + \delta^2\\
&\chi^{4,\{2,2\}} = \delta^2\\
&\chi^{4,\{3,1\}} = \chi^2\delta - \delta^2\\
&[GL(2,C)]_4 = \Gamma_{4,\{4,0\}} \oplus 2\Gamma_{4,\{2,2\}} \oplus 3\Gamma_{4,\{3,1\}}\\
&\Gamma_{4,\{4,0\}} = \Gamma_{4,2} \quad \Gamma_{4,\{2,2\}} = \Gamma_{4,0} \quad \Gamma_{4,\{3,1\}} = \Gamma_{4,1}.
\end{aligned}$$

To find the molecular terms we must still reduce the product (neglecting $\mathscr{S}(N)$ and Γ_σ)

$$\begin{aligned}
\Gamma = \Gamma_H \otimes \Gamma_C &= \Gamma_H \otimes (T_1 \times \Gamma_{6,1})\\
&= [(A_2 \times \Gamma_{4,2}) \otimes (T_1 \times \Gamma_{6,1})]\\
&\quad \oplus [(E \times \Gamma_{4,0}) \otimes (T_1 \times \Gamma_{6,1})]\\
&\quad \oplus [(T_1 \times \Gamma_{4,1}) \otimes (T_1 \times \Gamma_{6,1})]\\
&= [(A_2 \otimes T_1) \times (\Gamma_{4,2} \otimes \Gamma_{6,1})]\\
&\quad \oplus [(E \otimes T_1) \times (\Gamma_{4,0} \otimes \Gamma_{6,1})]\\
&\quad \oplus [(T_1 \otimes T_1) \times (\Gamma_{4,1} \otimes \Gamma_{6,1})].
\end{aligned}$$

The individual products reduce as follows:

$$\begin{aligned}
&A_2 \otimes T_1 = T_2\\
&E \otimes T_1 = T_1 \oplus T_2\\
&T_1 \otimes T_1 = A_1 \oplus E \oplus T_1 \oplus T_2\\
&\Gamma_{4,2} \otimes \Gamma_{6,1} = \Gamma_{10,3} \oplus \Gamma_{10,2} \oplus \Gamma_{10,1}\\
&\Gamma_{4,0} \otimes \Gamma_{6,1} = \Gamma_{10,1}\\
&\Gamma_{4,1} \otimes \Gamma_{6,1} = \Gamma_{10,2} \oplus \Gamma_{10,1} \oplus \Gamma_{10,0}.
\end{aligned}$$

Hence

$$\begin{aligned}
\Gamma &= (T_2 \times \Gamma_{10,3}) \oplus (T_2 \times \Gamma_{10,2}) \oplus (T_2 \times \Gamma_{10,1})\\
&\quad \oplus (T_1 \times \Gamma_{10,1}) \oplus (T_2 \times \Gamma_{10,1})\\
&\quad \oplus (A_1 \times \Gamma_{10,2}) \oplus (A_1 \times \Gamma_{10,1}) \oplus (A_1 \times \Gamma_{10,0})\\
&\quad \oplus (E \times \Gamma_{10,2}) \oplus (E \times \Gamma_{10,1}) \oplus (E \times \Gamma_{10,0})\\
&\quad \oplus (T_1 \times \Gamma_{10,2}) \oplus (T_1 \times \Gamma_{10,1}) \oplus (T_1 \times \Gamma_{10,0})\\
&\quad \oplus (T_2 \times \Gamma_{10,2}) \oplus (T_2 \times \Gamma_{10,1}) \oplus (T_2 \times \Gamma_{10,0})\\
&= (T_2 \times \Gamma_{10,3}) \oplus 2(T_2 \times \Gamma_{10,2}) \oplus 3(T_2 \times \Gamma_{10,1})\\
&\quad \oplus 2(T_1 \times \Gamma_{10,1}) \oplus (A_1 \times \Gamma_{10,2}) \oplus (A_1 \times \Gamma_{10,1}) \oplus (A_1 \times \Gamma_{10,1})\\
&\quad \oplus (E \times \Gamma_{10,2}) \oplus (E \times \Gamma_{10,1}) \oplus (E \times \Gamma_{10,1}) \oplus (T_1 \times \Gamma_{10,2})\\
&\quad \oplus (T_1 \times \Gamma_{10,1}) \oplus (T_2 \times \Gamma_{10,0}).
\end{aligned}$$

The corresponding 13 different molecular terms are

$$^7T_2,\ ^5T_2,\ ^3T_2,\ ^3T_1,\ ^5A_1,\ ^3A_1,\ ^1A_1,\ ^5E,\ ^3E,\ ^1E,\ ^5T_1,\ ^1T_1,\ ^1T_2.$$

The ground state should be a $^1A_1$ term.

The ground state of a free carbon atom is a ^3P state. On the other hand, it seems likely that a free carbon atom is excited to a ^5S state in forming a methane molecule. This term generates the representation $\Gamma_0^{(-)} \times \Gamma_{6,2} \times \Gamma_\sigma$ of $O(3) \times GL(2,C) \times \mathcal{S}(6)$, so $\Gamma_C = A_2 \times \Gamma_{6,2} \times \Gamma_\sigma$. Neglecting the symmetric group we have

$$\begin{aligned}\Gamma = \Gamma_H \otimes \Gamma_C &= \Gamma_H \otimes (A_2 \times \Gamma_{6,2})\\ &= (A_2 \times \Gamma_{4,2}) \otimes (A_2 \times \Gamma_{6,2}) \oplus (E \times \Gamma_{4,0}) \otimes (A_2 \times \Gamma_{6,2})\\ &\quad \oplus (T_1 \times \Gamma_{4,1}) \otimes (A_2 \times \Gamma_{6,2})\\ &= [(A_2 \otimes A_2) \times (\Gamma_{4,2} \otimes \Gamma_{6,2})] \oplus [(E \otimes A_2) \times (\Gamma_{4,0} \otimes \Gamma_{6,2})]\\ &\quad \oplus [(T_1 \otimes A_2) \times (\Gamma_{4,1} \otimes \Gamma_{6,2})].\end{aligned}$$

Using the relations

$$\begin{aligned}&A_2 \otimes A_2 = A_1\\ &E \otimes A_2 = E\\ &T_1 \otimes A_2 = T_2\\ &\Gamma_{4,2} \otimes \Gamma_{6,2} = \Gamma_{10,4} \oplus \Gamma_{10,3} \oplus \Gamma_{10,2} \oplus \Gamma_{10,1} \oplus \Gamma_{10,0}\\ &\Gamma_{4,0} \otimes \Gamma_{6,2} = \Gamma_{10,2}\\ &\Gamma_{4,1} \otimes \Gamma_{6,2} = \Gamma_{10,3} \oplus \Gamma_{10,2} \oplus \Gamma_{10,1},\end{aligned}$$

we find (dropping the subscript 10 from the representations of $GL(2,C)$)

$$\begin{aligned}\Gamma = (A_1 \times \Gamma_4) \oplus (A_1 \times \Gamma_3) \oplus (A_1 \times \Gamma_2) \oplus (A_1 \times \Gamma_1) \oplus (A_1 \times \Gamma_1)\\ \oplus (E \times \Gamma_2) \oplus (T_2 \times \Gamma_3) \oplus (T_2 \times \Gamma_2) \oplus (T_2 \times \Gamma_1).\end{aligned}$$

The corresponding nine terms are: $^9A_1$, $^7A_1$, $^5A_1$, $^3A_1$, $^1A_1$, ^5E, $^7T_2$, $^5T_2$, $^3T_2$. All of these terms except $^9A_1$ and $^7A_1$ can occur in the combination of a ^3P carbon atom.

5. Nuclear Structure

The structure of nuclei will now be briefly investigated in a manner very similar to that used for the investigation of atomic structure (190, 192). The main mathematical difference will be the use of a spin-spin space instead of a spin space.

We shall assume the nucleus to be an N-nucleon system which is describable by a Schrödinger-Pauli type wave equation. Because of the use of an isotopic spin variable to describe the charge state of a nucleon, an N-nucleon wave function will depend on N sets of arguments $\mathbf{r}_i$, s_i, and t_i as well as on time. If we let $\mathcal{H}$ be the space of N-particle spatial wave functions (i.e., wave functions for spinless particles), Σ be the 2^N-dimensional spin space for a system of N spin 1/2 particles, and T be the 2^N-dimensional isotopic spin space for a system of N nucleons, then the wave function for an N-nucleon system lies in the space $\mathcal{H} \times \Sigma \times T$.

The Hamiltonian for an N-nucleon system will be an operator in the space $\mathscr{H} \times \Sigma \times T$. We shall consider two types of Hamiltonians, the second of which is a refinement of the first. In fact, it is doubtful if the first Hamiltonian is satisfactory for the lowest approximation.

Both Hamiltonians will contain only 2-body forces. In the first approximation it will be assumed that the energy of the system depends only on spatial coordinates and is independent of charge and spin. In the second approximation charge independence will still be assumed but spin dependence will be allowed. Since both approximations assume charge independence, both exclude Coulomb forces, and are therefore good only for light nuclei.

A. Spatial Coordinate Approximation

$$H_A = H_A(\nabla_i^2, r_{ij}, P_{kl}^M) \tag{8:5.1}$$

where $r_{ij} = |\mathbf{r}_i - \mathbf{r}_j|$ is the distance between the ith and jth nucleons, and P_{kl}^M is the transposition operator which interchanges the coordinate vectors of nucleons k and l. The Hamiltonian is also assumed to be invariant under any permutation of nucleons.

Let us call the 4^N-dimensional space $\Omega = \Sigma \times T$ spin-spin space. The symmetry group of H_A is

$$\begin{aligned} G_A &= [O_1(3) \otimes \ldots \otimes O_N(3)] \times \mathscr{S}_S(N) \times GL(4^N, \mathrm{C}) \\ &= O(3) \times \mathscr{S}(N) \times GL(4^N, C). \end{aligned} \tag{8:5.2}$$

A typical irreducible representation is

$$\Gamma_A = \Gamma_L \times \Gamma_{\{\lambda\}} \times GL(4^N, C), \tag{8:5.3}$$

where Γ_L is a $(2L+1)$-dimensional irreducible representation of $O(3)$, and $\Gamma_{\{\lambda\}}$ is an irreducible representation of $\mathscr{S}(N)$ belonging to the partition $\{\lambda\}$ of N. We see that energy depends on L and $\{\lambda\}$ but not on spin or charge.

However, we want only antisymmetric functions (because of the Pauli exclusion principle), and since an antisymmetric function is not antisymmetric after being transformed by an element of $GL(4^N, C)$ we must consider a smaller symmetry group. The new group is

$$\begin{aligned} G_A^{(P)} &= [O_1(3) \times \ldots \times O_N(3)] \times [GL_1(4, C) \otimes \ldots \otimes GL_N(4, C)] \\ &\quad \times [\mathscr{S}_S(N) \otimes \mathscr{S}_A(N)] = O(3) \times GL(4, C) \times \mathscr{S}(N) \end{aligned} \tag{8:5.4}$$

A typical irreducible representation of $G_A^{(P)}$ which subduces the alternating representation of $\mathscr{S}(N)$ is

$$\Gamma_A{}^{(P)} = \Gamma_L \times \Gamma_{N,\{\Lambda\}} \times \Gamma_\sigma, \tag{8:5.5}$$

where $\Gamma_{N,\{\Lambda\}}$ is the $\{\Lambda\}$-symmetrized power of $GL(4, C)$, and $\{\Lambda\}$ is a quaternary partition of N.

Let us discuss for a moment the reason for $\Gamma_{\{\Lambda\}}$ being a typical irreducible representation of $GL(4, C)$. Let us consider the groups

$$G_S = [O_1(3) \otimes \ldots \otimes O_N(3)] \times \mathscr{S}_S(N) = O(3) \times \mathscr{S}(N). \quad (8:5.6)$$

$$G_\Omega = [GL_1(4,C) \otimes \ldots \otimes GL_N(4,C)] \times \mathscr{S}_\Omega(N) = GL(4,C) \times \mathscr{S}(N). \quad (8:5.7)$$

According to Chapter VII, Section 3, items (20) and (3), the representation Γ_Ω of G_Ω generated by Ω is

$$\Gamma_\Omega = \sum_{\{\Lambda\}} \Gamma_{N,\{\Lambda\}} \times \Gamma_{\{\Lambda\}}, \quad (8:5.8)$$

where $\Gamma_{N,\{\Lambda\}}$ is again the $\{\Lambda\}$-symmetrized power of $GL(4,C)$, $\Gamma_{\{\Lambda\}}$ is the irreducible representation of $\mathscr{S}(N)$ belonging to the partition $\{\Lambda\}$ of N, and the sum is over all quaternary partitions $\{\Lambda\}$ of N.

Let S be the space of all spatial eigenvectors of H_A belonging to a particular energy level. Then all total (space-spin-isotropic spin) eigenvectors of H_A belonging to this energy level must lie in the space $S \times \Omega$. If Γ_S is the representation of G_S generated by S, then the representation of $G_S \times G_\Omega$ generated by $S \times \Omega$ is $\Gamma_S \times \Gamma_\Omega$.

Since $G_A^{(P)}$ is a subgroup of $G_S \times G_\Omega$ we can find the irreducible representations of $G_A^{(P)}$ generated by eigenfunctions of H_A by decomposing the representations of $G_A^{(P)}$ subduced by irreducible representations of $G_S \times G_\Omega$ which are themselves generated by eigenfunctions of H_A. A typical irreducible representation of G_S is $\Gamma_L \times \Gamma_{\{\lambda\}}$, where $\Gamma_{\{\lambda\}}$ is an irreducible representation of $\mathscr{S}(N)$ belonging to the partition $\{\lambda\}$ of N. Hence, from (8:5.8) we see that a typical irreducible representation of $G_S \times G_\Omega$ is $\Gamma_L \times \Gamma_{\{\lambda\}} \times \Gamma_{N,\{\Lambda\}} \times \Gamma_{\{\Lambda\}}$. This subduces the representation

$$\Gamma_L \times \Gamma_{N,\{\Lambda\}} \times [\Gamma_{\{\lambda\}} \otimes \Gamma_{\{\Lambda\}}]$$

of $G_A^{(P)}$. We see now why $\Gamma_{N,\{\Lambda\}}$ is a typical irreducible representation of $GL(4,C)$.

We note incidentally that $\Gamma_{\{\lambda\}} \otimes \Gamma_{\{\Lambda\}}$ contains Γ_σ as a component exactly once if $\Gamma_{\{\lambda\}} = \bar{\Gamma}_{\{\Lambda\}}$, and not at all otherwise.

A linearly independent set of eigenfunctions of H_A generating a representation $\Gamma_L \times \Gamma_{N,\{\Lambda\}} \times \Gamma_\sigma$ of $G_A^{(P)}$ can be called a superterm and can be specified by the four numbers L, Λ_1, Λ_2, and Λ_3 since

$$\Lambda_4 = N - \Lambda_1 - \Lambda_2 - \Lambda_3.$$

If the ordering $\Lambda_1 \leqslant \Lambda_2 \leqslant \Lambda_3 \leqslant \Lambda_4$ is adopted, then it is customary to introduce the three partition numbers

$$\begin{aligned} P &= \tfrac{1}{2}(\Lambda_4 - \Lambda_3 - \Lambda_2 - \Lambda_1) \\ P' &= \tfrac{1}{2}(\Lambda_4 - \Lambda_3 + \Lambda_2 - \Lambda_1) \\ P'' &= \tfrac{1}{2}(\Lambda_4 - \Lambda_3 - \Lambda_2 + \Lambda_1) \end{aligned} \quad (8:5.9)$$

so that a superterm is specified by the four numbers L, P, P', and P''. The degeneracy of a superterm is $(2L+1)\delta_{\{\Lambda\}}$, where $\delta_{\{\Lambda\}}$ is given in Chapter

VII, Section 3, item (2). A superterm is usually called a supermultiplet, but it is more analogous to a term of atomic spectroscopy than to a multiplet.

B. Spin Approximation

$$H_B = H_A + H'(r_{ij}, \nabla_i, \boldsymbol{\sigma}_i, P^B_{kl}, P^H_{kl}), \tag{8:5.10}$$

where H' is assumed to be invariant under all permutations of nucleons as well as under equal simultaneous rotation of space and spin, P^B_{kl} is the transposition operator for the spins of the kth and lth nucleons, and P^H_{kl} is the transposition operator for both the coordinate vectors and spins of the kth and lth particles. The operators P^M_{kl}, P^B_{kl}, and P^H_{kl} are the Majorana, Bartlett, and Heisenberg exchange operators, and they are related by the equation

$$P^H_{kl} = P^M_{kl} P^B_{kl}. \tag{8:5.11}$$

The symmetry group of H_B, assuming that the spin terms actually occur, is

$$\begin{aligned} G_B = \{&[R_1(3) \otimes U_1(2)] \otimes \dots \otimes [R_N(3) \otimes U_N(2)]\} \\ &\times [\mathscr{S}_S(N) \otimes \mathscr{S}_\Sigma(N)] \times GL(2^N, C) = R(3) \times \mathscr{S}(N) \times GL(2^N, C). \end{aligned} \tag{8:5.12}$$

A typical irreducible representation of G_B is

$$\Gamma_B = \Gamma_J \times \Gamma_{\{\lambda\}} \times GL(2^N, C). \tag{8:5.13}$$

If we want to impose the Pauli exclusion principle we are again forced to consider a smaller group. In this case we can consider the group

$$\begin{aligned} G_B^{(P)} &= \{[R_1(3) \otimes U_1(2)] \otimes \dots \otimes [R_N(3) \otimes U_N(2)]\} \\ &\quad \times [GL_1(2, C) \otimes \dots \otimes GL_N(2, C)] \times [\mathscr{S}_S(N) \otimes \mathscr{S}_\Sigma(N) \otimes \mathscr{S}_T(N)] \\ &= R(3) \times GL(2, C) \times \mathscr{S}(N), \end{aligned} \tag{8:5.14}$$

where all isotopic spins are transformed the same, and spatial coordinates, spins, and isotopic spins are simultaneously permuted. A typical irreducible representation of $G_B^{(P)}$ which subduces the alternating representation of $\mathscr{S}(N)$ is

$$\Gamma_B^{(P)} = \Gamma_J \times \Gamma_T \times \Gamma_\sigma, \tag{8:5.15}$$

where Γ_T is the $(2T + 1)$-dimensional irreducible representation of $GL(2, C)$ generated by the independent components of the tensor $Y_{\{\frac{1}{2}N+T, \frac{1}{2}N-T\}} T_{i_1 \dots i_N}$.

A linearly independent set of eigenfunctions of H_B generating an irreducible representation $\Gamma_B^{(P)}$ of $G_B^{(P)}$ can be called a supermultiplet, but is usually called an isotopic spin multiplet. The degeneracy of a supermultiplet is $(2J + 1)(2T + 1)$.

To find how a superterm generating the irreducible representation $\Gamma_L \times \Gamma_{N,\{\Lambda\}} \times \Gamma_\sigma$ of $G_A^{(P)}$ splits into supermultiplets generating the irreducible representations $\Gamma_J \times \Gamma_T \times \Gamma_\sigma$ of $G_B^{(P)}$ we must reduce the representation of $G_B^{(P)}$ subduced by the irreducible representation $\Gamma_L \times \Gamma_{N,\{\Lambda\}} \times \Gamma_\sigma$ of $G_A^{(P)}$. This is difficult to do in the general case and will not be attempted here.

6. Selection Rules

In this section we shall consider transitions of a system from one state to another in which energy is released or absorbed by the system in the form of photons. In brief, then, we shall consider radiative transitions. By means of group theory we shall be able to see that the symmetry of a system can rule out certain radiative transitions. In other words, we shall use group theory to derive selection rules. Actually only one example will be treated because the myriad of others can be treated analogously.

Let us assume that the rate R at which energy is spontaneously radiated by a system into electric dipole radiation is given by

$$R_{if} = \frac{64}{3}\frac{\pi^4}{c^3}\,\nu_{if}^4 |\langle i|\mathbf{P}|f\rangle|^2, \tag{8:6.1}$$

where

$$|i\rangle = \text{the initial energy eigenfunction}$$

$$|f\rangle = \text{the final energy eigenfunction}$$

$$\nu_{if} = \frac{E_i - E_f}{h} > 0$$

$$\mathbf{P} = \sum_{i=1}^{N} e_i \mathbf{r}_i = \text{electric dipole vector operator}$$

$$N = \text{number of charges of system}$$

$$e_i = \text{amplitude of } i\text{th charge.}$$

R_{if} is then the rate at which electric dipole energy is radiated via the transition $|i\rangle \to |f\rangle$.

Let us now apply formula (8:6.1) to an atomic system in which the initial and final states are multiplet levels. Thus

$$|i\rangle = |{}^{2S'+1}L'_{J'}\rangle \tag{8:6.2a}$$

$$|f\rangle = |{}^{2S+1}L_J\rangle \tag{8:6.2b}$$

The rate of radiation R_{if} will be zero whenever $\langle i|P|f\rangle$ is zero, so let us consider $\langle i|P|f\rangle$ and determine when it must be zero.

The matrix element can be written out as

$$\langle i|\mathbf{P}|f\rangle = e\sum_{k=1}^{N}\langle i|\mathbf{r}_{(k)}|f\rangle$$

so the jth ($j = 1, 2, 3$) component of the vector matrix element is

$$\langle i|\mathbf{P}|f\rangle_j = e\sum_{k=1}^{N}\langle i|x_j^{(k)}|f\rangle = e\sum_{k=1}^{N}\langle\, {}^{2S'+1}L'_{J'}|x_j^{(k)}|{}^{2S+1}L_J\,\rangle. \tag{8:6.3}$$

Let us now consider the set of functions

$$x_j^{(k)}|{}^{2S+1}L_J\,\rangle \qquad j = 1,2,3 \qquad k = 1,2,\dots,N.$$

Further, let us expand one of these functions in a series of atomic energy eigenfunctions, and compute the matrix element

$$\langle {}^{2S'+1}L'_{J'}|x_j^{(k)}|{}^{2S+1}L_J\rangle$$

by taking the inner product of $\langle {}^{2S'+1}L'_{J'}|$ with each term of the series. We know that every term in which $\langle {}^{2S'+1}L'_{J'}|$ is multiplied by an atomic energy eigenfunction $|{}^{2S''+1}L''_{J''}\rangle$, $J'' \neq J'$, must be zero. This follows from the fact that the $(2J+1)$ multiplet eigenfunctions $|{}^{2S+1}L_J\rangle$ generate the irreducible representation $\Gamma_J \times \Gamma_\sigma$ of $R(3) \times \mathcal{S}(N)$.

Let us therefore determine what values of J can occur in the eigenfunctions in the expansion of $x_j^{(k)}|{}^{2S+1}L_J\rangle$. To do this we will first consider the symmetry of the functions $x_j^{(k)}|{}^{2S+1}L_J\rangle$. Since the three functions $x_j^{(k)}$ (k fixed) generate the representation Γ_1 of $R(3)$, and the $(2J+1)$ functions $|{}^{2S+1}L_J\rangle$ generate the representation Γ_J of $R(3)$, we see that the $3(2J+1)$ functions $x_j^{(k)}|{}^{2S+1}L_J\rangle$ (k fixed) generate the representation $\Gamma_1 \otimes \Gamma_J$ of $R(3)$. Further, the N functions $x_j^{(k)}$ (j fixed) generate the representation $\Gamma\binom{N}{1}$ of $\mathcal{S}(N)$,§ and each function $|{}^{2S+1}L_J\rangle$ generates the representation Γ_σ of $\mathcal{S}(N)$, so the N functions $x_j^{(k)}|{}^{2S+1}L_J\rangle$ (fixed j) generate the representation $\Gamma\binom{N}{1} \otimes \Gamma_\sigma$ of $\mathcal{S}(N)$. Hence, the set of all functions $x_j^{(k)}|{}^{2S+1}L_J\rangle$ generates the representation $\Gamma = (\Gamma_1 \otimes \Gamma_J) \times \left(\Gamma\binom{N}{1} \otimes \Gamma_\sigma\right)$ of $R(3) \times \mathcal{S}(N)$.

We know also from Chapter IV, Section 9 that only eigenfunctions transforming like the original functions can occur in the expansion of $x_j^{(k)}|{}^{2S+1}L_J\rangle$. In this case that means that only eigenfunctions transforming according to one of the irreducible components of

$$\Gamma = (\Gamma_1 \otimes \Gamma_J) \times \left(\Gamma\binom{N}{1} \otimes \Gamma_\sigma\right)$$

can enter. But

$$\Gamma_1 \otimes \Gamma_J \cdot\!\equiv\!\cdot\ \Gamma_{J+1} \oplus \Gamma_J \oplus \Gamma_{J-1} \tag{8:6.4a}$$

$$\begin{aligned} \Gamma\binom{N}{1} &\cdot\!\equiv\!\cdot\ \Gamma_{\{N\}} \otimes \Gamma_{\{N-1,1\}} && \text{if } N > 1 \\ &\cdot\!\equiv\!\cdot\ \Gamma_{\{1\}} = \bar{\Gamma}_{triv.} && \text{if } N = 1 \end{aligned} \tag{8:6.4b}$$

§ See Chapter VII, Section 3, items (21), (24), and (23).

$$\Gamma\binom{N}{1} \otimes \Gamma_\sigma \cdot\!\equiv\!\cdot\, \Gamma_\sigma \oplus \bar{\Gamma}_{\{N-1,1\}} \qquad \text{if } N > 1$$
$$\cdot\!\equiv\!\cdot\, \Gamma_{triv.} \qquad \text{if } N = 1. \tag{8:6.4c}$$

Hence

$$\Gamma \cdot\!\equiv\!\cdot\, (\Gamma_{J+1} \times \Gamma_\sigma) \oplus (\Gamma_J \times \Gamma_\sigma) \oplus (\Gamma_{J-1} \times \Gamma_\sigma)$$
$$\oplus\, (\Gamma_{J+1} \times \bar{\Gamma}_{\{N-1,1\}}) \oplus (\Gamma_J \times \bar{\Gamma}_{\{N-1,1\}}) \tag{8:6.5}$$
$$\oplus\, (\Gamma_{J-1} \times \bar{\Gamma}_{\{N-1,1\}}).$$

Thus we see that the only possible values of J'' are $J + 1$, J, and $J - 1$. Hence

$$\langle {}^{2S'+1}L'_{J'}|\mathbf{P}|{}^{2S+1}L_J\rangle$$

is zero unless $J' = J + 1$, J, or $J - 1$. In other words, only electric dipole radiative transitions are allowed for which $\Delta J = 0, \pm 1$.

There is still another selection rule for electric dipole radiation. To derive this additional selection rule let us suppose that the atomic energy eigenvectors $|{}^{2S+1}L_J\rangle$ are chosen so that the representation of the abelian subgroup of rotations about some fixed axis generated by every multiplet of $(2J + 1)$ eigenvectors is diagonalized. For simplicity we can choose the fixed axis to be the z-axis. The irreducible representation Γ_J of $R(3)$ is easily seen to subduce the representation

$$\Gamma_J^{(s)} = \sum_{m=-J}^{J} \Gamma_m \tag{8:6.6}$$

of $R(2)$, where Γ_m is the 1-dimensional representation

$$R(\theta) \to e^{-im\theta} \tag{8:6.7}$$

Let us now rewrite the eigenfunctions $|{}^{2S+1}L_J\rangle$ so as to indicate the representation of $R(2)$ according to which each transforms. For simplicity let us simply write ϕ_J^m so

$$\mathscr{R}(\theta)\phi_J^m = e^{-im\theta}\phi_J^m. \tag{8:6.8}$$

Also let us use the variables

$$\xi = x + iy \tag{8:6.9a}$$
$$\xi^* = x - iy \tag{8:6.9b}$$
$$z = z \tag{8:6.9c}$$

so that

$$\mathscr{R}(\theta)\xi = e^{i\theta}\xi \tag{8:6.10a}$$
$$\mathscr{R}(\theta)\xi^* = e^{-i\theta}\xi^* \tag{8:6.10b}$$
$$\mathscr{R}(\theta)z = z. \tag{8:6.10c}$$

If we now consider matrix elements of the type $\langle\phi_{J+\Delta J}^{m'}|\xi|\phi_J^m\rangle$, we have

$$\langle\mathscr{R}(\theta)\phi_{J+\Delta J}^{m'}|\mathscr{R}(\theta)\xi|\mathscr{R}(\theta)\phi_J^m\rangle = e^{i(m'-m+1)}\langle\phi_{J+\Delta J}^{m'}|\xi|\phi_J^m\rangle. \tag{8:6.11}$$

But a rotation of the coordinate system does not change the value of the matrix element, so

$$\langle \mathscr{R}(\theta)\phi^{m'}_{J+\Delta J}|\mathscr{R}(\theta)\xi|\mathscr{R}(\theta)\phi^{m}_{J}\rangle = \langle \phi^{m'}_{J+\Delta J}|\xi|\phi^{m}_{J}\rangle. \quad (8{:}6.12)$$

Thus from (8:6.11) and (8:6.12) we obtain

$$[e^{i(m'-m+1)\theta} - 1]\langle \phi^{m'}_{J+\Delta J}|\xi|\phi^{m}_{J}\rangle = 0 \quad (8{:}6.13)$$

From (8:6.13) we see that either $\langle \phi^{m'}_{J+\Delta J}|\xi|\phi^{m}_{J}\rangle = 0$ or $m' = m - 1$. Similarly, we find

$$[e^{i(m'-m-1)\theta} - 1]\langle \phi^{m'}_{J+\Delta J}|\xi^*|\phi^{m}_{J}\rangle = 0 \quad (8{:}6.14)$$

$$[e^{i(m'-m)\theta} - 1]\langle \phi^{m'}_{J+\Delta J}|z|\phi^{m}_{J}\rangle = 0. \quad (8{:}6.15)$$

Thus, we find

$$\Delta m = 0, \pm 1. \quad (8{:}6.16)$$

For the rates of magnetic dipole and electric quadrupole radiation, respectively, the following formulas can be used:

$$R_{if} = \frac{64}{3}\frac{\pi^4}{c^3}\nu_{if}^4|\langle i|\mathbf{M}|f\rangle|^2 \quad (8{:}6.17)$$

$$\mathbf{M} = \frac{1}{2c}\sum_{k=1}^{N}\frac{e_i}{m_i}(\mathbf{L}_i + 2\mathbf{S}_i) \quad (8{:}6.17\text{a})$$

= magnetic dipole vector operator

$$\mathbf{L}_k = -i\hbar\mathbf{r}_k \times \boldsymbol{\nabla}_k \quad (8{:}6.17\text{b})$$

$$\mathbf{S}_k = \tfrac{1}{2}\hbar\boldsymbol{\sigma}_k \quad (8{:}6.17\text{c})$$

$$R_{if} = \frac{32}{5}\frac{\pi^6}{c^5}\nu_{if}^6 \operatorname{tr}\left[\langle i|Q - \frac{1}{3}\operatorname{tr}(Q)I|f\rangle^\dagger\langle i|Q - \frac{1}{3}\operatorname{tr}(Q)I|f\rangle\right] \quad (8{:}6.18)$$

$$Q = \sum_{k=1}^{N} e_k\mathbf{r}_k\mathbf{r}_k = \text{electric quadrupole dyadic operator} \quad (8{:}6.18\text{a})$$

I = 3-dimensional identity matrix or dyadic. (8:6.18b)

The concept of a selection rule can be generalized to include any rule which states that a matrix element determining the rate of some process is zero.

REFERENCES

1. Alexander, E., Systematics of the one-dimensional space groups. *Z. Krist.* **70**, 367 (1929).
2. Alexander, E., Remarks on the systematics of one-dimensional space groups. *Z. Krist.* **89**, 606 (1934).
3. Anonymous, Report on notation for the spectra of polyatomic molecules. *J. Chem Phys.* **23**, 1997 (1955).
4. Astbury, W. T., and Yardley, K., Tabulated data for the examination of the 230 space groups by homogeneous X-rays. *Phil. Trans. Roy. Soc.* **A224**, 221 (1924).
5. Baker, G. A., Degeneracy of the n-dimensional, isotropic, harmonic oscillator. *Phys. Rev.* **103**, 1119 (1956).
6. Bäbler, F., On a law on the theory of crystal classes. *Comment. Math. Helv.* **20**, 65 (1947).
7. Barnes, R. B., Brattain, R. R., and Seitz, F., On the structure and interpretaton of the infrared absorption spectra of crystals. *Phys. Rev.* **48**, 582 (1935).
8. Bauer, E., Introduction to the theory of groups and its applications to quantum physics. *Ann. inst. Henri Poincaré* **4**, 1 (1933).
9. Bauman, R. P., Selection rules for a freely rotating ethane-type molecule. *J. Chem. Phys.* **24**, 13 (1956).
10. Begbie, G. H., and Born, M., Thermal scattering of X-rays by crystals. *Proc. Roy. Soc.* **A188**, 179 (1947).
11. Bell, D. G., Group theory and crystal lattices. *Revs. Modern Phys.* **26**, 311 (1954).
12. Bell, D. G., Hum, D. M., Pincherle, L., Sciama, D. W., and Woodward, P. M., The electronic band structure of PbS. *Proc. Roy. Soc.* **A217**, 71 (1953).
13. Belova, E. N., Belov, N. V., and Subnikov, A. V., On the number and the character of the abstract groups corresponding to the 32 crystal classes. *Doklady. Akad. Nauk S.S.S.R.* **63**, 669 (1948).
14. Bethe, H. A., Term splitting in crystals. *Ann. Phys.* **3**, 133 (1929).
15. Bhagavantam, S., Photo-elastic effect in crystals. *Proc. Indian Acad. Sci.* **16**, 359 (1942).
16. Bhagavantam, S., and Suryanarayana, D., Method of enumerating the physical constants of crystals. *Acta Cryst.* **2**, 21 (1949).
17. Bieberbach, L., On the motion groups of Euclidean space. *Math. Ann.* **70**, 297 (1910); **72**, 400 (1912).
18. Bieberbach, L., Counting up of the finite rotation groups of three-dimensional Euclidean space. *Deut. Math.* **1**, 145 (1936).
19. Bieberbach, L., On the volume equality of Brillouin zones. *Monatsh. Math. Phys.* **48**, 509 (1939).
20. Bivins, R. L., Metropolis, N., Stein, P. R., and Wells, M. B., Characters of the symmetric groups of degree 15 and 16. *Math. Tables Aids Comput.* **8**, 212 (1954).
21. Bouckaert, L. P., Smoluchowski, R., and Wigner, E. P., Theory of Brillouin zones and symmetry properties of wave functions in crystals. *Phys. Rev.* **50**, 58 (1936).
22. Brandenberger, E., Systematic presentation of the selection rules important for the crystal structures of triclinic, monoclinic, and rhombic space groups. *Z. Krist.* **68**, 330 (1928).
23. Brandenberger, E., and Niggli, P., The systematic presentation of the selection rules important for crystal structure. *Z. Krist.* **68**, 301 (1928).
24. Buckley, Transformations of the fundamental equations of thermodynamics. *J. Research Natl. Bur. Standards* **33**, 213 (1944).

25. Buerger, M. J., Application of plane groups to the interpretation of Weissenberg photographs. *Z. Krist.* **91**, 255 (1935).

26. Buerger, M. J., Derivative crystal structures. *J. Chem. Phys.* **15**, 1 (1947).

27. Buerger, M. J., Crystallographic symmetry in reciprocal space. *Proc. Natl. Acad. Sci. U.S.* **35**, 198 (1949).

28. Buerger, M. J., The crystallographic symmetries determinable by X-ray diffraction. *Proc. Natl. Acad. Sci. U.S.* **36**, 324 (1950).

29. Buerger, M. J., Vector sets. *Acta Cryst.* **3**, 87 (1950).

30. Buerger, M. J., Tables of the characteristics of the vector representations of the 230 space groups. *Acta Cryst.* **3**, 465 (1950).

31. Burckhardt, J. J., Remarks on the arithmetic calculation of motion groups. *Comment. Math. Helv.* **2**, 91 (1930).

32. Burckhardt, J. J., On linear inhomogeneous substitution groups. *Compt. rend. congr. intern. math. Oslo* **2**, 25 (1936).

33. Burckhardt, J. J., Motion groups in many-dimensional spaces. *Comment. Math. Helv.* **9**, 284 (1937).

34. Case, K. M., Karplus, R., and Yang, C. N., Strange particles and the conservation of isotopic spin. *Phys. Rev.* **101**, 874 (1956).

35. Chodorow, M. I., and Manning, M. F., Energy bands in the body-centered lattice. *Phys. Rev.* **52**, 731 (1937).

36. Corson, E. M., Note on the Dirac character operator. *Phys. Rev.* **73**, 57 (1948).

37. Decius, J. C., Complete sets and redundancies among small vibrational coordinates. *J. Chem. Phys.* **17**, 1315 (1949).

38. Delbrück, M., Extension of the group theory of terms. Z. *Physik.* **51**, 181 (1928).

39. Devonshire, A. F., The rotation of molecules in fields of cotahedral symmetry. *Proc. Roy. Soc.* **A153**, 601 (1936).

40. Döring, W., and Zehler, V., Group-theoretic investigation of the electron bands in the diamond lattice. *Ann. Physik.* **13**, 214 (1953).

41. Dresselhaus, G., Spin-orbit coupling effects in zinc blende structures. *Phys. Rev.* **100**, 580 (1955).

42. Eckart, C., The application of group theory to the quantum dynamics of monatomic systems. *Revs. Modern Phys.* **2**, 205 (1930).

43. Eckart, C., Some studies concerning rotating axes and polyatomic molecules. *Phys. Rev.* **47**, 552 (1935).

44. Edmonds, A. R., and Flowers, B. H., Studies in jj-coupling. *Proc. Roy. Soc.* **A214**, 515 (1952); **A215**, 120 (1952).

45. Elert, W., On the rotation spectrum and the vibration spectrum of a molecule of type CH_4. *Z. Phys.* **51**, 6 (1928).

46. Elliott, R. J., Spin-orbit coupling in band theory—character tables for some double space groups. *Phys. Rev.* **96**, 280 (1954).

47. Eyring, H., Frost, A. A., and Turkevich, J., Molecular symmetry and the reduction of the secular equation. *J. Chem. Phys.* **1**, 777 (1933).

48. Fedorov, E. S., Elements of the study of form. *Verhandl. russ. Min. Ges.* **21**, 1 (1885).

49. Feenberg, E., and Wigner, E. P., On the structure of nuclei between helium and oxygen. *Phys. Rev.* **51**, 95 (1937).

50. Finkelstein, R. J., and Moe, M., Scattering by a symmetric potential. *Phys. Rev.* **100**, 1775 (1955).

51. Fletcher, T. J., Campanological groups. *Amer. Math. Monthly* **63**, 619 (1956).

52. Flowers, B. H., The classification of states of the nuclear f-shell. *Proc. Roy. Soc.* **A210**, 497 (1952).

53. Flowers, B. H., Studies in jj-coupling. *Proc. Roy. Soc.* **A212**, 248 (1952); **A215**, 398 (1952).
54. Flowers, B. H., jj-coupling in nuclei. *Phys. Rev.* **86**, 254 (1952).
55. Flowers, B. H., Excited states of nuclei in jj-coupling. *Physica* **18**, 1101 (1952).
56. Fock, V., Theory of the hydrogen atom. *Z. Physik* **98**, 145 (1935).
57. Fokker, A. D., Crystal symmetry and lattice vibrations. *Physica* **13**, 1 (1933).
58. Frobenius, G., On the undecomposable discrete motion groups. *Sitzber. kgl. preuss. Akad. Wiss.* **654** (1911).
59. Frobenius, G., Group theoretic derivation of the 32 crystal classes. *Sitzber. kgl. preuss. Akad. Wiss.* **681** (1911).
60. Fues, E., Vector relations of the atom in quantum mechanics. *Z. Physik* **51**, 817 (1928).
61. Fumi, F. G., Analytical representation of the crystal axes of translation. *Atti accad. naz. Lincei, Rend. Classe sci. fis. mat. enat.* **3**, 370 (1947).
62. Fumi, F. G., The elementary cells of Bravais and the primitive translations of Seitz. *Atti accad. naz. Lincei, Rend. Classe sci. fis. mat. enat.* **3**, 376 (1947).
63. Fumi, F. G., Matter tensors in symmetrical systems. *Nuovo cimento* **9**, 739 (1952).
64. Gamba, A., Remarks on the applications of group theory to quantum physics. *Rev. sci.* **90**, 11 (1952).
65. Gamba, A., The number of independent components of tensors in symmetrical systems. *Nuovo cimento* **10**, 1343 (1953).
66. Gamba, A., Strange particles and the conservation of isotopic spin. *Nuovo cimento* **3**, 1486 (1956).
67. Gamba, A., and Verde, M., On a question of nuclear spectroscopy. *Nuovo cimento* **9**, 544 (1952).
68. Ganzhorn, K., Quantum mechanics of the body-centered cubic transition metals. *Z. Naturforsch.* **7**, 291 (1952).
69. Ganzhorn, K., Group theory and quantum mechanics of transition metal structures. *Z. Naturforsch.* **8**, 330 (1953).
70. Gårding, L., and Wightman, A., Representations of the anticommutation relations. *Proc. Natl. Acad. Sci. U.S.* **40**, 617 (1954).
71. Garnir, H., A question in the theory of space groups, and its application to a vibration problem posed by theoretical chemistry. *Bull. soc. roy. sci. Liège* **15**, 357 (1946).
72. Garrido, J., On the classification of crystalline forms. *Anais fac. cient. Pôrto* **30**, 22 (1945).
73. Hall, G. G., The molecular orbital theory of chemical valency. *Proc. Roy. Soc.* **A202**, 336 (1950).
74. Hauptman, H., and Karle, J., Structure invariants and semi-invariants for non-centrosymmetric space groups. *Acta Cryst.* **9**, 45 (1956).
75. Hayes, W. D., Transformation groups of the thermodynamic variables. *Quart. Appl. Math.* **4**, 227 (1946).
76. Heesch, H., On systematic structure theory *Z. Krist.* **71**, 95 (1929); **72**, 177 (1929); **73**, 325, 346 (1930).
77. Heisenberg, W., The theory of ferromagnetism. *Z. Physik.* **49**, 619 (1928).
78. Heitler, W., Group theory of homopolar chemical combination. *Z. Physik.* **47**, 835 (1928).
79. Heitler, W., Group theory of the reciprocal action of atoms. *Z. Physik* **51**, 805 (1928).
80. Heitler, W., Present state of the quantum mechanical theory of homopolar valency. *Physik. Z.* **31**, 185 (1930).

81. Heitler, W., and Rumer, G., Quantum theory of chemical combination for polyatomic molecules. *Z. Physik.* **68**, 12 (1931).
82. Herring, C., Effect of time-reversal symmetry on energy bands of crystals. *Phys. Rev.* **52**, 361 (1937).
83. Herring, C., Accidental degeneracy in the energy bands of crystals. *Phys. Rev.* **52**, 365 (1937).
84. Herring, C., Character tables for two space groups. *J. Franklin Inst.* **233**, 525 (1942).
85. Hermann, C., On systematic structure theory. *Z. Krist.* **68**, 257 (1928); **69**, 226 (1928).
86. Herrmann, K., Roentgenographic extinction tables. *Z. Krist.* **68**, 288 (1928).
87. Herrmann, K., Tensors and crystal symmetry. *Z. Krist.* **89**, 32 (1934).
88. Hornig, D. F., The vibrational spectra of molecules and complex ions in crystals. *J. Chem. Phys.* **16**, 1063 (1948).
89. Howarth, D. J., and Jones, H., The cellular method of determining electronic wave functions and eigenvalues in crystals, with applications to sodium. *Proc. Phys. Soc.* (*London*) **A65**, 355 (1952).
90. Hund, F., Symmetry characteristics of terms for systems of similar particles in quantum mechanics. *Z. Physik* **43**, 788 (1927).
91. Hund, F., Symmetry properties of the forces in atomic nuclei. *Z. Physik* **105**, 202 (1937).
92. Ito, D., Janaka, H., Watanabe, Y., and Yamazaki, M., Group theoretical aspects in S-matrix theory. *Progr. Theoret. Phys.* (*Japan*) **7**, 128 (1952).
93. Ito, H., On the density matrix in Hartree field. *Progr. Theoret. Phys.* **7**, 406 (1952).
94. Jahn, H. A., Rotation and vibration of the methane molecule. *Ann. Physik* **23**, 529 (1935).
95. Jahn, H. A., Note on the Bhagavantam-Suryanarayana method of enumerating the physical constants of crystals. *Acta Cryst.* **2**, 30 (1949).
96. Jahn, H. A., Theoretical studies in nuclear structure. *Proc. Roy. Soc.* **A201**, 516 (1950); **A205**, 192 (1951).
97. Jahn, H. A., Direct evaluation of fractional parentage coefficients using young operators. *Phys. Rev.* **96**, 989 (1954).
98. Jahn, H. A., and Hope, J., Symmetry properties of the Wigner 9j symbol. *Phys. Rev.* **93**, 318 (1954).
99. Jahn, H. A., and Teller, E., Stability of polyatomic molecules in degenerate electronic states. *Proc. Roy. Soc.* **A161**, 220 (1937).
100. Jahn, H. A., and Van Wieringen, H., Theoretical studies in nuclear structure. *Proc. Roy. Soc.* **A209**, 502 (1951).
101. Jordan, P., and Wigner, E., On the Pauli equivalence prohibition. *Z. Physik* **47**, 631 (1928).
102. Kar, S. C., Contribution to the group theory of valence states. *Z. Physik* **81**, 139 (1933).
103. Kerns, D. M., Analysis of symmetrical waveguide junctions. *J. Research Natl. Bur. Standards* **46**, 267 (1951).
104. Koenig, F. O., Families of thermodynamic equations. *J. Chem. Phys.* **3**, 29 (1935).
105. Kondô, K., Table of characters of the symmetric group of degree 14. *Proc. Phys. Math. Soc. Japan* **3**, 585 (1940).

106. Koster, G. F., Localized functions in molecules and crystals. *Phys. Rev.* **89**, 67 (1953).
107. Kotani, M., Note on the theory of electronic states of polyatomic molecules. *Proc. Phys. Math. Soc. Japan* **19**, 460 (1937).
108. Kotani, M., and Siga, M., Valence theory of the methane molecule. *Proc. Phys. Math. Soc. Japan* **19**, 471 (1937).
109. Ledinegg, E., and Urban, P., On the group-theoretical treatment of the linear atomic chain. *Acta Phys. Austriaca* **6**, 7 (1952).
110. Liehr, A. D., On the use of local symmetry in analyzing the infrared spectra of complex molecules. *J. Chem. Phys.* **24**, 162 (1956).
111. Lord, R. C., and Teller, E., Structure of benzene. *J. Chem. Soc.* 1728 (1937).
112. Lunn, A. C., and Senior, J. K., Isomerism and configuration. *J. Phys. Chem.* **33**, 1027 (1929).
113. Mair, R. D., and Hornig, D. F., The vibrational spectra of molecules and complex ions. *J. Chem. Phys.* **17**, 1236 (1949).
114. Mathis, F., On the determination of the frequencies of proper vibration of polyatomic molecules. *Ann. fac. sci. univ. Toulouse sci. math. sci. phys.* **18**, 193 (1954).
115. Matossi, F., Irreducible representations of cubic groups. *J. Chem. Phys.* **19**, 1612 (1951).
116. McLachlan, D., Symmetry in reciprocal space. *Acta Cryst.* **9**, 318 (1956).
117. McWeeny, R., On the basis of orbital theories. *Proc. Roy. Soc.* **A232**, 114 (1955).
118. Meijer, P. H. E., Calculation of wave functions in a symmetric crystalline field. *Phys. Rev.* **95**, 1443 (1954).
119. Meister, A. G., Cleveland, F. F., and Murray, M. J., Interpretation of the spectra of polyatomic molecules by use of group theory. *Am. J. Phys.* **11**, 239 (1943).
120. Melvin, M. A., Simplification in finding symmetry-adapted eigenfunctions. *Revs. Mod. Phys.* **28**, 18 (1956).
121. Meyer, B., On the symmetries of spherical harmonics. *Can. J. Math.* **6**, 135 (1954).
122. Miheev, V. I., The number of homology classes of crystals. *Doklady Akad. Nauk. S.S.S.R.* **71**, 667 (1950).
123. Miller, G. A., A new chapter in trigonometry. *Quart. J. Math.* **37**, 26 (1906).
124. Minden, H. T., The complete symmetry group for internal rotation in CH_3CF_3 and like molecules. *J. Chem. Phys.* **20**, 1964 (1952).
125. Misra, R. D., Lattice sums of cubic crystals. *Proc. Natl. Acad. Sci. India* **13**, 275 (1943).
126. Motzok, D., Theory of substitutions in the analysis of the study of symmetry. *Z. Krist.* **72**, 249 (1929).
127. Motzok, D., Composition and transformation in the study of symmetry. *Z. Krist.* **73**, 434 (1930).
128. Mueller, E., The study of ornaments as application of the theory of finite groups. *Euclides* (*Madrid*) **6**, 42 (1946).
129. Mulliken, R. S., Electronic states of polyatomic molecules. *Phys. Rev.* **43**, 279 (1933).
130. Murnaghan, F. D., On the decomposition of tensors by contraction. *Proc. Natl. Acad. Sci. U.S.* **38**, 973 (1952).
131. Nagamiya, T., On the zero point entropy of methane crystals. *Progr. Theoret. Phys.* **6**, 702 (1951).
132. Nielson, J. R., and Berryman, L. H., A general method of obtaining molecular symmetry coordinates. *J. Chem. Phys.* **17**, 659 (1949).

133. Niggli, P., The surface symmetries of homogeneous discontinua. *Z. Krist.* **60,** 282 (1924).

134. Niggli, P., The regular point distribution along a line in a plane. *Z. Krist.* **63,** 255 (1926).

135. Niggli, P., Topological structure analysis. *Z. Krist.* **65,** 391 (1927); **68,** 404 (1928).

136. Niggli, P., New formulation of crystallography. *Experientia* **2,** 336 (1946).

137. Niggli, P., Character tables as an expression of the symmetry properties of molecules and crystals. *Schweiz. mineralog. petrog. Mitt.* **33,** 21 (1953).

138. Niggli, A., and Niggli, P., Space group symmetries and methods of calculation of crystal structure study. *Z. angew. Math. Phys.* **2,** 217, 311 (1951).

139. Niggli, P., and Nowacki, W., The arithmetical concept of crystal classes and the derivation of the space groups based upon this concept. *Z. Krist.* **91,** 321 (1935).

140. Nowacki, W., The non-crystallographic point groups. *Z. Krist.* **86,** 19 (1933).

141. Nowacki, W., On the number of different space groups. *Schweiz. Mineralog. petrog. Mitt.* **34,** 160 (1954).

142. Opechowski, W., On double crystallographic groups. *Physica* **7,** 552 (1940).

143. Parmenter, R. H., Symmetry properties of the energy bands of the zinc blende structure. *Phys. Rev.* **100,** 573 (1955).

144. Placzek, G., Intensities and polarizations of Raman lines. *Z. Physik.* **70,** 84 (1931).

145. Placzek, G., and Teller, E., Rotation structure of the Raman bands of polyatomic molecules. *Z. Phys.* **81,** 209 (1933).

146. Polya, G., Concerning the analogy of crystal symmetry in the plane. *Z. Krist.* **60,** 278 (1924).

147. Polya, G., Combinatorial number determination for permutation groups and chemical binding. *Compt. rend. congr. intern. Math. Oslo* **2,** 19 (1936).

148. Polya, G., Number determination for groups, graphs, and chemical binding. *Acta Math.* **68,** 145 (1937).

149. Prins, J. A., A thermodynamical substitution group. *Physica* **13,** 417 (1947).

150. Racah, G., Theory of complex spectra. *Phys. Rev.* **61,** 186 (1942); **62,** 438 (1942); **63,** 367 (1943); **76,** 1352 (1949).

151. Racah, G., On the decomposition of tensors by contraction. *Revs.* Mod. *Phys.* **21,** 494 (1949).

152. Rahman, A., Enumeration of physical constants of crystals. *Acta Cryst.* **6,** 426 (1953).

153. Rosenthal, J. E., and Murphy, G. M., Group theory and the vibration of polyatomic molecules. *Revs. Mod. Phys.* **8,** 317 (1936).

154. Rumer, G., The theory of spin valence. *Göttinger Nachrichten* 337 (1932).

155. Schiff, L. I., Paper representations of the non-cubic crystal classes. *Am. J. Phys.* **22,** 621 (1954).

156. Seitz, F., A matrix-algebraic development of the crystallographic groups. *Z. Krist.* **88,** 433 (1934); **90,** 289 (1935); **91,** 336 (1935); **94,** 100 (1936).

157. Seitz, F., On the reduction of space groups. *Ann. Math.* **37,** 17 (1936).

158. Seitz, F., and Sherman, A., On the symmetric states of atomic configurations. *J. Chem. Phys.* **2,** 11 (1934).

159. Serber, R., The solution of problems involving permutation degeneracy. *J Chem. Phys.* **2,** 697 (1934).

160. Serber, R., Extension of the Dirac vector model to include several configurations. *Phys. Rev.* **45,** 461 (1934).

161. Shannon, C. E., Synthesis of two-terminal switching circuits. *Bell System Tech. J.* **28**, 59 (1949).

162. Shapiro, I. S., Symmetry properties in the theory of elementary particles and nuclear processes. *Uspekhi Fiz. Nayk* **57**, 7 (1954).

163. Sklar, A. L., Theory of color of organic compounds. *J. Chem. Phys.* **5**, 669 (1937)

164. Sponer, H., and Teller, E., Electronic spectra. *Revs. Mod. Phys.* **13**, 75 (1941).

165. Stearn, A. E., *et al.*, Molecular symmetry and the reduction of the secular equation. *J. Chem. Phys.* **2**, 410 (1934).

166. Stiefel, E., Two applications of group characters to the solution of boundary value problems. *J. Research Natl. Bur. Standards* **48**, 424 (1952).

167. Subnikov, A. V., On the symmetry of vectors and tensors. *Izvest. Akad. Nauk S.S.S.R.* **13**, 347 (1949).

168. Subnikov, A. V., The so-called homology of crystals. *Doklady Akad. Nauk S.S.S.R.* **88**, 453 (1953).

169. Sun, C. E., *et al.*, On the detection and determination of redundant vibrational coordinates. *J. Chem. Phys.* **17**, 840 (1949).

170. Tavger, B. A., and Vaitsev, V. M., Magnetic symmetry of crystals. *Soviet Physics JETP* **3**, 430 (1956).

171. Teller, E., and Topley, B., Vibration frequencies of ethylene and ethane. *J. Chem. Soc.*, 885 (1935).

172. Theimer, O., Selection rules and temperature dependence of the first-order Raman effect in crystals. *Can. J. Phys.* **34**, 312 (1956).

173. Tisza, L., Interpretation of the spectra of polyatomic molecules. *Z. Physik.* **82**, 48 (1933).

174. Venkatarayudu, T., Normal coordinates of symmetric point groups. *Proc. Indian Acad. Sci.* **17**, 50, 75 (1943).

175. Venkatarayudu, T., and Krishnamurty, T. S. G., Symmetry properties of wave functions in crystals. *Proc. Indian Acad. Sci.* **29**, 137, 148 (1949).

176. Venkatarayudu, T., and Krishnamurty, T. S G., Physical constants of isotropic Solids. *Acta Cryst.* **5**, 287 (1952.)

177. Voge, H. H., Relation of the states of the carbon atom to its valence in methane. *J. Chem. Phys.* **4**, 581 (1936).

178. von der Lage, F. C., and Bethe, H. A., A method of obtaining electronic eigenfunctions and eigenvalues in solids with an application to sodium. *Phys. Rev.* **71**, 612 (1947).

179. von Neumann, J., and Wigner, E., Explanation of certain spectrum properties by means of the quantum mechanics of rotating electrons. *Z. Physik.* **47**, 203 (1928); **49**, 73 (1928); **51**, 844 (1928).

180. Waser, J., Symmetry relations between structure factors. *Acta Cryst.* **8**, 595 (1955).

181. Weber, L., The symmetry of homogeneous plane point systems. *Z. Krist.* **70**, 309 (1929).

182. Wells, A. F., The geometrical basis of crystal chemistry. *Acta Cryst.* **7**, 535, 545, 842, 849 (1954); **9**, 23 (1956).

183. Weyl, H., The quantum-theoretic calculation of molecular binding energies. *Göttinger Nachrichten* 285 (1930); 33 (1931).

184. Whiffen, D. H., The force field, vibration frequencies, normal coordinates, infrared and Raman intensities for benzene. *Phil. Trans. Roy. Soc.* **A248**, 131 (1955).

185. Wigner, E., Non-combining terms in the new quantum theory. *Z. Physik.* **40**, 492, 883 (1927).

186. Wigner, E., Some consequencies of the Schrodinger theory for term structures. *Z. Physik* **43**, 624 (1927); **45**, 601 (1928).

187. Wigner, E., On the characteristic elastic vibrations of symmetrical systems. *Göttinger Nachrichten* 133 (1930).

188. Wigner, E., On the operation of time reversal in quantum mechanics. *Göttinger Nachrichten* 546 (1932).

189. Wigner, E., Saturation of exchange forces. *Proc. Natl. Acad. Sci. U.S.* **22**, 662 (1936).

190. Wigner, E., On the consequences of the symmetry of the nuclear Hamiltonian on the spectroscopy of nuclei. *Phys. Rev.* **51**, 106 (1937).

191. Wigner, E., On the structure of nuclei beyond oxygen. *Phys. Rev.* **51**, 947 (1937).

192. Wigner, E., and Feenberg, E., Symmetry properties of nuclear energy levels. *Repts. Progr. Phys.* **8**, 274 (1941).

193. Wigner, E., and Witmer, E. E., Diatomic molecular spectra according to quantum mechanics. *Z. Physik.* **51**, 859 (1928).

194. Wilson, E. B., The degeneracy, selection rules, and other properties of the normal vibrations of certain polyatomic molecules. *J. Chem. Phys.* **2**, 432 (1934).

195. Wilson, E. B., The normal modes and frequencies of vibration of the plane hexagon model of the benzene molecule. *Phys. Rev.* **45**, 706 (1934).

196. Wilson, E. B., The statistical weights of the rotational levels of polyatomic molecules, including methane, ammonia, benzene, cyclopropane and ethane. *J. Chem. Phys.* **3**, 276 (1935).

197. Winston, H., The electronic energy levels of molecular crystals. *J. Chem. Phys.* **19**, 156 (1951).

198. Winston, H., Studies on localized orbitals. *Phys. Rev.* **94**, 328 (1954).

199. Winston, H., and Halford, R. S., Motions of molecules in condensed systems. *J. Chem. Phys.* **17**, 607 (1949).

200. Wintgen, G., On the representation theory of space groups. *Math. Ann.* **118**, 195 (1941).

201. Yamanouchi, T., On the calculation of atomic energy levels. *Proc. Phys. Math. Japan* **17**, 274 (1935); **18**, 10, 23, 623 (1936).

202. Yamanouchi, T., On the construction of unitary irreducible representations of the symmetric group. *Proc. Phys. Math. Soc. Japan* **19**, 436 (1937).

203. Yamanouchi, T., On the binding energy of the atomic nuclei. *Proc. Phys. Math. Soc. Japan* **19**, 557 (1937).

204. Yamanouchi, T., On Heisenberg's theory of ferromagnetism. *Proc. Phys. Math. Soc. Japan* **19**, 1003 (1937).

205. Yamanouchi, T., Tables useful for construction of irreducible representation matrices of symmetric groups. *J. Phys. Soc. Japan* **3**, 245 (1948).

206. Yanagawa, S., Theory of the normal modes of vibrations in crystals. *Progr. Theoret. Phys.* **10**, 83 (1953).

207. Yanagawa, S., Mathematical formulations of physical quantities for jj-coupling nuclear shell model. *J. Phys. Soc. Japan* **8**, 302 (1953).

208. Zassenhaus, H., On an algorithm for the determination of space groups. *Comment. Math. Helv.* **21**, 117 (1948).

209. Zehler, V., The calculation of the energy bands in the diamond crystal. *Ann. Physik* **13**, 229 (1953).

210. Zia-ud-Din, M., The characters of the symmetric group of order 11!. *Proc. London Math. Soc.* **39**, 200 (1935).

211. Zia-ud-Din, M., The characters of the symmetric groups of degrees 12 and 13. *Proc. London Math. Soc.* **42**, 340 (1937).
212. Zocher, H., Considerations of spatial and temporal asymmetry. *Z. Phys.* **139**, 147 (1954).
213. Zocher, H., and Torok, C., About space-time asymmetry in the realm of classical general and crystal physics. *Proc. Natl. Acad. Sci. U.S.* **39**, 681 (1953).

Appendix I

PROOF OF THE KEY THEOREM OF REPRESENTATION THEORY

Theorem. Every group has exactly r inequivalent irreducible representations, and if Γ_p and Γ_q are any two of these, then the matrix elements satisfy the orthogonality relations

$$\sum_{A\in G} [D^{(p)-1}(A)]_{ij}[D^{(q)}(A)]_{kl} = \frac{g}{d_p}\delta_{i,l}\delta_{j,k}\delta_{p,q}$$

where $\sum_{A\in G}$ means the sum over all elements of G,

$$d_p = \text{dimension of } \Gamma_p$$

$$\delta_{p,q} = \begin{cases} 0 \text{ if } \Gamma_p \neq \Gamma_q \\ 1 \text{ if } \Gamma_p = \Gamma_q \end{cases}$$

and the equation does not apply if Γ_p is equivalent to but not identical with Γ_q.

Proof.

The proof will be divided into several distinct parts which will be numbered. In the first section we shall derive an equation which will be used in the next two sections to derive the orthogonality relations.

(1) Let G be any finite group, $\Gamma_1 = \{D^{(1)}\}$ and $\Gamma_2 = \{D^{(2)}\}$ any representations of G, d_1 and d_2 the dimensions of Γ_1 and Γ_2, X any $d_1 \times d_2$ matrix, and $P \equiv \sum_{B\in G} D^{(1)}(B)XD^{(2)-1}(B)$. Then it will be shown that $D^{(1)}(A)P = PD^{(2)}(A)$ is valid for all A in G.

$$\begin{aligned} PD^{(2)}(A) &= \sum_{B\in G} D^{(1)}(B)XD^{(2)-1}(B)D^{(2)}(A) \\ &= D^{(1)}(A)\sum_{B\in G} [D^{(1)-1}(A)D^{(1)}(B)]X[D^{(2)-1}(A)D^{(2)}(B)]^{-1} \\ &= D^{(1)}(A)\sum_{C\in G} D^{(1)}(C)XD^{(2)-1}(C) \qquad (C = A^{-1}B) \\ &= D^{(1)}(A)P \end{aligned}$$

(2) Let Γ_p and Γ_q be two inequivalent irreducible representations of a group G. Letting $P = \sum_{B\in G} D^{(q)}(B)XD^{(p)-1}(B)$ we see from the equation $PD^{(q)}(A) = D^{(q)}(A)P$ together with Schur's lemma that $P = 0$. Hence $\sum_{B\in G} D^{(q)}(B)XD^{(p)-1}(B) = 0$. Putting $X_{mn} = \delta_{mj}\delta_{kn}$ (fixed j, k) we find $\sum_{B\in G} D^{(q)}_{ij}(B)D^{(p)-1}_{kl}(B) = 0$.

(3) Let $\Gamma_p = \Gamma_q = \Gamma$. Letting $P = \sum_{B\epsilon G} D(B)XD^{-1}(B)$ we see from the equation $PD^{(q)}(A) = D^{(q)}(A)P$ and the irreducibility of Γ that P must be a scalar matrix, $P = \lambda I$. Hence, $\sum_{B\epsilon G} D(B)XD^{-1}(B) = \lambda I$. Taking the trace of both sides, we find that $\lambda = \frac{g}{d}\,\mathrm{tr}\,(X)$. Letting $X_{mn} = \delta_{mj}\delta_{kn}$ we find $\lambda = \frac{g}{d}\delta_{jk}$ and $\sum_{B\epsilon G} D_{ij}(B)D^{-1}_{kl}(B) = \frac{g}{d}\delta_{jk}\delta_{il}$.

(4) It must still be shown that G possesses exactly r (r = number of conjugate classes of G) inequivalent irreducible representations. Let Γ be any representation and let $v^{(\Gamma)}$ be an r-dimensional column matrix defined by

$$v^{(\Gamma)} \equiv \begin{pmatrix} \sqrt{\frac{r_1}{g}} & \chi_1^{(\Gamma)} \\ \sqrt{\frac{r_2}{g}} & \chi_2^{(\Gamma)} \\ \vdots & \\ \sqrt{\frac{r_r}{g}} & \chi_r^{(\Gamma)} \end{pmatrix}$$

Then if Γ_p and Γ_q are irreducible representations, it follows easily from the preceding orthogonality relations that $v^{(p)\dagger}v^{(q)} = \delta_{p,q}$. Hence, the character vectors $v^{(p)}$ belonging to the irreducible representations of G form an orthonormal set in an r-dimensional vector space. Consequently, the number of inequivalent irreducible representations is $\leqslant r$.

(5) In this section we shall derive two equations which will be used in the next section to show that the number of irreducible representations is $\geqslant r$. We know that a reducible representation must be completely reducible, so that every representation is equivalent to a direct sum of irreducible representations. If Γ is a representation of G, and $\Gamma \cdot\!\equiv\!\cdot \sum_{p=1}^{R} c^p \Gamma_p$ (R = number of inequivalent irreducible representations of G) then it follows easily that $v^{(\Gamma)} = \sum_{p=1}^{R} c^{(p)} v^{(p)}$ and $c^{(p)} = v^{(p)\dagger}v^{(\Gamma)}$. For the regular representation of the group

$$v = \begin{pmatrix} \sqrt{g} \\ 0 \\ 0 \\ \vdots \\ 0 \end{pmatrix}$$

so $c^p = v^{(p)\dagger}v = \chi_1^{(p)} = d_p$. Hence

$$\Gamma_{\text{reg}} \cdot\!\equiv\!\cdot \sum_{p=1}^{R} d_p \Gamma_p$$

From the equation $v^{(\text{reg})} = \sum_{p=1}^{R} d_p v^{(p)}$ it follows that

$$\frac{1}{g}\sum_{p=1}^{R} d_p^{\,2} = 1$$

$$\sum_{p=1}^{R} d_p \chi_j^{(p)} = 0 \qquad (j = 2, 3, \ldots, r)$$

(6) Now let us define

$$S_j^{(p)} \equiv \sum_{A \epsilon C_j} D^{(p)}(A)$$

Then $D^{(p)-1}(B) S_j^{(p)} D^{(p)}(B) = S_j^{(p)}$ so $S_j^{(p)}$ is by Schur's lemma a scalar matrix.

$$S_j^{(p)} = \mu I$$

But $\operatorname{tr}(S_j^{(p)}) = r_j \chi_j^{(p)}$ so

$$\mu = \frac{r_j \chi_j^{(p)}}{d_p}$$

$$S_j^{(p)} = \frac{r_j \chi_j^{(p)}}{d_p} I$$

From the class multiplication formula (see Chapter II)

$$C_i C_j = \sum_{k=1}^{r} h_{ij,k} C_k$$

it follows that

$$S_i S_j = \sum_{k=1}^{r} h_{ij,k} S_k$$

or

$$r_i r_j \left(\frac{\chi_i^{(p)}}{d_p}\right)\left(\frac{\chi_j^{(p)}}{d_p}\right) = \sum_{k=1}^{r} h_{ij,k} r_k \frac{\chi_k^{(p)}}{d_p}$$

Summing over all irreducible representations we have (using the equations of section 5)

$$r_i r_j \sum_{p=1}^{R} \chi_i^{(p)} \chi_j^{(p)} = \sum_{k=1}^{r} h_{ij,k} r_k \sum_{p=1}^{R} d_p \chi_k^{(p)}.$$

$$= g h_{ij,1}$$

$$= g r_i \delta_{i,j'}$$

So

$$\sum_{p=1}^{R} \chi_i^{(p)} \chi_j^{(p)} = \frac{g}{r_j} \delta_{i,j'}$$

where

$$\delta_{ij'} = 1 \text{ if } C_j \text{ is the class inverse to } C_i$$
$$= 0 \text{ otherwise}$$

Now let us define r vectors of dimension R as follows:

$$u_j \equiv \begin{pmatrix} \chi_j^{(1)} \\ \chi_j^{(2)} \\ \vdots \\ \chi_j^{(R)} \end{pmatrix} \qquad j = 1, 2, \ldots, r$$

From the preceding orthogonality relation we see that

$$u_j^t u_k = \frac{g}{r_j} \delta_{j,k'}$$

so none of the vectors is the null vector. Furthermore, they are linearly independent, because if $a_1, \ldots, a_r$ are constants satisfying

$$\sum_{j=1}^{r} a_j u_j = 0$$

then by multiplying by u_{k}^t., we find

$$a_k = 0$$

But if r column matrix vectors are linearly independent, they must be at least r-dimensional. Hence $R \geqslant r$.

Appendix II

IRREDUCIBLE REPRESENTATIONS OF D_3, D_4, D_6, T, O, AND $\mathscr{I}$

In this appendix the two orthogonal generators of the 2- and 3-dimensional irreducible representations of the groups D_3, D_4, D_6, T, and O will be given. Also the three orthogonal generators of the 3-, 4-, and 5-dimensional irreducible representations of the icosahedral group $\mathscr{I}$ will be given.

Group	$D(A_1)$	$D(A_2)$	*Irreducible Representation*
D_3	$\begin{pmatrix} -1 & 0 \\ 0 & 1 \end{pmatrix}$	$\begin{pmatrix} -\frac{1}{2} & -\frac{1}{2}\sqrt{3} \\ \frac{1}{2}\sqrt{3} & -\frac{1}{2} \end{pmatrix}$	Γ_3
D_4	$\begin{pmatrix} -1 & 0 \\ 0 & 1 \end{pmatrix}$	$\begin{pmatrix} 0 & -1 \\ 1 & 0 \end{pmatrix}$	Γ_5
D_6	$\begin{pmatrix} -1 & 0 \\ 0 & 1 \end{pmatrix}$	$\begin{pmatrix} \frac{1}{2} & -\frac{1}{2}\sqrt{3} \\ \frac{1}{2}\sqrt{3} & \frac{1}{2} \end{pmatrix}$	Γ_5
	$\begin{pmatrix} -1 & 0 \\ 0 & 1 \end{pmatrix}$	$\begin{pmatrix} -\frac{1}{2} & \frac{1}{2}\sqrt{3} \\ -\frac{1}{2}\sqrt{3} & -\frac{1}{2} \end{pmatrix}$	Γ_6
T	$\begin{pmatrix} 1 & 0 & 0 \\ 0 & -1 & 0 \\ 0 & 0 & -1 \end{pmatrix}$	$\begin{pmatrix} 0 & 0 & 1 \\ 1 & 0 & 0 \\ 0 & 1 & 0 \end{pmatrix}$	Γ_4
O	$\begin{pmatrix} -1 & 0 \\ 0 & 1 \end{pmatrix}$	$\begin{pmatrix} -\frac{1}{2} & -\frac{1}{2}\sqrt{3} \\ \frac{1}{2}\sqrt{3} & -\frac{1}{2} \end{pmatrix}$	Γ_3
	$\begin{pmatrix} -1 & 0 & 0 \\ 0 & 0 & -1 \\ 0 & 1 & 0 \end{pmatrix}$	$\begin{pmatrix} 0 & 0 & 1 \\ 1 & 0 & 0 \\ 0 & 1 & 0 \end{pmatrix}$	Γ_4
	$\begin{pmatrix} 1 & 0 & 0 \\ 0 & 0 & 1 \\ 0 & -1 & 0 \end{pmatrix}$	$\begin{pmatrix} 0 & 0 & 1 \\ 1 & 0 & 0 \\ 0 & 1 & 0 \end{pmatrix}$	Γ_5

Icosahedral Group $\mathscr{I}$

$D(A_1)$	$D(A_2)$	$D(A_3)$	Irreducible Representation
$\begin{pmatrix} 1 & 0 & 0 \\ 0 & -\frac{1}{2} & -\frac{1}{2}\sqrt{3} \\ 0 & \frac{1}{2}\sqrt{3} & -\frac{1}{2} \end{pmatrix}$	$\begin{pmatrix} -\frac{1}{3} & -\frac{2}{3}\sqrt{2} & 0 \\ -\frac{2}{3}\sqrt{2} & \frac{1}{3} & 0 \\ 0 & 0 & -1 \end{pmatrix}$	$\begin{pmatrix} -1 & 0 & 0 \\ 0 & -\frac{1}{4} & -\frac{1}{4}\sqrt{15} \\ 0 & -\frac{1}{4}\sqrt{15} & \frac{1}{2} \end{pmatrix}$	Γ_2
$\begin{pmatrix} -\frac{1}{2} & -\frac{1}{2}\sqrt{3} & 0 \\ \frac{1}{2}\sqrt{3} & -\frac{1}{2} & 0 \\ 0 & 0 & 1 \end{pmatrix}$	$\begin{pmatrix} -1 & 0 & 0 \\ 0 & \frac{1}{3} & \frac{2}{3}\sqrt{2} \\ 0 & \frac{2}{3}\sqrt{2} & -\frac{1}{3} \end{pmatrix}$	$\begin{pmatrix} \frac{1}{4} & -\frac{1}{4}\sqrt{15} & -0 \\ -\frac{1}{4}\sqrt{15} & -\frac{1}{4} & 0 \\ 0 & 0 & -1 \end{pmatrix}$	Γ_3
$\begin{pmatrix} 1 & 0 & 0 & 0 \\ 0 & 1 & 0 & 0 \\ 0 & 0 & -\frac{1}{2} & \frac{1}{2}\sqrt{3} \\ 0 & 0 & -\frac{1}{2}\sqrt{3} & -\frac{1}{2} \end{pmatrix}$	$\begin{pmatrix} 1 & 0 & 0 & 0 \\ 0 & -\frac{1}{3} & \frac{2}{3}\sqrt{2} & 0 \\ 0 & \frac{2}{3}\sqrt{2} & \frac{1}{3} & 0 \\ 0 & 0 & 0 & -1 \end{pmatrix}$	$\begin{pmatrix} -\frac{1}{4} & \frac{1}{4}\sqrt{15} & 0 & 0 \\ \frac{1}{4}\sqrt{15} & \frac{1}{4} & 0 & 0 \\ 0 & 0 & 1 & 0 \\ 0 & 0 & 0 & -1 \end{pmatrix}$	Γ_4
$\begin{pmatrix} 1 & 0 & 0 & 0 & 0 \\ 0 & -\frac{1}{2} & \frac{1}{2}\sqrt{3} & 0 & 0 \\ 0 & -\frac{1}{2}\sqrt{3} & -\frac{1}{2} & 0 & 0 \\ 0 & 0 & 0 & -\frac{1}{2} & \frac{1}{2}\sqrt{3} \\ 0 & 0 & 0 & -\frac{1}{2}\sqrt{3} & -\frac{1}{2} \end{pmatrix}$	$\begin{pmatrix} -\frac{1}{3} & \frac{2}{3}\sqrt{2} & 0 & 0 & 0 \\ \frac{2}{3}\sqrt{2} & \frac{1}{3} & 0 & 0 & 0 \\ 0 & 0 & -1 & 0 & 0 \\ 0 & 0 & 0 & 1 & 0 \\ 0 & 0 & 0 & 0 & 1 \end{pmatrix}$	$\begin{pmatrix} 1 & 0 & 0 & 0 & 0 \\ 0 & -\frac{1}{2} & 0 & \frac{1}{2}\sqrt{3} & 0 \\ 0 & 0 & \frac{1}{2} & 0 & -\frac{1}{2}\sqrt{3} \\ 0 & \frac{1}{2}\sqrt{3} & 0 & \frac{1}{2} & 0 \\ 0 & 0 & -\frac{1}{2}\sqrt{3} & 0 & -\frac{1}{2} \end{pmatrix}$	Γ_5

Since $\mathscr{I}$ is isomorphic to the alternating group on five symbols $\mathscr{A}(5)$, a correspondence between A_1, A_2, A_3 and permutations can be established. One such correspondence is

$$\begin{aligned} A_1 &\leftrightarrow (1\,2\,3) = (1\,2)(2\,3) \\ A_2 &\leftrightarrow (1\,2)(3\,4) \\ A_3 &\leftrightarrow (1\,2)(4\,5). \end{aligned}$$

Appendix III

THE LORENTZ GROUPS

A brief survey of the principal algebraic properties of the Lorentz groups will be presented here.

Let

$$G = \begin{pmatrix} -1 & 0 & 0 & 0 \\ 0 & 1 & 0 & 0 \\ 0 & 0 & 1 & 0 \\ 0 & 0 & 0 & 1 \end{pmatrix}.$$

A *Lorentz matrix* L is defined to be any real 4-dimensional matrix satisfying the equation

$$L^t G L = G.$$

The determinant of a Lorentz matrix is ± 1.

$$\det(L) = \pm 1.$$

Also L and L^{-1} have the same eigenvalues so that if λ is an eigenvalue of L, then so is λ^{-1}.

The set of all Lorentz matrices forms an infinite group when the group product of two Lorentz matrices is defined to be the matrix product. The group of all Lorentz matrixes is called the *full homogeneous Lorentz group*.

The Lorentz matrices, in contrast to the matrices of finite matrix groups, are not all diagonalizable.

The full homogeneous Lorentz group has several subgroups which are also called Lorentz groups. The subgroup consisting of all Lorentz matrices with positive upper left diagonal element is called the *orthochronous, homogeneous Lorentz group*. The subgroup consisting of all Lorentz matrices with positive determinant is called the *proper homogeneous Lorentz group*, The subgroup consisting of all Lorentz matrices with positive upper left diagonal element and positive determinant is called the *proper, orthochronous, homogeneous Lorentz group*. The subgroup consisting of all Lorentz matrices whose determinant and upper left element have the same sign will be called the *antichronous, homogeneous Lorentz group*.

Let

$$S = \begin{pmatrix} 1 & 0 & 0 & 0 \\ 0 & -1 & 0 & 0 \\ 0 & 0 & -1 & 0 \\ 0 & 0 & 0 & -1 \end{pmatrix} \qquad T = \begin{pmatrix} -1 & 0 & 0 & 0 \\ 0 & 1 & 0 & 0 \\ 0 & 0 & 1 & 0 \\ 0 & 0 & 0 & 1 \end{pmatrix}$$

so*

$$ST = TS = -I = \begin{pmatrix} -1 & 0 & 0 & 0 \\ 0 & -1 & 0 & 0 \\ 0 & 0 & -1 & 0 \\ 0 & 0 & 0 & -1 \end{pmatrix}.$$

The orthochronous homogeneous Lorentz group, the antichronous homogeneous Lorentz group, the proper homogeneous Lorentz group, and the full homogeneous Lorentz group are obtained from the proper, orthochronous, homogeneous Lorentz group by adding to it the matrices $\{S\}$, $\{T\}$, $\{-I\}$, and $\{S, T\}$, respectively, together with all matrices generated by forming products of the respective matrices and Lorentz matrices of the proper, orthochronous, homogeneous Lorentz group.

Let us adopt the following notation for these groups:

1. proper, orthochronous, homogeneous Lorentz group $\mathscr{L}(O, O, O)$.
2. orthochronous, homogeneous Lorentz group $\mathscr{L}(S, O, O)$.
3. antichronous, homogeneous Lorentz group $\mathscr{L}(O, T, O)$.
4. proper homogeneous Lorentz group $\mathscr{L}(O, O, -I)$.
5. full homogeneous Lorentz group $\mathscr{L}(S, T, -I)$.

Besides the homogeneous Lorentz groups defined above there are also inhomogeneous Lorentz groups. Let

$$x = \begin{pmatrix} x^0 \\ x^1 \\ x^2 \\ x^3 \end{pmatrix}$$

be a four-component, real, column matrix. Then besides homogeneous, linear transformations of the form

$$x' = Lx,$$

we can define inhomogeneous, linear transformations of the form

$$x' = Lx + a,$$

where a is any real, four-component column matrix. Such a transformation will be denoted by the symbol $(L|a)$. Inhomogeneous linear transformations satisfy the relations§

$$(L_1|a_1)(L_2|a_2) = (L_1 L_2|L_1 a_2 + a_1)$$

$$(L|a)^{-1} = (L^{-1}|-L^{-1}a)$$

$$(L|a)^{-1}(L_0|a_0)(L|a) = (L^{-1}L_o L|L^{-1}L_o a + L^{-1}a_o - L^{-1}a).$$

* Note that $T = G$. Two symbols are used to facilitate discussion of the two uses of the matrix.

§ One sees that inhomogeneous Lorentz transformations have the faithful 5-dimensional representation

$$(L|a) \rightarrow \begin{pmatrix} L & a \\ 0 & 1 \end{pmatrix}.$$

Corresponding to each homogeneous Lorentz group we can now form an inhomogeneous Lorentz group. If we let $\mathscr{L}$ denote any one of the homogeneous Lorentz groups, then the corresponding inhomogeneous Lorentz group $\mathscr{I}\mathscr{L}$ is defined as the group of all inhomogeneous transformations $(L|a)$ which can be formed from all real a and all L in $\mathscr{L}$. We thus obtain the five inhomogeneous Lorentz groups $\mathscr{I}\mathscr{L}(O,O,O)$, $\mathscr{I}\mathscr{L}(S,O,O)$, $\mathscr{I}\mathscr{L}(O,T,O)$, $\mathscr{I}\mathscr{L}(O,O,-I)$, $\mathscr{I}\mathscr{L}(S,T,-I)$.

Let $\mathscr{I}\mathscr{L}$ be any one of the above five inhomogeneous Lorentz groups, and let $\mathscr{T}$ be the subgroup of all translations $\mathscr{T} = \{(I|v)\}$. Then $\mathscr{T}$ is a normal subgroup of $\mathscr{I}\mathscr{L}$ and

$$\frac{\mathscr{I}\mathscr{L}}{\mathscr{T}} = \mathscr{L}.$$

Furthermore

$$\mathscr{I}\mathscr{L} = \mathscr{T} \boxed{S} \mathscr{L};$$

i.e., $\mathscr{I}\mathscr{L}$ is the semidirect product of $\mathscr{T}$ and $\mathscr{L}$.

Ten Lorentz groups have now been defined. Several of them will be discussed individually in the remainder of the appendix.

1. The Proper, Orthochronous, Homogeneous Lorentz Group $\mathscr{L}(O, O, O)$

(1) $\mathscr{L}(O,O,O)$ is not Abelian.

(2) $\mathscr{L}(O,O,O)$ is simple.

(3) $\mathscr{L}(O,O,O)$ is a normal subgroup of each of the other four homogeneous Lorentz groups.

(4) $\mathscr{L}(O,O,O)$ contains a subgroup which is isomorphic to the 3-dimensional rotation group. This subgroup consists of all matrices of the form

$$\begin{pmatrix} 1 & 0 & 0 & 0 \\ 0 & R_{11} & R_{12} & R_{13} \\ 0 & R_{21} & R_{22} & R_{23} \\ 0 & R_{31} & R_{32} & R_{33} \end{pmatrix},$$

where $R = ||R_{ij}||$ is a rotation matrix. Such a Lorentz matrix is frequently referred to as a rotation.

(5) Every Lorentz matrix L of $\mathscr{L}(O,O,O)$ can be expressed in the form

$$L = R_1 L_x R_2 ,$$

where

$$L_x = \begin{pmatrix} \cosh\theta & \sinh\theta & 0 & 0 \\ \sinh\theta & \cosh\theta & 0 & 0 \\ 0 & 0 & 1 & 0 \\ 0 & 0 & 0 & 1 \end{pmatrix}$$

and θ is real and R_1 and R_2 are rotations.

(6)

$$\begin{pmatrix} \cosh\theta & \sinh\theta \\ \sinh\theta & \cosh\theta \end{pmatrix} = e^{\theta\left(\begin{smallmatrix} 0 & 1 \\ 1 & 0 \end{smallmatrix}\right)}.$$

(7) $\mathscr{L}(O, O, O)$ is a 6-parameter group, i.e., the elements of the group can be specified by six real continuously varying parameters.

(8) Let us write the six parameters of $\mathscr{L}(O, O, O)$ in the form $\omega^{\mu\nu}$ $(\mu, \nu = 0, 1, 2, 3)$ where $\omega^{\mu\nu} = -\omega^{\nu\mu}$ and $L = I$ for $\omega^{\mu\nu} = 0$. Next let us expand $L(\omega^{\mu\nu})$ in a power series in $\omega^{\mu\nu}$.

$$L(\omega_{\mu\nu}) = I - \tfrac{1}{2}\omega^{\mu\nu}K_{\mu\nu} + \ldots,$$

where the K's are real 4-dimensional matrices chosen so that

$$K_{\mu\nu} = -K_{\nu\mu} .$$

If for infinitesimal $\omega^{\mu\nu}$ the matrix $L(\omega^{\mu\nu})$ transforms x^μ $(\mu = 0, 1, 2, 3)$ according to the equation

$$x'^\mu = L^\mu{}_\nu x^\nu \qquad \mu, \nu = 0, 1, 2, 3,$$

$$L^\mu{}_v = \delta^\mu_\nu + \omega^{\mu\lambda}g_{\lambda\nu}$$

$$\begin{aligned} g_{\lambda\nu} &= -1 \quad \text{if } \lambda = \nu = 0 \\ &= 1 \quad \text{if } \lambda = \nu = 1, 2, 3 \\ &= 0 \quad \text{otherwise.} \end{aligned}$$

$$L = \begin{pmatrix} L^0{}_0 & L^0{}_1 & . & . & . & L^0{}_3 \\ L^1{}_0 & L^1{}_1 & . & . & . & L^1{}_3 \\ . & . & . & . & . & . \\ . & . & . & . & . & . \\ . & . & . & . & . & . \\ L^3{}_0 & L^3{}_1 & . & . & . & L^3{}_3 \end{pmatrix}$$

then

$$K_{01} = \begin{pmatrix} 0 & -1 & 0 & 0 \\ -1 & 0 & 0 & 0 \\ 0 & 0 & 0 & 0 \\ 0 & 0 & 0 & 0 \end{pmatrix} \qquad K_{02} = \begin{pmatrix} 0 & 0 & -1 & 0 \\ 0 & 0 & 0 & 0 \\ -1 & 0 & 0 & 0 \\ 0 & 0 & 0 & 0 \end{pmatrix}$$

$$K_{03} = \begin{pmatrix} 0 & 0 & 0 & -1 \\ 0 & 0 & 0 & 0 \\ 0 & 0 & 0 & 0 \\ -1 & 0 & 0 & 0 \end{pmatrix}$$

$$K_{23} = \begin{pmatrix} 0 & 0 & 0 & 0 \\ 0 & 0 & 0 & 0 \\ 0 & 0 & 0 & -1 \\ 0 & 0 & 1 & 0 \end{pmatrix} \qquad K_{31} = \begin{pmatrix} 0 & 0 & 0 & 0 \\ 0 & 0 & 0 & 1 \\ 0 & 0 & 0 & 0 \\ 0 & -1 & 0 & 0 \end{pmatrix}$$

$$K_{12} = \begin{pmatrix} 0 & 0 & 0 & 0 \\ 0 & 0 & -1 & 0 \\ 0 & 1 & 0 & 0 \\ 0 & 0 & 0 & 0 \end{pmatrix}$$

These six matrices satisfy the commutation relations

$$[K_{\kappa\lambda}, K_{\mu\nu}]_- = g_{\kappa\mu} K_{\lambda\nu} + g_{\lambda\nu} K_{\kappa\mu} - g_{\kappa\nu} K_{\lambda\mu} - g_{\lambda\mu} K_{\kappa\nu} \; .$$

If $L \to D^{(\Gamma)}(L)$ is any representation of $\mathscr{L}(O, O, O)$ and if

$$L = I - \tfrac{1}{2}\omega^{\mu\nu} K_{\mu\nu}$$

$$D^{(\Gamma)}(L) = I - \tfrac{1}{2}\omega^{\mu\nu} K^{(\Gamma)}_{\mu\nu},$$

then these $K^{(\Gamma)}$'s must also satisfy the above commutation relations. The $K^{(\Gamma)}$'s belonging to a representation Γ are called the infinitesimal transformations of the representation Γ. If Γ is irreducible so are the $K^{(\Gamma)}$'s.

(9) $\mathscr{L}(O, O, O)$ has both finite-dimensional and infinite-dimensional irreducible representations.

(10) Only finite-dimensional representations will be considered in this section.

(11) Every reducible finite-dimensional representation is completely reducible.

(12) The only unitary irreducible finite-dimensional representation is the trivial one $L \to 1$.

(13) Let $S(2)$ be the group of all unimodular 2-dimensional matrices. Then $S(2)$ is two-to-one homomorphic to $\mathscr{L}(O, O, O)$.

(14) An explicit form of a homomorphism between $S(2)$ and $\mathscr{L}(O, O, O)$ is presented.

$$\begin{pmatrix} \alpha\beta \\ \gamma\delta \end{pmatrix} \to \begin{pmatrix} \frac{1}{2}(|\alpha|^2+|\beta|^2+|\gamma|^2+|\delta|^2) & \mathrm{Re}(\alpha\beta^*+\gamma\delta^*) & -\mathrm{Im}(\alpha\beta^*+\gamma\delta^*) & \frac{1}{2}(|\alpha|^2-|\beta|^2+|\gamma|^2-|\delta|^2) \\ \mathrm{Re}(\alpha\gamma^*+\beta\delta^*) & \mathrm{Re}(\alpha\delta^*+\beta\gamma^*) & -\mathrm{Im}(\alpha\delta^*-\beta\gamma^*) & \mathrm{Re}(\alpha\gamma^*-\beta\delta^*) \\ \mathrm{Im}(\alpha\gamma^*+\beta\delta^*) & \mathrm{Im}(\alpha\delta^*+\beta\gamma^*) & \mathrm{Re}(\alpha\delta^*-\beta\gamma^*) & \mathrm{Im}(\alpha\gamma^*-\beta\delta^*) \\ \frac{1}{2}(|\alpha|^2+|\beta|^2-|\gamma|^2-|\delta|^2) & \mathrm{Re}(\alpha\beta^*-\gamma\delta^*) & -\mathrm{Im}(\alpha\beta^*-\gamma\delta^*) & \frac{1}{2}(|\alpha|^2-|\beta|^2-|\gamma|^2+|\delta|^2) \end{pmatrix}$$

(15) For some particular matrices this homomorphism takes the form indicated as follows.

$$\pm\begin{pmatrix} \cos\frac{1}{2}\theta & i\sin\frac{1}{2}\theta \\ i\sin\frac{1}{2}\theta & \cos\frac{1}{2}\theta \end{pmatrix} \to \begin{pmatrix} 1 & 0 & 0 & 0 \\ 0 & 1 & 0 & 0 \\ 0 & 0 & \cos\theta & -\sin\theta \\ 0 & 0 & \sin\theta & \cos\theta \end{pmatrix}$$

$$\pm\begin{pmatrix} \cos\frac{1}{2}\theta & -\sin\frac{1}{2}\theta \\ \sin\frac{1}{2}\theta & \cos\frac{1}{2}\theta \end{pmatrix} \to \begin{pmatrix} 1 & 0 & 0 & 0 \\ 0 & \cos\theta & 0 & \sin\theta \\ 0 & 0 & 1 & 0 \\ 0 & -\sin\theta & 0 & \cos\theta \end{pmatrix}$$

$$\pm\begin{pmatrix} e^{\frac{1}{2}i\theta} & 0 \\ 0 & e^{-\frac{1}{2}i\theta} \end{pmatrix} \to \begin{pmatrix} 1 & 0 & 0 & 0 \\ 0 & \cos\theta & -\sin\theta & 0 \\ 0 & \sin\theta & \cos\theta & 0 \\ 0 & 0 & 0 & 1 \end{pmatrix}$$

$$\pm\begin{pmatrix} \cosh\frac{1}{2}\theta & \sinh\frac{1}{2}\theta \\ \sinh\frac{1}{2}\theta & \cosh\frac{1}{2}\theta \end{pmatrix} \to \begin{pmatrix} \cosh\theta & \sinh\theta & 0 & 0 \\ \sinh\theta & \cosh\theta & 0 & 0 \\ 0 & 0 & 1 & 0 \\ 0 & 0 & 0 & 1 \end{pmatrix}$$

$$\pm\begin{pmatrix} \cosh\frac{1}{2}\theta & i\sinh\frac{1}{2}\theta \\ -i\sinh\frac{1}{2}\theta & \cosh\frac{1}{2}\theta \end{pmatrix} \to \begin{pmatrix} \cosh\theta & 0 & \sinh\theta & 0 \\ 0 & 1 & 0 & 0 \\ \sinh\theta & 0 & \cosh\theta & 0 \\ 0 & 0 & 0 & 1 \end{pmatrix}$$

$$\pm\begin{pmatrix} e^{\frac{1}{2}\theta} & 0 \\ 0 & e^{-\frac{1}{2}\theta} \end{pmatrix} \to \begin{pmatrix} \cosh\theta & 0 & 0 & \sinh\theta \\ 0 & 1 & 0 & 0 \\ 0 & 0 & 1 & 0 \\ \sinh\theta & 0 & 0 & \cosh\theta \end{pmatrix}$$

(16) We can take the reverse point of view and consider $S(2)$ as a two-valued representation of $\mathscr{L}(O, O, O)$.

(17) $S(2)$ is an irreducible representation of $\mathscr{L}(O, O, O)$.

(18) $S(2)$ is not equivalent to $S^*(2)$.

(19) The infinitesimal matrices $K_{\mu\nu}$ for this representation ($S(2)$) are

$$K_{23} = \frac{1}{2i}\begin{pmatrix} 0 & 1 \\ 1 & 0 \end{pmatrix}, \quad K_{31} = \frac{1}{2i}\begin{pmatrix} 0 & -i \\ i & 0 \end{pmatrix}, \quad K_{12} = \frac{1}{2i}\begin{pmatrix} 1 & 0 \\ 0 & -1 \end{pmatrix},$$

$$K_{01} = -\frac{1}{2}\begin{pmatrix} 0 & 1 \\ 1 & 0 \end{pmatrix}, \quad K_{02} = -\frac{1}{2}\begin{pmatrix} 0 & -i \\ i & 0 \end{pmatrix}, \quad K_{03} = -\frac{1}{2}\begin{pmatrix} 1 & 0 \\ 0 & -1 \end{pmatrix}.$$

(20) $S(2)$ is the covering group of $\mathscr{L}(O, O, O)$.

(21) $\mathscr{L}(O, O, O)$ has a countably infinite number of inequivalent, finite-dimensional, irreducible representations.

(22) The inequivalent, finite-dimensional, irreducible representations of

$\mathscr{L}(O, O, O)$ can be labeled by two discrete, non-negative indices m and n which can assume the values 0, $\frac{1}{2}$, 1, $\frac{3}{2}$, 2, $\frac{5}{2}$,... .

(23) The irreducible representation of $\mathscr{L}(O, O, O)$ belonging to the indices m and n will be denoted by $\Gamma_{m,n}$.

(24) $\Gamma_{m,n}$ is the Kronecker product of the $2m$th symmetrized Kronecker power of $S(2)$ with the $2n$th symmetrized Kronecker power of $S^*(2)$

$$\Gamma_{m,n} \cdot\!\equiv\!\cdot [S(2)]_{(2m)} \otimes [S^*(2)]_{(2n)} \;.$$

(25) $S(2) \cdot\!\equiv\!\cdot \Gamma_{1/2,0}\;, \quad S^*(2) \cdot\!\equiv\!\cdot \Gamma_{0,1/2}\;.$

(26) The dimension of $\Gamma_{m,n}$ is $(2m+1)(2n+1)$.

(27) $\Gamma_{m,n}$ is single-valued if $m+n$ is an integer, and double-valued otherwise. $\Gamma_{m,m}$ is a real, single-valued representation.

(28) The Kronecker product of two irreducible representations of $\mathscr{L}(O, O, O)$ can be reduced by a Clebsch-Gordan series as follows:

$$\Gamma_{m,n} \otimes \Gamma_{M,N} \cdot\!\equiv\!\cdot \sum_{j=|m-M|}^{m+M} \sum_{k=|n-N|}^{n+N} \Gamma_{j,k}\;,$$

where the summation indices change by unit increments.

(29) If

$$\mathbf{K} = (K_{23}, K_{31}, K_{12})$$
$$\mathscr{K} = (K_{01}, K_{02}, K_{03})$$

then

$$[K_1, K_2]_- = K_3(\text{cycl})$$
$$[\mathscr{K}_1, \mathscr{K}_2]_- = -\mathscr{K}_3(\text{cycl})$$
$$[K_1, \mathscr{K}_2]_- = [\mathscr{K}_1, K_2]_- = \mathscr{K}_3(\text{cycl}).$$

(30) The operators

$$C_1 = \mathbf{K}^2 - \mathscr{K}^2$$
$$C_2 = \mathbf{K} \cdot \mathscr{K}$$

commute with the infinitesimal operators $K_{\mu\nu}$ and are therefore scalar matrices in an irreducible representation. The operators C_1 and C_2 are called Casimir operators.

(31) Let

$$\mathbf{J} = \tfrac{1}{2}i(\mathbf{K} + i\mathscr{K})$$
$$\mathscr{J} = \tfrac{1}{2}i(\mathbf{K} - i\mathscr{K}).$$

Then,

$$[J_1, J_2]_- = iJ_3(\text{cycl})$$
$$[\mathscr{J}_1, \mathscr{J}_2]_- = i\mathscr{J}_3(\text{cycl})$$
$$[J_i, \mathscr{J}_j]_- = 0 \qquad i, j = 1, 2, 3.$$

(32) The J's and the $\mathscr{J}$'s both satisfy the commutation relations for angular momentum operators.

(33) The irreducible representation $\Gamma_{m,n}$ of the J's and $\mathscr{J}$'s is

$$\mathbf{J} \rightarrow \boldsymbol{\sigma}_m \otimes I_n$$
$$\mathcal{J} \rightarrow I_m \otimes \boldsymbol{\sigma}_n$$

where $\boldsymbol{\sigma}_m$ and $\boldsymbol{\sigma}_n$ are the irreducible spin matrix vectors of dimension $(2m + 1)$ and $(2n + 1)$, respectively, and I_m and I_n are the identity matrices of dimension $(2m + 1)$ and $(2n + 1)$ respectively.

(34)
$$C_1 = -2(\mathbf{J}^2 + \mathcal{J}^2)$$
$$C_2 = i(\mathbf{J}^2 - \mathcal{J}^2).$$

(35) In the irreducible representation $\Gamma_{m,n}$ the scalar Casimir matrices are given by

$$C_1 = -2\{m(m + 1) + n(n + 1)\}I_{m,n}$$
$$C_2 = i\{m(m + 1) - n(n + 1)\}I_{m,n} \, ,$$

where $I_{m,n}$ is the identity matrix of dimension $(2m + 1)(2n + 1)$.

(36) The eigenvalues of the Casimir operators can also be used to label the irreducible representations of $\mathscr{L}(O, O, O)$.

(37) Since $\mathscr{L}(O, O, O)$ is a matrix group it is a representation of itself. Also it is irreducible and is equivalent to $\Gamma_{1/2,1/2}$.

(38) A two-component spinor is a tensor which transforms under $\Gamma_{1/2,0}$. A two-component conjugate spinor is a tensor which transforms under $\Gamma_{0,1/2}$.

(39) A Dirac four-spinor, or undor, is a tensor which transforms under $\Gamma_{1/2,0} \oplus \Gamma_{0,1/2}$.

(40) A spinor with $2m$ undotted upper indices and $2n$ dotted lower indices is a tensor which transforms under $[\Gamma_{1/2,0}]_{2m} \otimes [\Gamma_{0,1/2}]_{2n}$.

(41) A spinor with $2m$ undotted upper indices and $2n$ dotted lower indices which is symmetric in the undotted indices and in the dotted indices is a tensor whose independent components transform under $\Gamma_{m,n}$.

2. The Proper Homogeneous Lorentz Group $\mathscr{L}(O, O, -I)$

$\mathscr{L}(O, O, -I)$ is easily seen to be isomorphic to $\mathscr{L}(O, O, O) \times C_2$. Hence the irreducible representations of $\mathscr{L}(O, O, -I)$ are outer Kronecker products of those of $\mathscr{L}(O, O, O)$ and the two of C_2.

3. The Orthochronous, Homogeneous Lorentz Group $\mathscr{L}(S, O, O)$ and the Antichronous, Homogeneous Lorentz Group $\mathscr{L}(O, T, O)$

These two groups are easily seen to be isomorphic to each other (by letting S correspond to T). Consequently only one group need be discussed. This will be $\mathscr{L}(S, O, O)$.

(1) $\mathscr{L}(O, O, O)$ is a normal subgroup of $\mathscr{L}(S, O, O)$.

(2) $\dfrac{\mathscr{L}(S, O, O)}{\mathscr{L}(O, O, O)} = C_2$.

(3) The finite-dimensional irreducible representations of $\mathscr{L}(S,O,O)$ are as follows. Letting $\Gamma_{m,n}$ be the previously defined irreducible representation of $\mathscr{L}(O,O,O)$, the irreducible representations of $\mathscr{L}(S,O,O)$ are $\Gamma^{(\mathscr{I})}_{m,n}(m\neq n)$ and $\Gamma^{(\text{ext})}_{m,m}$. By $\Gamma^{(\mathscr{I})}_{m,n}$ is meant the representation of $\mathscr{L}(S,O,O)$ induced by $\Gamma_{m,n}$, and by $\Gamma^{(\text{ext})}_{m,m}$ is meant a representation of $\mathscr{L}(S,O,O)$ which subduces $\Gamma_{m,m}$ on $\mathscr{L}(O,O,O)$ (i.e., $\Gamma^{(\text{ext})}_{m,m}$ is an extension of $\Gamma_{m,m}$).

(4) The irreducible representations of $\mathscr{L}(S,O,O)$ defined in (3) include all p-inequivalent irreducible finite-dimensional representations of $\mathscr{L}(S,O,O)$.

(5) Let $\Gamma_{mn}(S)$ be the representation

$$L\to D^{(m,n)}(SLS)$$

of $\mathscr{L}(O,O,O)$. Then for $m\neq n$

$$\Gamma_{mn}(S)\cdot\!\equiv\!\cdot\Gamma^{*}_{mn}\cdot\!\equiv\!\cdot\Gamma_{nm}\,.$$

(6) For $m\neq n$,

$$\Gamma^{(\mathscr{I})}_{mn}\cdot\!\equiv\!\cdot\Gamma^{(\mathscr{I})}_{nm}\,.$$

(7) For $m\neq n$, $\Gamma^{(\mathscr{I})}_{mn}$ is given by

$$L\to\begin{pmatrix} D^{(m,n)}(L) & 0\\ 0 & D^{(m,n)}(SLS)\end{pmatrix}\ \text{all } L \text{ in } \mathscr{L}(O,O,O)$$

$$S\to\pm\begin{pmatrix}0 & I\\ I & 0\end{pmatrix}\ \text{where } \dim I=(2m+1)(2n+1).$$

(8) $\Gamma^{(\text{ext})}_{m,m}$ can be chosen to be a real single-valued vector representation.

(9) In $\Gamma^{(\text{ext})}_{m,m}$ the matrix $D^{(m,m)}(S)$ can be chosen to be a diagonalizable square root of the identity matrix with the degeneracy of the eigenvalue $+1$ being $m(2m+1)$ and the degeneracy of the eigen. value -1 being $(m+1)(2m+1)$.

(10) Let $\Gamma_{m,m}$ be expressed in the form

$$L\to[D^{(1/2,0)}(L)]_{(2m)}\otimes[D^{(1/2,0)}(SLS)]_{(2m)}\,.$$

Then $D(S)$ can be chosen to have the form

$$D(S)=-\sum_{k=0}^{2m}a_k(\boldsymbol{\sigma}_1\cdot\boldsymbol{\sigma}_2)^k,$$

where

$\boldsymbol{\sigma}_1=\boldsymbol{\sigma}\otimes I$

$\boldsymbol{\sigma}_2=I\otimes\boldsymbol{\sigma}$

$\boldsymbol{\sigma}=$ irreducible $(2m+1)$-dimensional spin-vector matrix

$I=(2m+1)$-dimensional identity matrix

and the a_k's are numerical coefficients defined as follows:

Let

$$a = \begin{pmatrix} a_0 \\ a_1 \\ \vdots \\ a_{2m} \end{pmatrix} \qquad b = (-1)^{2m} \begin{pmatrix} 1 \\ -1 \\ 1 \\ -1 \\ \vdots \\ (-1)^{2m} \end{pmatrix}$$

$$\Delta_{rs} = \tfrac{1}{2}[r(r+1) - m(m+1)]^s \qquad r, s = 0, 1, 2, \ldots, 2m$$

$$\Delta = ||\Delta_{rs}||.$$

Then

$$a = \Delta^{-1} b.$$

(11)
$$D^{(1/2,1/2)}(S) = -\tfrac{1}{2} - 2\boldsymbol{\sigma}_1 \cdot \boldsymbol{\sigma}_2$$

$$D^{(1,1)}(S) = 1 - \boldsymbol{\sigma}_1 \cdot \boldsymbol{\sigma}_2 - (\boldsymbol{\sigma}_1 \cdot \boldsymbol{\sigma}_2)^2.$$

(12) Let Γ_1 and Γ_2 be any two single-valued finite-dimensional vector representations of $\mathscr{L}(S, O, O)$ which subduce on $\mathscr{L}(O, O, O)$ the same irreducible representation. Then

$$D^{(\Gamma_2)}(S) = \pm\, D^{(\Gamma_1)}(S).$$

(13)
$$\begin{gathered} [S, K_{23}]_- = [S, K_{31}]_- = [S, K_{12}]_- = 0 \\ [S, K_{01}]_+ = [S, K_{02}]_+ = [S, K_{03}]_+ = 0 \\ [T, K_{23}]_- = [T, K_{31}]_- = [T, K_{12}]_- = 0 \\ [T, K_{01}]_+ = [T, K_{02}]_+ = [T, K_{03}]_+ = 0. \end{gathered}$$

4. The Full Homogeneous Lorentz Group $\mathscr{L}(S, T, -I)$

(1) All four other homogeneous Lorentz groups are normal subgroups of $\mathscr{L}(S, T, -I)$.

(2)
$$\frac{\mathscr{L}(S, T, -I)}{\mathscr{L}(O, O, O)} = D_2.$$

$$\frac{\mathscr{L}(S, T, -I)}{\mathscr{L}(S, O, O)} = \frac{\mathscr{L}(S, T, -I)}{\mathscr{L}(O, T, O)} = \frac{\mathscr{L}(S, T, -I)}{\mathscr{L}(O, O, -I)} = C_2.$$

(3) $\mathscr{L}(S, T, -I)$ is isomorphic to the direct product of $\mathscr{L}(S, O, O)$ and C_2.

$$\mathscr{L}(S, T, -I) = \mathscr{L}(S, O, O) \times C_2.$$

If L denotes any element of $\mathscr{L}(S, O, O)$ and if $C_2 = \{I, -I\}$, then the isomorphism is

$$(L, I) \leftrightarrow L$$
$$(L, -I) \leftrightarrow -L.$$

(4) The finite-dimensional irreducible representations of $\mathscr{L}(S, T, -I)$ are all outer Kronecker products of finite-dimensional irreducible

representations of $\mathscr{L}(S, O, O)$ and irreducible representations of C_2.

(5) Let Γ_1 and Γ_2 be any two single-valued finite-dimensional vector representations of $\mathscr{L}(S, T, -I)$ which subduce on $\mathscr{L}(O, O, O)$ the same irreducible representation.
Let $A_1 = I$, $A_2 = -I$, $A_3 = S$, $A_4 = T$ (so $\{A_i\} = D_2$). Then

$$D^{(\Gamma_1)}(A_i) = \chi(A_i) D^{(\Gamma_2)}(A_i) \quad (i = 1, 2, 3, 4)$$

where χ is one of the four 1-dimensional characters of D_2.

5. The Proper, Orthochronous, Homogeneous Lorentz Group $\mathscr{L}(O, O, O)$: Irreducible, Infinite-Dimensional, Unitary Representations§

(1) The 2-dimensional unimodular group $S(2)$ is two-to-one homomorphic to $\mathscr{L}(O, O, O)$.

(2) Every nontrivial unitary representation of $\mathscr{L}(O, O, O)$ is infinite dimensional.

(3) Let $L_2(Z)$ be the separable Hilbert space of all measurable functions of $z = x + iy$, $-\infty \leqslant x, y \leqslant \infty$, such that

$$\int_{-\infty}^{\infty} dx \int_{-\infty}^{\infty} dy |f(z)|^2 < \infty,$$

and

$$\langle f_1 | f_2 \rangle = \int_{-\infty}^{\infty} dx \int_{-\infty}^{\infty} dy\, f_1^*(z) f_2(z).$$

Let

$$a = \begin{pmatrix} a_{11} & a_{12} \\ a_{21} & a_{22} \end{pmatrix}$$

be any matrix in the 2-dimensional unimodular group $S(2)$. Let $D^{(m,\rho)}(a)$ be an operator in $L_2(Z)$ defined for every integer m and every real number ρ by

$$D^{(m,\rho)}(a) f(z) = |a_{12} z + a_{21}|^{-m+i\rho-2} (a_{12} z + a_{22})^m f\left(\frac{a_{11} z + a_{21}}{a_{12} z + a_{22}}\right).$$

Then

$$a \to D^{(m,\rho)}(a)$$

is an irreducible unitary representation of $S(2)$ (and therefore of $\mathscr{L}(O, O, O)$). Let us denote this representation by $\Gamma_{m,\rho}$.

---

§ The outline here follows the discussion by M. A. Naimark, Linear representations of the Lorentz group, Amer. *Math. Soc. Translation* (2) **6**, **379** (1957).

(4) The set of representations $\Gamma_{m,\rho}$ is called the *principal series* of representations.

(5) Two unitary representations $a \to U(a)$, $a \to U'(a)$ in the spaces V and V' are said to be equivalent if there exists an isometric mapping of V onto V' under which $U(a)$ goes into $U'(a)$.

(6) $\Gamma_{m,\rho} \cdot\!\equiv\!\cdot \Gamma_{-m,-\rho}$.

(7) Let Γ_j be the $(2j+1)$-dimensional irreducible representation of the 3-dimensional rotation group. Let $\Gamma^{(s)}_{m,\rho}$ be the representation of the rotation subgroup of $\mathscr{L}(O,O,O)$ subduced by $\Gamma_{m,\rho}$. Then $\Gamma^{(s)}_{m,\rho}$ contains Γ_j as a component at most once. Furthermore $\Gamma^{(s)}_{m,\rho}$ contains Γ_j if and only if $m/2$ is one of the numbers $j, j-1, \ldots, -j$.

(8) The infinitesimal operators $K_{\mu\nu}$ in $\Gamma_{m,\rho}$ have the following representation in $L_2(Z)$.

$$K_{23} \to \frac{i}{2}(1-z^2)\frac{\partial}{\partial z} - \frac{i}{2}(1-z^{*2})\frac{\partial}{\partial z^*} + \frac{i}{2}\left\{\left(\frac{m}{2}+\frac{i\rho}{2}-1\right)z - \left(-\frac{m}{2}+\frac{i\rho}{2}-1\right)z^*\right\}$$

$$K_{31} \to \frac{1}{2}(1+z^2)\frac{\partial}{\partial z} + \frac{1}{2}(1+z^{*2})\frac{\partial}{\partial z^*} - \frac{1}{2}\left\{\left(\frac{m}{2}+\frac{i\rho}{2}-1\right)z + \left(-\frac{m}{2}+\frac{i\rho}{2}-1\right)z^*\right\}$$

$$K_{12} \to iz\frac{\partial}{\partial z} - iz^*\frac{\partial}{\partial z^*} - \frac{im}{2}$$

$$K_{01} \to -\frac{1}{2}(1-z^2)\frac{\partial}{\partial z} - \frac{1}{2}(1-z^{*2})\frac{\partial}{\partial z^*} - \frac{1}{2}\left\{\left(\frac{m}{2}+\frac{i\rho}{2}-1\right)z + \left(-\frac{m}{2}+\frac{i\rho}{2}-1\right)z^*\right\}$$

$$K_{02} \to \frac{i}{2}(1+z^2)\frac{\partial}{\partial z} - \frac{i}{2}(1+z^{*2})\frac{\partial}{\partial z^*} - \frac{i}{2}\left\{\left(\frac{m}{2}+\frac{i\rho}{2}-1\right)z - \left(-\frac{m}{2}+\frac{i\rho}{2}-1\right)z^*\right\}$$

$$K_{03} \to -z\frac{\partial}{\partial z} - z^*\frac{\partial}{\partial z^*} + \frac{1}{2}(i\rho-2).$$

(9) In the principal series of irreducible representations, the Casimir operators are given by

$$C_1 = \left[\left(\frac{\rho}{2}\right)^2 - \left(\frac{m}{2}\right)^2 + 1\right]I$$

$$C_2 = -\frac{m\rho}{4}I.$$

(10) Let σ be a real parameter such that $0 < \sigma \leqslant 2$. Let $\mathfrak{h}_\sigma'$ be the set of all measurable functions $f(z)$, $(z = x + iy, -\infty \leqslant x, y \leqslant \infty)$ such that

$$\int_{-\infty}^{\infty} dx_1 \int_{-\infty}^{\infty} dx_2 \int_{-\infty}^{\infty} dy_1 \int_{-\infty}^{\infty} dy_2 |z_1 - z_2|^{\sigma-2} f_1^*(z_1) f_2(z_2)$$

converges absolutely, and let

$$\langle f_1 | f_2 \rangle = \int_{-\infty}^{\infty} dx_1 \int_{-\infty}^{\infty} dx_2 \int_{-\infty}^{\infty} dy_1 \int_{-\infty}^{\infty} dy_2 |z_1 - z_2|^{\sigma-2} f_1^*(z_1) f_2(z_2).$$

Let $\mathfrak{h}_\sigma$ be the closure of $\mathfrak{h}_\sigma'$ (so $\mathfrak{h}_\sigma'$ is a separable Hilbert space). Let a be any matrix of $S(2)$ and let $D^{(\sigma)}(a)$ be an operator in $\mathfrak{h}_\sigma$ defined for every σ by

$$D^{(\sigma)}(a)f(z) = |a_{12}z + a_{22}|^{-2-\sigma} f\left(\frac{a_{11}z + a_{21}}{a_{12}z + a_{22}}\right).$$

Then

$$a \to D^{(\sigma)}(a)$$

is an irreducible unitary representation of $S(2)$ (and therefore of $\mathscr{L}(O, O, O)$). Let us denote this representation by Γ_σ.

(11) The set of representations Γ_σ is called the *supplementary series* of representations.

(12) Γ_2 is the trivial 1-dimensional representation of $\mathscr{L}(O, O, O)$.

(13) Again let Γ_j be the $(2j + 1)$-dimensional irreducible representation of the 3-dimensional rotation, and let $\Gamma_\sigma^{(s)}$ be the representation of the rotation subgroup of $\mathscr{L}(O, O, O)$ subduced by Γ_σ. Then $\Gamma_\sigma^{(s)}$ contains Γ_j at most once as a component. Furthermore Γ_j occurs as a component if and only if j is an integer.

(14) The infinitesimal operators $K_{\mu\nu}$ in Γ_σ have the following representation in $\mathfrak{h}_\sigma$.

$$K_{23} \to \frac{i}{2}(1 - z^2)\frac{\partial}{\partial z} - \frac{i}{2}(1 - z^{*2})\frac{\partial}{\partial z^*} - \frac{i}{2}\left(\frac{\sigma}{2} + 1\right)(z - z^*)$$

$$K_{31} \to \frac{1}{2}(1 + z^2)\frac{\partial}{\partial z} + \frac{1}{2}(1 + z^{*2})\frac{\partial}{\partial z^*} + \frac{1}{2}\left(\frac{\sigma}{2} + 1\right)(z + z^*)$$

$$K_{12} \to iz\frac{\partial}{\partial z} - iz^*\frac{\partial}{\partial z^*}$$

$$K_{01} \to -\frac{1}{2}(1 - z^2)\frac{\partial}{\partial z} - \frac{1}{2}(1 - z^{*2})\frac{\partial}{\partial z^*} + \frac{1}{2}\left(\frac{\sigma + 1}{2}\right)(z + z^*)$$

$$K_{02} \to \frac{i}{2}(1 + z^2)\frac{\partial}{\partial z} - \frac{i}{2}(1 + z^{*2})\frac{\partial}{\partial z^*} + \frac{i}{2}\left(\frac{\sigma}{2} + 1\right)(z - z^*)$$

$$K_{03} \to -z\frac{\partial}{\partial z} - z^*\frac{\partial}{\partial z^*} - \left(\frac{\sigma}{2} + 1\right).$$

(15) In the supplementary series of irreducible representations the Casimir operators are given by

$$C_1 = \left[1 - \left(\frac{\sigma}{2}\right)^2\right] I$$

$$C_2 = 0.$$

(16) Every irreducible unitary representation of $\mathscr{L}(O, O, O)$ is unitarily equivalent to a representation of the principal series or of the supplementary series.

6. The Proper, Orthochronous, Inhomogeneous Lorentz Group $\mathscr{IL}(O, O, O)$

The only irreducible finite-dimensional representations of $\mathscr{IL}(O, O, O)$ are those engendered by the finite-dimensional representations of the quotient group $\mathscr{L}(O, O, O) = \dfrac{\mathscr{IL}(O, O, O)}{\mathscr{T}}$. Consequently, attention will be focussed on the irreducible infinite-dimensional representations, and in particular on the unitary representations. The irreducible unitary representations of $\mathscr{IL}(O, O, O)$ will be developed by the method of little groups,* and those of physical interest will receive the most attention.

(1) Let k be any real four-component column matrix and $\mathcal{O}(k)$ the set of all four-component matrices of the form Lk, where L is any matrix in $\mathscr{L}(O, O, O)$. $\mathcal{O}(k)$ will be called the orbit§ of k.

(2) All vectors in an orbit have the same length‡ $k^\mu k_\mu = k^t G k$.

(3) The space of all real 4-vectors can be decomposed into disjoint orbits. These orbits are equivalence classes.

(4) The orbits themselves will be classified into six types.

(a) The vectors of $\mathcal{O}(k)$ are all future timelike, i.e.

$$k^\mu k_\mu < 0 \qquad k^0 > 0.$$

---

* The outline here follows the discussions by E. P. Wigner, On unitary representations of the inhomogeneous Lorentz group, *Ann. Math., Princeton* **40**, 149 (1939); and V. Bargmann and E. P. Wigner, Group theoretical discussion of relativistic wave equations, *Proc. Natl. Acad. Sci. U.S.* **34**, 211 (1948). See also Iu. M. Shirokov, A Group-Theoretical Consideration on the Basis of Relativistic Quantum Mechanics, *Soviet Physics JETP* **6**, 664, 919, 929 (1958); G. W. Mackey, The Theory of Group Representations (Notes) (1955), p. 171, Univ. Chicago; and E. P. Wigner, Relativistic wave equations, *Z. Physik* **124**, 665 (1947).

§ In the discussion of space groups the corresponding entity was called the star of k.

‡ Note: $g_{00} = -g_{11} = -g_{22} = -g_{33} = -1$
$g_{\mu\nu} = 0 \quad \mu \neq \nu.$

(b) The vectors of $\mathcal{O}(k)$ are all past timelike, i.e.

$$k^\mu k_\mu < 0 \qquad k^0 < 0.$$

(c) The vectors of $\mathcal{O}(k)$ are all spacelike, i.e.

$$k^\mu k_\mu > 0.$$

(d) The vectors of $\mathcal{O}(k)$ are all future null, i.e.

$$k^\mu k_\mu = 0 \qquad k^0 > 0.$$

(e) The vectors of $\mathcal{O}(k)$ are all past null, i.e.

$$k^\mu k_\mu = 0 \qquad k^0 < 0.$$

(f) $\mathcal{O}(k)$ contains only the zero vector, i.e.

$$k^\mu = 0 \qquad \mu = 0, 1, 2, 3.$$

(5) In types (a), (b), and (c) above there is one and only one orbit for each value of the length $k^\mu k_\mu$. Types (d), (e), and (f) contain only one orbit apiece.

(6) Let k be any real 4-vector, and let $L^{(I)}(k)$ be the set of all Lorentz matrices L in $\mathscr{L}(O, O, O)$ leaving k invariant i.e.,

$$Lk = k.$$

$L^{(I)}(k)$ will be called the little group of the first kind belonging to k. Subsequently this concept of a little group will be related to the older one.

(7) All little groups $L^{(I)}$ belonging to vectors in the same orbit $\mathcal{O}$ are isomorphic.

(8) All little groups $L^{(I)}$ belonging to orbits of the same type are isomorphic.

(9) The six little groups $L^{(I)}$ belonging to the six types of orbits are as follows:

(a) The 3-dimensional rotation group.

(b) The 3-dimensional rotation group.

(c) The 2 + 1-dimensional homogeneous Lorentz group.*

(d) The 2-dimensional Euclidean group† $\mathscr{E}(2)$.

(e) The 2-dimensional Euclidean group $\mathscr{E}(2)$.

(f) The proper, orthochronous, homogeneous Lorentz group $\mathscr{L}(O, O, O)$.

(10) The little group $\mathscr{E}(2)$ for types (d) and (e) is not obvious, so it will be discussed further. For type (d) let

---

* For a complete discussion of this group see V. Bargmann, Irreducible unitary representations of the Lorentz group, *Ann. Math., Princeton* **48**, 568 (1947).

† $\mathscr{E}(2)$ is the group of all linear transformations of the form

$$x' = Rx + b,$$

where x, x', and b are real 2-dimensional column matrices, and R is a rotation matrix.

$$k = \begin{pmatrix} 1 \\ 1 \\ 0 \\ 0 \end{pmatrix}.$$

Then the Lorentz matrices leaving k invariant have the form

$$L(x, y, \theta) = L(x, y) L(\theta),$$

where

$$L(x,y) = \begin{pmatrix} 1 + \dfrac{x^2+y^2}{2} & -\dfrac{x^2+y^2}{2} & x & y \\ \dfrac{x^2+y^2}{2} & 1 - \dfrac{x^2+y^2}{2} & x & y \\ x & -x & 1 & 0 \\ y & -y & 0 & 1 \end{pmatrix} -\infty < x, y < \infty$$

$$L(\theta) = \begin{pmatrix} 1 & 0 & 0 & 0 \\ 0 & 1 & 0 & 0 \\ 0 & 0 & \cos\theta & -\sin\theta \\ 0 & 0 & \sin\theta & \cos\theta \end{pmatrix}$$

These matrices satisfy the relations

$$L(x,y)L(x',y') = L(x + x', y + y')$$

$$L(\theta)L(\theta') = L(\theta + \theta')$$

$$L(\theta)L(x,y) = L(x\cos\theta - y\sin\theta, x\sin\theta + y\cos\theta)L(\theta).$$

Consequently, $L(x, y, \theta)$ represents a translation with components x, y and a rotation through angle θ.

Letting

$$T_x = \left(\frac{\partial L(x,y,\theta)}{\partial x}\right)_0 = \begin{pmatrix} 0 & 0 & 1 & 0 \\ 0 & 0 & 1 & 0 \\ 1 & -1 & 0 & 0 \\ 0 & 0 & 0 & 0 \end{pmatrix}$$

$$T_y = \left(\frac{\partial L(x,y,\theta)}{\partial y}\right)_0 = \begin{pmatrix} 0 & 0 & 0 & 1 \\ 0 & 0 & 0 & 1 \\ 0 & 0 & 0 & 0 \\ 1 & -1 & 0 & 0 \end{pmatrix}$$

$$M = \left(\frac{\partial L(x,y,\theta)}{\partial \theta}\right)_0 = \begin{pmatrix} 0 & 0 & 0 & 0 \\ 0 & 0 & 0 & 0 \\ 0 & 0 & 0 & -1 \\ 0 & 0 & 1 & 0 \end{pmatrix}$$

be the infinitesimal transformations, we see that

$$[T_x, T_y]_- = 0 \qquad [T_x, M]_- = -T_y \qquad [T_y, M]_- = T_x .$$

We also see that

$$Tx = -K_{02} - K_{12}$$
$$Ty = -K_{03} + K_{31}$$
$$M = K_{23},$$

where the $K_{\mu\nu}$'s are the infinitesimal transformations of the representation of $\mathscr{L}(O, O, O)$ by itself.

Furthermore, if

$$\Xi = -T_x^2 - T_y^2,$$

then

$$[\Xi, T_x]_- = [\Xi, T_y]_- = [\Xi, M]_- = 0,$$

so Ξ is a Casimir operator for $\mathscr{E}(2)$.

(11) The irreducible unitary representations of $\mathscr{E}(2)$ will be discussed briefly here.*

The translations $L(x, y)$ form a normal abelian subgroup of $\mathscr{E}(2)$ whose irreducible representations are

$$\omega(l)\colon \quad L(x, y) \to e^{i\mathbf{l}\cdot\mathbf{x}},$$

where $\mathbf{x} = (x, y)$, and $\mathbf{l} = (l_x, l_y)$ is a real 2-vector. The little group of the second kind $L^{(II)}$ belonging to $\omega(l)$ is either the whole group $\mathscr{E}(2)$ (when $\mathbf{l} = \mathbf{0}$), or the translation subgroup $\mathscr{T}(2)$ (when $\mathbf{l} \neq \mathbf{0}$).

In the first case ($\mathbf{l} = \mathbf{0}$) the irreducible representations of $\mathscr{E}(2)$ are engendered by irreducible representations of the quotient group $\mathscr{R}(2) = \dfrac{\mathscr{E}(2)}{\mathscr{T}(2)}$. The irreducible representations of $\mathscr{R}(2)$ are $L(\theta) \to e^{\pm is\theta}$ $(s = 0, 1, 2, 3, \ldots)$. The irreducible representations of $\mathscr{E}(2)$ engendered by these will be called $\Omega_s^{(\pm)}$. In the second case ($\mathbf{l} \neq \mathbf{0}$), the induced representations $\omega^{(\mathscr{I})}(\mathbf{l})$ are irreducible representations of $\mathscr{E}(2)$. Furthermore, all $\mathbf{l}$'s of the same length yield the same $\omega^{(\mathscr{I}}(\mathbf{l})$.

In the representations $\Omega_s^{(\pm)}$ the Casimir operator Ξ is equal to zero, whereas in the representation $\omega^{(\mathscr{I})}(\mathbf{l})$ it equals $l^2 I$. Thus the eigenvalue of Ξ characterizes the representations $\omega^{(\mathscr{I})}(\mathbf{l})$. Consequently they will be denoted by Ω_Ξ, where Ξ denotes the eigenvalue. In the representations $\Omega_s^{(\pm)}$ the infinitesimal operator M is represented by is.

It is also possible and desirable to obtain two-valued unitary representations of $\mathscr{E}(2)$. In the first case ($\mathbf{l} = \mathbf{0}$) this can be done

---

* For more complete discussions see E. P. Wigner, The Application of Group Theory to the Special Functions of Mathematical Physics (Notes) (1955), p. 116, Princeton Univ., and N. Ya. Vilenkin, Bessel Functions and Representations of the Group of Euclidean Motions, *Uspehi Mat. Nauk.* **11**, 69 (1956).

simply by letting s assume the values $\frac{1}{2}$, $\frac{3}{2}$,.... The resulting 1-dimensional two-valued representations of $\mathscr{E}(2)$ will still be denoted by $\Omega_s^{(\pm)}$. In the second case ($\mathbf{l} \neq \mathbf{0}$) we make use of the two-valued representation $\Gamma_{\frac{1}{2}}$ of $\mathscr{L}(O, O, O)$. This allows us to map every matrix $L(x, y, \theta)$ onto two 2-dimensional unimodular matrices $\pm D^{(\frac{1}{2})}(x, y, \theta)$. These matrices form a group $\mathscr{E}'(2)$, and the matrices $\pm D^{(\frac{1}{2})}(x, y, 0)$ form a normal abelian subgroup $\mathscr{T}'(2)$. The unitary irreducible representations $\mathscr{T}'(2)$ are

$$\omega(\mathbf{l}):\ \pm D^{(\frac{1}{2})}(x, y, 0) \rightarrow e^{i\mathbf{l}\cdot\mathbf{x}}$$

$$\omega'(\mathbf{l}):\ \pm D^{(\frac{1}{2})}(x, y, 0) \rightarrow \pm e^{i\mathbf{l}\cdot\mathbf{x}}.$$

The little group $L^{(II)}$ in the case $\mathbf{l} \neq \mathbf{0}$ is the group consisting of all translations $\pm D^{(\frac{1}{2})}(x, y, 0)$. The representations $\omega(\mathbf{l})$ and $\omega'(\mathbf{l})$ are also representations of $L^{(II)}$. The representations $\omega^{(\mathscr{I})}(\mathbf{l})$ and $\omega'^{(\mathscr{I})}(\mathbf{l})$ are therefore irreducible representations of $\mathscr{E}'(2)$ (and hence of $\mathscr{E}(2)$). The irreducible representations $\omega'^{(\mathscr{I})}(\mathbf{l})$ are new two-valued representations of $\mathscr{E}(2)$ whereas the representations $\omega^{(\mathscr{I})}(\mathbf{l})$ are the old $\omega^{(\mathscr{I})}(\mathbf{l})$. In $\omega'^{(\mathscr{I})}(\mathbf{l})$ the Casimir operator $\Xi = l^2 I$. Hence the irreducible two-valued representations $\omega'^{(\mathscr{I})}(\mathbf{l})$ will be denoted by Ω'_{Ξ}.

In summary, the 2-dimensional Euclidean group $\mathscr{E}(2)$ has the irreducible unitary representations $\Omega_s^{(\pm)}$, Ω_{Ξ}, and Ω'_{Ξ}.

(12) We can now return to $\mathscr{I}\mathscr{L}(O, O, O)$. The irreducible unitary representations of $\mathscr{T}$ are

$$\Delta(k):\ (I|a) \rightarrow e^{ik\cdot a},$$

where k is a real 4-vector and $k\cdot a = k^t G a$.

(13) The little group of the first kind $L^{(I)}$ belonging to $\Delta(k)$ is just $L^{(I)}(k)$. Also, the $\Delta(k')$'s occurring in the orbit of $\Delta(k)$ belong to k's in the orbit of k.

(14) Since $L^{(II)}(k)$ is the semidirect product of $\mathscr{T}$ with $L^{(I)}(k)$, it follows that $\Delta(k)$ can be extended as a vector representation to $L^{(II)}(k)$. The extension is

$$\Delta_{ext.}(k):\ (L|a) \rightarrow e^{ik\cdot a}$$

(15) Every allowable irreducible representation γ_{allow} of $L^{(II)}(k)$ has the form

$$\gamma_{\text{allow}} = \Delta_{\text{ext}}(k) \otimes \Omega,$$

where Ω is an irreducible representation of $L^{(II)}(k)$ engendered by an irreducible representation of $L^{(I)}(k) = \dfrac{L^{(II)}(k)}{\mathscr{T}}$.

Furthermore, every representation $\Delta_{\text{ext}}(k) \otimes \Omega$ of $L^{(II)}(k)$ is allowable.

(16) Every induced representation $\gamma_{\text{allow}}^{(\mathscr{I})} = (\Delta_{\text{ext}}(k) \otimes \Omega)^{(\mathscr{I})}$ of $\mathscr{I}\mathscr{L}(O,O,O)$ is irreducible, and every irreducible unitary representation of $\mathscr{I}\mathscr{L}(O,O,O)$ is one of these. Furthermore, by using one k from each orbit together with all irreducible unitary representations Ω of the corresponding $L^{(I)}(k)$ we obtain in this way all irreducible unitary representations of $\mathscr{I}\mathscr{L}(O,O,O)$.

(17) From (16) we see that corresponding to every orbit $\mathscr{O}$ and every Ω corresponding to $\mathscr{O}$ there is an irreducible unitary representation $\Gamma(\mathscr{O},\Omega)$ of $\mathscr{I}\mathscr{L}(O,O,O)$.

(18) Let us introduce more specific notation for the six types of orbits $\mathscr{O}(k)$.
(a) K_+ is the orbit of type (a) with $k_\mu k^\mu = -K, K > 0, k^\circ > 0$.
(b) K_- is the orbit of type (b) with $k^\mu k_\mu = -K, K > 0, k^\circ < 0$.
(c) K_0 is the orbit of type (c) with $k^\mu k_\mu = -K, K < 0$.
(d) O_+ is the orbit of type (d) $(k^\mu k_\mu = 0, k^\circ > 0)$.
(e) O_- is the orbit of type (e) $(k^\mu k_\mu = 0, k^\circ < 0)$.
(f) O_0 is the orbit of type (f) $(k = 0)$.

(19) The irreducible representations $\Gamma(K_+,\Omega)$, $\Gamma(K_-\,,\Omega)$, $\Gamma(K_0,\Omega)$, and $\Gamma\,(O_-,\Omega)$ of $\mathscr{I}\mathscr{L}(O,O,O)$ can be obtained from the irreducible representations $\Gamma(1_+,\Omega)$, $(-1_0,\Omega)$, and (O_+,Ω) as follows:

$$D^{(K_+,\Omega)}(L\,|a) = D^{(1_+,\Omega)}(L\,|\sqrt{K}a)$$

$$D^{(K_-,\Omega)}(L\,|a) = D^{(1_+,\Omega)}(L\,|-\sqrt{K}a)$$

$$D^{(K_0,\Omega)}(L\,|a) = D^{(-1_0,\Omega)}(L\,|\sqrt{-K}a)$$

$$D^{(O_-,\Omega)}(L\,|a) = D^{(O_+,\Omega)}(L\,|-a)$$

(20) Let $\Gamma(\mathscr{O},\Omega)$ be an irreducible representation of $\mathscr{I}\mathscr{L}(O,O,O)$, and $\Gamma^{(s)}(\mathscr{O},\Omega)$ the representation of $\mathscr{T}$ subduced by $\Gamma(\mathscr{O},\Omega)$. Let $\Delta(\mathscr{O})$ be the direct sum of all $\Delta(k)$ in $\mathscr{O}$. Then $\Gamma^{(s)}(\mathscr{O},\Omega)$ is a multiple of $\Delta(\mathscr{O})$.

(21) Let V be the carrier spce of $\Gamma(\mathscr{O},\Omega)$. Then V contains a basis which diagonalizes $\Gamma^{(s)}(\mathscr{O},\Omega)$. These basis vectors can be labelled by the vectors k in $\mathscr{O}$ together with an auxiliary parameter ξ (which has the same range for each k). The basis is $v(k,\xi)$. Let us assume that an inner product is defined such that these basis vectors are orthonormal.

$$D^{(\mathscr{O},\Omega)}(I\,|a)v(k,\xi) = e^{ik\cdot a}\,v(k,\xi).$$

(22) Let $P(L)$ be a linear operator in V defined for each L in $\mathscr{L}(O,O,O)$ by

$$P(L)v(k,\xi) = v(Lk,\xi),$$

and let us assume that $P(L)$ is unitary. Let

$$Q(L) = D^{(\mathscr{O},\Omega)}(L\,|0)P^{-1}(L).$$

Then

$$[Q(L), D^{(\mathscr{O},\Omega)}(I\,|a)]_- = 0.$$

Consequently, if $V(k)$ is the subspace of V spanned by all $v(k, \xi)$ belonging to a fixed k, we see that $V(k)$ must be invariant under Q. Thus Q (considered as a matrix) has nonzero blocks along the diagonal corresponding to the subspaces $V(k)$. Let $Q(k, L)$ be such a block. Then $Q(k, L)$ (fixed k) furnishes an irreducible representation of the little group $L^{(I)}(\mathscr{O})$. Let k_0 be a vector in $\mathscr{O}$, and let L_k be a Lorentz matrix in $\mathscr{L}(O, O, O)$ defined uniquely for each k in $\mathscr{O}$ such that L_k is an almost everywhere continuous function of k, $L_{k_0} = I$, and $L_k k_0 = k$. Then

$$Q(k, L) = Q(k_0, L_k^{-1}\, LL_{L^{-1}k}),$$

i.e.,

$$\langle k\xi\,|Q(L)\,|k\xi'\rangle = \langle k_0\,\xi|Q(L_k^{-1}LL_{L^{-1}k})|k_0\,\xi'\rangle.$$

Also

$$Q(L_1^{-1}k, L_2) = Q^{-1}(k, L_1)Q(k, L_1\, L_2),$$

i.e.,

$$\langle L_1^{-1}k|Q(L_2)|L_1^{-1}k, \xi'\rangle = \langle k\xi|Q^{-1}(L_1)Q(L_1\, L_2)|k, \xi'\rangle.$$

Finally, we observe that

$$D^{(\mathscr{O},\Omega)}(L\,|a)v(k, \xi) = e^{iLk\cdot a}Q(L)v(Lk, \xi).$$

(23) The vectors $v(k, \xi)$ can be expressed in terms of $v(k_0, \xi)$ by the equation

$$v(k, \xi) = D^{(\mathscr{O},\Omega)}(L_k\,|0)v(k_0, \xi).$$

(24) Let

$$D^{(\mathscr{O},\Omega)}(I - \tfrac{1}{2}\omega^{\mu\nu}K_{\mu\nu}|0) = I - \tfrac{1}{2}\omega^{\mu\nu}K_{\mu\nu}^{(\mathscr{O},\Omega}$$

$$D^{(\mathscr{O},\Omega)}(I\,|a) = I + ia^{\mu}P_{\mu} \quad \text{(for small } a\text{)}.$$

Dropping the superscripts we have

$$[P_{\mu}, P_{\nu}]_- = 0, \qquad (\mu, \nu = 0, 1, 2, 3),$$

$$[K_{\kappa\lambda}, P_{\mu}]_- = g_{\kappa\mu}\,P_{\lambda} - g_{\lambda\mu}\,P_{\kappa} \qquad (\kappa, \lambda, \mu = 0, 1, 2, 3).$$

We see also that $\mathscr{I}\mathscr{L}(O, O, O)$ is a 10-parameter group.

(25) If P_{λ} and $K_{\mu\nu}$ satisfy the commutation relations in (24), if $L = ||\,L^{\kappa}{}_{\nu}||$ is any Lorentz matrix, and if $P'^{\kappa} \equiv L^{\kappa}{}_{\nu}P^{\nu}$, $K'^{\mu\nu} \equiv L^{\mu}{}_{\kappa}\, L^{\nu}{}_{\lambda}\, K^{\kappa\lambda}$, then P'_{μ} and $K'_{\mu\nu}$ satisfy the same commutation relations.

(26) Let

$$C_1 = -P^{\mu}P_{\mu}$$

$$C_2 = \tfrac{1}{2}K^{\lambda\mu}K_{\lambda\mu}\,P^{\nu}P_{\nu} - K^{\lambda\mu}K_{\lambda\nu}\,P_{\mu}\,P^{\nu}.$$

Then

$$[C_1, K_{\lambda\mu}]_- = 0, \qquad [C_1, P_\mu]_- = 0,$$
$$[C_2, K_{\lambda\mu}]_- = 0, \qquad [C_2, P_\mu]_- = 0,$$

so C_1 and C_2 are Casimir operators.

(27) In the irreducible representation $\Gamma(\mathcal{O}, \Omega)$ of $\mathscr{IL}(0,0,0)$

$$C_1 = -k^2 I,$$

where k is any vector in $\mathcal{O}$.

(28) Let us from now on concentrate our attention on the orbits K_+ and O_+. The corresponding little groups are $\mathscr{R}(3)$ and $\mathscr{E}(2)$. The irreducible representations of $\mathscr{R}(3)$ are Ω_s $(s = 0, \frac{1}{2}, 1, \frac{3}{2}, \ldots)$; the irreducible unitary representations of $\mathscr{E}(2)$ are $\Omega_s^{(\pm)}$ $(s = 0, \frac{1}{2}, 1, \frac{3}{2}, \ldots)$, Ω_Ξ, and Ω_Ξ'. The corresponding irreducible unitary representations of $\mathscr{IL}(0,0,0)$ are $\Gamma(K_+, \Omega_s)$, $\Gamma(O_+, \Omega_s^{(\pm)})$, $\Gamma(O_+; \Omega_\Xi)$, and $\Gamma(O_+, \Omega_\Xi')$. Let us denote these more briefly by K_s, $O_s^{(\pm)}$, O_Ξ, and O_Ξ'.

(29) The values of C_2 in the above irreducible representations are as follows:

$$\begin{array}{ll} K_s: & C_2 = Ks(s+1)I \\ O_s^{(+)}: & C_2 = 0 \\ O_s^{(-)}: & C_2 = 0 \\ O_\Xi: & C_2 = \Xi > 0 \\ O_\Xi': & C_2 = \Xi > 0 \end{array}$$

(30) It is convenient now to introduce the operators w_μ which are defined in terms of the operators

$$v_{\lambda\mu\nu} = P_\lambda K_{\mu\nu} + P_\mu K_{\nu\lambda} + P_\nu K_{\lambda\mu}$$

by the equation

$$w_\mu = (v_{123}, v_{230}, v_{310}, v_{012}) \quad (\mu = 0, 1, 2, 3).$$

These operators satisfy the relations

$$\begin{aligned} &[w_\mu, P_\nu]_- = 0 \\ &[w_\lambda, K_{\mu\nu}]_- = g_{\lambda\nu} w_\mu - g_{\lambda\mu} w_\nu \\ &[w^\kappa, w^\lambda]_- = -\epsilon^{\kappa\lambda\mu\nu} w_\mu P_\nu \qquad \epsilon^{0123} = 1 \\ &w_\mu P^\mu = 0 \\ &w_\mu w^\mu = -C_2. \end{aligned}$$

The operators $u_\mu = K_{\mu\nu} P^\nu$ are also useful and satisfy the following relations

$$\begin{aligned} &[u_\mu, P_\nu]_- = - P_\mu P_\nu - g_{\mu\nu} C_1 \\ &[u_\lambda, K_{\mu\nu}]_- = -g_{\lambda\mu} u_\nu + g_{\lambda\nu} u_\nu \\ &[u_\mu, w_\nu]_- = - w_\mu P_\nu \\ &[u_\mu, u_\nu]_- = C_1 K_{\mu\nu} \\ &u^\mu P_\mu = 0 \\ &w_\mu u^\mu = 0 \end{aligned}$$

(31) In the representations $O_s^{(\pm)}$ the subspaces $V(k)$ are all 1-dimensional.

(32) In the representation $O_s^{(+)}$

$$w_\mu = -isP_\mu$$

and in the representation $O_s^{(-)}$

$$w_\mu = isP_\mu.$$

These operator equations can be used to distinguish $O_s^{(+)}$ and $O_s^{(-)}$.

(33) Let $K_{\lambda\mu}$, P_ν be the 10 infinitesimal operators for the irreducible representation $\Gamma(\mathcal{O}, \Omega)$ of $\mathcal{IL}(O, O, O)$ (note that superscripts have been omitted). Then it is possible to express $K_{\lambda\mu}$ in the form

$$K_{\lambda\mu} = \underset{0}{K}_{\lambda\mu} + \underset{s}{K}_{\lambda\mu}$$

where the operators $\underset{0}{K}_{\lambda\mu}$ and $\underset{s}{K}_{\lambda\mu}$ obey the same commutation relations as the $K_{\lambda\mu}$'s (i.e., if $[K_{\kappa\lambda}, K_{\mu\nu}]_- = c^{\alpha\beta}_{\kappa\lambda\mu\nu} K_{\alpha\beta}$ then

$$[\underset{0}{K}_{\kappa\lambda}, \underset{0}{K}_{\mu\nu}]_- = c^{\alpha\beta}_{\kappa\lambda\mu\nu} \underset{0}{K}_{\alpha\beta} \text{ and } [\underset{s}{K}_{\kappa\lambda}, \underset{s}{K}_{\mu\nu}]_- = c^{\alpha\beta}_{\kappa\lambda\mu\nu} \underset{s}{K}_{\alpha\beta}),$$

$$[\underset{0}{K}_{\kappa\lambda}, \underset{s}{K}_{\mu\nu}]_- = 0$$

$$[\underset{s}{K}_{\lambda\mu}, P_\nu]_- = 0$$

$$\langle k\xi|\underset{s}{K}_{\lambda\mu}|k\xi'\rangle = \langle k'\xi|\underset{s}{K}_{\lambda\mu}|k'\xi'\rangle \quad (\text{all } k, k' \text{ in } \mathcal{O})$$

$$\langle k\xi|\underset{0}{K}_{\lambda\mu}|k'\xi'\rangle = \delta(\xi, \xi')f(k, k').$$

The operators $\underset{0}{K}_{\lambda\mu}$ and $\underset{s}{K}_{\lambda\mu}$ are the orbital and spin parts respectively of $K_{\lambda\mu}$.

(34) The remaining part of this section will be devoted to constructing explicit realizations of the irreducible representations. The functions in the carrier space of an irreducible representation will be defined only for k's lying in the relevant orbit $\mathcal{O}$.

(35) K_s. Here the representations K_s will be treated. Let $\zeta_1, \ldots, \zeta_{2s}$ be $2s$ 4-valued variables, and let $\psi(k; \zeta_1, \ldots, \zeta_{2s})$ be any function which is symmetric in the $2s$ variables $\zeta_1, \ldots, \zeta_{2s}$ and satisfies

$$(\gamma^\mu_n k_\mu - i\kappa)\psi(k; \zeta_1, \ldots, \zeta_{2s}) = 0 \quad n = 1, \ldots, 2s,$$

where $[\gamma^\mu_n, \gamma^\nu_n]_+ = 2g^{\mu\nu}$

$$[\gamma^\mu_m, \gamma^\nu_n]_- = 0 \qquad m \neq n$$

$$\kappa^2 = K$$

and γ^μ_n operates* on the index ζ_n. The carrier space of K_s is the

* This notation can be understood as follows. Let V_4 be a 4-dimensional vector space, and $V_{4,2s}$ the $2s$th Kronecker power of V_4. Then ψ is a vector in the symmetric subspace of $V_{4,2s}$ which depends on k. Furthermore if γ^μ ($\mu = 0, 1, 2, 3$) are the ordinary Dirac matrices, then

$$\gamma^\mu_n = I \otimes I \otimes \ldots \otimes I \otimes \gamma^\mu \otimes I \otimes \ldots \otimes I,$$

where the I's are 4-dimensional unit operators and γ^μ is in the nth position.

set of all such functions with finite norm, where the inner product is defined by

$$\langle\phi|\psi\rangle = \int \phi^+\beta_1\beta_2\ldots\beta_{2s}\psi\frac{d^3k}{|\sqrt{k^2+K}|},$$

where $k^0 = |\sqrt{\mathbf{k}^2+K}\,|$.

The infinitesimal operators are*

$$P_\mu\psi(k;\zeta_1,\ldots,\zeta_{2s}) = k_\mu\psi(k;\zeta_1,\ldots,\zeta_{2s})$$

$$\underset{0}{K_{\mu\nu}} = -\left(k_\mu\frac{\partial}{\partial k^\nu} - k_\nu\frac{\partial}{\partial k^\mu}\right)$$

$$\underset{s}{K_{\mu\nu}} = \frac{-1}{4}\sum_{n=1}^{2s}[\gamma_{n\mu},\gamma_{n\nu}]_-.$$

(36) $O_s^{(\pm)}$. The equations are the same as for K_s with $\kappa = 0$ except that, for $O_s^{(+)}$, ψ must also satisfy the condition

$$\gamma_{n5}\psi = \psi, \qquad n = 1,\ldots,2s$$

where

$$\gamma_{n5} = i\gamma_{n0}\gamma_{n1}\gamma_{n2}\gamma_{n3} \qquad n = 1,\ldots,2s,$$

and for $O_s^{(-)}$

$$\gamma_{n5}\psi = -\psi \qquad n = 1,\ldots,2s.$$

(37) Since $k^\mu\gamma_\mu$ has only two linearly independent eigenvectors when $k^\mu k_\mu = 0$ and $k^0 > 0$ it is easily seen that $O_s^{(+)}$ and $O_s^{(-)}$ have just one linearly independent ψ for each k.

(38) O_Ξ. Let ξ be a real spacelike 4-vector orthogonal to k and let $\psi(k;\xi)$ be any function satisfying

$$k^\mu k_\mu\psi = 0$$

$$k^\mu\xi_\mu\psi = 0$$

$$\xi^\mu\xi_\mu\psi = \psi$$

$$k^\mu\frac{\partial}{\partial\xi_n}\psi = -i\Xi^{\frac{1}{2}}\psi.$$

To construct the inner product, let $u(k)$ and $v(k)$ be two real spacelike unit vectors defined for every nonxero null k such that $u(k)$ and

* For other forms of the infinitesimal operators see Iu. M. Shirokov, A Group, Theoretical Consideration on the Basis of Relativistic Quantum Mechanics, *Soviet Physics JETP* **6**, 664, 919, 929 (1958); T. S. Chang, Calculations of some operators in relativistic quantum mechanics, *Acta Math. Sinica* **3**, 59 (1953); and L. L. Foldy-Synthesis of covariant particle equations, *Phys. Rev.* **102**, 568 (1956).

$v(k)$ are orthogonal to each other and to k. Then ξ can be expressed in the form

$$\xi = \alpha k + \beta u(k) + \gamma v(k),$$

where

$$\beta^2 + \gamma^2 = 1.$$

Let

$$\tau = -i\ln(\beta + i\gamma).$$

Then

$$\psi(k, \xi) = \psi(k, \alpha, \tau)$$

and

$$\langle\phi|\psi\rangle = \int \phi^*(k, 0, \tau)\psi(k, 0, \tau)\frac{d^{(3)}k}{|\mathbf{k}|}d\tau,$$

where $k^2 = |\mathbf{k}|$. The carrier space is the set of all ψ's with finite norm.

The infinitesimal operators are

$$P_\mu \psi(k; \xi) = k_\mu \psi(k; \xi)$$

$$\underset{0}{K}_{\mu\nu} = -\left(k_\mu \frac{\partial}{\partial k^\nu} - k_\nu \frac{\partial}{\partial k^\mu}\right)$$

$$\underset{s}{K}_{\mu\nu} = -\left(\xi_\mu \frac{\partial}{\partial \xi^\nu} - \xi_\nu \frac{\partial}{\partial \xi^\mu}\right).$$

(39) O_Ξ'. In addition to the parameter ξ used with O_Ξ, a 4-valued parameter ζ is needed. Let $\psi(k; \xi, \zeta)$ be any function satisfying

$$\gamma^\mu k_\mu \psi = 0$$

$$\xi^\mu k_\mu \psi = 0$$

$$k^\mu \frac{\partial}{\partial \xi^\mu}\psi = -i\Xi^{\frac{1}{2}}\psi,$$

and let

$$\langle\phi|\psi\rangle = \int \phi^*(k, 0, \tau)\psi(k, 0, \tau)\, \frac{d^{(3)}k}{|\mathbf{k}|^2}\, d\tau$$

where $k^0 = |\mathbf{k}|$. The carrier space is the set of all ψ's with finite norm.

The infinitesimal operators are

$$P_\mu \psi(k; \xi, \zeta) = k_\mu \psi(k; \xi, \zeta)$$

$$\underset{0}{K}_{\mu\nu} = -\left(k_\mu \frac{\partial}{\partial k^\nu} - k_\nu \frac{\partial}{\partial k^\mu}\right)$$

$$\underset{s}{K}_{\mu\nu} = -\left(\xi_\mu \frac{\partial}{\partial \xi^\nu} - \xi_\nu \frac{\partial}{\partial \xi^\mu}\right) - \tfrac{1}{4}\,[\gamma_\mu, \gamma_\nu]_-$$

where the γ's operate on the index ζ.

7. The Proper Inhomogeneous Lorentz Group $\mathscr{IL}(O,O,-I)$

$\mathscr{IL}(O,O,-I)$ is isomorphic to $\mathscr{IL}(O,O,O) \times C_2$ so the irreducible representations of $\mathscr{IL}(O,O,-I)$ are outer Kronecker products of those of $\mathscr{IL}(O,O,O)$ and those of C_2.

8. The Orthochronous, Inhomogeneous Lorentz Group $\mathscr{IL}(S,O,O)$ and the Antichronous, Inhomogenous Lorentz Group $\mathscr{IL}(O,T,O)$

Since these two groups are isomorphic we shall consider only $\mathscr{IL}(S,O,O)$.

(1) $\mathscr{IL}(O,O,O)$ is a normal subgroup of $\mathscr{IL}(S,O,O)$.

(2) $\dfrac{\mathscr{IL}(S,O,O)}{\mathscr{IL}(O,O,O)} = C_2$.

(3) The unitary irreducible representations of $\mathscr{IL}(S,O,O)$ of physical interest are $K_s^{(\mathrm{ext})}$, $O_0^{(\mathrm{ext})}$, $O_\Xi^{(\mathrm{ext})}$, $O'^{(\mathrm{ext})}_\Xi$, and $O_s^{(\pm)(\mathscr{I})}$ (for $s \neq 0$).

(4) For $O_s^{(\pm)(\mathscr{I})}$.

$$(L|a) \rightarrow \begin{pmatrix} D^{(o_s^{(\pm)})}(L|a) & \\ & D^{(o_s^{(\pm)})}(SLS|Sa) \end{pmatrix}$$

$$(S|0) \rightarrow \pm \begin{pmatrix} O & I \\ I & O \end{pmatrix}.$$

(5) From the faithful 5-dimensional representation, one finds

$$[S,P_0]_- = 0, \qquad [S,P_i]_+ = 0,$$
$$[T,P_0]_- = 0, \qquad [T,P_i]_+ = 0.$$

9. The Full Inhomogeneous Lorentz Group $\mathscr{IL}(S,T,-I)$

(1) All four other inhomogeneous Lorentz groups are normal subgroups of $\mathscr{IL}(S,T,-I)$.

(2) $\dfrac{\mathscr{IL}(S,T,-I)}{\mathscr{IL}(O,O,O)} = D_2$

$$\frac{\mathscr{IL}(S,T,-I)}{\mathscr{IL}(S,O,O,)} = \frac{\mathscr{IL}(S,T,-I)}{\mathscr{IL}(O,T,O)} = \frac{\mathscr{IL}(S,T,-I)}{\mathscr{IL}(O,O,-I)} = C_2.$$

(3) $\mathscr{IL}(S,T,-I)$ is isomorphic to the direct product of $\mathscr{IL}(S,O,O)$ and C_2.

$$\mathscr{IL}(S,T,-I) = \mathscr{IL}(S,O,O) \times C_2.$$

(4) The irreducible representations of $\mathscr{IL}(S,T,-I)$ are outer Kronecker products of those of $\mathscr{IL}(S,O,O)$ and those of C_2.

SUBJECT INDEX

Q

R

S